PHYSICS

Mantles of the Earth

and

Terrestrial Planets

NATO ADVANCED STUDY INSTITUTE

Conference organized by

the School of Physics at the University

of Newcastle upon Tyne, England

30 March–7 April 1966

Director of Institute	PROFESSOR S. K. RUNCORN, F.R.S.
Organizing Committee	MR. F. R. BREARY
	DR. R. W. GIRDLER
	MR. M. J. GROSS
	MRS. J. ROBERTS
	DR. D. J. TRITTON

Mantles of the Earth

and

Terrestrial Planets

Edited by S. K. RUNCORN, F.R.S.

School of Physics, University of Newcastle upon Tyne, England

1967

INTERSCIENCE PUBLISHERS

a division of John Wiley & Sons

LONDON   NEW YORK   SYDNEY

First published 1967 by John Wiley & Sons

Library of Congress Catalog Card Number 67-26566

MADE AND PRINTED IN GREAT BRITAIN BY
HAZELL WATSON AND VINEY LTD, AYLESBURY, BUCKS

Contributors

PROFESSOR H. ALFVÉN   Institutionen für Plasmafysik, Stockholm 70, Sweden

DR. D. W. ALLAN   Department of Mathematics, King's College, London W.C.2, England

DR. R. R. ALLAN   Ministry of Aviation, Space Department, Royal Aircraft Establishment, Farnborough, Hampshire, England

MR. R. J. ANDERLE   Naval Weapons Laboratory, Dahlgren, Virginia, U.S.A.

DR. D. L. ANDERSON   Seismological Laboratory, 220 N. San Rafael Avenue, Pasadena, California 91105, U.S.A.

PROFESSOR H. P. BERLAGE   Soestdijkseweg 123a, De Bilt, Netherlands

PROFESSOR K. E. BULLEN, F.R.S.   Department of Applied Mathematics, University of Sydney, Sydney, N.S.W., Australia

MLLE. O. CALAME   Observatoire du Pic du Midi, 65 Bagnères de Bigorre, Hautes-Pyrénées, France

PROFESSOR G. COLOMBO   via S. Piox 19, Padova, Italy

MR. A. M. COODE   School of Physics, University of Newcastle upon Tyne, England

DR. K. M. CREER   School of Physics, University of Newcastle upon Tyne, England

DR. A. DOLLFUS   Observatoire de Paris, Section d'Astrophysique, 78 Meudon, Seine-et-Oise, France

DR. W. J. ECKERT   IBM, Computing Laboratory, Columbia University, 612 W. 115th Street, New York, N.Y. 10025, U.S.A.

DR. J. W. ELDER   Department of Applied Mathematics and Theoretical Physics, University of Cambridge, Silver Street, Cambridge, England

DR. T. ERNST   852 Erlangen, Schlossgarten 5a, Mineralogisches Institut, W. Germany

DR. G. FIELDER   University of London Observatory, Mill Hill Park, London N.W.7, England

DR. E. A. GAUGLER   Office of Space Science and Applications, NASA, Washington D.C. 20546, U.S.A.

DR. P. W. GAST   Lamont Geological Observatory, Palisades, New York, U.S.A.

DR. H. GERSTENKORN   3001 Isernhagen NB/Hannover, Grünberger Steg 1, W. Germany

DR. R. W. GIRDLER   School of Physics, University of Newcastle upon Tyne, England

DR. P. GOLDREICH   Institute of Geophysics and Planetary Physics, University of California, Los Angeles, California 24, U.S.A.

MRS. B. M. GRAY   Computing Centre, University of East Anglia, Norwich, England

DR. P. GRJEBINE   Centre des Faibles, Radioactivités, C.N.R.S., Gif-sur-Yvette Seine-et-Oise, France

MR. M. J. GROSS   School of Physics, University of Newcastle upon Tyne, England

DR. P. G. HARRIS   Department of Earth Sciences, The University, Leeds, England

PROFESSOR J. HOPMANN   Türkenschanz Str. 17, 1180 Vienna, Austria

PROFESSOR J. HOSPERS   Geological Institute, 130 Nieuwe Prinsengracht, Amsterdam-C, Netherlands

SIR HAROLD JEFFREYS, F.R.S.   160 Huntingdon Road, Cambridge, England

DR. J. F. KERRIDGE   Crystallography Department, Birkbeck College, Malet Street, London W.C.1, England

DR. P. LÄMMERZAHL   69 Heidelberg, Postfach 1248, W. Germany

DR. J. F. MCCAULEY   1626 N. Navajo Drive, Flagstaff, Arizona 86001, U.S.A.

MR. D. P. MCKENZIE   Department of Geodesy and Geophysics, University of Cambridge, Madingley Rise, Madingley Road, Cambridge, England

DR. A. H. MARCUS   Statistical Laboratory, Department of Mathematics, Case Institute of Technology, Cleveland, Ohio 44106, U.S.A.

DR. G. D. NICHOLLS   Department of Geology, University of Manchester, Manchester 13, England

DR. S. PEALE   Institute of Geophysics and Planetary Physics, University of California, Los Angeles, California 24, U.S.A.

DR. R. A. PHINNEY   Department of Geology, Princeton University, Princeton, New Jersey, U.S.A.

DR. S. I. RASOOL   475 Riverside Drive, Room 431, New York, N.Y. 10027, U.S.A.

DR. S. J. B. REED   Mineralogy Department, British Museum (Natural History), Cromwell Road, London S.W.7, England

DR. L. B. RONCA   Air Force Cambridge Research Laboratories, Space Physics Laboratory, Lunar-Planetary Research Branch, L. G. Hanscom Field, Bedford, Massachusetts, U.S.A.

PROFESSOR S. K. RUNCORN, F.R.S.   School of Physics, University of Newcastle upon Tyne, England

MR. J.-G. SCHILLING   Department of Geology and Geophysics, Room 54-1220, Massachusetts Institute of Technology, Cambridge, Massachusetts, U.S.A.

DR. I. I. SHAPIRO   Lincoln Laboratory, Massachusetts Institute of Technology, Lexington, Massachusetts, U.S.A.

DR. L. R. SYKES   Lamont Geological Observatory, Palisades, New York, U.S.A.

DR. H. I. S. THIRLAWAY   U.K. Atomic Energy Authority, Blacknest, Brimpton, Nr. Reading, Berkshire, England

DR. W. B. THOMPSON   Department of Physics, University of California, San Diego, La Jolla, California, U.S.A.

DR. J. H. THOMSON   Jodrell Bank, University of Manchester, Macclesfield, Cheshire, England

DR. D. J. TRITTON   School of Physics, University of Newcastle upon Tyne, England

PROFESSOR H. C. UREY   Department of Chemistry, University of California, San Diego, P.O. Box 109, La Jolla, California 92038, U.S.A.

DR. A. VOGEL   Geophysical Laboratory, University of Uppsala, Husbyborg, Uppsala, Sweden

DR. N. O. WEISS   Department of Applied Mathematics and Theoretical Physics, University of Cambridge, Silver Street, Cambridge, England

DR. G. A. WILKINS   H.M. Nautical Almanac Office, Herstmonceux Castle, Hailsham, Sussex, England

DR. J. W. WINCHESTER   Department of Geology and Geophysics, Massachusetts Institute of Technology, Cambridge, Massachusetts, U.S.A.

DR. J. A. WOOD   Smithsonian Astrophysical Observatory, 60 Garden Street, Massachusetts 02138, U.S.A.

MR. M. N. ZARRAGA   School of Physics, University of Newcastle upon Tyne, England

Preface

Clues to Earth and Planet Interiors[*]

That planetary astronomy is again 'fashionable' is due to two factors—the advent of space technology, and growth in knowledge of our own planet, the Earth.

It was through observations of the planets, three centuries ago, that scientific revolution really began. Galileo discovered, by his telescope, that Venus had phases like the Moon—persuasive evidence that Copernicus was correct in supposing the planets to move about a fixed Sun, not a fixed Earth. Also the fortunate fact that the Earth's next-nearest neighbour, Mars, has an orbit which departs considerably from a circle enabled Kepler to discover that the paths followed by the planets about the Sun are ellipses. From this Newton derived the universal law of gravitation.

By the beginning of the present century this inverse square law was shown to explain all the intricate details of the motions of the planets. One discrepancy remained—an unexplained rotation of Mercury's orbit—and this, in the hands of Einstein, became a cornerstone of the general theory of relativity. The other important anomalies in the Moon's motion have led to the discovery of variations in the Earth's rotation—basic data for the geophysicist.

Meantime, bigger telescopes, and the introduction of photography as a tool, had shifted the astronomers' interest to greater distances—to stars and galaxies. Thus, the planets and Moon were left mainly to amateurs. Then revitalizing ideas came from other branches of science. Thus arguments based on physical chemistry, and advanced by Professor Harold Urey, reopened, shortly after the war, the question of the origin of the Earth and planets. It was argued that they were formed, along with the Sun, by accretion from a primeval dust cloud, already flattened by rotation.

Galileo first used his telescope to look at the nearest celestial object, the Moon. He interpreted what he saw in terms of the Earth's topography: mountain ranges, dark depressions (maria), and craters. Though these features would have seemed familiar to him, it represented a radical change in outlook to interpret the heavens in terms of the Earth. But in 1893 an American geologist, G. K. Gilbert, broke away from this interpretation. He argued, in particular, that the Moon's craters differed in contour from terrestrial volcanic craters, and were caused by the impact of meteorites.

The meteorite impact theory is now widely accepted, helped by the discovery of similar craters on the Earth. On the Moon, with neither atmosphere nor water, there can be little erosion, and its surface preserves almost perfectly the record of its bombardment over thousands of millions of years.

In its primeval surface, we see the final events of its formation, and strong support is given to the accretion theory of the origin of planets. The photographs of Mars, transmitted from *Mariner IV*, show a surface cratered with similar frequency. Because meteorites may have been formed from the remains of such a dust cloud, their study has been vital to understanding of the evolution of the solar system.

[*] Adapted by permission of *The Times* from an article in the edition dated 30th March 1966.

Surprisingly, we appear to know more about the interiors of stars than of planets. This is because stars consist of gases, whose physical behaviour can be predicted confidently. Meteorites are mostly stony or iron. So the interiors of planets involve us in the behaviour of silicate minerals and iron under a wide range of conditions, including pressures hundreds of thousands of times that of the atmosphere.

Such materials are too complex at an atomic level for dependable prediction to be yet possible. However, since the beginning of this century, earthquake shocks have been recorded at seismograph stations over the globe and the speeds at which various kinds of waves travel through the Earth are known.

Seismologists conclude from such evidence that the Earth has a fluid iron core, of 3500 kilometres radius, and that around this there is a solid silicate mantle, 2900 kilometres thick, on which the lighter 35 kilometres thick continents float like islands. It is with the object of drilling deep enough in an ocean area to sample the mantle that the American Mohole project—now in its final stage near Hawaii—has been planned [now discontinued]. Geochemists argue that particularly dense silicates, brought up through cracks in the crust, are just such a sample, in the form of olivine nodules, and one much more cheaply available. It is also possible, by using the measures obtained by seismologists of the degree of compression that silicates and iron undergo in the Earth, that the composition and structures of Mars and other planets can be predicted with confidence.

How far can guidance from the Earth be relied upon? The science of geology, which so impressed the young Charles Darwin with its reasoning, has unravelled complex events in the Earth's crust which, compared with the Moon or Mars, we now see to be highly active. Long ago, the Alps and Andes were recognized as consisting of highly folded sedimentary strata, suggesting strong compression on the Earth's crust. This, it was argued, could be produced on a cooling, contracting Earth. Signs of the opposite effect—tension—were on a much less impressive scale, except for the great east African rift valleys. Geophysical exploration of the ocean floor since the war has, however, revealed tensional features in the Mid-Atlantic Ridge and other oceanic ridges.

These discoveries have even caused theorists to suggest an expanding Earth. However, both compression and extension occur and this leads inevitably to the hypothesis that great convection currents move within it—transporting heat from the deep interior, compressing the crust where they descend, and causing tension where they rise. These currents, moving a few centimetres a year, can explain continental drift. The mantle is not as solid as seismologists had concluded from studying its response to stresses of a few seconds to a few minutes period, but shows creep over millions of years. Mars and the Moon give no indications of such vigorous internal movements, but their interiors may not be so dead as used to be thought. Careful study of telescopic and *Ranger* photographs shows that small volcanic cones and faults exist, and opinion is hardening that the maria are lava which could have issued from the interior. The convection current hypothesis may apply to their interiors.

The thick atmosphere of Venus and the nearness of Mercury to the Sun have prevented the rotation of their solid surface from being followed, as that of Mars has long been. As the lengths of their days were then not known, they were assumed always to present the same faces to the Sun, as the Moon does to the Earth. Radar measurements now enable their rotation rates to be determined. Mercury rotates about its axis in two-thirds of its year and Venus once in 250 days in a retrograde direction.

An explanation of these curious results leads to the conclusion that the shapes of these planets deviate from that suggested theoretically by about a kilometre, as has long been known in the case of the Moon. The shape of Mars is still a problem, for there is some conflict of evidence. Was it in their early history that these planets were distorted—or are they distorted like the Earth by currents within them now?

Two issues concerning the Moon provoke debate. It is retreating from the Earth at a rate which can be measured astronomically. This is due to the action of the tides, and the rate seems to have been constant through most of geological time. The Moon, if so, was astonishingly close to the Earth 2000 million years ago—and, since the Earth's age is about 4500 million years, the question arises where the Moon was during the first half of the Earth's life. Was it captured by the Earth, did it come from the Earth, or did it begin as a disk of dust girdling the Earth? The second issue is that calculations based on the orbital motion of the Moon lead to the surprising conclusion that the Moon is hollow. This is much too implausible to accept—so there is a problem ready made for some young research student.

In arranging this NATO Advanced Study Institute I would like to acknowledge the great help received from the staff of the School of Physics, especially from the organizing committee. As in similar institutes held in the past four years, we were much indebted to the help of the NATO science office and the University authorities. In particular, Dr. C. I. C. Bosanquet, the Vice-Chancellor, has given unfailing support in the endeavours to bring together scientists and research students from many different countries and from various disciplines.

S. K. RUNCORN

Contents

Preface *S. K. Runcorn*   vii

I   Evidence from meteorites and cosmochemistry   1

II   Determination of basic physical constants of the planets   75

III   Radial variation of physical properties in planetary
       interiors   107

IV   Physical evidence for non-hydrostatic conditions
       in the planets   139

V   Planetary rotation   187

VI   The origin of the Moon   223

VII   Geochemical evidence on the nature of the Earth's
       mantle   265

VIII   Surface evidence relating to planetary evolution   329

IX   Thermal convection in planets   481

       Author Index   567

       Subject Index   575

I

Evidence from meteorites and cosmochemistry

1. The early thermal history of planets: evidence from meteorites (J. A. WOOD) 3

2. Chemical and mineralogical evidence from iron meteorites on the nature of the parent body (S. J. B. REED) . . 15

3. The mineralogy and genesis of the carbonaceous meteorites (J. F. KERRIDGE) 35

4. Rare-gas isotope studies on meteorites (P. LÄMMERZAHL) . 49

5. Abundance of cosmic dust (T. GRJEBINE) . . . 63

1

J. A. WOOD

Smithsonian Institution
Astrophysical Observatory
Cambridge, Massachusetts, U.S.A.

The early thermal history of planets: evidence from meteorites

Meteorites are broken pieces of alien planets. Many lines of evidence lead us to believe that their substance is still in a very primitive state, that nothing has happened to change it importantly since the earliest eons of the solar system. The imprint of events that occurred at the very beginning is still borne by the meteorites, and we study them in order to learn of these early events and processes. This chapter discusses recent evidence of the early thermal history of the parent meteorite planets.

The evidence is contained in metallic Ni–Fe minerals. Some meteorites (the 'irons', $\sim 6\%$ of all observed falls) are composed almost wholly of Ni–Fe metal. This cannot be primordial planetary material; the composition is too specialized. Only melting, followed by gravitational separation of dense molten metal from lighter silicate magma, blast-furnace fashion, seems capable of having produced compact metallic masses like the iron meteorites. One supposes heating and melting occurred in the interiors of parent meteorite planets, and that metal droplets sank to the centers of the planets, there to collect into Ni–Fe cores analogous to Earth's high-density core. Urey[1] has postulated a different model, however, in which planetary surfaces are heated and melted, and numerous small zones of liquid metal collect at the base of the melted zone.

Most ($\sim 75\%$) iron meteorites, the *octahedrites*, contain a curious and striking internal structure, the *Widmanstätten* structure (figure 1). This consists of octahedrally oriented arrays of plates of *kamacite* (α Ni–Fe, body-centered cubic), with the spaces between them filled by *taenite* (γ Ni–Fe, face-centered cubic) and *plessite* (figure 2). 'Plessite' is sometimes a fine-grained mixture of kamacite and taenite, sometimes a martensitic alloy (α_2 Ni–Fe, distorted body-centered cubic). The concentration of Ni is highly variable in these metallic minerals, as an electron microprobe profile across them shows (figure 3).

The phase diagram of the binary Fe–Ni system (figure 4) contains a two-phase field beneath 900 °C. The bulk Ni content of octahedrites (7–15%) is such that they must have entered this field when they cooled. Formation of the Widmanstätten structure can be understood straightforwardly in terms of slow cooling in the kamacite-plus-taenite field[2, 5, 6]. Let us consider what would happen in the case of an alloy of 10% bulk Ni content.

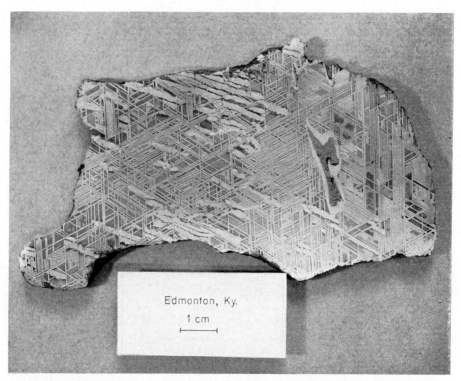

FIGURE 1   Widmanstätten pattern in an iron meteorite (octahedrite). A flat surface
sawed through the specimen has been smoothed and polished, then etched in dilute acid
to reveal the pattern. The fine parallel bands are plates of kamacite which run through the
meteorite. [Photograph by courtesy of the Smithsonian Institution]

Slow cooling would have allowed the molten metal to solidify into very coarse crystals of taenite. When these cooled to 700 °C (A in figure 4), equilibrium requires that kamacite of composition A' should have nucleated. Apparently it did so in the form of plates along {111} lattice planes in the host taenite, accounting for the octahedral geometry of the Widmanstätten structure. During further cooling, equilibrium requires that the two alloys change in composition: kamacite along A'B'C'D' in figure 4, taenite along ABCD. Thus the Ni content was required to increase in both alloys (until the system cooled to ∼450 °C); this is possible in a system of constant total Ni content only if the amount of low-Ni alloy (kamacite) grows at the expense of high-Ni alloy (taenite).

Alloy compositions can have changed only by virtue of lattice diffusion, which carried Ni from the kamacite–taenite interfaces (where reaction was occurring) into the interiors of kamacite and taenite crystals (Fe moved in the reverse direction, of course). But lattice diffusion coefficients are temperature dependent, so temperatures must eventually have been reached where diffusion could no longer supply Ni to crystal interiors. The effective range of diffusion grew shorter and shorter; the Ni content of taenite continued to increase near interfaces, but not in crystal interiors; the final result must have been roughly M-shaped Ni distributions in taenite crystals, like those observed in octahedrites (figure 3).

The interactions (during cooling) of kamacite growth, changes of composition, and

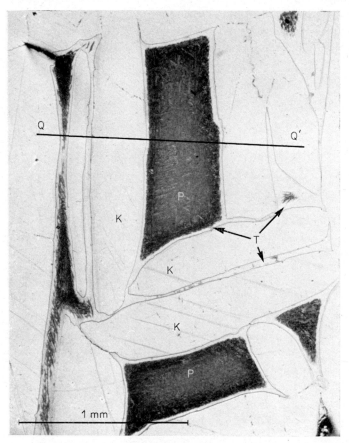

FIGURE 2   A photomicrograph of Widmanstätten structure in the Anoka (Minnesota) octahedrite: K, kamacite; T, taenite; P, plessite. Profile of Ni content across QQ′ appears in figure 3. [From Wood²]

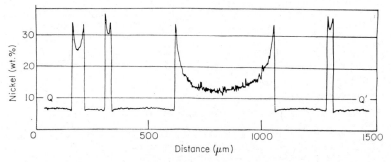

FIGURE 3   Variation of Ni content across the Widmanstätten structure: an electron microprobe profile taken across QQ′ in figure 2. [From Wood²]

failure of diffusion are shown schematically in figure 5. Failure of diffusion in kamacite after the temperature fell beneath ∼450 °C (i.e. below **C′**, where the phase boundary bends back) would have produced kamacite inhomogeneities like those in figure 3. Finally, cooling would have brought about the transformation of low-Ni taenite

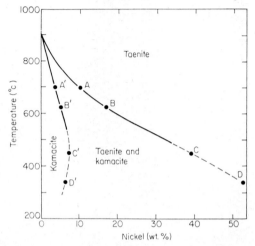

FIGURE 4   Phase diagram of the binary system Fe–Ni (at 1 atm pressure) by Goldstein
and Ogilvie[3]. [From Wood[4]]

interiors to martensite, and this in turn is capable of decomposing to a fine mixture of kamacite and taenite (plessite).

Clearly the final distribution of Ni in a given taenite or taenite-and-plessite area,

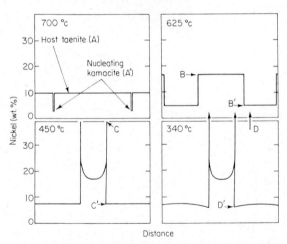

FIGURE 5   Growth of the Widmanstätten structure in a cooling Ni–Fe alloy (schematic).
A, A′, etc., refer to points in figure 4. [From Wood[4]]

the detailed shape of the 'M' profile that is obtained by microprobing across it, depends upon the rate at which the system cooled. All other things being equal, the slower it cooled, the lower the temperature at which Ni diffusion will have failed, the more Ni will have been able to penetrate to its interior, and the higher the final Ni content at this center will be. The effect can be seen in figure 6: here Ni profiles generated by a computer, for a given set of starting conditions but assuming various cooling rates, are compared.

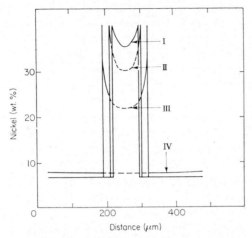

FIGURE 6   Computer-simulated Ni profiles in taenite showing the effect of varying the cooling rate of the system. Curve I, 0·01 degc per million years; curve II, 0·1 degc per million years; curve III, 1 degc per million years; curve IV, 10 degc per million years. [From Wood[2]]

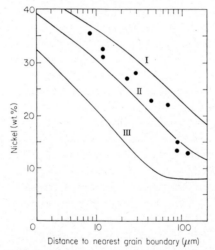

FIGURE 7   Relationship between the size of a taenite crystal (abscissa), the rate at which it cooled (degc per million years), and the amount of Ni it will contain at its center after cooling (ordinate). Curves show the theoretical (computer-simulated) relationships for three cooling rates: curve I, 1 degc per million years; curve II, 10 degc per million years; curve III, 100 degc per million years. Points are measurements of taenite crystals in the Toluca octahedrite. [From Wood[4]]

Computer simulations of this type, which take account of the Fe–Ni phase diagram[3] and the coefficient of diffusion of Ni in taenite[7], have been used to determine rates at which the octahedrites cooled[2, 8]. The author's approach to this problem has been to determine, via computer simulation, the relationship that ought to exist

between the Ni concentration at the center of a taenite crystal (after cooling is completed), the dimension of the crystal, and the cooling rate of the system. The first two
parameters could then be measured in real octahedrites and used to derive the third.
An example is shown in figure 7: here the computed relationships are shown by full
lines, and points represent real taenite crystals in an octahedrite (Toluca). The seven
upper points indicate that Toluca cooled through 600–500 °C at about 5 degc per million years. The displacement of the three lower points can be attributed to super-
cooling of the taenite to about 100 degc beneath the taenite/taenite-plus-kamacite
boundary before kamacite nucleated.

This technique, applied to eight octahedrites, has consistently yielded cooling rates
in the range 2–40 degc per million years[2, 8]. An error analysis, which takes into account uncertainties in the phase diagram and coefficient of diffusion, and the possible
effects of pressure and trace elements on them, as well as analytical error, indicates
that these cooling rates can be inaccurate in absolute value by as much as a factor of
2·5 in either direction[4]; they should be regarded as order-of-magnitude values.

These are relatively rapid cooling rates, and not consistent with any great thickness
of insulating overburden. If octahedrites cooled in the cores of planets, they were
very small planets (asteroids). Heat-flow calculations equate a central cooling rate
of 2 degc per million years ($\pm 2\cdot 5 \times$) with a planetary radius of 100–200 km, and 40
degc per million years ($\pm 2\cdot 5 \times$) with 30–60 km (see Wood[2]). If octahedrites cooled in
the mantles of planets, it was at depths of no greater than a few tens of kilometers.

Kamacite and taenite occur not only in irons, but also in most stony meteorites[9].
The *chondrites*, stony masses that comprise $\sim 85\%$ of the meteorites seen to fall,
contain tiny, dispersed metal grains (figure 8). These are almost always crystals of
pure kamacite or pure taenite; the two alloys rarely occur in actual contact with one
another. They have essentially the same compositions[10] and compositional inhomogeneities[4] (see figure 9) as kamacite and taenite in octahedrites. In particular, as
figure 9 shows, taenite crystals have M-shaped Ni distributions even though they are
surrounded by silicate minerals, not kamacite.

The chondrites have passed through a period of high temperature (1000 °c?), which
metamorphosed them. It can be shown that the metal grains grew *in situ* in the chondrites during this event (and during subsequent cooling). Kamacite and taenite must
have behaved during cooling just as they did in octahedrites, in order to end up with
the same Ni profiles. Yet this requires reaction between the kamacite and taenite
(as we have seen), a thing that seems impossible in chondrites, where the two alloys
are physically separated. Evidently during metamorphism Ni and Fe were able to
move from one metal grain to another, through intervening silicate material, with
great facility. How this was accomplished is not known: grain boundary diffusion is
one possibility; vapor transfer in the form of volatile compounds is another.

In any case, since chondritic metal has behaved like octahedrite metal during cooling,
the technique discussed above for determining the rates at which octahedrites cooled
can be extended to chondrites (figure 10). It has been found that the 'ordinary' (i.e. highly
metamorphosed) chondrites cooled at rates comparable with the octahedrites,
2–10 degc per million years. 'Pigeonite' or grade-3 (less severely metamorphosed)
chondrites generally cooled more slowly, 0·2–2 degc per million years[4]. Uncertainties
of $\pm 2\cdot 5 \times$ apply to these numbers also. Thus most chondrites, like the octahedrites,
were not more deeply buried than a few tens of kilometers when they cooled.

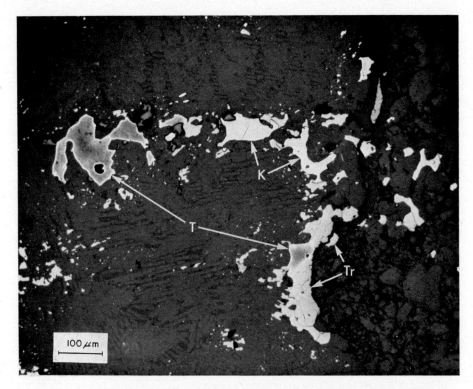

FIGURE 8   Photomicrograph of minerals in a chondrite (Bjurböle, Finland): K, kamacite; T, taenite; Tr, troilite (FeS), embedded in silicate minerals (dark gray). Metallic minerals have formed *in situ* in the meteorite. [From Wood[4]]

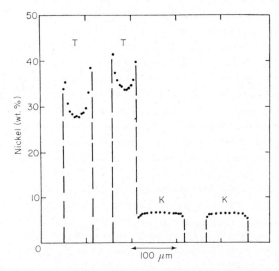

FIGURE 9   Electron microprobe profiles of Ni content across individual metal grains in several chondrites. Left, taenite grain in Mocs (Rumania); center, composite grain in Bjurböle; right, kamacite grain in Forest City (Iowa). [From Wood[11]]

What was the source of the heat that melted irons and metamorphosed chondrites? Five possibilities come to mind, but most of these can be discarded with considerable confidence.

(i) The first possibility is original heat. Perhaps the planets accreted from material that was already hot, in some cases molten. Urey[12] has argued against this on the basis that many volatile elements (e.g. Zn, Se, Cd, and Te) would have remained uncondensed at high temperature, and so should not be present in the meteorites as abundantly as they are. Actually this is true only of some of the meteorites (such as

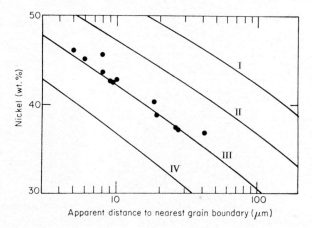

FIGURE 10   Relationship between dimension and central Ni content for taenite crystals (points plotted) in an 'ordinary' chondrite (Forest City). Curve I, 0·1 degc per million years; curve II, 1 degc per million years; curve III, 10 degc per million years; curve IV, 100 degc per million years. [From Wood[11]]

carbonaceous chondrites—a low-temperature origin for these is also indicated by their high content of water and organic compounds). The ordinary and grade-3 chondrites and iron meteorites discussed in the present chapter are, in fact, to some degree depleted (relative to the cosmic abundance) in the elements referred to by Urey (see Anders[13]). It is difficult to exclude the possibility that they had a different, hotter origin than the carbonaceous chondrites. However, rather complicated arguments involving the whole question of chondrite genesis can be raised, which make hot accretion seem improbable. For example, if the ordinary chondrites accreted at high ($> \sim 300$ °c) temperatures in the presence of a gas of cosmic composition, they should not have incorporated as much S and O as they do contain. Above 300 °c the cosmic gas acts to reduce oxidized Fe, Fe silicates, and troilite to metallic Fe plus H_2O and H_2S (unaccretable vapors).

(ii) Secondly, there is the possibility of long-lived radioactivity. This is the only source of planetary heat of which we have sure knowledge (other than solar radiation, of course). It seems quite inadequate to have heated the parent meteorite planets. Let us assume the planets accreted cold $\sim 4·6 \times 10^9$ years ago (the traditional 'age of the solar system', based on results from several geochronological techniques), and contained the same levels of ^{40}K, U, and Th as did chondritic meteorites at that time. Under these circumstances the cores of planets 60 and 200 km in radius (limiting instances of the positions where the octahedrites appear to have formed, as discussed above) would not have been heated above -60 °C and 300 °C, respectively, by radio-active decay (figure 11). The situation is not improved if we suppose that the octa-hedrites were formed in the upper mantles of larger bodies. In order to heat the planets to the melting point of Fe (1535 °C), more than four times the chondritic concentration of ^{40}K, U, Th would have to be assumed, an extravagant assumption because of cosmic abundance considerations.

An even stronger argument against ^{40}K, U, Th heating is raised by the chondritic cooling rates. On the assumption that the parent chondrite planets (there is no evidence that chondrites and octahedrites came from the same planets) were heated to meta-morphic temperatures by ^{40}K, U, Th decay, they could have cooled subsequently

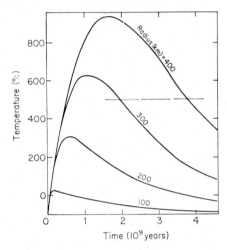

FIGURE 11   Thermal histories at centers of planets of various size, assuming cold accre-tion 4.6×10^9 years ago, and chondritic levels of long-lived radionuclides (^{40}K, U, Th). Cooling rates, dictated by the decay constant of ^{40}K, are about 0·3 degc per million years at 500 °C. (Curves generated by numerical solution of the heat-flow equation. Thermal parameters used appear in the paper by Wood[2], appendix 1)

only by virtue of decreases in ^{40}K, U, Th levels brought about by decay, and so the cooling rate would have been fixed by the decay constant of ^{40}K (the most important heat generator of the three, for chondritic compositions). Under these circumstances, the cooling rate in the neighborhood of 500 °C has to be $\sim$0·3 degc per million years (figure 11). Yet we have seen that the ordinary chondrites cooled much more rapidly, 2–10 degc per million years. Even taking into account the uncertainties in derived cooling rates, many chondrites cooled too rapidly to be consistent with ^{40}K decay.

The preceding argument cannot be used in the case of octahedrites, because melting and differentiation in the parent octahedrite planets may have brought about a re-distribution of ^{40}K, U, Th, which allowed subsequent cooling to be determined by the thermal inertia of the planets rather than the ^{40}K decay constant. It is valid for the chondrites, however, because these have not suffered bulk melting, certainly not bulk melting accompanied by any degree of gravity differentiation, or their content of dense metal and troilite minerals would have been removed from them.

(iii) The third possibility is long-lived radioactivity and planetary breakup. Levin[14] has pointed out that ^{40}K, U, Th heating, melting, and metamorphism might have occurred in a large parent planet, which was then broken up by a collision or by tidal stresses, after which the fragments cooled more rapidly than the original body could have. This model gets around the difficulties noted in (ii). ^{40}K, U, Th heat is generated slowly, however; so, for melting and differentiation to have been achieved $\sim 4 \cdot 6 \times 10^9$ years ago (as indicated by ^{87}Rb–^{87}Sr and ^{207}Pb–^{206}Pb dating (see Anders[15])), the planet would have to have been formed considerably earlier. If we assume that ^{40}K, U, Th levels are consistent with the present-day chondritic abundances, it appears the planet would have to have predated the melting event by $\sim 10^9$ years.

Such a long planetary prehistory seems inconsistent with the recent discovery that live ^{244}Pu was still present in the parent meteorite planet(s) when melting occurred. Independent studies based on fission tracks[16] and noble-gas abundances (^{136}Xe is a fission product of ^{244}Pu)[17] have produced convincing evidence that ^{244}Pu was present in Moore County and Pasamonte (achondrites), and Toluca (octahedrite): these are all meteorites that have been melted. Not many half-lives of ^{244}Pu can have elapsed between the time when the elements that make up the solar system were created, and the crystallization and cooling of melted planetary interiors (after which ^{136}Xe and fission tracks could begin to accumulate). The half-life of ^{244}Pu is only 76×10^6 years; so it seems highly unlikely that any important amount would persist after $\sim 10^9$ years of planetary heating.

(iv) Next there is external heating. Urey[1] has postulated that the newly formed planets, lunar in dimension, were surrounded by large gas spheres. The latter, in a condition of Helmholtz–Kelvin contraction, grew hot inside. The gas heated the surfaces of the planets, causing superficial melting and gravity fractionation of rock types, which left small pods of molten metal at the base of the melted zone. These cooled to form iron meteorites. Urey's model in its present form does not explicitly account for chondrites or the heating event that metamorphosed them.

No specific thermal argument can be raised against this model. By a proper choice of parameters any maximum temperature and subsequent cooling rate desired can be obtained in the upper mantles of Urey's lunar-sized objects. The model can be criticized only in the context of the whole problem of meteorites and the origin of the solar system, a discussion that would be beyond the scope of this chapter. The reader is referred to a recent review paper by Anders[13], in which objections are raised to Urey's model in general (pp. 701–3), and to Urey's interpretation of the significance of cavities that occur in the surface of some iron meteorites (pp. 614–5) in particular. Since Urey's model is to a large extent based on the premise that these cavities are primary features, it is also worth reading Henderson and Perry's original description and discussion of them in the Goose Lake meteorite[18], and aerodynamic studies (e.g. Thomas[19]) which appear to show that the cavities could have been formed by ablation when these meteorites penetrated the Earth's atmosphere.

(v) The last possibility is that of short-lived radioactivity. Brown[20] first pointed out that nuclides with half-lives of less than 10^8 years might have been present in the newly formed planets, if the planets accreted sufficiently soon after nucleosynthesis, although of course the Earth does not contain such nuclides any longer. Urey[21] suggested that short-lived radioactivity might have been an important heat source in the parent meteorite planets, but later discarded the idea. Fish, Goles, and Anders[2] have subsequently advocated it as the most plausible way of accounting for the time scale of thermal events that have affected the meteorites.

The eight most important short-lived radionuclides, in terms of the heat-generating potential, are listed in table 1. Evidence has already been found that two of these were present in the parent meteorite planets: ^{244}Pu (discussed above) and ^{129}I (discussed by Reynolds[23]). However, they would not have heated planetary matter significantly. By far the likeliest heat source in the list is ^{26}Al. Unfortunately, it is all but impossible to prove that ^{26}Al was present, since it decays to ^{26}Mg, which is already contained in planetary material in great abundance.

TABLE 1   Important short-lived radionuclides

	Half-life (million years)	Estimated initial heat output[a] (microcalories per gram of rock per year)
^{10}Be	2·5	53
^{26}Al	0·72	56000
^{36}Cl	0·3	6600
^{60}Fe	~0·3	~120000
^{129}I	16	0·39
^{237}Np	2·2	72
^{244}Pu	76	0·51
^{247}Cm	> 40	<0·21

[a] At the time when the elements were formed (see Fish, Goles, and Anders[22] for the basis of estimates).

^{26}Al heating seems the most probable cause of melting and metamorphism in the parent meteorite planets. It might seem unlikely that the solar system could have been created rapidly enough to preserve any of such a short-lived (720 000 years half-life) radionuclide, but recent studies (e.g. that by Ezer and Cameron[24]) have shown that only $\sim 2 \times 10^6$ years elapsed while the Sun contracted on to the main sequence. Before that time it existed as interstellar gas, into which supernovae could inject newly formed nuclides including, presumably, ^{26}Al. Two million years of ^{26}Al decay before the planets were formed would have decreased the rate of heat generation (table 1) by an order of magnitude but even then enough decay energy would be left to cause melting.

If ^{26}Al heating affected all the terrestrial planets, it may mean that they had an early history quite different from that which is often assumed (i.e. cold or warm accretion followed by a very gradual buildup of K, U, Th heat). They may have accreted cold, but reached an almost completely molten state within a few million years. (However, a discussion of ^{26}Al heating in the Earth or Venus is more or less academic. If these bodies accreted rapidly enough to incorporate undecayed ^{26}Al, it turns out that enough gravitational energy would have been retained as heat to occasion melting.)

From the point of view of a planetary geophysicist, the evidence in favor of ^{26}Al heating is obviously less than satisfactory. What can be said with some certainty is that when we consult the one (now available) source of detailed information about the very early events that affected planets, namely the meteorites, we see evidence of a great deal of heat. The possibility that all the terrestrial planets were similarly affected is worth keeping in mind.

References

1. H. C. Urey, *Monthly Notices Roy. Astron. Soc.*, **131**, 199 (1966).
2. J. A. Wood, *Icarus*, **3**, 429 (1964).
3. J. I. Goldstein and R. E. Ogilvie, *Trans. Met. Soc. AIME*, **233**, 2083 (1965).
4. J. A. Wood, *Icarus*, in press (1966).
5. G. Derge and A. R. Kommel, *Am. J. Sci.*, **34**, 203 (1937).
6. S. H. Perry, 'The metallography of meteoric iron', *U.S. Natl. Museum, Bull.*, **184** (1944).
7. J. I. Goldstein, R. E. Hanneman, and R. E. Ogilvie, *Trans. Met. Soc. AIME*, **233**, 812 (1964).
8. J. I. Goldstein and R. E. Ogilvie, *Geochim. Cosmochim. Acta*, **29**, 893 (1965).
9. H. C. Urey and T. Mayeda, *Geochim. Cosmochim. Acta*, **17**, 113 (1959).
10. S. J. B. Reed, *Nature*, **204**, 374 (1964).
11. J. A. Wood, *Nature*, **208**, 1085 (1965).
12. H. C. Urey, *Geochim. Cosmochim. Acta*, **2**, 269 (1952).
13. E. Anders, *Space Sci. Rev.*, **3**, 583 (1964).
14. B. Yu. Levin, private communication.
15. E. Anders, *Rev. Mod. Phys.*, **34**, 287 (1962).
16. R. L. Fleischer, P. B. Price, and R. M. Walker, *J. Geophys. Res.*, **70**, 2703 (1965).
17. M. W. Rowe and P. K. Kuroda, *J. Geophys. Res.*, **70**, 709 (1965).
18. E. P. Henderson and S. H. Perry, *Proc. U.S. Natl. Museum*, **107**, 339 (1958).
19. R. N. Thomas, 'Meteors', *J. Atmos. Terrest. Phys., Suppl.*, **2**, 1 (1955).
20. H. Brown, *Phys. Rev.*, **72**, 348 (1947).
21. H. C. Urey, *Proc. Natl. Acad. Sci. U.S.*, **41**, 127 (1955).
22. R. A. Fish, G. G. Goles, and E. Anders, *Astrophys. J.*, **132**, 243 (1960).
23. J. H. Reynolds, *J. Geophys. Res.*, **68**, 2939 (1963).
24. D. Ezer and A. G. W. Cameron, *Icarus*, **1**, 422 (1963).

2

S. J. B. REED

Mineralogy Department
British Museum (Natural History)
London, England

Chemical and mineralogical evidence from iron meteorites on the nature of the parent body

---

The Chemistry and Mineralogy of Iron Meteorites

Out of a total of 1789 meteorite specimens known, 591 are irons[1], i.e. one-third of the total. However, taking the 781 which were seen to fall, only 43 are irons, which is less than 6%. These 'falls' represent a reasonably unbiased sample; so the latter figure may be taken as the approximate fraction of all meteorites reaching the Earth's surface which are irons. The gross over-representation of irons in museum collections is due to their being much more easily recognized than stone meteorites. The average mass of an iron is more than a stone, so that the fraction by mass of falls which are irons is more than 6%. However, in estimating the relative abundance of iron meteorite material in space, it is necessary to allow for the greater loss of mass suffered by stones compared with irons owing to atmospheric ablation. Allowing for this it is estimated that irons contribute about 10% of the mass of the original meteoritic material. It is widely thought that irons are fragments of the core of one or more planetary bodies. On the assumption that the density of the metallic core is twice that of the stony mantle, the observed proportion of iron meteorites would be consistent with a core radius of about 37% of the total (compared with 45% for Earth). However, the significance of this estimate is doubtful, since the data are too dependent on a few large falls to be a satisfactory statistical sample. Moreover, it is likely that there was more than one parent body, and the fragmented material which happens to be in orbits which permit capture by Earth may well be biased with respect to the iron to stone ratio.

A large number of chemical analyses of iron meteorites has been published: from these the approximate mean composition of irons is Fe 90%, Ni 9%, Co 0·5%, and S, P, C, and trace elements 0·5%. The elements S, P, and C occur mainly in large grains of sulphide, phosphide and carbide minerals, and graphite. Analyses for these elements are therefore very liable to sampling errors, and results vary according to the procedure adopted. However, it is fairly certain that the amounts of these elements present are of the order of one- or two-tenths of one per cent each. The amount of

Co seems to be rather constant at around one-half of one per cent, and, as Co is distributed fairly evenly, there is no sampling problem. The Ni concentration in irons is highly variable, the minimum being about 5% and the maximum over 60%. Hey[2] has shown that several old analyses in which the Ni concentrations quoted are well under 5% are erroneous: there are probably very few irons really containing appreciably less than 5%. The distribution of Ni contents is skew, with the main peak around 8% and a tail extending to high Ni contents, although there are relatively few with more than 20%. Also it is not completely smooth: there is a marked peak just below 6%, and in the high-Ni region there is distinct clustering around 17%.

The classification of iron meteorites is governed by the macroscopic structures revealed by etching. The great majority (about 80%) of irons have a Widmanstätten structure which consists of oriented lamellae of the Fe–Ni alloy phase kamacite, bordered by strips of another Fe–Ni alloy taenite, with the interstices filled with dark-etching plessite, a microscopic or submicroscopic intergrowth of kamacite and taenite. The kamacite lamellae in the Widmanstätten structure lie in planes parallel to the faces of an octahedron, which gives rise to the name 'octahedrite' for the class of irons which have a Widmanstätten structure. This class is divided according to the width of the kamacite lamellae into 5 subclasses: coarsest, coarse, medium, fine, and finest octahedrites. About half of all octahedrites are classified as medium, with kamacite lamellae between 0·5 and 1·5 mm wide. There is a general tendency for a high Ni content to be associated with a fine Widmanstätten structure, but the correlation is not exact. Octahedrites contain down to about 6% Ni, where there is a fairly sharp cut-off. Irons with less than 6% Ni fall into one of two classes, hexahedrites and Ni-poor ataxites. The hexahedrites are characterized by the appearance on etching of Neumann lines, which are actually narrow twin lamellae produced by deformation, lying in hexahedral planes. The Ni-poor ataxites (ataxite meaning without structure, Ni-poor to distinguish from a separate class of Ni-rich ataxites) form a small group differing from the hexahedrites only in the absence of Neumann lines, which is probably not a distinction of great significance. At the Ni-rich end of the spectrum the octahedrites merge into the Ni-rich ataxites, which are macroscopically structureless, but most of them consist almost entirely of microscopic fine plessite intergrowth. The boundary between octahedrites and Ni-rich ataxites in terms of Ni content is not sharp, and there is a zone of overlap between 10% and 16%.

The minerals in iron meteorites are as follows:

kamacite	α Fe–Ni alloy (body-centred cubic)
taenite	γ Fe–Ni (face-centred cubic)
plessite	$\alpha + \gamma$ intergrowth (not a true mineral)
troilite	FeS
schreibersite ⎱ rhabdite ⎰	$(Fe, Ni)_3 P$
cohenite	$(Fe, Ni)_3 C$
graphite	C
daubréelite	$FeCr_2 S_4$
lawrencite	$FeCl_2$

The minerals are listed in approximate order of importance. A few others have been identified in irons, but are found only in insignificant amounts. Not all these minerals are present in all irons. Hexahedrites and Ni-poor ataxites contain no taenite, and both graphite and cohenite are found mainly in irons containing less than about 8% Ni. The rhabdite form of iron–nickel phosphide is also more abundant in the more Ni-poor types, whereas schreibersite and troilite are common in all types. Kamacite is chemically fairly homogeneous, containing 6% to 7·5% Ni (slightly less in hexahedrites and Ni-poor ataxites), while taenite is highly inhomogeneous, containing about 25% to 50% Ni. The mean composition of plessite is variable according to the proportions of kamacite and taenite in the intergrowth. Troilite is pure stoichiometric FeS with only trace amounts of other elements. Schreibersite and rhabdite are quite variable in their Fe to Ni ratio, the Ni content ranging from 12% to 50%, though apparently always maintaining stoichiometry. Cohenite contains 1% to 3% Ni.

The crystallography of the metal phases is actually rather more complex than indicated above. There is a distorted body-centred cubic phase referred to as α_2, which is produced by the diffusionless (martensitic) transformation of taenite at

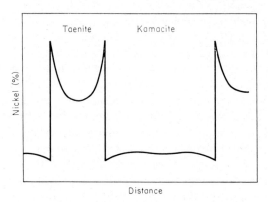

FIGURE 1   Typical Ni profile in an octahedrite

low temperatures. A transformation structure resulting from the shock-induced conversion of kamacite to the high-pressure ε phase is found in some irons[3-8]. There is evidence of ordering, in both kamacite and taenite, from superlattice lines found in their X-ray diffraction patterns[9,10]. In taenite there is some evidence of Fe_3Ni and possibly FeNi ordered structures.

Techniques previously used to obtain information about the distribution of elements in iron meteorites, such as microhardness measurements, thermomagnetic analysis, and mechanical separation of phases followed by wet chemical analysis, have been largely superseded by electron-probe microanalysis. The combination in this technique of high spatial resolution (about 1 μm) with reasonable accuracy (about 1% of the amount analysed) has proved most useful in elucidating the details of the distribution of the main elements present. The amount of Co in the metal phases is small, and that of other elements excluding Fe and Ni even smaller; so these phases can be regarded as Fe–Ni alloys, the composition of which is essentially determined by the Ni concentration alone. Figure 1 shows the normal form of the Ni distribution in kamacite and taenite in an octahedrite from electron-probe data[11-18]. The concentration of Ni in taenite rises very rapidly up to the boundary with kamacite, and with a resolution of 1 μm the apparent maximum at the boundary is probably several per cent of Ni too low. The boundary Ni concentration, with some allowance for limited resolution, varies from 35% to 50% in different specimens. In the microscope the low-Ni centre of the M-shaped profile is shown, on etching, to consist of plessite, but the Ni profile is more or less smooth across the unresolved intergrowth in the centre of the M. Kamacite is far more homogeneous than taenite, the only variation in Ni concentration being a slight depression in the centre of kamacite lamellae and a a more marked decrease in Ni immediately adjacent to taenite. The latter phenomenon has been called the 'Agrell effect', having been first demonstrated conclusively by Agrell, Long, and Ogilvie[14], who proved that it is not an artefact produced during preparation of the specimen.

The Formation of the Widmanstätten Structure

The fact that iron meteorites exist at all proves that they must at one time have been molten, since it is possible to visualize a process of large-scale separation of metal and silicates in a parent body only if the metal was liquid. This requires a temperature of at least 1500 °C. The kamacite lamellae of the Widmanstätten structure are oriented parallel to the (111) planes of taenite, and a specific lattice orientation relationship between the two phases exists, which indicates that the kamacite lamellae grew by a process of exsolution in the solid state, and that prior to the appearance of kamacite during cooling the metal consisted entirely of taenite. The fact that kamacite lamellae maintain a constant orientation throughout some of the largest known specimens, with dimensions of the order of metres, shows that at the all-taenite stage the material was in the form of very large single crystals, and this indicates very slow cooling in the temperature range in which only taenite is stable, estimated to be about 1500–700 °C for octahedrites. Most of the growth of kamacite lamellae is thought to have taken place in the temperature range 700–500 °C (approximately). The coarseness and regularity of the Widmanstätten structure compared with comparable structures produced in the laboratory is such as to suggest very slow cooling during its formation. It therefore seems that iron meteorites originate from metallic masses which cooled exceedingly slowly over a temperature range of at least 1000 degC, and this obviously requires a very long cooling period.

The equilibrium phase diagram of the Fe–Ni binary system has been intensively investigated, and in the more recent work there has been a good measure of agreement. Figure 2 shows the subsolidus area of the phase diagram relevant to discussion of the Widmanstätten structure in octahedrites. The positions of the boundaries are taken from the data of Owen and Liu[19], Ringwood and Kaufman[20], Kachi, Bando, and Higuchi[21], and Goldstein and Ogilvie[22]. The experimental data below 500 °C are of doubtful accuracy because the γ–α transformation is inhibited by the extreme slowness of diffusion at such low temperatures, but it is possible to extrapolate the experimentally determined boundaries to lower temperatures by thermodynamic calculations. The γ–α transformation in pure Fe occurs at 910 °C; the addition of Ni lowers the transformation temperature until with 50% Ni it is below 400 °C. The equilibrium Ni content of the α phase (kamacite) increases steadily with falling temperature down to some temperature below 500 °C, after which it is thought to decrease, though this has not been proved experimentally. The maximum Ni content of the α phase is probably around 7% to 8%. This binary phase diagram has been extensively used to explain the Widmanstätten structure and the distribution of Ni in it, but it must be borne in mind that the presence of other elements (particularly P and C) may shift the boundaries quite appreciably; also the pressure in the parent body could have a marked effect.

The typical distribution of Ni in the Widmanstätten structure shown in figure 1 can be explained by reference to the Fe–Ni phase diagram in figure 2. A typical octahedrite containing, say, 9% Ni will consist entirely of taenite until it cools to about 700 °C when it enters the $\alpha + \gamma$ field. There may be some undercooling before nucleation and growth of kamacite commences, but at a temperature not too far below 700 °C kamacite starts to exsolve. The habit and lattice orientation of the kamacite are governed by the criterion of minimum free energy, and this gives rise to the observed

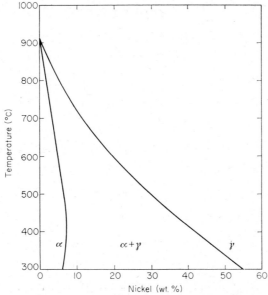

FIGURE 2   Low-temperature area of the Fe–Ni equilibrium phase diagram

characteristics of the Widmanstätten structure. During further cooling both kamacite and taenite increase in Ni content, the total Ni being kept constant by the continuing transformation of taenite to kamacite. The observed inhomogeneities develop because of increasingly restricted diffusion as the temperature falls. The Ni concentration in the centre of the M profile of large taenite–plessite areas corresponds to a temperature in the region of 600 °C. Diffusion in taenite is so slow at this temperature that it is impossible for more Ni to diffuse into the centre to maintain the equilibrium Ni content. Equilibrium is, however, still maintained close to the kamacite–taenite interface, so that Ni builds up at the interface, giving the characteristic M profile. Diffusion in kamacite is very much faster than in taenite at a given temperature, so kamacite remains virtually homogeneous down to lower temperatures. Inhomogeneity in kamacite seems to develop in the region in which the slope of the α-phase boundary reverses. The centres of wide kamacite lamellae have Ni contents corresponding to temperatures just above the temperature of maximum Ni content, while, at the interface with taenite, equilibrium is maintained down to temperatures appreciably below this. The shape of the α-phase boundary in the phase diagram thus explains the Ni profile in kamacite, including the Agrell effect. The Ni concentrations in kamacite and taenite at the interface between them correspond to a certain temperature, obtainable from the phase diagram, at which the Ni profile becomes completely frozen in. These interface compositions can be measured with the electron probe, though the gradient in taenite is so steep that a correction for the limited resolution of the probe is necessary. Figure 3 shows the results of such measurements on 17 octahedrites by Reed[18]. Although there is some scatter, at least part of which could be due to experimental error (mostly in the taenite), there is a clear correlation between the Ni concentrations in kamacite and taenite. Since increasing Ni in taenite is definitely associated with decreasing temperature, it follows that freezing in must occur below the

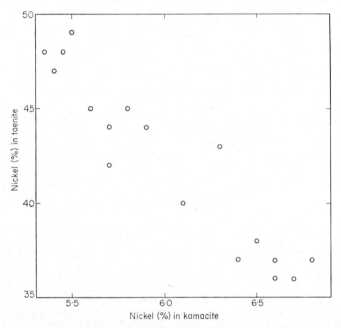

FIGURE 3   Ni concentration in kamacite and taenite at their mutual interface in
17 octahedrites

reversal of slope of the α-phase boundary, because the Ni content decreases in kamacite while increasing in taenite. From the phase diagram in figure 2, the observed range of taenite compositions corresponds to freezing-in temperatures of about 350–450 °C. The kamacite compositions are useful in giving information about the shape of the α-phase boundary at temperatures too low for accurate experimental data to be obtained, rather than for deducing freezing-in temperatures. The information obtained applies to the Fe–Ni system modified by the effects of pressure (if any) and other elements present. The measurement of interface compositions by conventional electron-probe microanalysis is handicapped by the limited spatial resolution. This difficulty could be largely overcome by using a thin-film specimen in a high-resolution instrument, such as that described by Duncumb[23], with which resolution better than 0·2 μm is obtainable.

Freezing-in temperatures deduced from interface compositions may be regarded as an indication of relative cooling rates. In principle it should be possible to calculate absolute cooling rates from interface compositions, but a method of doing this has not yet been evolved. The same applies to freezing-in temperatures arrived at in other ways, such as measuring the volume fraction occupied by the main kamacite lamellae and finding the corresponding temperature from the phase diagram by applying the lever rule, as carried out by Massalski and Park[24]. This procedure gives a freezing-in temperature, which is the temperature below which no significant further growth of the main kamacite lamellae could take place (though γ–α transformation to form plessite would continue). Anders[25], using preferred values for total Ni contents, re-calculated the results obtained by Massalski and Park for five octahedrites and found a range of freezing-in temperatures of 433–515 °C. Both this and the interface composi-tion method thus indicate a range of cooling rates which must be quite large, in view of the rapid change of diffusion coefficients with temperature.

Wood[15] has evolved a method of determining absolute cooling rates in which a computer model of the development of the M profile is set up, making use of experi-mental data on the Fe–Ni phase diagram and diffusion coefficients. This model predicts the Ni concentration in taenite–plessite areas as a function of the distance from the interface with kamacite for various cooling rates. Comparison with electron-probe measurements then enables cooling rates to be deduced. Values of 1–10 degc per million years were found for octahedrites. Comparable results have been obtained by Short and Anderson[26] and Goldstein and Ogilvie[16] using methods which are similar in principle.

Profile synthesis by computer is clearly a very powerful technique, since it offers the possibility of quantitative determination of cooling rates, but there are certain limita-tions. Firstly, it is possible to deduce only a mean linear cooling rate over the range of temperatures in which the γ–α transformation takes place (say 700–400 °C), and noth-ing can be said about the cooling rate outside this range. Secondly, there are several possible sources of error, some of them quite serious, which affect the accuracy of calculated cooling rates. For instance, there is a margin of error in the location of the boundaries in the phase diagram, particularly below 500 °C. Diffusion coefficients have been measured only at relatively high temperatures, and the error in experi-mentally determined activation energies is sufficient to cause large errors in calculated diffusion coefficients for low temperatures. It is assumed that it is appropriate to use the phase diagram for the binary Fe–Ni system at one atmosphere pressure, but this is not strictly correct, since there are appreciable amounts of other elements present, and pressures of more than one atmosphere must have existed in any parent body of plausible size. The addition of 0·1 % of P raises the γ–α transformation temperature of Fe by about 60 degc while adding the same amount of C reduces it by about 30 degc, according to phase diagrams given by Hansen[27]. Quite small concentrations of these elements can evidently change the starting temperature of the γ–α transformation quite appreciably, besides altering the equilibrium Ni contents of kamacite and taenite at any given temperature. One of the main uncertainties of the computer approach is the amount of undercooling of taenite to allow after entering the $\alpha + \gamma$ field, before kamacite nucleates. Goldstein and Ogilvie[16] state that, as nucleation of kama-cite is presumably homogeneous, some undercooling is inevitable, and suggest 100 degc as a reasonable amount to assume. It is doubtful if metallurgical intuition can be relied on, because of the time available being vastly greater than in the laboratory. Wood[15] also assumed undercooling of around 100 degC on the grounds that this gave the best agreement between computed and experimental profiles for the ten octahedrites studied. The validity of this assumption is questionable, in view of the other uncertainties in the computation, and the fact that the boundary had already been adjusted to give profiles of the correct shape. In view of the large number of possible sources of error, computer profile synthesis, though a very promising technique, cannot at present be expected to produce accurate absolute cooling rates, though the observation of differences of cooling rate between different specimens is almost certainly valid.

The main conclusion which has been drawn from the estimated cooling rates for octahedrites is that, for a parent body of the size required to cool at 1–10 degC per million years (50–250 km radius), it is necessary to invoke some heating process such as the decay of short-lived radionuclides (possibly ^{26}Al) to explain how the temperature in the interior of the body rose initially to over 1500 °C, which would clearly also be of great importance in the thermal history of the Earth and other planets. If cooling rates are underestimated, then the parent body or bodies must have been smaller, making it even more necessary to invoke an extra heat source to cause initial melting. If the reverse is true, it might appear to eliminate the necessity for such extra heating, but other evidence must be considered. Cooling through 1000 degC must have taken place within the age of the solar system, which implies a mean cooling rate of at least 0·2 degC per million years. Wood[15] estimated that a planetary body of radius greater than about 420 km would not cool to below 500 °C at the centre within the age of the solar system. Therefore any proposed parent body must in any case be restricted to dimensions comparable with asteroids (Ceres, the largest, has a radius of 365 km) rather than the Moon (radius 1740 km), and a size approaching that of the planets (e.g. Earth, radius 6360 km) is completely impossible. This conclusion is confirmed by the evidence against pressures of greater than a few kilobars in the parent body, which is discussed on p. 25. The evidence for asteroidal-sized parent bodies and the consequent necessity for postulating early heating by short-lived radionuclides is therefore largely independent of the absolute cooling rates obtained by the profile synthesis technique. The most useful function of cooling-rate calculations is to indicate differences in cooling rate, which can also be deduced from freezing-in temperatures. The implications of these differences with respect to a possible multiplicity of parent bodies are discussed in conjunction with the evidence from Ga–Ge groups on p. 27.

The Role of Phosphorus

The presence of P in irons is important, partly because of its effect on the equilibrium of the metal phases, and partly because of the universal occurrence of iron–nickel phosphide in the form of schreibersite and rhabdite. The main source of information on the ternary Fe–Ni–P system is the work of Vogel and Baur[28], who produced detailed phase diagrams, but it is doubtful whether the experimental basis was adequate to justify the apparent precision of the diagrams. Vogel[29–31] has given a comprehensive explanation of the occurrence of schreibersite and rhabdite, and the origin of the Widmanstätten structure. Vogel's interpretation is based on the 'δ–γ hypothesis', according to which the kamacite lamellae of the Widmanstätten structure were formed direct from the melt as dendrites of δ phase (high-temperature body-centred cubic alloy), which is stabilized by P and therefore remains unaltered during cooling, instead of transforming to γ phase. This hypothesis has not received support, owing to the difficulty in reconciling it with the known facts about the Widmanstätten structure. It is, of course, in direct conflict with the 'γ–α hypothesis' expounded in the previous section. Since the γ–α hypothesis provides much the more satisfactory explanation for the Widmanstätten structure, Vogel's account of the formation of schreibersite and rhabdite must be rejected.

Adler and Dwornik[32], Goldstein and Ogilvie[33], and Reed[34] have carried out electron-probe investigations on schreibersite and rhabdite. Henderson and Perry[35] had already discovered that the Ni content of schreibersite in a given specimen is variable, with a tendency for the largest grains to have the least Ni. This fact has been confirmed by electron-probe microanalysis, and the size correlation has been found to extend over the whole size range down to schreibersite grains only a few micrometres across. The range of Ni contents is from just over 10% up to 50%. It seems that the formula M_3P, where M is Ni, Fe, and a little Co, is strictly adhered to, and the variation in Ni content is accompanied by a compensating variation in Fe. Despite the large variation in Ni content from grain to grain, there is no detectable variation within each grain. If we assume a simple diffusion-limited growth process, this implies that diffusion of Ni and Fe in the surrounding material (which is almost always kamacite) must be much slower than in the phosphide. The different compositions of different grains must be due to the freezing-in at varying temperatures, governed by the limitation of diffusion of Ni and Fe in kamacite. The equilibrium Ni content of schreibersite must increase with falling temperature. The largest grains have the lowest Ni content because they nucleated first at the highest temperature and, at lower temperatures, when only limited diffusion in kamacite was possible, they were less able to raise their Ni content because of having a smaller surface area to volume ratio compared with small grains. The very smallest grains of schreibersite are found at kamacite–taenite interfaces, and it appears that schreibersite nucleated in the taenite at the interface. This is a favourable site with regard to the availability of Ni, and may also be preferred for crystallographic reasons. It is possible that all schreibersite nucleated in this manner, but this is difficult to prove, as the larger grains are no longer close to kamacite–taenite interfaces. Experiments by Clark[36] show that in the three-phase $\alpha + \gamma + $ phosphide field, the equilibrium Ni contents of γ phase (taenite) and phosphide (schreibersite) are similar over a range of temperatures well above the freezing-in temperature of octahedrites, which suggests that chemical factors would tend to favour nucleation of schreibersite in taenite at all temperatures.

Rhabdite occurs as numerous small regular needles scattered within the kamacite of hexahedrites and octahedrites. It is chemically identical with schreibersite: each grain is homogeneous, but there is a size-correlated variation from grain to grain, though the range of sizes and Ni contents is much less than that of schreibersite. Rhabdite is presumably the result of homogeneous nucleation of phosphide at low temperatures when the rate of growth of schreibersite was too low to prevent super-saturation of kamacite with P. It is interesting to note that the Ni content of the small-est schreibersite grains equals, and even exceeds, that of rhabdite in octahedrites with both forms present. This suggests that at low temperatures nucleation and growth of both varieties occurs simultaneously, and the minute schreibersite grains adjacent to, or embedded in, taenite are actually the latest phosphide to precipitate.

The preceding account shows that the observed features of schreibersite and rhabdite in irons can be explained in general terms. In the absence of an accurate ternary phase diagram it is impossible to make quantitative estimates of cooling rates, pressures, etc., from the Ni content of the phosphide phase. An alternative indicator of these conditions is the P content of kamacite. Reed[34] has noted that the measured P concentration in kamacite in octahedrites indicates freezing-in at around 300 °C to 400 °C on the basis of the reasonably well-established P solvus curve for α-iron, with a small allowance for the Ni in kamacite. This range is comparable with that estimated for the freezing in of the kamacite–taenite equilibrium.

Perhaps the most important aspect of the role of P in irons is its effect on the Widmanstätten structure. If the Vogel phase diagram is qualitatively correct, then the only way schreibersite could have formed is by precipitation in the solid state after the start of the γ–α transformation, i.e. after kamacite had begun to exsolve from taenite. There are only two alternatives to this: either the δ–γ hypothesis is correct, which raises profound difficulties, or else the ternary phase diagram is basically incorrect. The thermodynamically plausible ways of constructing the diagram, given the known binary Fe–Ni and Fe–P diagrams, must be strictly limited, and experimental evidence (as far as it goes) agrees qualitatively with Vogel's ternary diagram, so the latter alternative is improbable. The foregoing explanation, involving the precipitation of phosphide after the start of the γ–α transformation, is therefore probably correct. Clark[36] found experimentally that the Ni content of $(Fe, Ni)_3P$ in equilibrium with α and γ Fe–Ni alloys is about 12% at 700 °C (at one atmosphere pressure). This is about equal to the minimum Ni content of schreibersite, which suggests that schreibersite must have nucleated appreciably above 700 °C. From the Fe–Ni phase diagram for one atmosphere pressure, 700 °C is about the temperature at which kamacite starts to appear (assuming no undercooling) in octahedrites, which is inconsistent with the requirement that kamacite should start to appear before the precipitation of phosphide. This discrepancy might be accounted for by the presence of other elements (of which C is probably the only one which could have an appreciable effect), or it may be due to the assumption that the binary Fe–Ni phase diagram gives correctly the temperature at which kamacite started to exsolve, whereas in fact the effect of P could be to raise this temperature well above 700 °C. The concentration of P in kamacite in octahedrites is 0·05% to 0·10% according to Goldstein and Ogilvie[33] and Reed[34]. With the rhabdite included, the mean P content of kamacite in the Canyon Diablo coarse octahedrite was found by Reed to be 0·15%. If we allow for the larger but less numerous grains of schreibersite, the overall P content is probably around 0·2%. Taenite contains much less P than kamacite, but the proportion of taenite in a coarse octahedrite is small. The effect of adding 0·2% P to iron is to raise the temperature at which the γ–α transformation starts by about 100 degC. A comparable effect is likely in the ternary Fe–Ni–P system, which has serious implications for the accuracy of the Ni profile synthesis technique. The effect of P on the frozen-in Ni concentrations in kamacite and taenite at their mutual interface, representing equilibrium at a temperature of the order of 400 °C, is probably less serious because most of the P has already gone from the metal phases into precipitated phosphide.

Consideration of the effect of P throws doubt on the accuracy of calculated cooling rates. On the positive side, it has been shown that the facts are best explained by processes which are completely compatible with the account of the origin of the Widmanstätten structure given in the previous section, and do not require the assumption of very high pressure during cooling. In fact the evidence is clearly against any pressure high enough to have a drastic effect on the phase diagram, although it is difficult to set a precise upper limit. It is highly desirable that more experimental work on the Fe–Ni–P system should be carried out to improve our understanding of the role of P in irons.

The Pressure in the Parent Body

There has been much debate in the last few years about the pressure which existed in the parent body or bodies from which iron meteorites originate. At present the evidence points to low pressures (up to a few kilobars), since the arguments put forward in favour of high pressure have largely been discredited, and there is some positive evidence against high pressures. A brief outline of some of the main arguments is given here.

Diamond

Small diamonds have been found in a few meteorites, notably in the Canyon Diablo octahedrite associated with the famous crater in Arizona. The formation of diamond as a stable phase requires pressures of several tens of kilobars, and it has been proposed that its presence is indicative of such static pressures in the parent body, which would require it to be of the order of size of the Moon or larger. However, Nininger[37], Lipschutz and Anders[38,39], and Heymann and others[8] have argued that a more probable explanation is that they were produced by impact shock, since diamond-bearing specimens always show other signs of shock, while unshocked specimens do not contain diamonds.

Cliftonite

The name cliftonite is used to describe small regular graphite crystals found in a number of irons. It has been suggested that these are pseudomorphs after diamond and therefore indicate high pressures. However, Anders and Lipschutz[39] have put forward strong arguments against a diamond origin. The lattice orientations of artificially graphitized diamond and cliftonite are quite different; also cliftonite has been found coexisting with tridymite, which is unstable above 3 kb, in certain stone meteorites. Another difficulty with the diamond origin hypothesis is that there is a volume increase of 56% on conversion of diamond to graphite, no evidence for which can be seen in meteoritic cliftonite.

Cohenite

The mineral cohenite, $(Fe, Ni)_3C$, is commonly present in the more Ni-poor types of iron meteorite. Pure Fe_3C (cementite) is unstable at one atmosphere pressure below about 1000 °c, and tends to decompose into metallic iron and graphite. Ni is known as a graphitizing element because its presence promotes the decomposition of cementite in steel. Since iron meteorites were certainly in equilibrium down to temperatures well below 1000 °c and cohenite clearly formed as a stable phase, its presence is difficult to explain. Ringwood[40] and others have suggested that pressures of a few tens of kilobars would suitably stabilize cohenite during cooling. However, Lipschutz and Anders[41] have argued that, as experiments have failed to confirm the predicted stabilizing effect, the assumption of high pressures does not solve the problem, and whatever the pressure it is necessary to suppose that decomposition during cooling was drastically inhibited. There is some experimental evidence that a lack of nuclei slows down decomposition by a large factor. Moreover, Lovering[42] has observed that cohenite exists in metallic masses in basalt from Disko Island, West Greenland, which proves that it can survive during slow cooling at low pressures.

Widmanstätten structure

Uhlig[43] thought that the distribution of Ni between kamacite and taenite could only be accounted for on the basis of a 100 kb phase diagram, but his argument was based on an assumed Ni concentration in taenite of 30%, which is now known to be considerably lower than that actually existing close to interfaces with kamacite. The evidence now available is entirely consistent with formation at low pressure. It is difficult to set a precise upper limit, but a pressure much above 10 kb is unlikely, in view of the effects of pressure on the Fe–Ni phase diagram calculated by Kaufman and Ringwood[44].

Ni-rich ataxites

A further argument advanced by Uhlig was that there is no apparent reason why Ni-rich ataxites should not have developed Widmanstätten structures, since fine Widmanstätten structures have been reported in alloys containing comparable amounts of Ni cooled slowly at one atmosphere pressure. Uhlig proposed that this discrepancy could be accounted for by assuming that meteorites cooled at very high pressures, at which the starting temperature of the γ–α transformation would be depressed sufficiently for the transformation to be completely inhibited. However, Wood[15] has argued convincingly that the supposed Widmanstätten structures produced experimentally resulted from the diffusionless (martensitic) transformation of the γ phase to distorted α phase, and were not true Widmanstätten structures. This eliminates the necessity for high pressures, and the absence of Widmanstätten structures in Ni-rich ataxites can be explained as being merely due to the γ–α transformation starting at too low a temperature for kamacite lamellae to develop. The fine kamacite–taenite intergrowth in Ni-rich ataxites requires diffusion only over very short distances.

Tridymite

Anders[25] has pointed out that the stony-iron meteorite Steinbach contains tridymite, a form of silica which cannot exist at pressures above 3 kb, while the metal part contains a well-developed Widmanstätten structure. This shows that it is possible for a Widmanstätten structure to form at low pressures.

Internal cavities

Further evidence against high pressures cited by Anders is the presence of internal cavities in some irons, which could not exist with pressures of more than about 4 kb.

Ga–Ge Groups

Lovering and others[45] have shown that the Ga and Ge contents of iron meteorites are highly variable, but in a fairly systematic way. Firstly, there is a strong positive correlation between the concentrations of the two elements and, secondly, the distribution shows marked clustering. This led to the proposal that irons could be classified into four Ga–Ge groups defined by the range of Ga and Ge concentrations found in each group. Wasson[46] divided group 4 into two clearly resolved groups which he designated 4a and 4b, based on analyses of 20 specimens belonging to Lovering's group 4, using a more sensitive analytical technique.

Several authors have noted a degree of correlation between Ga–Ge groups, structural classes, and Ni contents. Wasson found that group 4a irons are fine octahedrites, while group 4b are Ni-rich ataxites. The range of Ni contents in both groups is quite narrow. Group 1 is also very well defined in terms of structural class and Ni content. Groups 2 and 3 cover a wider range, but group 2 appears to be a combination of a rather narrow group of hexahedrites and Ni-poor ataxites, and a more diffuse group of octahedrites. Table 1 gives the range of Ga and Ge concentrations in the five groups, together with the structural classes which predominate in each group, and the range of Ni contents taken from the analytical data collected by Hey[1], based on

TABLE 1   Ga–Ge groups

Group	Ga (parts per million)	Ge (parts per million)	Predominant structural classes	Range of Ni contents (%)
1	80–100	300–420	coarsest octahedrites coarse octahedrites	6·5–7·3
2	40–65	130–230	Ni-poor ataxites hexahedrites	5·4–5·9[a]
			coarsest octahedrites coarse octahedrites medium octahedrites	6·4–9·5
3	8–24	15–80	medium octahedrites fine octahedrites finest octahedrites	7·4–13·5
4a	1·7–2·3	0·1–0·14	fine octahedrites	7·4–9·2
4b	0·2–0·4	0·03–0·06	Ni-rich ataxites	16·2–18·2

[a] Excluding one anomalously high-Ni hexahedrite.

Lovering's classification, with Wasson's groups 4a and 4b. The distribution of the 103 analysed specimens listed by Hey among the Ga–Ge groups is as follows:

group 1	12
2	24
3	30
4 (a and b)	21
anomalous	16

Groups 1, 4a, 4b, and part of 2 seem to be well defined, and from Hey's data about 40% of analysed irons fall into these groups. The existence of at least some well-

defined groups, within which the Ga, Ge, and Ni contents and the structure vary only
slightly, is therefore well established. The remaining 60%, consisting of group 3 and
the rest of group 2, together with all anomalous cases, could represent an unresolved
mixture of a number of groups. The present Ga–Ge groups should not be regarded
as definitive: it is to be expected that ideas about grouping will be modified as more
data on these and other trace elements become available. Nevertheless, the existence
of distinct groups is already a fact requiring explanation. Their origin can conveniently
be attributed to different parent bodies, thus avoiding the awkward necessity of
explaining drastic differentiation of Ga and Ge, with independent Ni differentiation,
within one body. There remains the problem of explaining the large difference in the
abundance of Ga and Ge in the parent bodies. The concentrations in groups 1 and 2
are comparable with cosmic abundances. The other groups are depleted, and no
correspondingly enriched material has been observed. According to Anders[25], the
only plausible explanation for this depletion is selective volatilization. The problem
of the processes involved in the initial accretion of the meteorite parent bodies is
complex and controversial, and will not be discussed here. It is sufficient to note that
the evidence points to the existence of several separate parent bodies, and that the
origin of the Ga–Ge groups is unlikely to lie in mantle–core differentiation or other
processes occurring within a single parent body.

There is abundant evidence of marked differences in cooling rates among the iron
meteorites. Differences in cooling rate between the centre and edge of the core of a
single parent body would no doubt exist, but could hardly be as great. Furthermore,
if the differences were due to the original location of the meteorite in a single core,
and if there were a monotonic variation in Ni content from centre to edge, then a
simple correlation between cooling rate and Ni content would exist. Irons with the
same Ni content often have different cooling rates, which suggests either a multiplicity of parent bodies, or a single parent body with rather peculiar properties. One
indication of cooling rate is the width of the kamacite lamellae for a given total Ni
content, and Yavnel[47] has shown that a degree of correlation between lamella width
and Ga–Ge groups exists, suggesting different cooling rates for different parent bodies.
The results of electron-probe studies tend to confirm this observation, although it is
not yet possible to assign with confidence a unique cooling rate to each group. There
is, however, a general trend towards faster cooling with decreasing Ga–Ge content,
and group 4a irons seem to have cooled perhaps 20 times faster than group 1. Other
things being equal, this would correspond to parent bodies with radii differing by a
factor of about 4.

The Nature of the Parent Body

A plausible explanation for the range of Ni contents in irons is selective oxidation of
Fe, which is observed in the commonest type of stone meteorites, the ordinary
chondrites. The redox conditions under which a metal plus silicate system equilibrates
determine the proportion of Fe which is oxidized and enters the silicate minerals.
The Ni remains virtually entirely in the metal phases, so that the stronger the
oxidation the more Fe-rich the silicates and the more Ni-rich the metal. The metal
in chondrites has a range of Ni contents closely correlated with the Fe to Mg ratio
of the main silicate minerals olivine and pyroxene, resulting from equilibration under a

range of redox conditions. The range of Ni contents of metal in chondrites is from around 5% to over 50%, which closely parallels that in irons. This shows that the selective oxidation mechanism operating in a meteorite parent body is capable of producing the range of Ni contents found in irons.

Lovering[48] has proposed an alternative mechanism by which differentiation with respect to Ni content arises during solidification. According to the Fe–Ni phase diagram, the first metal to solidify from a melt containing 11% Ni (the value assumed by Lovering) contains 5·5% Ni. If the solid metal is effectively removed from the system, the Ni content of the solidifying metal increases with falling temperature, until the last drop of liquid containing 68% Ni solidifies. Lovering calculated the distribution of iron meteorites with respect to Ni content predicted by this theory. There is agreement between the observed and predicted distributions, in that both show a preponderance of low-Ni irons, but there are considerable discrepancies in detail. However, the observed distribution may be influenced by biased sampling, so comparison with the prediction is not a critical test. Furthermore, it is assumed that there was only one parent body, which is unlikely in view of the existence of Ga–Ge groups: if there were several, the observed distribution would be composite.

It seems likely that some differentiation would occur during solidification of a massive metallic body. Whether or not the resulting inhomogeneity would be retained during cooling is dependent on the rate of diffusion in the solid γ phase and the time available. The interdiffusion coefficient of Fe and Ni in the γ phase at temperatures just below the melting point is of the order of 10^{-9} cm^2/sec according to Goldstein, Hannemann, and Ogilvie[49]. The time available for diffusion in a temperature range of, say, 100 degc below the melting point could hardly have been much more than 10^8 years. Under these conditions, homogenization is impossible in bodies more than a few tens of metres across. If solidification of the core of the parent body proceeded from the centre outwards, then differentiation would give rise to an increasing Ni content in each successive layer and, if the core were more than a few tens of metres across, the non-uniform Ni distribution would be frozen in. In this way the whole range of Ni contents observed in irons would be produced within a single core, but this is not in accordance with the evidence from Ga–Ge groups. About 40% of irons analysed for Ga and Ge belong to groups in which the range of Ni contents is only 1% or 2% Ni, and the remainder seem more likely to belong to a number of poorly resolved groups than to represent a continuum. It is almost essential to assume that different Ga–Ge groups originate in different parent bodies: there is thus no evidence of more than a rather small variation in Ni content within each parent body. It is widely thought that iron meteorites are fragments of the cores of a number of asteroidal bodies with radii of 50 to 250 km. On any reasonable estimate of core to mantle ratio, such bodies would have cores with diameters of not less than several tens of kilometres. If cores of such dimensions differentiated by the Lovering mechanism, the whole range of Ni contents would be frozen in. The rather small variation observed within each Ga–Ge group suggests that this mechanism did not operate to an appreciable extent. If Ga–Ge groups do indeed come from different parent bodies, then another explanation must be sought for the large variation in Ni content between the groups.

It is possible to envisage mechanisms by which a solid core, more or less homogeneous throughout, could be formed. A kind of dendritic structure might have appeared at the start of solidification. This would divide the core into enclosed cells

M.E.—2*

within which differentiation could take place during further solidification. The size of these cells would determine whether or not the inhomogeneity arising from the differentiation would be retained in the solid core. Alternatively, solidification might have started with the nucleation of crystals more or less simultaneously throughout the core. If the viscosity of the melt were great enough and the gravitational field weak enough, in relation to the dimensions of the core and the time available, these crystals might not have been able to sink to the centre to an appreciable extent, so that solidification would proceed by the growth of the crystals throughout the core, rather than by outward growth from a central solid mass. Either of these mechanisms would enable a liquid metal core to solidify without large compositional variations being frozen in.

The observation of appreciable differences in Ni content and the width of kamacite lamellae in different specimens of the Canyon Diablo meteorite is of great interest. As noted by Heymann and others[8], this constitutes evidence for compositional variations over distances of less than 100 m, since estimates of the size of the meteorite at impact, based on the size of the crater, range from 25 to 86 m. The change in the Widmanstätten structure from coarse to medium and the variation in Ni content observed in what are thought to be fragments from different parts of the meteorite are of comparable magnitude with the variations found within the more well-defined of the Ga–Ge groups. Such compositional variations over distances of a few tens of metres could be due to the Lovering differentiation mechanism operating during solidification, but the rather narrow range of Ni contents in each Ga–Ge group indicates that a considerable amount of homogenization must have taken place. Therefore the original metallic masses must either have been limited in size to the order of the Canyon Diablo meteorite, or else if larger they must have been divided into cells of comparable dimensions.

Two of the most probable sources of error in cooling-rate calculations are neglecting the effect of P and overestimating the amount of undercooling. Both of these would lead to underestimating the cooling rate, although this might be partially offset by the effects of C and pressure. It therefore seems that the estimated sizes of the parent bodies are more likely to be too large than too small. The development of a well-defined core plus mantle structure is dependent on the temperature, which governs the physical state of the material and the viscosity of any liquid phases, the size of the body, which governs the gravitational field and the distances over which material has to be transported to achieve separation of metal and silicate, and the time available. The effect of these factors is to make the formation of a metal core less probable as the size of the body decreases. The estimated radii of 50 to 250 km calculated by the profile synthesis technique[15,16,26] are based on a metal core plus silicate mantle model. This model may be inaccurate if the calculated cooling rates are considerably too slow, since the corresponding parent body might be too small for a core to form. In such small bodies there could be partial separation of metal and silicate, with relatively small metal masses scattered within the body, in which case it is difficult to estimate the total size from the cooling rate of the metal. In such a body it is still necessary for the temperature to have been high enough to melt the metal, though metal mixed with troilite melts more easily than metal alone; so the temperature required to achieve some separation of metal and silicate might be appreciably below 1500 °C.

Most of the stone meteorites are chondrites, which characteristically consist of small (typically around 1 mm in diameter), approximately spherical chondrules embedded in a fine-grained matrix. The chemical composition of chondrites is fairly uniform, and the total amount of Fe present is almost always within the range 20–30% by weight. It is possible to describe a given specimen fairly completely by two quantities: the degree of oxidation and the degree of metamorphism (i.e. heating). Most chondrites contain both metallic and oxidized iron, and the range of Ni contents in the metal, governed by the degree of oxidation, parallels that of iron meteorites. The degree of metamorphism is indicated by mineralogical alteration and textural changes. There is no sign of appreciable amounts of metal having been lost; so it seems likely that chondrites represent meteoritic material which has not been heated enough to permit large-scale separation of metal and silicates. The achondrites are characterized by being poor in metal and not having chondrules. It is tempting to interpret achondrites as the silicate complement of irons, deriving perhaps from material similar to the chondrites which has been strongly heated and separated into metal and silicate fractions. There are some difficulties in this interpretation when details are considered, but it does provide an explanation for some of the basic properties of meteorites. Chondrites fall into five fairly well-defined groups, which might originate from different parent bodies. Yavnel[50] and Ringwood[51] have produced schemes in which complementary irons, achondrites, and chondrites are grouped together. These groupings are not entirely satisfactory, and may be an oversimplification of the true picture, but some such system seems preferable to any conceivable single parent body theory. It is worthy of note that, as 85% of falls are chondrites, it seems that temperatures high enough for separation of metal and silicate to take place were the exception rather than the rule.

The metal grains in chondrites are too small for Widmanstätten structures to have formed, but the same phases, kamacite and taenite, are found as in irons. Electron-probe studies have shown that the Ni distribution in kamacite and taenite in chondrites is generally similar to that in irons[52] but, if the results are interpreted in terms of cooling rates, chondrites seem to have cooled somewhat more slowly[53, 54]. Furthermore, from the metal phase compositions, the cooling rate for the more primitive (unmetamorphosed) types is, if anything, lower than for the metamorphosed types. These results are surprising, since the more primitive chondrites would be expected to have come from near the surface of the parent body, the irons from the central core, and the metamorphosed chondrites from the intermediate region. However, the calculated cooling rates are only for the temperature range 700–400 °C approximately, and Wood[53] has suggested that this result is possible in a core–mantle body, given an appropriate distribution of heat-producing radionuclides. In any case, the comparison of calculated cooling rates for chondrites and irons may not be valid, since the effects of pressure and minor constituents could be important, and the conditions of nucleation and growth of kamacite are different. An alternative, somewhat improbable, explanation is that the least metamorphosed chondrites are the most deep seated, while the metamorphosed chondrites and irons originate from nearer the surface of the parent body. This requires stronger heating near the surface than at the centre, which might be due to chemical reactions involving the atmosphere. The central region would be heated less but would cool more slowly than the surface region. This model requires partial separation of metal from silicate near the surface in at least some of the parent bodies to account for the metal masses of which the irons are fragments.

Evidence from meteorites is clearly of great interest in view of its bearing on the origin of the solar system as a whole, but full discussion of this requires consideration of stone meteorites, particularly the critical question of the origin of chondrules, and must take into account data not touched on here, such as isotopic measurements. The most recent and comprehensive review of these topics is by Anders[25]. The main purpose of this account of the evidence from irons has been to try to set boundary conditions on the processes by which iron meteorites came into being. It is in the nature of the problem that the observational data are open to different interpretations, and the evidence from irons is consistent with more than one parent body model. However, it is fairly certain that irons originated from several bodies of asteroidal rather than planetary size. Details of the origin and history of irons and of meteorites in general remain controversial, but the subject is evolving rapidly, and more definite answers to some of the critical questions may soon be possible.

References

1. M. H. Hey, *Catalogue of Meteorites*, British Museum (Natural History), London, 1967.
2. M. H. Hey, private communication.
3. C. S. Smith, *Trans. AIME*, **212**, 574 (1958).
4. R. E. Maringer and G. K. Manning, in *Researches in Meteorites* (Ed. C. B. Moore), Wiley, New York, 1962, pp. 123–44.
5. T. Takashi and W. A. Bassett, *Science*, **145**, 383 (1964).
6. R. L. Clendenen and H. G. Drickamer, *J. Phys. Chem. Solids*, **25**, 865 (1964).
7. F. P. Bundy, *J. Appl. Phys.*, **36**, 616 (1965).
8. D. Heymann, M. E. Lipschutz, B. Nielson, and E. Anders, *J. Geophys. Res.*, **71**, 619 (1966).
9. A. R. Ramsden and E. N. Cameron, *Am. Mineralogist*, **51**, 37 (1966).
10. N. N. Stulov, *Meteoritika*, **19**, 63 (1960).
11. A. A. Yavnel, I. B. Borovskii, N. P. Ilyin, and I. D. Marchukova, *Dokl. Akad. Nauk SSSR*, **123**, 256 (1958).
12. R. E. Maringer and G. K. Manning, *WADC Tech. Rept. No.* 59-164 (1959).
13. M. Feller-Kniepmeyer and H. H. Uhlig, *Geochim. Cosmochim. Acta*, **21**, 257 (1961).
14. S. O. Agrell, J. V. P. Long, and R. E. Ogilvie, *Nature*, **198**, 749 (1963).
15. J. A. Wood, *Icarus*, **3**, 429 (1964).
16. J. I. Goldstein and R. E. Ogilvie, *Geochim. Cosmochim. Acta*, **29**, 893 (1965).
17. J. I. Goldstein, *J. Geophys. Res.*, **70**, 6223 (1965).
18. S. J. B. Reed, *Geochim. Cosmochim. Acta*, **29**, 535 (1965).
19. E. A. Owen and Y. K. Liu, *J. Iron Steel Inst.*, **163**, 132 (1949).
20. A. E. Ringwood and L. Kaufman, *Geochim. Cosmochim. Acta*, **23**, 1003 (1962).
21. S. Kachi, Y. Bando, and S. Higuchi, *Japan J. Appl. Phys.*, **1**, 339 (1962).
22. J. I. Goldstein and R. E. Ogilvie, *Trans. AIME*, **233**, 2083 (1965).
23. P. Duncumb, in *X-ray Optics and X-ray Microanalysis* (Eds. H. H. Pattee and others), Academic Press, New York, 1963, pp. 431–9.
24. T. B. Massalski and F. R. Park, *J. Geophys Res.*, **67**, 2925 (1962).
25. E. Anders, *Space Sci. Rev.*, **3**, 583 (1964).
26. J. M. Short and C. A. Anderson, *J. Geophys. Res.*, **70**, 3745 (1965).
27. M. Hansen, *Constitution of Binary Alloys*, McGraw-Hill, New York, 1958.
28. R. Vogel and H. Baur, *Arch. Eisenhuettenw.*, **5**, 269 (1931).
29. R. Vogel, *Neues Jahrb. Mineral., Abhandl.*, **84**, 327 (1952).
30. R. Vogel, *Chem. Erde*, **19**, 147 (1958).
31. R. Vogel, *Neues Jahrb. Mineral., Monatsh.*, **1964**, 63.

32. I. Adler and E. J. Dwornik, *U.S., Geol. Survey, Profess. Papers,* **1961**, 263.
33. J. I. Goldstein and R. E. Ogilvie, *Geochim. Cosmochim. Acta,* **27**, 623 (1963).
34. S. J. B. Reed, *Geochim. Cosmochim. Acta,* **29**, 513 (1965).
35. E. P. Henderson and S. H. Perry, *Proc. U.S. Natl. Museum,* **107**, 339 (1958).
36. S. P. Clark, *Ann. Rept. Geophys. Lab. Wash., 1961/2,* 166 (1962).
37. H. H. Nininger, *Arizona's Meteorite Crater,* American Meteorite Museum, Sedona, Arizona, 1956.
38. M. E. Lipschutz and E. Anders, *Science,* **134**, 2095 (1961).
39. E. Anders and M. E. Lipschutz, *J. Geophys. Res.,* **71**, 643 (1966).
40. A. E. Ringwood, *Geochim. Cosmochim. Acta,* **20**, 155 (1960).
41. M. E. Lipschutz and E. Anders, *Geochim. Cosmochim. Acta,* **28**, 699 (1964).
42. J. F. Lovering, *Geochim. Cosmochim. Acta,* **28**, 1745 (1964).
43. H. H. Uhlig, *Geochim. Cosmochim. Acta,* **6**, 282 (1954).
44. L. Kaufman and A. E. Ringwood, *Acta Met.,* **9**, 941 (1961).
45. J. F. Lovering, W. Nichiporuk, A. Chodos, and H. Brown, *Geochim. Cosmochim. Acta,* **11**, 263 (1957).
46. J. T. Wasson, *Geochim. Cosmochim. Acta,* in press (1966).
47. A. A. Yavnel, *Dokl. Akad. Nauk SSSR,* **131**, 1049 (1960).
48. J. F. Lovering, *Geochim. Cosmochim. Acta,* **12**, 238 (1957).
49. J. I. Goldstein, R. E. Hannemann, and R. E. Ogilvie, *Trans. AIME,* **233**, 812 (1964).
50. A. A. Yavnel, *Meteoritika,* **15**, 115 (1958).
51. A. E. Ringwood, *Geochim. Cosmochim. Acta,* **24**, 159 (1961).
52. S. J. B. Reed, *Nature,* **204**, 374 (1964).
53. J. A. Wood, *Icarus,* in press (1966).
54. R. A. Binns and S. J. B. Reed, to be published.

3

J. F. KERRIDGE

Crystallography Department
Birkbeck College
London, England

The mineralogy and genesis of the carbonaceous meteorites

Introduction

Although the organic complex permeating the carbonaceous meteorites has received extensive study recently[1,2], the mineral suite comprising the bulk of each of these meteorites has enjoyed little attention. This chapter is an attempt to summarize such physical, chemical, and crystallographic data as have been obtained from this material with indications of their genetical relevance. No attempt is made to review all recent theories of meteorite evolution. Most of such theories are based on their ability to explain the ordinary, equilibrated chondrites and can only be made to include the carbonaceous, disequilibrium meteorites by means of *ad hoc* assumptions.

The starting point in most theories of cosmogony is the chondritic structure common to most stone meteorites. Theories can basically be divided into two categories which can be labelled 'volcanic' and 'nebular' referring to the mode of chondrule formation. Arguments are advanced against the former, and in favour of the nebular, mode of formation. A tentative picture is presented of a nebular genesis for chondrules which leads naturally to the disequilibrium structures found in carbonaceous meteorites and logically to the equilibrium arrangement of ordinary chondrites.

The majority, if not all, of the meteorites are debris following collisions between bodies in the asteroid belt. Consequently they represent random samples of the structures present in small members of the solar system which are clearly related, at some distant time, to the terrestrial planets. It is almost certain that the meteorites are the most primitive material which we have available for study, being significantly less altered than the surface layers of the Earth.

There are approximately 1000 stone meteorites in collections throughout the world. The carbonaceous meteorites form a very small class within these and Mason[3] lists 17 stones as falling into this category. From his list should be deleted Renazzo which, despite its 1·44 wt. % of carbon, is mineralogically quite different from the rest. To his list should be added Kaba, Mokoia, Pollen, and Revelstoke. Two others, Bali and Essebi, await more detailed study. Carbonaceous meteorites are divided into two categories on the basis of carbon content: type I containing more than about 2·7 wt. % and type II less than this.

Superficial examination of the carbonaceous meteorites reveals four principal constituents which in varying proportions make up the different stones. One of these constituents is a high-temperature silicate phase which occurs generally as chondrules or irregular fragments embedded in an opaque, fine-grained ground mass (figure 1). This ground mass contains the other three constituents: an amorphous low-temperature silicate, magnetite, and water-soluble sulphates. In addition, several trace minerals can be found including sulphides of iron, carbonates, and metallic nickel–iron. The amounts of low-temperature silicate, magnetite, and water-soluble sulphates

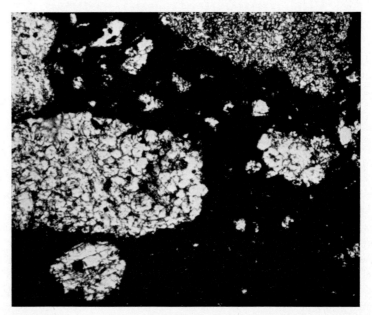

FIGURE 1   Thin section of the Cold Bokkeveld carbonaceous meteorite. Chondrules and irregular fragments of olivine and pyroxene can be seen embedded in an opaque ground mass consisting principally of semiamorphous layer-lattice silicate impregnated with carbonaceous matter. [By courtesy of G. Mueller]

increase with increasing carbon content, other constituents decreasing. The impregnation of the fine-grained matrix with organic matter renders conventional petrography extremely difficult, and little useful genetical information has been derived in this way.

Although the oxides and sulphides of iron and the water-soluble sulphates are in quasiequilibrium among themselves and with some of the low-temperature silicates[4, 5], there is considerable disequilibrium between high- and low-temperature silicates and within each silicate phase. This suggests that these meteorites are mechanical mixtures and not different arrested stages in the conversion of some common starting phase into another. There is no unequivocal evidence that any *in situ* transformations have occurred among the silicates since the aggregation of the meteorites in their present form. Du Fresne and Anders[4] observed composite grains in which polycrystalline low-temperature silicate separated high-temperature olivine crystals with identical orientations, suggesting that the olivine had been altered to form the low-temperature silicate. However, Keil and Fredriksson[6] put forward an alternative explanation, namely that the olivine crystal was split apart and penetrated by coexisting low-

temperature silicate. Microprobe measurements revealing markedly different compositions for the high- and low-temperature minerals suggest that the latter interpretation
is correct.

Bulk chemical analyses have been performed on most of the carbonaceous meteorites, but are of limited genetical value. Scant correlation can be discerned between
elemental variations and physical structure, except that carbon, sulphur, and water
tend to increase with increasing proportion of low-temperature silicate, and there
is little evidence for fractionation of elements according to affinities established in
geochemistry. This lends weight to the idea that these meteorites are mechanical
mixtures of minerals which were formed in different environments before being
accumulated into the aggregate now seen.

It is clear that any information about elemental fractionations from which genetical
conclusions can be derived should come from a study of specific minerals from within
the meteorites rather than from bulk analyses. The next section of this chapter will
consist of a review of the sparse information available at the present time on the
minerals of the carbonaceous meteorites.

Mineralogy

High-temperature silicates

High-temperature silicates are those which on Earth are known to be formed
either by magmatic processes or by thermal metamorphism above about 500 °C. The
most common such species are the orthosilicate olivine and the metasilicate pyroxene,
both of which can exist with cationic compositions between pure iron and pure
magnesium. In type II meteorites both olivine and pyroxene can be found, the former
predominating by a factor of about four[7]. They occur both as chondrules, essentially
the same as those occurring in ordinary chondrites, and also as fragments, though it
is not clear whether or not these fragments are bits of broken chondrules. In type I
stones apparently only olivine is found[8] and then as a rarity, usually in the form of
minute droplets[9].

Chondrules in general, including those in the carbonaceous meteorites, are roughly
spherical, crystalline masses, of about a millimetre in size, which have not been found
on Earth and which have consequently excited wide study and a large number of
explanatory theories[10,11]. As a working hypothesis it is assumed that the solar system
has witnessed only one chondrule-forming mechanism at work. It is now accepted
that the form of the chondrules was imposed by external physical conditions at the
time of solidification. This indicates that the chondrule-forming mechanism involved
the cooling of molten silicate droplets while in a free fall state. Opinion is divided as to
whether this state was achieved above the surface of the meteorite parent body or
bodies as a result of volcanic activity, or by volatilization and recondensation of
material while dispersed in space prior to formation of the planets and the rest of the
solar system. From the frequent occurrence within chondrules of glass and the high-
temperature monoclinic form of pyroxene and the elongate morphology of both
olivine and pyroxene, it is clear that cooling times were rapid, solidification times
probably being of the order of minutes[11]. In view of the smaller scale of the operations
involved, this observation would seem to favour the volcanic model, but evidence is

building up against this picture and in favour of what might be termed a nebular origin for chondrules.

High-temperature silicates have been extracted from type II carbonaceous meteorites for detailed analyses. Microprobe results[7], X-ray[12] and electron diffraction patterns[13], and optical microscopy[14] have shown that olivines and pyroxenes from these meteorites, unlike most other types, show a wide range of composition. Microprobe results for olivine from the Murray meteorite are illustrated in figure 2. Two points are obvious from these results: first, that iron contents extend to much higher values than are normally found in chondrites and, secondly, that the average of observed iron contents lies substantially below the mean for chondrules from ordinary chondrites of both H and L groups. Bulk chemical analyses for carbonaceous meteorites correspond in general to ordinary H group chondrites. (The classification of

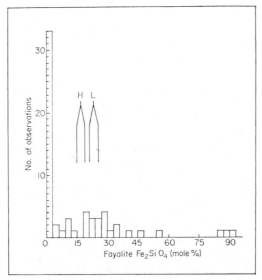

FIGURE 2   Electron microprobe results from individual olivine grains in the Murray carbonaceous meteorite showing variations in iron content from grain to grain. The olivine is considered as a solid solution of fayalite, the pure iron silicate, in forsterite, the pure magnesium equivalent. H and L represent the range of compositions observed in olivines from ordinary H and L group chondrites respectively. [After Fredriksson and Keil[7]]

meteorites into H and L groups is based on their bulk iron content, H being high iron content and L low[15]. These groups represent genetically different evolutionary paths.)

Clearly the composition of these minerals was established before aggregation, either during the chondrule-forming solidification process, or else by metamorphism in some later localities destroyed before accumulation of the meteorites in their present form. Establishment of composition during solidification requires there to have been a wide range in redoxy conditions throughout the regions in space where chondrule formation occurred. This follows because it is known that the equilibrium iron content of a condensing silicate is critically dependent on the partial pressure of hydrogen in the system. Variation of hydrogen concentration, with either distance or time, in order to achieve the observed range in silicate iron contents is relatively easy to visualize in a volcanic model for chondrule formation, but is less obvious in the case of a nebular model. Composition of the solar nebula at the time of condensation is commonly equated with the present solar composition, and the silicate iron content in equilibrium with the solar hydrogen content has been shown to be extremely small[11]. However, this point will be dealt with in greater detail below.

Acquisition of the present range in iron contents by means of metamorphic diffusion creates the problem of accounting for the regular composition of most other meteoritic silicates and seems to lead for ordinary chondrites to a picture involving two distinct periods of metamorphism separated by dispersal and reaccumulation of material. While not impossible, this model multiplies postulates beyond necessity.

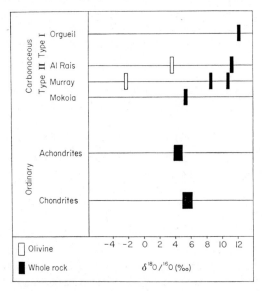

FIGURE 3 Comparison of oxygen isotope analyses for olivine and whole rock samples from ordinary and carbonaceous meteorites. The δ notation employed relates observed values to terrestrial standard mean ocean water. A δ value of $+10$ corresponds to a specimen 1 % richer in ^{18}O than is standard mean ocean water. [After Taylor and others[16]]

Taylor and others[16] have analysed the oxygen isotope ratios of olivines and pyroxenes extracted from ordinary and type II carbonaceous meteorites and also of whole rock samples of types I and II carbonaceous meteorite (figure 3). High-temperature silicates from ordinary chondrites and achondrites give ratios that fall consistently into two groups, implying two distinct genetical sequences. Similar material from carbonaceous meteorites, however, reveals a much greater spread in isotope ratios than is found for ordinary meteorites and is substantially depleted in ^{18}O relative to ordinary meteoritic silicate. This is interpreted to mean that the olivine and pyroxene in carbonaceous meteorites could not have been simply derived from, nor converted into, corresponding phases in ordinary stone meteorites. It is possible, however, that ordinary meteoritic silicate could have been derived by homogenization of a mixture of olivine or pyroxene such as is now found in carbonaceous meteorites and some other silicate enriched in ^{18}O. Whether such a homogenization process is compatible with the physical structures of all ordinary chondrites is not certain.

Chondrules in general, including those in carbonaceous meteorites, contain trace amounts of noble gases in what are thought to be primordial isotopic ratios, compatible with their formation as discrete droplets in irradiation conditions similar to those believed to have existed early in the formation of the solar system. Also it seems that they must have been dispersed and subjected to such irradiation for appreciable lengths of time[17]. This is thought to argue against a volcanic origin for chondrules.

Two further arguments against volcanic chondrule formation can be voiced. The first is that it is 'impossible' (see Levin[18]) for volcanism to convert the whole of the silicate mantle of a planetary body into chondritic structure which would be required in view of the superabundance of chondrites *vis-à-vis* other meteorite species. The second is that, supposing such a process were in fact possible, it would, for the same reasons, take a long time and thus during the lifetime of the process gravitational segregation within the magma should have produced marked changes in chondrule composition, so that a much wider range of compositions should be observed in ordinary chondrites than is found in practice[17].

If we summarize, therefore, what is known about the high-temperature silicates of the carbonaceous meteorites in comparison with those of ordinary stone meteorites, it is clear that a process capable of producing the latter with their uniform olivines and pyroxenes cannot readily be made to accommodate the heterogeneous high-temperature silicates of the carbonaceous meteorites. If, however, it is possible to account for the production of these disequilibrium silicates at some early stage in the evolution of the solar system, then ordinary chondritic, and achondritic, material can basically be formed from them by homogenization within the parent bodies.

Low-temperature silicates

The opaque, fine-grained ground mass of the carbonaceous meteorites consists mainly of a semiamorphous silicate not unlike a terrestrial clay. Several attempts have been made to identify this phase with specific terrestrial minerals. Wöhler and Harris[19,20] and Pisani[21] referred to it as serpentine, Kvasha[22] as chlorite or serpentine, Zachariasen[23] identified it as 'chrysotile', and Mason[24] called it 'chlorite or a related mineral with the structure of serpentine'. Nagy and others[5] recognized that positive identification was not possible and decided that chlorite and/or montmorillonite may be present, referring to the phase as a whole as micaceous silicate. Du Fresne and Anders[4] resolved three species which they referred to as characteristic minerals but did not identify them with terrestrial species. Boström and Fredriksson[25] concluded that the mineral was a chlorite resembling ferric chamosite.

The author's opinion, in view of the state of knowledge on the subject, is that specific identification is presumptuous and that the most that can be currently said about the bulk of this phase is that it consists of ill-crystallized layer-lattice silicates. Terms such as chlorite, serpentine, or chamosite infer the presence of structural schemes for which there is no direct evidence, only the observation of some secondary characteristics.

X-ray diffraction patterns give a limited amount of information concerning the nature of these silicates. The general form of the patterns corresponds closely to that for ultra-fine-grained terrestrial clays with layer-lattice structures. Basal spacings for the layer structure are about 7 Å for meteoritic material, similar to those for terrestrial kaolinite or antigorite, but no reflections are observed at 14 Å (chamosite, montmorillonite), 21 Å (mica), or 28 Å (chlorite). The observed basal reflections are diffuse

as, indeed, are all X-ray reflections from this material. The remaining unit cell parameters can only be roughly estimated from X-ray patterns. Although the diffuse
nature of the basal reflections is probably due to disordered stacking of the structural
layers, the broad nature of the prismatic reflections is more likely to be due to heterogeneous distribution of the silicate cations, resulting in a wide spread in composition
of the silicate particles. Single-crystal electron diffraction patterns of individual
particles lying on their basal planes show sharp reflections from which accurate unit
cell parameters can be calculated (with the exception of the basal spacing which is
always unknown in such measurements). Results from such a study reveal a wide
spread in values, in agreement with the suggestion above that this silicate phase has a
very heterogeneous composition[8]. The question of chemical composition of the low-
temperature silicates will be taken up again later in this section.

As mentioned above, oxygen isotope ratios have been determined for whole rock
samples of carbonaceous meteorites[16] and as a first approximation the values for the
low-temperature phase can be taken as the difference between these values and those
found for separated high-temperature silicates. This is compatible with observations:
the whole rock values are not only higher than the high-temperature silicate values
but tend to increase with increasing content of low-temperature silicate, implying
that the carbonaceous meteorites are mixtures of high-temperature silicates, depleted
in ^{18}O relative to ordinary meteorites, and low-temperature silicates enriched in ^{18}O.
These were clearly formed in different environments.

Taylor and coworkers concluded that the carbonaceous meteorites could not have
been formed by alteration of ordinary chondritic material. This conclusion was based
on the difference between the high-temperature silicates, and is certainly sound.
However, one cannot be dogmatic about the origin of the low-temperature silicate
phase, as this could have been formed from high-temperature silicates of either ordinary or carbonaceous meteorite type by reaction with water enriched in ^{18}O. The reverse process is not plausible, necessitating as it does either preferential loss of high
^{18}O water or combination with an ultra-low ^{18}O silicate phase. It seems reasonable
to suppose that ordinary chondritic material could have been formed by homogenization of a mixture of silicates corresponding roughly to the present type II
carbonaceous meteorites. The chondritic structure itself clearly predated this homogenization stage which involved the thermally activated redistribution of heavy
oxygen atoms, a process which has not occurred in the carbonaceous meteorites. It
does not seem possible, on the basis of the oxygen isotope determinations, to see far
beyond that genetic step and discern the paths followed by the two phases prior to
accumulation. As argued above, although it is possible to convert high-temperature
silicate such as is found in carbonaceous meteorites into low-temperature silicate,
the reverse process is improbable. The idea that low-temperature silicates, of which
some remain in the carbonaceous meteorites, formed the primitive material from which
the chondrules were formed, by volcanism, does not seem compatible with these
observations. Two broad genetic paths are left which can lead to the observed pattern
of oxygen isotope ratios. On one, the two silicate phases were formed independently
in separate environments, the high-temperature silicates in the form of chondrules
with low ^{18}O content, the low-temperature silicate in the form of dust with high
^{18}O content. Accumulation of these two phases produced the meteorite parent
bodies. On the other, chondrules were formed as the only primitive silicate phase,

with low ^{18}O content, and were accumulated together with high ^{18}O water into the parent bodies. Reaction between some of the chondrules and water produced the observed low-temperature silicates and homogenization of them, and remaining high-temperature silicate produced the present ordinary chondrites. The genetical picture will be further elaborated later in this chapter.

Very little is known about the chemical composition of the low-temperature silicates. The only classical analysis in the literature is a spectrographic determination by Du Fresne and Anders[4] on material extracted from the type II stone Mighei. Principal constituents found were iron (17%), magnesium (15%), and silicon (14%). These values lead to an unusually high cation to silicon ratio, and it is possible that this material was somewhat contaminated with magnetite which can form intimate intergrowths with clay minerals.

The diffuse nature of X-ray reflections from this material, referred to above, prevents the unit cell from being determined with sufficient accuracy to permit calculations of the chemical composition. Electron diffraction patterns can be measured with greater accuracy, but have proved of limited value. Although a rough correlation exists between unit cell size and cationic composition among terrestrial clays, applying this to meteoritic results indicates an overwhelming abundance of aluminium-rich silicates and this is clearly at odds with the bulk chemical analyses[8].

Electron microprobe analyses from the matrix of carbonaceous meteorites[7] are suspect because of the small grain size and the intimate mixture of these silicates with magnetite, leading to apparent iron contents which are both excessive and too homogeneous. The Orgueil silicate composition quoted by Boström and Fredriksson[25] was derived from microprobe data with allowance made for interference from magnesium sulphate but not from magnetite. Their value for the composition lay between the limits $(Mg, Fe^{2+}, Ni, Al)_{5.93}OH_{7.86}O_{0.14}Si_4O_{10}$ for the case in which the iron was totally ferrous, and $(Mg, Fe^{3+}, Ni, Al)_{5.93}OH_{5.75}O_{2.25}Si_4O_{10}$ for the ferric case. They pointed out that in fact most of the iron was known to be in the ferric state. On the basis of this composition, the bulk chemical analysis, and a rough knowledge of the proportions of the other principal constituents in the mineral suite, they calculated that the quantities of the mineral species in Orgueil were the following:

chlorite	62·6 wt. %
magnesium sulphate	6·7
troilite	4·6
magnetite	6·0
gypsum	2·9

plus several relatively minor components. The figures for magnetite, sulphate, and chlorite are in disagreement with the results of Du Fresne and Anders[4] and of the present author. Du Fresne and Anders quoted a value for the amount of magnesium sulphate in Orgueil as 16·96% by weight of the whole and stated that the insoluble remainder contained roughly equal amounts of magnetite and layer-lattice silicate.

The author has conducted a set of calculations similar to, but simpler than, those of Boström and Fredriksson, aimed at determining the average composition of the silicate phase from quantitative estimates of the mineral proportions rather than the reverse. This was deemed possible because of the small number of major components in the system. The bulk chemical analysis used was that of Wiik[26], as quoted by Du Fresne and Anders[4], in terms of atoms per 100 silicon atoms, and provides the following:

> 105 atoms of magnesium
> 88 atoms of iron
> 46 atoms of sulphur
> 9 atoms of aluminium
> 6 atoms of calcium
> 6 atoms of sodium
> 4 atoms of nickel

Mineral proportions were taken as the following:

layer-lattice silicate	50% by weight
magnetite	17%
sulphate	17%
troilite	6%
remainder	10%
total	100%

Free sulphur is ignored and it is assumed that all sulphur is combined in water-soluble sulphate and iron sulphide.

Starting with 46 atoms of sulphur, 6 are combined with the 6 calcium atoms to form 6 molecules of gypsum leaving 40, which are divided, on the basis of known proportions of sulphide to sulphate, to form 12 molecules of troilite, thus accounting for 12 atoms of iron-plus-nickel, and 28 molecules of magnesium sulphate, accounting for 28 atoms of magnesium.

All remaining magnesium, 77 atoms, and all aluminium and sodium, 15 atoms combined, are assigned to silicate.

From the known proportions of silicate to magnetite the number of iron-plus-nickel atoms in the silicate is calculated. For purposes of calculating its molecular weight it is assumed that there are 3 water molecules per 4 silicon atoms in the silicate. It is found that of the 80 iron-plus-nickel atoms remaining after earlier steps, 23 reside in the silicate and 57 in magnetite.

This leads to an average formula for the layer-lattice silicate of

$$Mg_{3.08} Fe^{3+}_{0.92} Al_{0.36} Na_{0.24} Si_4O_{10}(OH)_6O_{0.12}$$

It is assumed that all the iron is in the trivalent state and this is obviously an over-simplification but in the author's opinion the data do not justify any more detailed an approach. It is interesting to note that the formula above leads to a cation to silicon ratio of 1·15:1, significantly below average for meteoritic silicates, and to an $Fe/(Fe + Mg)$ ratio of 23%, corresponding to silicates from L group chondrites, although bulk analyses of carbonaceous meteorites put them in the H group.

Although the bulk of the meteoritic layer-lattice silicates can be only roughly identified, a limited number of specific identifications have been made of individual minor minerals of this type. Antigorite has been recognized in Pollen, a type II meteorite[27], clino-chrysotile in Orgueil, Murray, Staroye Boriskino, Cold Bokkeveld, and Mokoia, and sepiolite in Orgueil, Staroye Boriskino, and Kaba[8]. It is worth noting that all these minerals are pure magnesium silicates. The chrysotile and sepiolite were in general quite well crystallized, indicating strongly that they were formed over a period of time by hydrothermal reaction rather than directly from the vapour phase.

On the basis of these last observations it seems certain that some at least of the low-temperature silicates have been formed by the aqueous alteration of an earlier generation of silicate, although no conclusions can be drawn regarding the identity of this primitive silicate. It has been pointed out on a number of occasions[17,25,28] that the high content of relatively volatile elements, such as mercury, lead, and bismuth, in the carbonaceous meteorites argues against a high-temperature stage at any time in its history for the bulk of the material. This suggests that the starting material in the hydrothermal transformations was layer-lattice silicate in the form of fine cosmic dust formed by direct condensation from the vapour phase. This is certainly compatible with the observations. However, it is not necessary, nor even possible, to rule out a high-temperature stage for at least a small proportion of the type I meteorite material on account of the presence within it of olivine and also of the spheroidal magnetite described in the next section.

This section might best be concluded by quoting Anders[17] to the effect that type I carbonaceous meteorites represent (predominately) primitive, volatile-rich condensate 'slightly altered due to storage in a damp environment'.

Magnetite

Magnetite is apparently omnipresent in carbonaceous meteorites, its content increasing with that of carbon. Some type II stones show both metallic iron in process of being converted into magnetite[29] and vice versa[30], lending weight to the mechanical mixture hypothesis.

Spheroidal magnetite has been observed in Orgueil, which is often taken to mean that this material has passed through a high-temperature stage, the spheroidal form being characteristic of the molten state rather than of a solid-state reaction product[31,32]. It is suggested that the spherules of magnetite were formed originally as cores to silicate chondrules which have been 'weathered' in the damp region of the parent body, although this process did not take place *in situ* but before the present accumulation took place. Such cored chondrules have in fact been observed in some carbonaceous meteorites[9,30,32].

Water-soluble sulphates

Magnesium sulphate and gypsum have been extracted from most type I and II stones[4,5,8]. In type I meteorites, Orgueil and Ivuna, they occur partly in veins[4] and comprise a substantial proportion of the whole meteorite. In these the magnesium sulphate predominates. In type II, Murray in particular, there seems to be considerable heterogeneity within the meteorite, some samples yielding a mixture as from type I and some only pure calcium sulphate[8]. Full correlation of salt sample with bulk chemical analysis has not been done, but it seems that the variation in sulphate is not matched by similar bulk chemical variations, implying that the sulphates were formed *in situ* and not transported into the sampled regions[4,8,17]. This would indicate that reaction with sulphur trioxide, or dioxide and oxygen, produced the salts. It also suggests that the water-soluble salts were about the last phases to be produced in the history of this material, a conclusion also reached by Boström and Fredriksson[25].

Trace minerals

Metallic nickel–iron occurs in most type II stones as very rare small droplets[29,33]. It has also been reported in two type I stones, Orgueil[29] and Tonk[30], which disturbs the equilibrium referred to above as postulated for the iron oxide–sulphide mixture.

In type II meteorites the metal phase occurs as droplets included within olivine, though whether only in chondrules[33] or in any olivine grains[7] is a matter of some dispute. There is universal agreement, however, that the iron was formed before accumulation of the meteorite, probably, in fact, at the same time as the chondrules crystallized. This implies a locally high cation to silicon ratio at the time of chondrule formation, so that the occurrence of apparently contemporary pyroxene indicates that some heterogeneity existed at that stage, possibly related to the volatility of silicon.

Dolomite occurs in very small quantities in Orgueil, but forms a valuable genetical key as from its crystal perfection crystallization times, in the presence of water, of greater than 1000 years have been calculated[4]. Thus the damp environment on the parent body lasted for at least this length of time.

Primordial noble gases

The presence within chondrules of trace amounts of primordial noble gases has already been mentioned. Within the carbonaceous meteorites as whole units there is significantly more of this primordial gas than in ordinary meteorites, which is taken to mean that a substantial fraction of the carbonaceous meteorite material has not lost all of its original gas content, that is it has never undergone a high-temperature stage in its evolution[17,32]. This is in agreement with the observations made earlier with regard to the high content of relatively volatile non-gaseous elements.

Genesis

There is good evidence that both the high-temperature chondrules and a part of the low-temperature silicate matrix of the unmetamorphosed carbonaceous meteorites were formed quite early in the history of the solar system. It is not possible to derive one phase from the other within a closed system; so it is necessary to construct at least two evolutionary paths during that period of solar system evolution culminating in accumulation of the meteorite parent bodies.

A crucial property of the chondrules from the carbonaceous meteorites, which must be accounted for in any theory of meteorite genesis, is the heterogeneous distribution, and relatively high content, of oxidized iron in the silicates. These iron contents are apparently primordial and reflect a range in redoxy conditions, that is to say, a heterogeneous distribution of hydrogen, at the time of chondrule formation. This chondrule formation is thought to have occurred while cosmic matter was in a dispersed state preceding aggregation into planets and asteroids. Therefore it is necessary to explain how a suitable distribution of hydrogen existed to enable material with a high oxidized iron content to condense in an atmosphere which is commonly equated with that of the present Sun in which the hydrogen to oxygen ratio is 10^3 (see Goldberg, Müller, and Aller[34]).

If a rapid heating and cooling cycle is postulated for the chondrules, which is consistent with their structure, a simple mechanical separation of the hydrogen from the solid fraction of the nebula, over distances of the order of an astronomical unit, suffices to explain the apparent lack of equilibrium reached by the oxidized iron in the chondrules. If the nebular hydrogen were distributed with spherical uniformity while the solid fraction were retained or concentrated within the ecliptic plane, this could provide the necessary separation. The agency for such a divorce could be either mechanical or magnetic, or a combination of both.

The broad features of the evolutionary path of meteoritic material are therefore visualized as follows. The outer regions of the primitive solar nebula cooled and condensed slowly into a cloud of dust contained within a sphere of hydrogen-rich gas. The dust fraction, or a part of it, was concentrated by some mechanism within the plane of the ecliptic.

A short-lived event rapidly heated most of the dust to above its melting point and allowed it to cool quickly. Igneous silicate chondrules were thus formed with a wide range in iron content reflecting local cationic variations as well as variations in hydrogen partial pressure related to distance from the ecliptic plane. The heating event is commonly identified either with a T Tauri type of shock wave emanation[11] or else with lightning discharges generated by interparticle friction[35].

Chondrules and unreheated dust, plus a second generation of dust formed from material which missed the liquid phase field on cooling, accumulated into planets and asteroids.

Within the asteroids, and planets, short-lived radioactive isotopes provided a source of heat which metamorphosed much of the primitive aggregate by varying amounts.

The ordinary chondrites are material which has been homogenized during this stage. Iron contents within the igneous silicates have been made uniform by solid-state diffusion, as have isotopic distributions. The carbonaceous meteorites suffered little or no heating during this stage and are thus thought to have come from the surface regions of their parent body or bodies. Water, driven off from the interior condensed at or near the surface to provide a source of cosmologically active water for upwards of 1000 years, the damp environment visualized by Anders. Subsequent mixing of unmetamorphosed and unhydrated olivine and pyroxene with low-temperature silicates of both primitive and secondary, hydrothermal, origin produced the material now available to us as type II carbonaceous meteorites. Type I meteorites are similar mixtures with only trivial quantities of high-temperature silicate.

The absence of any correlation between chondrule iron content and degree of metamorphism follows logically, because in this model metamorphism is employed to homogenize iron contents, not to create them. The chance existence of homogeneous but unmetamorphosed chondrules, as in Renazzo, is not ruled out.

Overall enrichment of stone meteorites in iron relative to the Sun suggests that possibly magnetic fields played a part in effecting the iron–hydrogen fractionation during chondrule formation.

Acknowledgements

The author would like to thank Professor J. D. Bernal for encouragement and advice during the preparation of this chapter.

References

1. H. C. Urey, *Space Research VI, Proc. Inten. Space Sci. Symp.*, *6th, Mar del Plata, Argentina, May, 1965*, North-Holland, Amsterdam, to be published.
2. M. H. Studier, R. Hayatsu, and E. Anders, *Science*, **149**, 1455 (1965).
3. B. Mason, *Meteorites*, 1st ed., Wiley, New York, 1962.
4. E. R. Du Fresne and E. Anders, *Geochim. Cosmochim. Acta*, **26**, 1085 (1962).
5. B. Nagy, W. G. Meinschein, and D. J. Hennessy, *Ann. N.Y. Acad. Sci.*, **108**, 534 (1963).
6. K. Keil and K. Fredriksson, private communication.
7. K. Fredriksson and K. Keil, *Meteoritics*, **2**, 201 (1964).
8. J. F. Kerridge, *Ann. N.Y. Acad. Sci.*, **119**, 41 (1964).
9. G. Mueller, 'Interpretation of micro-structures in carbonaceous meteorites', *Advances in Organic Geochemistry*, Pergamon Press, Oxford, 1963.
10. K. Fredriksson and A. E. Ringwood, *Geochim. Cosmochim. Acta*, **27**, 639 (1963).
11. J. A. Wood, *Icarus*, **2**, 152 (1963).
12. B. Mason, *Geochim. Cosmochim. Acta*, **27**, 1011 (1963).
13. J. F. Kerridge, unpublished.
14. G. Tschermak, *Die Mikroskopische Beschaffenheit der Meteoriten*, E. Schweizerbart'sche, Stuttgart, 1885 (English translation, J. A. Wood and E. M. Wood, Smithsonian Institution, Massachusetts, 1964).
15. H. C. Urey and H. Craig, *Geochim. Cosmochim. Acta*, **4**, 36 (1953).
16. H. P. Taylor, M. B. Duke, L. T. Silver, and S. Epstein, *Geochim. Cosmochim. Acta*, **29**, 489 (1965).
17. E. Anders, *Space Sci. Rev.*, **3**, 583 (1964).
18. B. J. Levin, *Planetary Space Sci.*, **13**, 243 (1965).
19. F. Wöhler and E. P. Harris, *Sitz. Ber. Akad. Wiss.*, *Wien*, **35**, 5 (1859).
20. F. Wöhler and E. P. Harris, *Sitz. Ber. Akad. Wiss.*, *Wien*, **41**, 565 (1860).
21. F. Pisani, *Compt. Rend.*, **59**, 132 (1864).
22. L. G. Kvasha, *Meteoritika*, **4**, 83 (1948).
23. W. H. Zachariasen, unpublished, quoted in reference 4.
24. B. Mason, *J. Geophys. Res.*, **65**, 2965 (1960).
25. K. Boström and K. Fredriksson, in press (1966).
26. H. B. Wiik, *Geochim. Cosmochim. Acta*, **9**, 279 (1956).
27. F. C. Wolff, *Geochim. Cosmochim. Acta*, **27**, 979 (1963).
28. H. C. Urey, *Rev. Geophys.*, **2**, 1 (1964).
29. P. Ramdohr, *J. Geophys. Res.*, **68**, 2011 (1963).
30. K. I. Sztrokay, V. Tolnay, and M. Földvari-Vogl, *Acta Geol.*, **7**, 57 (1961).
31. F. Fitch, H. P. Schwarcz, and E. Anders, *Nature*, **193**, 1123 (1962).
32. E. Anders, *Ann. N.Y. Acad. Sci.*, **108**, 514 (1963).
33. J. A. Wood, *Icarus*, in press (1966).
34. L. G. Goldberg, E. A. Müller, and L. H. Aller, *Astrophys. J.*, *Suppl.*, **5**, 1 (1960).
35. F. L. Whipple, in press (1966).

4

P. LÄMMERZAHL

Max-Planck-Institut für Kernphysik
Heidelberg, Germany

Rare-gas isotope studies on meteorites

Introduction

Many of the processes that meteoritic matter went through in the course of evolution effected changes in the isotopic abundances. Investigation of these variations provides valuable information about the meteorites' history, which is closely connected with that of other objects in planetary space. The setting-up of the time scale, in particular, would hardly be possible without the results of isotope studies.

The experimental conditions are most favourable for rare gases. They are highly volatile and had been almost completely lost when meteorites were formed. Thus, the initial rare-gas concentrations generally are extremely low, and even an admixture of small amounts with anomalous isotopic composition can be detected and measured by mass-spectrometric techniques.

We know a variety of sources of isotopic changes in meteorites. In their evolutionary history one can distinguish three main sections; for each of these the rare gases reveal some information. From the earliest stage, when matter condensed out of the solar nebula and accreted to primary bodies, primordial rare gases have been retained, which have approximately solar abundance ratios possibly altered by some fractionation process. It is quite astonishing that they could survive through the various processes of metamorphism which have occurred since that time. When the parent bodies had cooled down enough, accumulation of radiogenic isotopes, i.e. decay products of long-lived natural radioactivities, started. By measuring the radiogenic ^{4}He (from U and Th decay) and ^{40}Ar (from ^{40}K), the ages of the meteorites can be determined. The last period started with a breaking-up of the parent body, which caused the fragments to be exposed to cosmic radiation. The interaction of cosmic rays with matter is an extensive source of isotopic effects, producing a variety of stable and radioactive nuclides in the so-called spallation process. From the concentrations of these spallogenic isotopes, cosmic-ray exposure ages can be derived.

A complete review of the whole field of investigation is not the purpose of this chapter; that has been discussed comprehensively in other publications[1-4]. A brief outline can only be given, with special regard to recent contributions from the Max-Planck-Institut für Kernphysik.

Primordial Rare Gases

The rare gases found in meteorites sometimes cannot be attributed to radioactive decay or cosmic irradiation processes alone. The extremely high concentrations and the isotopic composition point to a component that was captured out of a gas, or plasma of solar composition. This is demonstrated by an example given in table 1.

TABLE 1   Rare-gas concentrations (in 10^{-8} cm^3 s.t.p./g) in two samples of the dark–light structured Fayetteville chondrite

	^{3}He	^{4}He	^{20}Ne	^{21}Ne	^{22}Ne	^{36}Ar	^{38}Ar	^{40}Ar	^{84}Kr	^{132}Xe
light	54	1880	12	8·6	8·4	1·50	1·23	2450	0·055	0·022
dark	474	1410000	5450	21·4	450	286	58	6100	0·17	0·10

[Data from Müller and Zähringer[5].]

In one sample (light) of the Fayetteville meteorite, the noble-gas concentrations are normal as for a chondrite—they mainly result from radioactivity (^{40}Ar and about 90% of ^{4}He) and from spallation; there are only small amounts of Kr, Xe, and an excess of ^{36}Ar and ^{20}Ne which are primordial. The gases in another (dark) sample of the same meteorite are quite different as concerns the total and relative abundances; they are essentially primordial, except for ^{40}Ar (the higher ^{40}Ar content is due to a higher K concentration).

Heavy primordial rare gases are rather common in stone meteorites. Quite a variety of processes occurring in the early stages of planetary evolution can be inferred from the isotope anomalies observed in meteoritic Kr and Xe. There is evidence of the former existence of extinct radioactivities, and spallation and fission processes must have occurred also (for a discussion of these topics, see publications by other authors[3,6-8]).

Only the minor isotopes of the heavy noble gases are affected by such processes. It seems that the main isotopes, together with primordial He, Ne, and Ar, originated from one common source of gas. The relative abundances are not identical with the cosmic values derived from stellar analysis, but it has been proposed[1,2,9,10] that the rare gases of the various meteorite classes and of the terrestrial atmosphere arose from initially solar composition by the action of a diffusion process in the solid state, which depleted the light rare gases more than the heavy ones. Strong diffusion losses are proved by the observed isotopic shifts. This effect is especially well pronounced for neon, where the ^{20}Ne to ^{22}Ne ratio varies by about 50%, and decreases with decreasing total neon concentration owing to the mass dependence of the diffusion coefficients.

Occasionally, meteorites are found to contain exceptionally large amounts of light primordial noble gases. They are mostly achondrites and bronzite chondrites; among them, Fayetteville has the highest He and Ne concentration ever observed. Quite remarkable is the correlation with a dark–light structure[11]. Centimetre-sized light parts are embedded in a matrix of much darker material. The nature of this effect has not yet been clarified; the dark appearance might be due to a finer grain size, possibly caused by shocks, or to a higher carbon content. Differences in the chemical composition have been measured for some other elements too[5]. The primordial rare gases are almost completely confined to the dark material, but even therein the distribution seems to be quite inhomogeneous. Eberhardt, Geiss, and Grögler[12,13] showed that the concentrations depend on the grain size, the rare gases being most enriched in the fraction of smallest grains.

By a method of fractionated dissolution, Hintenberger, Vilcsek, and Wänke[14] also proved the localization close to the crystal surfaces. Furthermore, they succeeded in showing that all the main minerals which the meteorites are composed of contain rare gases, but have been degassed each to a different degree. The $^{20}Ne/^{22}Ne$ values, ranging from 7·5 to 14, are highest in the metallic phase, which probably has retained

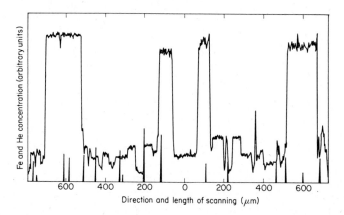

FIGURE 1   Linear scanning of the Fe concentration and the ^4He release in the Fayette-ville chondrite. The same path was scanned in both directions. [From Zähringer[15]]

nearly its original concentration. Assuming an inverse square-root mass dependence of the diffusion coefficients, the authors estimated the initial rare-gas contents of these meteorites to have been about 10 to 100 times higher.

An experimental technique that allows us to localize the rare gases even more specifically has been applied by Zähringer[15]. Polished sections of gas-rich meteorites are analysed by a microprobe; where the electron beam, of a few micrometres in diameter, hits the surface, the material is heated and the gases are released. The vacuum line of the microprobe analyser is connected to a sensitive mass spectrometer, adjusted to mass 4. By scanning the samples, the helium release has been measured as a function of the local iron concentration, the variations of which reflect the grain boundaries. The accuracy of this method requires still further improvement, but our preliminary results verified that primordial helium is preferentially located on the crystal surfaces. Sometimes, though less frequently, it seems to come from inner parts of the grains also. Figure 1 shows one of the measurements, where He release peaks and Fe concentration are recorded simultaneously.

From the experimental evidence, the taking-up of the rare gases in liquid solution can be excluded. As proposed by Fredriksson and Keil[16], they might have been intro-duced by supersonic shocks under high partial gas pressures. Possibly, they were trapped in collisions of the primary bodies that were still in contact with the gases of the solar nebula; cometary impacts, however, would also cause high momentary gas pressures. The possibility of a shock emplacement of rare gases was shown experimentally[17,18].

Another explanation is that the light primordial rare gases are trapped solar wind particles[12,13,19]. According to the model described by Wänke[20], these meteorites come from the outermost layer of their parent body where matter is exposed to solar particle irradiation; in addition, they might have collected cosmic dust that was also irradiated and caused the higher carbon content and the dark appearance. So, mixture with material from a somewhat greater depth produced the dark–light structure.

For either incorporation mechanism, confinement of the rare gases to the grain surfaces would be expected, especially for a particle irradiation model. In this respect, the microprobe investigation is, in principle, a crucial experiment. Helium that is found within the grains is perhaps located at inner crystal surfaces or lattice imperfections. Such sites might be accessible to shock-introduced gas, whereas solar particles cannot penetrate so deep. Obviously, this method would be very useful if it could be improved sufficiently, since the question about the nature of the primordial rare gases is of great interest in understanding the formation of meteorites.

Radiogenic Ages

The isotopic variations that are produced in the meteorites by the decay of long-lived radioactivities can be used to determine the time elapsed since their formation. Such variations occur because, after its condensation and accretion to large parent bodies, meteoritic matter underwent chemical differentiation. When radioactive elements are separated from their decay products, variations of the isotopic composition of the daughter elements arise in the course of time between samples of different mother to daughter ratio. To derive an age the relative amount of decayed radioactivity has to be measured.

Age determination with noble gases has the advantage, compared with methods based upon solid elements, that meteorites usually started with extremely low concentrations of helium and argon, and K–Ar and U–He dating therefore are possible just with single samples. Rb–Sr or Pb–Pb ages always require the measurement of at least two samples of cogenetic origin, but of different mother to daughter ratio.

The radiogenic ages define the time that passed since the last separation, which depends on the cooling-down of the parent body. The meaning is somewhat different for the various methods. As the formation of the minerals usually occurs at higher temperatures than the cessation of rare-gas escape, the solidification ages (Rb–Sr, Pb–Pb) are expected to be a little higher than the gas-retention ages (K–Ar, U,Th–He). Furthermore, the rare-gas ages may be affected by subsequent reheating, even to only moderate temperatures. Thus, the meteorites' thermal history can be studied by measuring their radiogenic ages.

Stony meteorites

In recent years, U,Th–He and K–Ar ages have been compiled[21-28] for a large number of stone meteorites. For rare-gas and potassium measurements, mass-spectrometric techniques are usually applied. In ordinary chondrites, the K content is in the narrow range of 800–900 parts per million (see Kirsten, Krankowsky, and Zäh-ringer[21]); the concentrations are lower in other meteorite classes. The small uranium and thorium concentrations could only be measured by neutron activation[29–32]; they are quite uniform for normal chondrites with 10–15 parts per billion U, but show stronger variations for achondrites and carbonaceous chondrites.

The K–Ar ages of stone meteorites range from a few hundred to about five thousand million years. The majority of them cluster around 4–4·5 × 10⁹ years, which is comparable with the Pb–Pb[33] and Rb–Sr ages [34,35]; a rather large number, however, have significantly lower ages. The U,Th–He ages are of the same order but a little lower on average. The K–Ar age distribution of chondritic meteorites is shown in a histogram (figure 2).

The ages which are much below 4 × 10⁹ years certainly result from some kind of

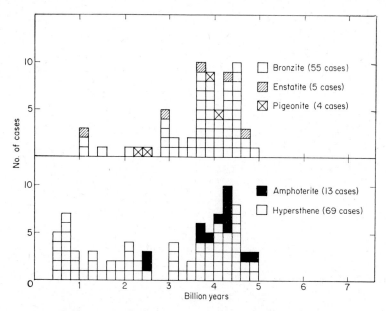

FIGURE 2   K–Ar ages of 146 chondrites [from Zähringer[22]]

reheating. As diffusion experiments[36,37] have shown, temperatures of about 100–200 °C already cause considerable rare-gas losses if they are maintained over longer periods of time. The critical temperature range can be exceeded in a close approach to the Sun and, from statistical considerations of orbital history, this is not an improbable event[38,39]. Another possible source of reheating and gas losses are collisions between the parent bodies.

The hypersthene chondrites have systematically lower ages than the bronzite chondrites. This must not necessarily reflect differences in the thermal history; different diffusion behaviour, which depends on the mineral composition as well as on the grain sizes, could have the same effect. The diffusion experiments, however, do not support such an explanation, although they cannot completely rule it out.

Quite informative is a comparison between the Ar and He ages as shown in figure 3, for hypersthene and bronzite chondrites. Most of the meteorites have about concordant He and Ar ages which are both high; obviously, these values give the true gas-retention ages, which are essentially not affected by any subsequent gas loss. There is a small group of meteorites of intermediate ages, the He ages being much lower than the K–Ar ages. This is what we would expect as the result of a diffusion process, for helium is released more easily than argon[21,36,37]. Only among the hypersthene chondrites are quite a number which have U,Th–He and K–Ar ages that are in rather good agreement, clustering around 1×10^9 years.

The latter group cannot result from an incomplete diffusion process at a time much

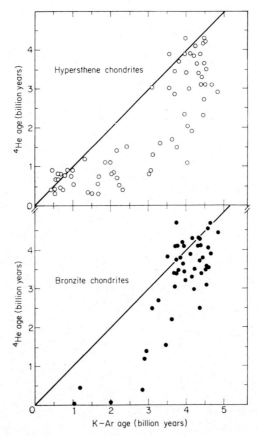

FIGURE 3   Comparison of ⁴He and K–Ar ages of chondrites [from Zähringer[22]]

later than that given by the age. Since helium escapes faster than argon, it is difficult to see how concordant K–Ar and U–He ages could be produced unless by resetting both radioactive clocks. It seems likely that the low-age hypersthene chondrites were commonly degassed some hundred million years ago. For several of these meteorites the degassing was not complete, which caused their somewhat higher ages. This explanation is supported by the gas release experiments of Fechtig, Gentner, and Lämmerzahl[36], where a strongly held ⁴⁰Ar component was observed in the Alfianello meteorite (a hypersthene with a K–Ar age of 0·7 billion years); this has been interpreted as the residual gas that was left only in the biggest grains. Recently, for the Bruderheim meteorite (a hypersthene with a K–Ar age of 1·8 billion years), a degassing

0·5 billion years ago has been measured by a diffusion experiment using the fast neutron-activated [39]Ar as a monitor for potassium[40,41].

The most likely explanation for an event which reheats quite a considerable part of all the hypersthene chondrites and which occurred so late in the history of our planetary system is a large collision of their parent body. Mineralogical observations also indicate a tendency for meteorites with extremely low radiogenic ages to have been severely shocked. A conclusion about their origin from a different parent body cannot be drawn from the absence of a corresponding group of bronzite chondrites with low radiogenic ages. The reheating observed for part of the hypersthene chondrites must have been a local event, as is seen from the very fact that most of the hypersthene chondrites have high radiogenic ages too. Then, the bronzite chondrites only need to have been sufficiently far from the centre of collision; they might have been deposited at greater depth.

Iron meteorites

The concentrations of potassium are several orders of magnitude smaller in iron meteorites than in chondrites. For K–Ar age determination, therefore, extreme experimental difficulties arise. Neutron activation techniques are sensitive enough to measure the small amounts of potassium and radiogenic argon; the main problem, however, is the contamination by non-radiogenic argon and non-meteoritic potassium.

The first attempt was made by Stoenner and Zähringer[42] who measured the [40]Ar and K contents by counting the activity of the unstable isotopes produced in the reactions $^{40}Ar(n, \gamma)^{41}Ar$ and $^{41}K(n, \gamma)^{42}K$. Their ages, ranging from 6 to 13 billion years, were unreasonably high.

A new programme of K–Ar dating on iron meteorites with improved experimental technique was lately started by Müller and Zähringer[43]. To examine whether the [40]Ar found in the meteorites is radiogenic, they looked for a proportionality between K and [40]Ar. Potassium is very inhomogeneously distributed and concentrated in inclusions; one can select different samples of the same meteorite with K contents varying more than an order of magnitude. Indeed, in such specimens where the potassium content is high, the [40]Ar to K ratio is constant.

The mean concentrations of the iron meteorites investigated are summarized in figure 4. For meteorites with low K content the ages are systematically high, which points to the existence of some kind of background [40]Ar of the order of 10^{-8} cm^3/g. This component is negligible for iron meteorites with more than 100 parts per billion K; such high K concentrations, however, are rather exceptional. The apparent ages of the four specimens richest in potassium (Carthage, Treysa, Canyon Diablo, Sikhote Alin) are between 6 and 7 billion years; the mean age is $6·3 \times 10^9$ years.

Troilite inclusions, with comparatively high K content, usually show much lower ages than the metal phase of the same meteorite. To explain this discrepancy two possibilities may be taken into consideration. One is that potassium migrated in the course of time from the metal to the inclusions. As the decay rate of [40]K was highest at the beginning, radiogenic [40]Ar is now in excess within the metallic phase; the true ages then must be somewhere between the apparent ages of the metal and those of the inclusions. Alternatively, the troilite might have been degassed at a later time, when the meteorite suffered a collision. From the cosmic-ray exposure ages it is seen that such catastrophic events occurred several hundred million years ago. In this case the better K–Ar age would be that of the metallic phase in which argon is more strongly fixed.

For a silicate nodule of one iron meteorite, a Rb–Sr age of 4.7×10^9 years has been reported[44]. Such material, however, is not typical for iron meteorites, and this measurement cannot disprove the K–Ar results which are based upon a much larger number of representative samples.

The existence of objects in the solar system that are much older than 4·5 billion years is incompatible with current hypotheses of its evolution. Moreover, ages of 6·3 billion years would be nearly in conflict with estimations of the age of matter

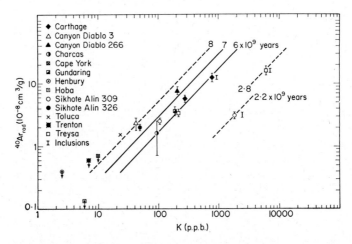

FIGURE 4   Mean concentrations of K and radiogenic ^{40}Ar in several iron meteorites. The straight lines are isochrones. [From Müller and Zähringer[43]]

based upon the uranium isotope ratio[45]. For these reasons, one has to be careful in the interpretation of the measured potassium and argon concentrations. Exact corrections to account for spallation are now possible[46], and the isotopic abundance of ^{40}K has been proved to be quite normal in iron meteorites[47,48]. The potassium–argon proportionality and the agreement of the measured age values of the iron meteorites with the highest K contents are strong arguments that the apparent K–Ar ages of about 6·3 billion years might be correct. But, at present, one cannot really exclude that some source of error is still involved.

Further experimental work is needed to improve the confidence in the results. The question about the age of iron meteorites is, of course, of fundamental importance in understanding the evolution of the planetary system.

Cosmic-ray Exposure Ages

Meteorites are fragments of one or more larger parent bodies which were broken up by a collision or some other unknown process. Up to that time, they were shielded from cosmic radiation which has a penetration depth of about one metre. But in the small fragments, meteoritic matter has been exposed to interaction with high-energy cosmic-ray particles. When such a particle hits an atomic nucleus, energetic protons, neutrons, and mesons are ejected in a cascade; the residual nucleus is highly excited, and is able to evaporate further particles including those of composite type such as deuterons, tritons, or helium nuclei. All stable and radioactive nuclides with mass numbers lower than the heaviest target element are produced. They can be detected by sensitive mass spectrometry and special low-level counting methods.

Meteorites are space probes from which we get information about cosmic radiation; fluctuations in time and variations along the orbit of meteorites are recorded by spallation-produced radioactivities of different half-lives[49−51]. One of the most important results is that the flux of cosmic radiation has been essentially constant over the last billion years.

The lifetime of meteorites as unshielded small bodies, the so-called cosmic-ray exposure age, can be determined too. The amount C of a stable spallation nuclide accumulated since the formation of the small-sized meteoritic body is a direct measure of the duration of the irradiation, t_e, which can be calculated from the equation

$$t_e = \frac{C}{dC/dt}$$

The production rate dC/dt, if it is assumed to be constant during the whole exposure, can be inferred from an unstable isotope which has come into radioactive equilibrium after a few half-lives; the number of newly produced nuclei is then equal to the number of nuclei disintegrating per unit time. The relative production rates of stable and radioactive isotopes are obtained from irradiations with artificially accelerated energetic particles[52]. Thus, an exposure age is derived from measurements of the concentration of a stable and of the specific activity of an unstable spallogenic nuclide.

^{3}H–^{3}He, ^{36}Cl–^{36}Ar, ^{39}Ar–^{38}Ar are such pairs of spallogenic nuclides, which are of practical importance for exposure age determinations. The half-lives are short compared with the exposure ages of meteorites, and radioactive equilibrium has been reached.

This is not the case for the long-lived radionuclide ^{40}K. Only small portions of the spallation-produced ^{40}K have decayed during the exposure times of iron meteorites, which are comparable with the half-life of $1\cdot3 \times 10^9$ years. By high precision isotope analysis of spallogenic potassium, exposure ages of iron meteorites have been derived from the deficient ^{40}K, relative to the stable ^{41}K (see Voshage and Hintenberger[51]). The same can be done by measuring spallogenic argon isotopes[46]. ^{40}Ar is directly produced but also arises, with some retardation, from the decay of spallogenic ^{40}K. The ^{40}Ar concentration, normalized to ^{38}Ar, is a function of time, which is illustrated in figure 5. The ^{40}Ar/^{38}Ar values, after a small correction to account for the different Ni content and radiation hardness, can be well fitted by a curve calculated for the cross-section parameters indicated.

For iron meteorites the most reliable exposure ages with the best statistics have been obtained by the ^{40}K–^{41}K method. The age distribution is shown in a histogram (figure 6). Apparently, most of the ages are clustered around 300, 600, and 900 million years, which points to an origin from a few distinct parent bodies. This is also supported by a correlation between the exposure ages, the mineralogical structure, and the Ga and Ge contents of the distinct groups[53].

The stony meteorites are younger than the irons by more than an order of magnitude. In figure 7 the ^{3}He exposure ages of 165 chondrites are shown. The best explanation for the strong discrepancy between the exposure ages of iron and stony meteorites is that they come from different places of the solar system. For objects originating in the

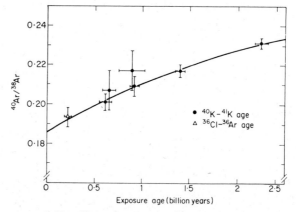

FIGURE 5   Spallogenic ^{40}Ar/^{38}Ar values as a function of the exposure age of iron meteorites. The curve is calculated for relative spallation cross sections of ^{40}Ar/^{38}Ar = 0·186 and ^{40}K/^{38}Ar = 0·97. [Data from Lämmerzahl and Zähringer[46]]

asteroidal belt, the travel times until they are captured by the Earth have been calculated to be several hundred million years[38, 39]. As the iron meteorites have ages of this order, they are most likely of asteroidal origin. The comparatively short ages of chondrites suggest a place of origin much closer to the Earth.

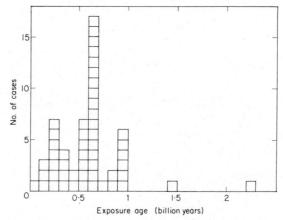

FIGURE 6   Exposure ages of 52 iron meteorites by the ^{40}K–^{41}K method [from Voshage[53]]

It is highly probable that the Moon's surface is a source of chondritic meteorites. The craters on it indicate a continuous bombardment by interplanetary objects. Very large bodies, either asteroids or comets, impinging on the Moon with cosmic velocities may throw away a substantial mass of lunar material. Ejecta that are accelerated to above escape velocity can move in free orbits round the Sun before they are captured by the Earth. Arnold[38, 39] has calculated that the lifetimes of such objects would have a distribution quite similar to the exposure ages of chondrites.

The fact that the ages of bronzite chondrites are sharply peaked at 4 million years points to one major event having formed these fragments; the few specimens of higher ages might be due to previous, less extensive events. One common parent body is highly probable for the bronzite chondrites.

As has already been seen from the radiogenic ages, the hypersthene chondrites have had a different history. The distribution of their exposure ages is decreasing slightly up to about 100 million years. If they were not preirradiated prior to the

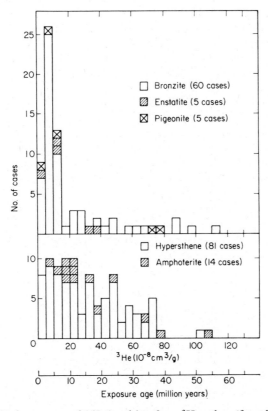

FIGURE 7   Exposure ages of 165 chondrites from ^{3}He values [from Zähringer[22]]

fragmentation, which seems unlikely, they must have been continuously created, i.e. in short intervals of time.

Zähringer[22] suggested the Moon as the source of both classes. The hypersthene chondrites, according to this idea, are material from close to the surface ejected in several smaller impacts; whereas the bronzite chondrites come from greater depth as fragments produced in one exceptionally catastrophic event.

Other theories presume different parent bodies for either chondritic class. Then the hypersthene chondrites have to come from a more distant source than the Moon, because of their higher exposure ages. To account for the fact that their exposure ages are still low compared with those of the iron meteorites, Anders[3] proposed the asteroids which cross the orbit of Mars as possible sources. From a statistical consideration combining exposure ages and daytimes of fall Wänke[54] concluded a place of origin outside the Earth's orbit for the hypersthenes, which he suggested to have been ejected from Mars itself. Sitte[55] has shown that multiple elastic scattering ought to be rather effective in deflecting asteroidal fragments into highly eccentric orbits, which would also lower the exposure ages considerably. He estimated that the Moon and the asteroidal belt should be sources of meteorites of comparable strength.

References

1. E. Anders, in *The Moon, Meteorites, and Comets, The Solar System IV* (Eds. B. Middlehurst and G. P. Kuiper), University of Chicago Press, Chicago, 1963, p. 402.
2. E. Anders, *Rev. Mod. Phys.*, **34**, 287 (1962).
3. E. Anders, *Space Sci. Rev.*, **3**, 583 (1964).
4. J. Zähringer, *Ann. Rev. Astron. Astrophys.*, **2**, 121 (1964).
5. O. Müller and J. Zähringer, *Earth Planetary Sci. Letters*, **1**, 25 (1966).
6. R. O. Pepin and P. Signer, *Science*, **149**, 253 (1965).
7. C. Merrihue, *J. Geophys. Res.*, **71**, 263 (1966).
8. K. Marti, P. Eberhardt, and J. Geiss, *Z. Naturforsch.*, **21a**, 398 (1966).
9. J. Zähringer, *Z. Naturforsch.*, **17a**, 460 (1962).
10. P. Signer and H. E. Suess, in *Earth Science and Meteoritics* (Eds. J. Geiss and E. D. Goldberg), North-Holland, Amsterdam, 1963, p. 241.
11. H. König, K. Keil, H. Hintenberger, F. Wlotzka, and F. Begemann, *Z. Naturforsch.*, **16a**, 1124 (1961).
12. P. Eberhardt, J. Geiss, and N. Grögler, *Mineral. Petrog. Mitt.*, **10**, 535 (1965).
13. P. Eberhardt, J. Geiss, and N. Grögler, *J. Geophys. Res.*, **70**, 4375 (1965).
14. H. Hintenberger, E. Vilcsek, and H. Wänke, *Z. Naturforsch.*, **20a**, 939 (1965).
15. J. Zähringer, *Earth Planetary Sci. Letters*, **1**, 20 (1966).
16. K. Fredriksson and K. Keil, *Geochim. Cosmochim. Acta*, **27**, 717 (1963).
17. K. Fredriksson and P. DeCarli, *J. Geophys. Res.*, **69**, 1403 (1964).
18. R. O. Pepin, J. H. Reynolds, and G. Turner, *J. Geophys. Res.*, **69**, 1406 (1964).
19. H. E. Suess, H. Wänke, and F. Wlotzka, *Geochim. Cosmochim. Acta*, **28**, 595 (1964).
20. H. Wänke, *Z. Naturforsch.*, **20a**, 946 (1965).
21. T. Kirsten, D. Krankowsky, and J. Zähringer, *Geochim. Cosmochim. Acta*, **27**, 13 (1963).
22. J. Zähringer, *Meteoritika*, **27**, 25 (1966).
23. W. Kaiser and J. Zähringer, *Z. Naturforsch.*, **20a**, 963 (1965).
24. A. P. Vinogradov and I. K. Zadorozhny, *Akad. Nauk SSSR*, **7**, 587 (1964).
25. D. Heymann, *J. Geophys. Res.*, **70**, 3735 (1965).
26. H. Hintenberger, H. König, L. Schultz, and H. Wänke, *Z. Naturforsch.*, **20a**, 983 (1965).
27. D. Krankowsky and J. Zähringer, in *Potassium Argon Dating* (Eds. O. A. Schaeffer and J. Zähringer), Springer-Verlag, Heidelberg, 1966, p. 174.
28. P. Eberhardt, O. Eugster, J. Geiss, and K. Marti, *Z. Naturforsch.*, **21a**, 414 (1966).
29. H. Hamaguchi, G. W. Reed, and A. Turkevich, *Geochim. Cosmochim. Acta*, **12**, 337 (1957).
30. G. L. Bate, J. R. Huizenga, and H. A. Potratz, *Geochim. Cosmochim. Acta*, **16**, 88 (1959).
31. G. W. Reed, K. Kigoshi, and A. Turkevich, *Geochim. Cosmochim. Acta*, **20**, 122 (1960).
32. J. F. Lovering and J. W. Morgan, *J. Geophys. Res.*, **69**, 1979 (1964).
33. C. Patterson, *Geochim. Cosmochim. Acta*, **10**, 230 (1956).
34. V. R. Murthy and W. Compston, *J. Geophys. Res.*, **70**, 5297 (1965).
35. W. H. Pinson Jr., C. C. Schnetzler, E. Beiser, H. W. Fairbairn, and P. M. Hurley, *Geochim. Cosmochim. Acta*, **29**, 455 (1965).
36. H. Fechtig, W. Gentner, and P. Lämmerzahl, *Geochim. Cosmochim. Acta*, **27**, 1149 (1963).
37. R. Bieri and W. Rutsch, preprint (1965).
38. J. R. Arnold, in *Isotopic and Cosmic Chemistry* (Eds. H. Craig, S. L. Miller, and G. J. Wasserburg), North-Holland, Amsterdam, 1964, p. 347.

39. J. R. Arnold, *Astrophys. J.*, **141**, 1536 (1965).
40. C. Merrihue and G. Turner, *J. Geophys. Res.*, **71**, 2852 (1966).
41. G. Turner, J. A. Miller, and R. L. Grasty, *Earth Planetary Sci. Letters*, **1**, 155 (1966).
42. R. W. Stoenner and J. Zähringer, *Geochim. Cosmochim. Acta*, **15**, 40 (1958).
43. O. Müller and J. Zähringer, *Geochim. Cosmochim. Acta*, **30**, 1075 (1966).
44. G. J. Wasserburg, D. S. Burnett, and C. Frondel, *Science*, **150**, 1814 (1965).
45. W. A. Fowler and F. Hoyle, *Ann. Phys. (N.Y.)*, **10**, 280 (1960).
46. P. Lämmerzahl and J. Zähringer, *Geochim. Cosmochim. Acta*, **30**, 1059 (1966).
47. W. Kempe and J. Zähringer, *Geochim. Cosmochim. Acta*, **30**, 1049 (1966).
48. D. S. Burnett, H. J. Lippolt, and G. J. Wasserburg, *J. Geophys. Res.*, **71**, 1249 (1966).
49. O. A. Schaeffer, R. Davis Jr., R. W. Stoenner, and D. Heymann, *Proc. Intern. Conf. on Cosmic Rays, Jaipur, 1963*, Vol. 3, Commercial Printing Press, Bombay, 1963, p. 480.
50. O. A. Schaeffer and D. Heymann, *J. Geophys. Res.*, **70**, 215 (1965).
51. H. Voshage and H. Hintenberger, *Symp. on Radioactive Dating, Athens*, International Atomic Energy Agency, Vienna, 1963, p. 367.
52. K. Goebel, H. Schultes, and J. Zähringer, *CERN* 64-12 (1964).
53. H. Voshage, private communication (1965).
54. H. Wänke, *Z. Naturforsch.*, **21a**, 93 (1966).
55. K. Sitte, *Z. Naturforsch.*, **21a**, 231 (1966).

5

T. GRJEBINE
Centre des Faibles Radioactivités
Gif-sur-Yvette, France

Abundance of cosmic dust

Cosmic dust can bring us very valuable information about the history of the solar system and the most primitive process of the formation of solid material in space. Recent measurements showing that the amount of cosmic dust is very abundant introduce another question: is cosmic dust one of the basic materials from which the Earth was formed and is this process still continuing? A partial answer can be given immediately: cosmic dust accounts for at least 1 % of the central oceanic sedimentation and may be responsible for 95 % of the total amount. But this process of accretion was not constant in time: there were periods when it was less important than at present, and other periods when it was more important. The absence of the criteria of cosmicity for all data collected makes evaluation dependent on the criteria chosen, and the abundance of cosmic dust is still usually subjected to an adjustment of some values previously found. The first review of the quantity of accretion of cosmic dust was published by Best[1].

In table 1 we have tabulated the different estimates of the accretion rate of cosmic dust on the Earth. The comparison of the results of the abundances found by different techniques is difficult because most of them measure the abundance of dust only in a range of sizes, whereas all the spectrum is composed of several magnitudes of sizes (figure 1).

Space Determination

Space determination started with the data collected by *Explorer I* in 1958 (sensor Alpha) and *Vanguard III* in 1959 (sensor Eta). An average flux of 10^{-2} m^{-2} sec^{-1} for particles of 10^{-9} g was detected. The mass evaluated by La Gow and Alexander[3] in the range of their detector was 6×10^2 tons/day. By extending the mass distribution as determined by *Explorer I* and *Vanguard III*, the daily influx of interplanetary matter on the Earth of particles of masses between $1 \cdot 2 \times 10^{-8}$ and $1 \cdot 2 \times 10^{-10}$ g was estimated at 10^4 tons/day (see La Gow and Alexander[3]). The size of cosmic dust that can be detected has since been considerably enlarged by photomultiplier detectors and by collection in free space.

Nazarova[4] reduced all data to one sensitivity and found that the flux depends strongly on the altitude; it was suggested by Nazarova that there was a concentration

TABLE 1   Different estimations of the mass yearly accreted by the Earth

Accretion rate per year	Authors	Year	Method
$4\cdot2 \times 10^9$	Hansa and Zacharov	1958	Ni in collection
$2\cdot5 \times 10^9$	Grjebine	1963	Fe in collection
$1\cdot7 \times 10^9$	Petterson	1958	Ni in air filtration
$9\cdot4 \times 10^8$	Zacharov	1961	Ni in collection
7×10^7	Link	1955	optical density of atmosphere
4×10^7	Lal	1966	cosmic Al^{26} in sea sediments
$3\cdot2 \times 10^7$	Petterson and Rotchi	1950	Ni in deep sea sediments
$1\cdot4 \times 10^7$	Petterson	1960	Ni in air filtration
5×10^6	Petterson	1960	deep sea sediments
$3\cdot6 \times 10^6$	McCracken and others	1961	satellite between $1\cdot2 \times 10^8$ and 10^{-10} g
$3\cdot6 \times 10^6$	La Gow and Alexander	1960	satellite between $1\cdot2 \times 10^8$ and 10^{-10} g
$3\cdot6 \times 10^6$	Dubin	1960	satellite between $1\cdot2 \times 10^8$ and 10^{-10} g
$3\cdot6 \times 10^6$	Whipple	1960	theoretical
$3\cdot6 \times 10^6$	Watson	1956	meteors
$3\cdot6 \times 10^6$	Mirtov	1962	optical measurements
$3\cdot1 \times 10^6$	Kreiken	1959	spherules in collection
2×10^6	Schaeffer	1965	cosmic ^{36}Cl in *large* particles of sea sediments
2×10^6	Thomson	1953	spherules in collection
$2\cdot8 \times 10^6$	Petterson	1960	air filtration
6×10^5	Grjebine	1964	spherules in Mediterranean Sea
5×10^5	Hodge and Wildt	1958	spherules in collection
$2\cdot5 \times 10^5$	Öpik	1956	astronomy
$1\cdot8 \times 10^5$	Thiel and Schmit	1961	spherules in snow
$1\cdot6 \times 10^5$	Crozier	1960	spherules in collection
$1\cdot2 \times 10^5$	Buddhue	1950	spherules
9×10^4	Crozier	1961	spherules in collection
4×10^4	Petterson and Rotchi	1950	deep sea spherules
3×10^4	Fireman and others	1961	air collection
$5\cdot8 \times 10^3$	Petterson and others	1958	deep sea spherules
5×10^2	Watson	1941	meteors
$1\cdot8 \times 10^2$	Milleman	1948	meteors
$1\cdot2 \times 10^2$	Petterson	1953	deep sea spherules

around the Earth. But it is difficult to explain, on the basis of geometrical consideration, an increase of three orders of magnitude between the data obtained close to the
Earth and those obtained far from the Earth. So, if the differences were not explained
by a dust belt around the Earth, they would lead to an accretion rate by the Earth of
$3\cdot6 \times 10^8$ tons/year for the detectors mounted on sounding rockets.

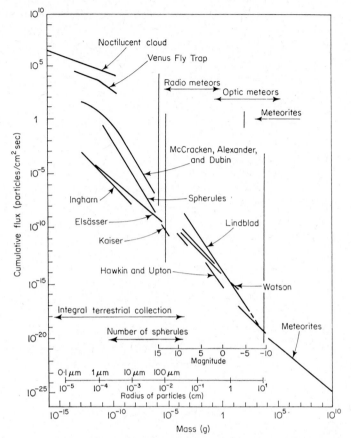

FIGURE 1 Cumulative flux of cosmic material against mass [the original curve is due to Alexander[2]]. The flux deduced from the noctilucent clouds NATTIP experiment is plotted using the 'minimal assumption'

Our purpose is not to review these experiments in detail but just to show how arbitrary the data of 10^4 tons/day of accreted material by the Earth ($3 \cdot 6 \times 10^6$ tons/day) actually appears. Besides the limit of size and the slope of the curve, it is important to know another fact in order to understand accretion—it is the direction of the particles. We have very few data about this as well, and it is impossible to say now whether we measure a spatial flux or an influx to the Earth.

Free-space Collection

The normalization of microphone detector data to data obtained by perforation or breaking of wire grids appeared to be difficult; the problem is even more striking when comparing the detection data for small particles, detected with a photomultiplier (this detects the light generated by the impact of a dust particle), with the data obtained through collection of cosmic dust.

The first results were obtained with the Venus Fly Trap Collector. The data published[5] showed a very important flux in the particle size range of 0·1–3 μm. Smaller particles were discounted because their cosmic origin was difficult to establish;

for larger ones the statistics were too poor. If an average bulk density of 3 g/cm^3 is assumed for these particles, a total rate of $1·5 \times 10^{-7}$ g/m^2 sec was being collected. If it can be assumed that the speed of the rocket was negligible compared with the speed of incoming particles, it would result in an amount of 3×10^5 to $1·2 \times 10^{-6}$ tons/day reaching the Earth in the $0·1–3$ μm window only. However, the opening of the collector occurred around 90 km and this strongly implies that the collector was sweeping dust already stopped in the atmosphere. Therefore, the accretion figure would be lower. Soberman and Hemenway[6] tried a computation of the data to correct the flux by accounting for the relative speed of the dust, but it was very difficult to find the real speed because many influencing factors are unknown, in particular the charge of the dust particle and the electrical drag resulting from that charge.

A second set of experiments was performed with collection made from noctilucent clouds. In this case the particles are definitely stopped and no free-space flux determination is possible.

The third series of experiments[7] performed by sounding rockets between 75 and 98 km in the absence of clouds has shown a flux very similar to the first Venus Fly Trap experiment. This implies that the particles in the Venus Fly Trap experiment were stopped as well, and therefore it is strongly evident that any calculation of the accreted mass on the basis of the existing Venus Fly Trap data cannot be made.

For the last experiment the authors did not publish any estimation of the total flux.

It is regrettable that until now all collections made with sounding rockets began at too low altitudes to give an unambiguous value for the incoming flux.

Upper Atmospheric Collection

The collection of particles between 78 and 95 km in and out of noctilucent clouds[8] provides us with very useful information for the evaluation of the accretion rate. We cannot calculate the accretion value directly from the experiments because they are also subject to indetermination; the speed of the particles and the statistical importance of noctilucent clouds or meteoric showers are unknown. Collection in the upper atmosphere can therefore only provide an upper and a lower limit for accretion.

The lower limit for accretion can be determined by assuming that there are no more than thirty clouds per year and that no particles are present in the absence of clouds. The total influx of accreted material is limited to the mass which could be collected in thirty clouds. These assumptions produce a lower limit of 1×10^7 tons/year arriving at the Earth in the window $0·05–4$ μm (box 14, density was assumed to be 3) (see Hemenway and others[8]). The upper limit can be set by assuming that the particles' speeds are considerably in excess of the rocket speed, and that the flux is independent of the visible appearance of clouds. This limit is unreasonably high.

Collection in the upper atmosphere made possible the extension of data collected with microphones and therefore the reevaluation of the accretion rates. All these experiments have shown that the curve of abundance against size was very similar to the curve determined by microphones. The most natural tendency is then to consider that space collection has determined the continuation of the curve, in the region of small particles, of the general flux detected by microphones. The contrary assumption would be that the small particles are simply the result of the breaking up of larger bodies. This assumption can hardly stand for the following reasons.

(i) The amount of large particles is not large enough (the lowest assumption deduced from noctilucent clouds, 1×10^7 tons/year, means that there are not enough large particles).

(ii) If the small particles were the result of the breaking down of larger particles, the distribution of particles (of size 5–50 μm) detected with microphones would be different from the statistics of spherules collected on the ground.

(iii) Very large particles (several hundred micrometres) have been detected on the ground with a different morphology than spherules; this implies that the slowing down in the atmosphere is progressive and that dust is apparently not even melted.

The same large particles have been detected by balloon and rocket collections,

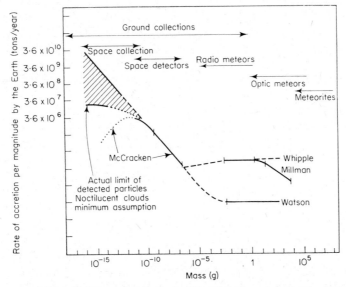

FIGURE 2 Rate of accretion per magnitude [the original curve is due to Alexander[2]]. The 'noctilucent cloud minimal assumption' is plotted assuming a flux of thirty clouds per year, with the amount of material collected by box 14 and an assumed density of 3

showing clearly that the number/size curve was not affected by any annihilation nor ablation of microscopic particles. Extending the general curve on this basis toward the 0·05 μm region (figure 2) brings the total accretion mass to 10^8 to 10^9 tons/year, a much higher range than was formerly supposed.

Atmospheric Determinations

A very interesting method utilizing the influence of the atmosphere in astronomic observation is used by Link to estimate the amount of dust present in the upper atmosphere[9]. Link considers several possible ways to estimate the importance of the diffusive layer at 100 km. One possible way is to estimate the falling speed of the dust, and from these data and the density calculate the mass accreted by the Earth.

The Bouguer curve of the luminosity of stars depending on their position presents an irregularity which was analysed on the basis of an absorption by an upper layer[10]. This absorbing layer at 100 km can also be studied during the eclipse of the Moon, or of a satellite, by the Earth. The shadow of the Earth appears larger than its geometrical size by approximately 1·5% (see Link[11]). The opacity of this shadow has an annual variation similar to the variation of meteors[9]. The time during which dust remains in the upper atmosphere has been studied by Link and Zacharov[12] with optical transparency measurements. These measurements yield an average of one month for the time it takes to decrease the dust density of the upper layer after a meteor shower.

Therefore purely astronomical observations can give a coherent set of figures from which to estimate the amount of cosmic dust accreted by the Earth. With these evaluations Link arrives at a value of 10^{-12} g/cm^2 sec or an annual accreted mass of $1·5 \times 10^8$ tons (see Link[9]).

In the atmosphere several different methods have been used to determine the concentration of dust. The earlier studies made by Friend and others[13] with aeroplanes have mainly shown particles smaller than 1 μm in size. The estimation of weight was 10^{-8} g/m^3. But when the estimation of weight was not based on counting but on the chemical analysis of the total material collected on the filters, the total amount was much higher. The detected calcium alone was as high as 10^{-7} g/m^3. If we use the general abundance of the elements to normalize the abundance of calcium, we obtain a total mass of the order of 10^{-5} g/m^3. Another type of measurement was made by Rosen with a balloon air-borne photomultiplier in conjunction with a microscope. This device counts the particles between 1 and 3 μm contained in a given stream of air. Rosen[14] found a distribution with a maximum around 20 km. In this layer, the concentration reached 1 particle/cm^3 yielding a density of about 1 to 2×10^{-5} g/m^3.

More recently, Grjebine[15] measured the concentration of a dust with an air-borne balloon technique. A surgical gauze exposed in a large box was lifted to 10 km, where the box was opened and the air permitted to pass through the gauze. When the balloon bursts at 30 km, the box is recovered by parachute. During the fall, the stream of air closes the box. The increase of weight of the gauze, after calcination, is measured on a precision scale and on a magnetic scale, which determines the amount of magnetic material. Over 10 km it was found that a large enrichment existed corresponding to 10^{-5} g/m^3 on the average and 10^{-4} g/m^3 after a meteoric shower. If this amount of material is assumed to be spread all over the World in a 10 km thick layer, this layer will represent at least 5×10^{13} g or $4·5 \times 10^7$ tons. If we assume the average falling time of this component is one month, as suggested by Link, there would be 6×10^8 tons/year of accreted material in the range of particles where the surgical gauze is efficient. The efficiency of the gauze was calculated to be 5% using radioactive bomb debris data. On the other hand, the accretion rate determined is in agreement with magnetic measurements made from the rate of fallout on the ground within a factor of 3.

One of the former integral measurements of dust on the ground was made by Petterson in Hawaii on Kilauea Mountain[16]. Petterson was measuring, by filtration, the amount of nickel present in the air. Similar measurements were made by Zacharov[17], and both groups of experimenters obtained very similar results. The total accreted masses to the Earth published by these authors ($1·4 \times 10^7$ tons and $9·4 \times 10^8$ tons) nevertheless depend on the assumption made regarding the percentage of nickel present in cosmic dust, and the residence time of the particles in the air. Petterson determined the residence time from the old semiempirical observation of the nebulosity of the atmosphere for 2 years after the big explosion of the volcano Krakatoa. It is difficult to say now if this nebulosity was really due to the explosion and to the introduction into the upper layer of the atmosphere of dust or of vapour. The only point is that modern measurements with dust or with radioactive debris have never shown such a long residence time. The amount of nickel in cosmic dust is very difficult to estimate. In the beginning it was thought that cosmic dust had a composition similar to that of iron meteorites and therefore the Ni to Fe ratio was supposed to be 10%. But later when a systematic analysis of spherules was made the ratio appeared to be much lower.

Averaging the amount of nickel in 500 spherules, Grjebine[18] obtained a figure of 0.3%. If we use this ratio and a residence time of one month, Petterson's figure becomes 1.7×10^9 tons/year and Zacharov's figure becomes 4.2×10^9 tons/year. In fact the real collected weight in the mountain top collector of Zacharov was very close to 4.2×10^9 tons/year.

A very large survey was made by Grjebine[19, 20] with the World-wide network of collectors of the Centre des Faibles Radioactivités of Gif-sur-Yvette. The collectors originally designed for the survey of radioactive bomb debris have been operating since 1958. They are made of a surgical gauze stretched over a funnel having a filtrating cotton and an ion-exchange resin at the bottom. The gauze and the cotton are calcinated and it appeared that it was quite possible to evaluate the amount of dust falling on the collector with magnetic measurements, even when direct weighing would be unreliable. The pollution from the ground was minimized this way, since the magnetic susceptibility of cosmic dust is much higher than that of the ground. The conversion of magnetic measurements into weight must be done with a very reliable sample, since all the data of all stations will depend on that conversion. The magnetic measurements have shown the following facts.

(i) The amount of magnetic dust falling in the collectors was nearly the same all over the World, magnetically equivalent to 2 mg Fe_2O_3 γ phase, with an exception, however, for the stations in the Sahara and northern Soudan, where aeolian transport of dust was obvious. The participation of aeolian material was detectable not only by abnormally high magnetic weights but also by considerable lowering of the magnetic susceptibility, showing therefore that it was the collection of old material where magnetite and metallic iron had been transformed into limonite.

(ii) The amount of magnetic dust falling on the sea was of the same order as that falling on the land, or higher.

(iii) The conversion ratio of magnetic attraction to weight was established with dust collected at sea level. The average data for the World was shown to be 4.8 g/m² year or 2.4×10^9 tons/Earth year.

(iv) Recently, during the Leonid shower in November 1965 we collected in the stratosphere a sufficiently large amount of dust to be able to weigh it directly as well as to carry out magnetic measurements. It appeared slightly more magnetic than the sample previously used. From the conversion factor of magnetic attraction to weight (the magnetic susceptibility of dust being higher), the figure of accretion decreased from 2.4 to 2×10^9 tons/Earth year.

(v) This very large amount of material exceeds all possible industrial pollution which is obviously unable to supply such a large amount of dust, except when the collectors were set in the middle of an industrial town or in the suburbs.

(vi) Some of the monthly maxima recorded in all the network were World wide and connected with meteor showers but most of the time, and even when it was a World-wide maximum, the monthly amount in each station was very irregular.

(vii) The monthly variation average over 7 years shows two maxima[21], one in spring and the other in the second part of the year around September. The first maximum was strikingly associated with radioactive debris, but the second one was associated much more with meteor showers. The most reasonable explanation for this process is the distinction of cosmic dust into two groups: the first one of over 10 μm reaches the ground very quickly, and the other one, smaller than 1 μm, behaves like the air mass in which it is included. The spring maximum of cosmic dust might be explained by small particles which have been stored in the stratosphere and which are injected in spring from the stratosphere to the troposphere at the same time as radioactive debris. The second maximum is the maximum due to larger particles which have reached the atmosphere with the spring meteoric showers. But recently Crozier published statistics of black spherules over 19 years, and it appears that he also observes two maxima which fit the maxima observed in meteor statistics; therefore, the spring maximum of magnetic dust may also be related to the flux of meteors.

(viii) Yearly values are also not constant and, by studying particles in the snow of the South Pole, Gliozzi[22] has shown that a period of about 2·5 years can be observed.

(ix) Longer periods exist as well. Since 1958 the total amount of magnetic dust has nearly doubled.

The main criticism which should be made about magnetic measurements is that it is a 'blind' type of measurement; the criteria of cosmicity is only found in a statistical analysis and in a high magnetic susceptibility, but of course it is difficult to expect a method to be integral and selective.

Ground Collection Sounding Techniques

The ground collection of cosmic dust has mainly been limited to magnetic spherules. The collections were made either with water pans or with greased plates[23,24] and by melting polar snow[25].

The values obtained in this way can hardly be considered as an estimation of the accretion rate for several reasons. Historically the spherules were considered as the only true cosmic material, and even among them only those with a small percentage of nickel were thought to be really cosmic, but further research has shown that the nickel criteria was probably wrong, and, moreover, that the spherules were a minority among cosmic dust. Besides, magnetic extraction introduces a very limiting factor as well. This limitation results in an accreted mass which is even smaller than that calculated from spatial data, ranging most of the time around 10^5 tons.

The most interesting result which was found with cosmic spherules extracted from sediment was the observation of a long variation in time. Petterson has shown that there was a strong increase of spherules in the last 5×10^4 years, so the actual rate for cosmic dust accretion must be considered as a high rate, at least compared with the rate during the Tertiary Era. This difference of rate will influence the comparison of actual measurements of flux with radioactive measurements of cosmonuclides in sediments.

Radioactive Methods

Cosmic dust during its stay in free space is a target for cosmic rays. They induce in it a series of radioactive nuclei which would not exist otherwise. The detection and utilization of this radioactivity for the appreciation of the accreted mass are subjected to a series of assumptions.

(i) The first possibility is to consider that cosmic dust, even when not identical with meteorites, is irradiated by the same cosmic flux and that the amount of radioactive nuclei will be identical with the activity per gramme of meteorite. This assumption is the most widely used.

(ii) Lack of secondaries, depending on the form of the spectrum of cosmic rays and size of the dust, is the second possibility; the lack of secondaries can produce a lower activation than in meteorites.

(iii) Loss by recoil is the next possibility; when a nuclear reaction occurs, the residual nucleus has a recoil. This recoil is large enough to expel the nuclei from a very small grain of dust; when a nucleus is expelled, it will be pushed away from the solar system by the radiation pressure and the solar wind. In this assumption, very fine dust which constitutes the main mass will be underactivated compared with the meteorite.

(iv) Next, there is activation by solar cosmic rays; the activation of meteorites is the result of the flux of cosmic galactic rays and of cosmic solar rays. The latter, which is much more abundant but less energetic, will activate large particles of dust as they will activate the superficial layer of the meteorite. If this layer is supposed to be very thin, it can also be supposed to be lost by fusion and ablation of the meteorite during entry into the atmosphere. In this series of assumptions the activity of dust can be 100 times higher than the activity of meteorites.

(v) The final assumption is the origin of cosmic dust; following some of the observations, the radioactivity of meteorites is not constant in time. The activation of meteorites by solar cosmic rays is not proved, but certainly not disproved.

If the dust is coming from the boundaries of the solar system or from interstellar space, the dust will be underactivated, as far as solar cosmic rays are concerned, through the recoil process. So, if the dust reaching the Earth is coming from the boundaries of the solar system, it will be underactivated at least as far as long periods are concerned. For instance, for the detection of ^{36}Cl or ^{26}Al, the dust should stay in orbit around the Sun for at least one million years, which is highly improbable. On the contrary, if the dust is coming from the Sun, for short periods it can be very overactivated, on the assumption that the long periods are more complicated to make and will depend on the dynamics of the dust in the Sun itself.

In all cases, one can see that the use of radioactive nuclei produced by cosmic rays is certainly a very good criterion of cosmicity but a very complicated one, and only very complete studies will give us the exact meaning of it.

The first two successful detections of radioactive nuclei formed by cosmic rays in cosmic dust were made by Fireman[26] and Schaeffer[27]. Schaeffer tried to detect

^{36}Cl, which is mainly formed from ^{40}Ca, in deep sea sediments. The radioactivity of ^{36}Cl is composed of a single beta without gamma rays; therefore it was necessary to eliminate all the chlorine in the sediment as otherwise the beta ray would be absorbed in the sample. The sediment was washed for one week with distilled water. A first attack with hydrochloric acid did not show any activity[28]; a second one with hydro-fluoric acid has shown the radioactivity of ^{36}Cl (see Schaeffer[27]).

If the radioactivity of ^{36}Cl per kilogramme of dust was the same as the radioactivity per kilogramme of meteorite, from the amount of ^{36}Cl detected by Schaeffer one can deduce a mass of dust of 2×10^6 tons/Earth year. This value corresponds only to the activity contained in big particles which have reached the bottom of the sea without corrosion. Since the number of small particles is largest and since even the large particles have a corrosion, this value must be multiplied by a corrosion factor to obtain the total accretion rate on the Earth. We do not have direct data from which we may measure the cosmic dust corrosion in the sea but we may estimate it as follows.

The comparison of the number of spherules in deep sea sediments and in lake sediments or in coastal geological deposits[29] shows that there are approximately 1000 times more spherules per gramme of sediment in fast sedimentation areas than in central oceanic regions; therefore, in spite of much smaller amounts of terrigenous sediment there are less spherules per gramme of sediment in central oceanic regions because they are destroyed. The recent discovery of bacterial life at the bottom of the ocean explains in a sense this process of destruction before they are covered with other sediments. Therefore the value of Schaeffer must be magnified by this corrosion factor and becomes 100 to 1000 times higher (2×10^8–2×10^9 tons/Earth year).

Another cosmonuclide determination was made by Lal and Venkatavaradam[30] in which deep sea sediments were treated with HCl, and ^{26}Al was detected. If the activation of dust was the same as the activation of meteorites, the amount detected shows that there is, approximately, from one to several per cent of cosmic material in deep sea sediments. This gives a value for accretion of 7×10^7 tons. Two comments must be made on this value.

(i) The portion of sediments from which ^{26}Al has been extracted has been dissolved in HCl. We have seen, with Schaeffer's detection of ^{36}Cl, that only a minor part of cosmic dust was soluble in HCl. There may be a larger amount of ^{26}Al in particles soluble only in hydrofluoric acid. The value of Lal must therefore be corrected by a 'non-total extraction factor'.

(ii) The second point refers to over- or underactivation. Lal calculated that the value matches the microphone flux and suggested an overactivation of dust.

On the other hand, Fireman[26] detected ^{60}Fe and ^{60}Co of cosmic origin but not ^{26}Al, and concluded that dust is underactivated for ^{26}Al when compared with the condition of irradiation of meteorites. So, when Fireman's and Lal's data are compared, we must also say that the total accreted mass must be over 7×10^7 tons. But we do not know the exact factor. This evidence shows very well that the method of mass determination through radioactivity induced by cosmic rays is very complicated and subject to many assumptions still not solved.

Historical data must be introduced as well to compare the different methods. Petterson has shown that the actual rate is very large. If we assume that the ratio of spherules to total cosmic dust has not changed through the Pliocene and Pleistocene Periods, we are in a particularly high period of accretion as we have seen before, and the radioactive data of ^{26}Al (period 8×10^8 years) and ^{36}Cl should be compared with the actual rate of accretion only when a correction factor has been applied.

Conclusion

Very interesting data have been published on the accretion rate of cosmic dust on the Earth. The main difference was due mostly to the fact that results referred to different components of cosmic dust and to different methods. Actually, it can be considered that a value of some 2×10^8 tons/Earth year can fit all the different determinations within a factor of $\times 10 \exp (\pm 1)$. A more careful analysis shows that a probable value is around 2×10^9 tons/Earth year but this value is not obtained with all the techniques. However, the importance of cosmic dust accretion will not be affected by those adjustments.

Actually, cosmic dust appears not only as a *major* constituent of oceanic sedimentation but also has an important role in meteorology and other geophysical processes[31]. But for the moment the large variation of cosmic dust flux and our ignorance of the dust origin forbid any conclusions on its role in the Earth's formation.

A very important point which has not been developed in this chapter, which is devoted to the amount of accreted material, is the chemical composition of cosmic dust. On the basis of present chemical analysis, it is clearly a source of valuable information on the history of the solar system.

References

1. G. T. Best, *Space Research I, Proc. Intern. Space Sci. Symp., Nice, 1960*, North-Holland, Amsterdam, 1961, pp. 1023–33.
2. W. M. Alexander, C. W. McCracken, L. Secretan, and O. E. Berg, *Space Research III, Proc. Intern. Space Sci. Symp., Washington, 1962*, North-Holland, Amsterdam, 1963, pp. 891–917.
3. H. E. La Gow and W. M. Alexander, *Space Research I, Proc. Intern. Space Sci. Symp., Nice, 1960*, North-Holland, Amsterdam, 1961, pp. 1033–41.
4. T. N. Nazarova, *Space Research II, Proc. Intern. Space Sci. Symp., Florence, 1961*, North-Holland, Amsterdam, 1962, pp. 639–44.
5. R. K. Soberman and C. L. Hemenway, *Astron. J.*, **67**, 121 (1962).
6. R. K. Soberman and C. L. Hemenway, *Astron. J.*, **67**, 256–66 (1962).
7. R. K. Soberman and C. L. Hemenway, *J. Geophys. Res.*, **70**, 2943 (1965).
8. C. L. Hemenway, E. F. Fullam, R. A. Skrivanek, and R. K. Soberman, *Tellus*, **16**, 96–102 (1964).
9. F. Link, *Texte des Conferences du Seminaire de L'Institut du Globe, Paris, 1965–66* Press Universitaire de France, C.E.A., Saclay, 1966.
10. F. Hausdorff, *Verhandl. Ber. Saechs. Akad. Wiss.*, **1895**, 401.
11. F. Link, *Osservatorio Astron. di Roma, Ser. III*, **N26**, 1 (1964).
12. F. Link, private communication.
13. J. F. Friend, H. W. Feel, P. W. Krey, J. Spar, and A. Walton, *High Altitude Sampling Program, D.A.S.A. Rept. No.* 1300 (1961).
14. J. M. Rosen, *J. Geophys. Res.*, **69**, 4673–6 (1964).
15. T. Grjebine, *Smithsonian Astrophys. Obs. Conf. on Meteor Orbit and Cosmic Dust, Cambridge, 1965*, in press.
16. H. Petterson, *Sci. Am.*, **202**, 123–32 (1960).

17. I. Zacharov, *Aerosols: Physical Chemistry and Applications, Proc. Natl. Conf. on Aerosols, 1st, Liblice, 1962*, Czechoslovak Academy of Sciences, Prague, 1964.
18. T. Grjebine, *Meteorite and Cosmic Dust Conf., Heidelberg, 1965.*
19. T. Grjebine, *Compt. Rend.*, **256**, 3735–8 (1963).
20. T. Grjebine, *Ann. N.Y. Acad. Sci.*, **119**, 126–42 (1964).
21. T. Grjebine, G. Lambert, and J. Labeyrie, *Compt. Rend.*, in press (1966).
22. J. Gliozzi, *J. Geophys. Res.*, **71**, 1993 (1966).
23. W. D. Crozier, *J. Geophys. Res.*, **66**, 2793–6 (1961).
24. P. W. Hodge and R. W. Wildt, *Geochim. Cosmochim. Acta*, **14**, 126–33 (1958).
25. R. A. Schmidt, *Ann. N.Y. Acad. Sci.*, **119**, 186–204 (1964).
26. E. Fireman, *Smithsonian Astrophys. Obs. Conf. on Meteor Orbit and Cosmic Dust, Cambridge, 1965*, in press.
27. O. A. Schaeffer, *Smithsonian Astrophys. Obs. Conf. on Meteor Orbit and Cosmic Dust, Cambridge, 1965*, in press.
28. O. A. Schaeffer, *Ann. N.Y. Acad. Sci.*, **119**, 347–50 (1964).
29. T. Grjebine, *Bull. Inst. Oceanog.*, **65**, 1–12 (1965).
30. D. Lal and V. S. Venkatavaradam, *Science*, **151**, 1381 (1966).
31. T. Grjebine, *Sci. Enseignement Sci.*, **35**, 45–55 (1965).

II

Determination of basic physical constants of the planets

1. The determination of the mass and oblateness of Mars from the orbits of its satellites (G. A. WILKINS) . 77

2. Optical diameter and ellipticity of the globe of the planet Mars (A. DOLLFUS) 85

3. Figure and density of the Moon (H. JEFFREYS) . . 93

4. The moment of inertia of the Moon determined from its orbital motion (W. J. ECKERT). . . . 97

1

G. A. WILKINS

H.M. Nautical Almanac Office
Royal Greenwich Observatory
Herstmonceux Castle
Sussex, England

The determination of the mass and oblateness of Mars from the orbits of its satellites

Introduction

The purposes of this chapter are to show how studies of the orbits of the satellites of Mars are used to give information about the principal parameters that define the structure of the planet, and to present the results obtained from a recent analysis of the observational material that is now available.

The two satellites, Phobos and Deimos, were discovered in 1877 by Hall[1] and it was soon found that they move in nearly circular orbits which lie close to the equatorial plane of Mars. The satellites are difficult to observe since they are faint, fast moving, and always comparatively close to the planet, the radii of the orbits being only 2·7 and 6·9 times the radius of Mars. The periods of revolutions are 7 hours 39 min and 30 hours 18 min, while the period of rotation of Mars is 24 hours 37 min. The mass of Mars is deduced from a modified form of Kepler's third law which connects the gravitational constant for the planet, the semimajor axis of the satellite orbit, and the period of revolution. The oblateness of Mars gives rise to a precession of the orbital plane of each satellite, and hence the so-called 'dynamical flattening' of Mars can be deduced from the rates of precession of the orbital planes. The value so obtained differs by an unexpectedly large factor from the value of the flattening of Mars that is deduced from optical measures of the equatorial and polar radii.

The results given below for the parameters, or elements, of the satellite orbits are in general agreement with those obtained previously by Struve[2] and Burton[3], and so the deduced values of the mass and oblateness of Mars are not significantly different. The new results, however, satisfy the theoretical relations given by Woolard[4] more closely than do the earlier ones. The additional interest of the recent studies, which used a larger number of observations including some made in 1941 and 1956, was in the attempt to confirm the suggestion made by Sharpless[5] that there were secular changes in the mean angular motions of the satellites. Several explanations, some more improbable than others, have been put forward to account for the large change for Phobos that was found by Sharpless, but the recent analysis suggests that any such secular change must be quite small.

The Orbits of the Satellites

The principal gravitational perturbations of the orbits of the satellites are due to the oblateness of Mars (or more precisely to the departure of the mass distribution from spherical symmetry). The only other significant perturbations are those due to the action of the Sun. The perturbations by the other planets are certainly negligible to the precision involved; the masses of the satellites and hence their mutual per-turbations are assumed to be negligible since the satellites are so faint. (The fact that the ratio of the mean angular motions cannot be expressed as a simple rational fraction also indicates that the mutual perturbations are not likely to be significant.)

The unperturbed orbital motion of each satellite would be Keplerian elliptic motion in a fixed plane, but the perturbing forces produce both periodic and secular (i.e. cumulative) changes in the elements defining the elliptic motion. The periodic per-turbations are small and have been neglected in the recent analysis. The principal secular perturbation due to the oblateness is a retrograde motion of the normal to the orbital plane about the principal axis of the planet, while the principal secular per-turbation due to the solar action is a similar motion about the normal to the plane of the orbit of Mars around the Sun. The net result is that the normal to the orbital plane precesses about an axis lying between the principal axis of the planet and the normal to the orbit of Mars; in the case of the satellites of Mars, this axis is close to the principal axis of the planet since the perturbations due to the oblateness are very much greater than those due to the solar action. This precession is such that the orbital plane maintains a constant inclination to the so-called Laplacian plane and the line of intersection of the two planes (i.e. line of nodes) regresses (i.e. moves in the opposite sense to the motion of the satellites) at a constant rate. In addition, the line of apsides in the orbital plane advances at (nearly) the same rate.

The positions of the satellites have only been measured at favourable oppositions over a period of one or two months at a time. It has therefore been the practice in the past to analyse the observations for each observer and each opposition separately in order to determine the set of elliptic elements (i.e. ignoring the perturbations) that would best fit the observations. These sets of elements have been analysed to determine the positions of the Laplacian planes and the secular motions for each satellite. In the recent analysis, however, all available observations of each satellite have been used to determine in a single least-squares solution the eleven parameters of an orbital model with the characteristics indicated above. (Solutions were also made for a model involving a twelfth parameter, corresponding to a secular change in the mean angular motion of the satellite.) Full details of the analysis will be pub-lished elsewhere, and so only the principal results (with formal standard errors) are given here in table 1, which gives the basic data from which the mass and dynamical flattening of Mars are to be deduced. The motions of the pericentron (i.e. of the line of apsides) could also be used, but their inclusion would not significantly improve or change the results obtained.

TABLE 1   Basic data for satellite orbits

Parameter	Phobos	Deimos
n daily mean angular motion	$1128 \cdot 8443° \pm 0 \cdot 0001°$	$285 \cdot 16188° \pm 0 \cdot 00001°$
a semimajor axis at unit distance	$12 \cdot 91'' \pm 0 \cdot 01''$	$32 \cdot 36'' \pm 0 \cdot 01''$
i inclination of orbital plane to Laplacian plane	$0 \cdot 9° \pm 0 \cdot 1°$	$1 \cdot 80° \pm 0 \cdot 02°$
$\dot N$ daily motion of node of orbital plane	$-0 \cdot 438° \pm 0 \cdot 001°$	$-0 \cdot 0180° \pm 0 \cdot 0003°$

Mass and Dynamical Flattening of Mars

From the observational data available we cannot expect to determine more than the first two terms in the expression for the gravitational potential of Mars. The potential at a point at a distance r astronomical units (A.U.) from the centre of Mars and at latitude ϕ is given by (1), where $k(= 0 \cdot 017\,202\,1)$ is the Gaussian gravitational con-

$$\frac{k^2 m}{r}\left\{1 - J_2\left(\frac{R_e}{r}\right)^2 P_2(\sin \phi)\right\} \tag{1}$$

stant, m is the mass of the planet in units of the Sun's mass, R_e is the planet's equatorial radius, J_2 is a coefficient that depends on the oblateness of the planet, and P_2 denotes the Legendre polynomial of second degree. The perturbing action of the Sun gives rise to another second-harmonic term, but with a coefficient proportional to $(r/r')^3$, where r' is the distance from the Sun; from Kepler's third law it can be seen that this term is proportional to $(n'/n)^2$, where $n'(= 0 \cdot 524\,033°$ per day) is the mean angular motion of Mars around the Sun. The masses of the satellites are assumed to be zero.

For each satellite the following relations hold; the mass of Mars is given by (2),

$$m = \frac{a^3 n^2}{k^2}\left\{1 - \frac{3}{2}J_2\left(\frac{R_e}{a}\right)^2 + \frac{1}{2}\left(\frac{n'}{n}\right)^2\right\} \tag{2}$$

while the angular motion of the node of the orbital plane on the Laplacian plane is given by (3).

$$\dot N = -n \cos i\left\{\frac{3}{2}J_2\left(\frac{R_e}{a}\right)^2 + \frac{3}{4}\left(\frac{n'}{n}\right)^2\right\} \tag{3}$$

The mean motions n and n' are both known accurately, and $\cos i$ is not critically dependent on the value of the i, so we see from equation (3) that the term $\frac{3}{2}J_2(R_e/a)^2$ can be determined directly from the observed value of $\dot N$ with a precision that is determined by the precision of that value. This term is small compared with unity, and so we see from equation (2) that we can determine the mass of Mars with a precision that is largely determined by the precision with which a can be determined. Substitution of the observational data from table 1 into equations (2) and (3) leads to the (rounded) results given in table 2.

TABLE 2   Intermediate values for each satellite

Quantity	Phobos	Deimos
$-\dot{N}/(n \cos i)$	$(0\cdot388 \pm 0\cdot001) \times 10^{-3}$	$(0\cdot632 \pm 0\cdot010) \times 10^{-4}$
$(n'/n)^2$	$0\cdot2155 \times 10^{-6}$	$3\cdot377 \times 10^{-6}$
$\frac{3}{2}J_2(R_e/a)^2$	$(0\cdot388 \pm 0\cdot001) \times 10^{-3}$	$(0\cdot606 \pm 0\cdot010) \times 10^{-4}$
n (rad/day)	$19\cdot7020$	$4\cdot97701$
a (A.U.)	$(0\cdot6259 \pm 0\cdot0005) \times 10^{-4}$	$(1\cdot5689 \pm 0\cdot0005) \times 10^{-4}$
m (solar masses)	$(0\cdot3215 \pm 0\cdot0007) \times 10^{-6}$	$(0\cdot3232 \pm 0\cdot0003) \times 10^{-6}$
$1/m$	3110000 ± 7000	3094000 ± 3000
$J_2R_e^2$ (A.U.^{2})	$(1\cdot013 \pm 0\cdot004) \times 10^{-12}$	$(0\cdot995 \pm 0\cdot016) \times 10^{-12}$

The weighted mean value for the mass of Mars (with the external standard error) is

$$m = (0\cdot3230 \pm 0\cdot0006) \times 10^{-6} \text{ solar masses}$$

while the corresponding value of the reciprocal mass is $3\,096\,000 \pm 6\,000$. Now the mass M of the Sun in grammes is given by

$$M = \frac{k^2L^3}{GT^2}$$

where G is the gravitational constant in c.g.s. units, T is the number of seconds ($86\,400$) in one day, and L is the number of centimetres in one astronomical unit. Adopting

$$G = (6\cdot668 \pm 0\cdot005) \times 10^{-8} \quad \text{and} \quad L = (1\cdot49600 \pm 0\cdot00001) \times 10^{13}$$

gives

$$M = (1\cdot9904 \pm 0\cdot0015) \times 10^{33} \text{ g}$$

Hence, the mass of Mars that we deduce from the satellite observations is

$$(0\cdot6428 \pm 0\cdot0013) \times 10^{27} \text{ g}$$

The weighted mean value of $J_2R_e^2$, when R_e is measured in astronomical units, is given by

$$J_2R_e^2 = (1\cdot013 \pm 0\cdot003) \times 10^{-12} \text{ A.U.}^2$$

In order to deduce the value of J_2 we must adopt a value for the equatorial radius of Mars. The most recent determination is that by Dollfus (see section II, chapter 2 of this book), who obtained $4\cdot715'' \pm 0\cdot015''$ for the apparent semidiameter at unit distance. Other comparatively recent determinations have, however, given a wide range of values, and it is clear that such measurements are particularly liable to systematic errors. We have adopted $4\cdot70'' \pm 0\cdot02''$. Hence we obtain

$$R_e = (0\cdot2279 \pm 0\cdot0010) \times 10^{-4} \text{ A.U.}$$

$$= (3\cdot409 \pm 0\cdot015) \times 10^8 \text{ cm}$$

and

$$J_2 = 0\cdot00195 \pm 0\cdot00002$$

Now the dynamical flattening (f) of the reference ellipsoid for a rotating oblate planet is given, to the first order of small quantities, by (4), where R_e and R_p are the

$$f \equiv \frac{R_e - R_p}{R_e} = \tfrac{3}{2}J_2 + \tfrac{1}{2}\sigma \qquad (4)$$

equatorial and polar radii of the reference ellipsoid and σ is the ratio of the centrifugal acceleration and the apparent acceleration at the equator. The reference ellipsoid is defined to be an equipotential surface, i.e. it would be the surface if the planet were covered by an ocean; it should be emphasized that in the derivation of the relation (4) between f, J_2, and σ no assumption is made about the internal structure of the planet. Now the centrifugal acceleration at the equator is $R_e\omega^2$, where ω is the angular speed of rotation of the planet. The sidereal period of rotation of Mars is 24 hours 37 min 22·67 sec, and so

$$\omega = 0{\cdot}708\,822 \times 10^{-4} \text{ rad/sec}$$

and

$$R_e\omega^2 = 1{\cdot}713 \pm 0{\cdot}007 \text{ cm/sec}^2$$

The apparent acceleration at the equator is given by

$$\frac{Gm}{R_e^{\,2}}\left(1 + \frac{3}{2}J_2\right) - R_e\omega^2 = 368{\cdot}3 \pm 3{\cdot}2 \text{ cm/sec}^2$$

and hence

$$\sigma = 0{\cdot}004\,65 \pm 0{\cdot}000\,05$$

and

$$f = 0{\cdot}005\,25 \pm 0{\cdot}000\,05$$

$$= (190{\cdot}4 \pm 1{\cdot}9)^{-1}$$

With these values the mean density ρ of Mars is given by

$$\rho = 3{\cdot}89 \pm 0{\cdot}05 \text{ g/cm}^3$$

The Motion of Phobos

The orbital elements given above were obtained by analysis of all suitable observations (about 2700 all told) that were made in the period 1877–1928, and it was found that there were no significant improvements in fit to the models used if quadratic terms were included in the expressions for the mean longitudes of Phobos and Deimos. The observational material for Phobos for that period, as well as additional observations made in 1941 and 1956, have now been studied in further detail since a reliable determination of the secular acceleration (if any) would be of considerable interest.

The observations fall naturally into groups, corresponding to measures of one coordinate (e.g. position angle) by one observer, at one opposition. The sums of squares of the residuals for each group were evaluated for five different values of the constant term (L_z) in the expression for the mean longitude, and the value giving the best fit in the least-squares sense was then estimated. For some groups there was no clear minimum, but for others it was clearly defined; the observations in position angle often gave quite a different estimate from those in distance, even for the same observer.

The residual differences between these estimates and the original value of L_z could show the presence of a steady change of rate of the mean motion or of a fluctuation in rate, such as would occur if air drag were significant but varied greatly with solar activity.

The observational material for 1941 and 1956 is almost entirely in the form of positions of Phobos relative to Deimos (rather than of the positions of each satellite with respect to the centre of Mars), and so could not be analysed directly by the computer program used for the main analysis. The assumption was therefore made that both sets of orbital elements were essentially correct except that the mean longitude of Phobos might be subject to fluctuations. The computer was used to evaluate positions of both Phobos and Deimos with respect to Mars for each time of observation, and the relative positions were then calculated by hand. For each ob- served coordinate it was then possible to estimate the value of L_z that would give the minimum residual. There was a considerable scatter but the general trend was plain.

A plot of the residual differences between the estimates of L_z and the value from the main analysis is given in figure 1. The size of each dot is a rough indication of its

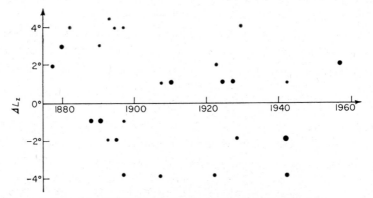

FIGURE 1   Residuals in mean longitude (ΔL_z) for Phobos.

The base value for L_z was obtained from a general least-squares fit for all observations from 1877 to 1929, whereas the individual estimates of L_z were obtained by examination of residuals for varying L_z by groups (1877–1929) or by individual observations (1941 and 1956)

weight as shown by the sharpness of the minimum, the number of observations concerned, and the accordance between different groups for the same opposition. (Discordant small groups are indicated by the smallest dots.) There is no trace of any systematic departure from the horizontal axis and so the original values of the zero and mean motion in longitude are confirmed. The scatter is greater than that given by Sharpless and the principal residual for the 1941 observations is of the opposite sign. The 1956 observations give a much smaller residual ($2°$) than the value ($6°$) that would be given by an acceleration of the magnitude suggested by Sharpless.

Discussion of the Results

The value for the reciprocal mass (which is the quantity usually used in dynamical astronomy) is in substantial agreement with the other direct determinations that are listed in table 3. In particular, the agreement between the determinations from the motions of the satellites and the space probe *Mariner IV* suggests that the conjecture

TABLE 3   Determinations of the mass of Mars

Author	Reciprocal mass	Method
Hall[1]	[a]3093500 ± 5000	satellites 1877
Van den Bosch[6]	3088000 ± 7500	satellites 1877–1909
Rabe[7]	3110000 ± 11000	Eros 1926–1945
NASA[b]	3099000 ± 3000	*Mariner IV* 1965
present analysis	3096000 ± 6000	satellites 1877–1928
present analysis	3094000 ± 3000	Deimos only 1877–1928

[a] This is the value currently adopted in the principal theories of the motions of the major planets.
[b] Results obtained by the National Aeronautics and Space Administration (NASA) which are presented elsewhere in this book.

by Marsden[8] that the determination of the mass from the satellites might be subject to a large systematic error is now even less likely.

The most recent visual determination of the flattening is that by Dollfus (see section II, chapter 2 of this book), who obtained

$$f = 0.011\,7 \pm 0.001\,17 = (85.5 \pm 8.6)^{-1}$$

Previous visual determinations have given values in the range 0·010 to 0·015 with a mean of 0·012 ± 0·002. There is thus a large discrepancy (almost by a factor of 2) between the visual and dynamical determinations. It has been suggested (e.g. by Öpik[9]) that the visual observations do not refer to the solid surface of the planet, but to some level in the atmosphere which is higher over the equator than over the poles. On the other hand, if the discrepancy between the two estimates of f is real it implies that the surface of Mars is not an equipotential surface; the possible consequences of such a conclusion are discussed by Runcorn (see section VIII, chapter 7 of this book).

Although the evidence against the existence of a large secular acceleration in the motion of Phobos appears to be strong, the scatter of the residuals in mean longitude does not rule out the existence of a significant secular acceleration. It is possible that the scatter in the principal residuals would be reduced if, as is intended, a rigorous theory of the motions were used in the analysis. It seems clear, however, that much of the scatter arises from the errors in the observations, and further progress will depend largely on new observations being made. Rakos[10] has, in fact, attempted to observe a series of partial eclipses of Phobos early in 1965; a preliminary analysis suggests that the mean longitude must be altered by about 30° in order to reconcile the present model with the observations. The reality of such a large effect must be in doubt until it has been confirmed by further observation or the observational data and the subsequent analysis have been subjected to close and independent scrutiny.

Further elucidation of the problems posed by Mars and its satellites depends on a further development of the theory and more observations. We hope to develop a rigorous theory of the motion of the satellites taking into account all sources of perturbations and to write a new program that will permit the direct analysis of positions of the satellites relative to each other, as well as positions relative to Mars.

We hope also that astronomers having access to large telescopes will take the opportunities at the next opposition in April 1967 to obtain new measures of the positions of the satellites and of the size and shape of Mars.

References

1. A. Hall, *Observations and Orbits of the Satellites of Mars with Data for Ephemerides in 1879*, Government Printing Office, Washington, 1878.
2. H. Struve, 'Über die Lage der Marsachse und die Konstanten in Marssystem', *Sitz. Ber. Preuss. Akad. Wiss. Berlin, Physik Math Kl*, **1911**, Nov. 30.
3. H. E. Burton, *Astron. J.*, **39**, 155–64 (1929).
4. E. W. Woolard, *Astron. J.*, **51**, 33–6 (1944).
5. B. P. Sharpless, *Astron. J.*, **51**, 185–6 (1945).
6. C. A. Van den Bosch, *De Massa's van de Groote Planeten*, Dissertation, University of Utrecht, p. 126 (1927).
7. E. Rabe, *Astron. J.*, **55**, 112–26 (1950).
8. B. G. Marsden, *Bull. Astron.*, **25**, 225–36 (1965).
9. E. J. Öpik, *Progr. Astronaut. Sci.*, **1**, 296–307 (1962).
10. K. D. Rakos, results communicated by R. L. Duncombe (1965).

2

A. DOLLFUS

Meudon Observatory
France

Optical diameter and ellipticity of the globe of the planet Mars

---

Introduction

The value of the equatorial and the polar diameters of the planet Mars are respectively $D_e = 6790$ km and $D_p = 6710$ km, these determinations being made with a precision of 0.3% corresponding to ∓ 20 km. Therefore, the apparent optical ellipticity of the globe amounts to $(D_e - D_p)/D_e = 0.0117$ with an accuracy of 10%. If we take the value of the mass given by Brouwer and Clemence[1], 0.1069 times the mass of the Earth, the density of Mars should be 4.09 as against 5.52 for the Earth.

Principle of the Method of Measurement

The above-mentioned values result from measurements made through a double-image micrometer. The instrument is mounted at the focus of a high resolving power telescope. It allows duplication of the image with two identical components A and B, the angular distance between which can be adjusted. The measurement is carried out by bringing the two images exactly tangential to each other, say image A on the right of image B; after that, the order of the images is inverted so that image B is exactly tangential to the right of image A. The total value of the two displacements given successively to the images is equal to twice the measured diameter of the disk. This method of measurement is very precise because it eliminates errors introduced by spreading of the image due to atmospheric effects and diffraction of the light by the objective glass. It allows the position of the exact contour of the planet to be determined with a precision far superior to the apparent angular width of the fuzzy limb of the planet.

Let us discuss the photometric profile across a diameter of the disk of the planet. In figure 1 we plot the intensity as a function of the distance to the centre of the disk. A disk of perfectly uniform brightness, observed under ideal conditions, should give the photometric profile ABCD. Diffraction of the light in the objective glass of the instrument, as well as loss of resolution by residual atmospheric agitation and possibly by aberrations, transform the profile ABCD into a profile which is partially blunted, aebcfd. It should be noted that if the diameter of the disk AD remains large compared with the apparent width of the blunted zone, the photometric profile aeb is symmetrical about the point e and eA = eB. If, therefore, we duplicate the image, as stated above, in order to bring the two new components exactly in contact with each other, the theoretical photometric profile will be ABCC′D in figure 2; the observed profile will be the sum of the two profiles abcd and a′b′c′d′. In view of the fact

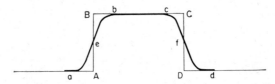

FIGURE 1   Intensity along a diametral section of the disk

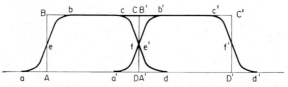

FIGURE 2   Theoretical photometric profile with the two images exactly superposed

that these profiles are respectively symmetrical to f and e′, their addition will give a repartition of the light which is exactly compensated, and the resulting profile will be aebcCB′b′c′f′d′; a uniform repartition of the light will be observed. If, on the contrary, the two images are not superposed exactly, but have been adjusted to be too close,

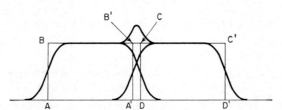

FIGURE 3   Theoretical photometric profile with the separation between the two images too small

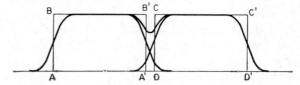

FIGURE 4   Theoretical photometric profile with the separation between the two images too large

a peak light intensity will be observed, as is shown in figure 3. If the separation of the two images is too large, a dip is observed as in figure 4. Therefore, the observer's task should be to adjust the distance of the images so that no peak and no dip is observed at the contact point. This is a very sensitive criterion which allows the observer to define the point of contact of the two limbs with a precision only a small fraction of the width of the blunted edge of the contour. Experiments carried out in the laboratory show that the precision thus obtained amounts to approximately one-fifth of the resolving power of the instrument, characterized by the width ε of the blunted zone aeb (figure 1). The precision of the measurements σ with the best observing conditions is, hence, given by $\sigma = \frac{1}{5}\varepsilon$.

New Double-image Birefrigent Micrometer

The most classical, first invented, double-image micrometers were the heliometer of Ramsden and the micrometer with birefringent prisms of Rochon. Neither of these instruments can be adapted for large-aperture telescopes.

More recently, two new types of such instruments have been produced, based on the birefringent properties of crystals: these are the birefringent micrometer of Muller[2] and the double-image micrometer of Lyot[3]. The optical properties are more or less equivalent and allow the measurement of planets having a diameter of up to twenty times the resolving power of the telescope. Beyond this limit, aberrations are introduced which affect the quality of the image. Consequently these instruments do not take the best advantage of large telescopes. As a matter of fact, under the best observing conditions, the apparent angular diameter of Mars can reach 24 seconds of arc. The largest telescope to be used for the diameter measurement on Mars through such a double-image micrometer should be one having a resolving power equal to 1/20 of the above value of the diameter of the planet, i.e. 1·2″. The diameter of the objective glass should be 10 cm only and the maximum possible precision of the measurements $(\sigma/\Delta) = (\varepsilon/5) \times (1/20) = 1\%$. The double-image micrometers of Lyot and Muller do not allow the measurement of planetary diameters with a precision higher than 1% at best; the necessity arose of having a double-image micrometer which would secure a much higher duplication without affecting the sharpness of the image. For this purpose, we produced a new instrument, *the large-range birefringent micrometer*. A description of this instrument was given in 1952[4]. This micrometer allows us to obtain a duplication of more than 200ε without affecting the fineness of the image.

Let us suppose that we use this micrometer on the 60 cm refractor of the Pic du Midi Observatory, which gives, under the best observing conditions, a resolving power $\varepsilon = 0·25″$. The precision of the measurement will be approximately $\frac{1}{5}$ of this value, i.e. 0·05″. During the most favourable apparitions of Mars, its apparent diameter is 24″; in this case, the precision given by the instrument is $\sigma/\Delta = 0·05/24 = 0·2\%$. This precision is higher than that obtained in all previous determinations.

Nevertheless, many phenomena interfere and may affect the above-stated precision. The three principal causes of errors or uncertainty are the following: limb darkening of the planet, curvature of the limb of the planet, and spreading of the image due to residual atmospheric agitation.

(i) Let us first consider the *limb darkening*. The photometric profile aeb is symmetrical about point e (figure 1) when the real image ABC has a limb AB, that is perfectly vertical. Practically this is not the case and planets show a darkening near the limb; the resulting photometric profile is rather similar to A″B″C, given by figure 5. The profile of A″B″C affected by the diffraction is a″e″b″C; it is distorted and the point e, corresponding to the half-height, does not coincide with the point e″ of the

real profile. A systematic error ee″ results, which tends to reduce the measured diameters. Naturally, the corresponding error becomes smaller with increased resolving
power.

(ii) Next let us consider the *curvature of the disk's limb*. In fact, the image of the
disk's limb is not rectilinear; the observer obtains contact of the two images by producing in the field of the telescope the configuration (*a*) (figure 6). If he sets the two
images too close, he obtains the configuration (*b*); if he sets the two images apart from

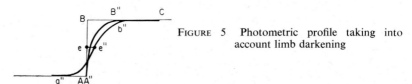

FIGURE 5   Photometric profile taking into
account limb darkening

each other he obtains the configuration (*c*). The repartition of the light at the contact
points of the two images in the configurations (*b*) and (*c*) is not symmetrical. Consequently, the observer will have difficulty in estimating the exact contact point. Naturally, this uncertainty is less important at increased resolving power. The error becomes
negligible when the apparent diameter of the disk of the planet is better than ten times
the diameter of the diffraction pattern or the spreading of the image.

(iii) Finally, we shall consider *the atmospheric agitation*. The turbulence of the air
produces a spreading of the image which affects its sharpness in two ways: (1) small-

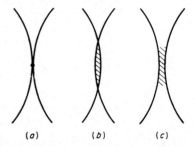

FIGURE 6   Configuration obtained (*a*) when
the images are exactly in contact, (*b*) when
the two images are too close, and (*c*) when
the two images are apart from each other

scale turbulence increases the fuzziness of the image and the contour of the profile
aeb (figure 1) is broadened—measurements taken in the laboratory show that this
small-scale turbulence tends to diminish the measured apparent diameter, and (2) large
undulations of the image rapidly displace the limbs and always destroy a precise
setting of contact. In case (2) the configurations alternatively take the aspects (*a*), (*b*),
and (*c*) of figure 6; there thus results a diminution in the precision of the measurements
and, in certain cases, a slight systematic error which tends to increase the measured
diameters.

Such errors as (1) and (2) are very small provided observing nights with particularly
steady images are selected.

Performance of the Measurements

The operation for measuring the diameters of Mars was carried out during the
exceptional approaches to the Earth in June 1954, September 1956, and November

1958. We chose, during each one of these apparitions, only the few days preceding or following opposition. Camichel, Focas, and the present author made the observations, in turn, with the 60 cm refractor of the Pic du Midi Observatory. The agreement between the three observers was around 0·05″ which represents $\frac{1}{5}$ of the width of the theoretical diffraction edge of the disk. Such a precision was generally maintained from night to night irrespective of observer. Measures were taken of the polar diameter D_p and the equatorial diameter D_e through five colour filters, covering the spectral range between the red and the blue. The following table contains the mean values of the measured diameters in red light only, after reduction to 1 A.U. (one astronomical unit). The dispersion of the measurements between observing nights was approximately 0·25%. The mean values correspond to D_e = 6·830 km and D_p = 6·750 km. If we take into consideration the error of the calibration of the micrometer, the accuracy of these measurements may be around 0·3%, i.e. ±20 km. The measurements taken in blue light are less accurate, but are used for the study of the properties of the Martian atmosphere; they are analysed in other publications[5, 6].

TABLE 1   Perihelic oppositions of Mars

Year	D_e at 1 A.U.	D_p at 1 A.U.	Ellipticity
1954 (5 nights)	9·41″	9·30″	0·0118
1956 (9 nights)	9·46″	9·35″	0·0117
1958 (8 nights)	9·41″	9·28″	0·0116
Mean (at 1 A.U.)	9·43″	9·31″	0·0117
(in km)	6830 km	6750 km	

Mean discrepancies between the observers = 0·05″ or 0·25%.
Mean dispersion on same nights = 0·05″ or 0·25%.
Measurements were made by H. Camichel, J. Focas, and A. Dollfus.

During the two or three nights preceding or following an opposition the phase is small enough to allow the determination of the equatorial diameter of the planet. A clear sky and a very good image are needed during these brief periods; fortunately this was the case during the above-mentioned three apparitions of Mars. By adjusting first the duplication in the polar direction and then turning the micrometer through 90° to the direction of the equator, it becomes immediately evident that the contact between the images, in the second case, is destroyed; the resulting difference in the duplication cannot be explained by the effect of the differential atmospheric refraction, but it involves an apparent ellipticity of the disk.

Corrections Due to the Atmosphere of Mars

The Martian atmosphere increases the apparent diameter of the planet slightly. The atmosphere is seen tangentially to the limb of the disk and its brightness is not negligible. The polarimetric determinations carried out over the last few years allow a determination of the brightness B_a of the atmosphere with reference to the brightness of the soil B_s at the disk's centre. By selecting polarimetric observations which were taken under the circumstances of apparently perfect purity of the Martian sky, we found $B_a/B_s = 0.010$ (see Dollfus[7]). Measurements for the case in which the atmosphere of Mars is not completely free of aerosols are perhaps more representative and these gave $B_a/B_s = 0.028$ (see Dollfus[8]).

Let us first compute the atmospheric effect for the value $B_a/B_s = 0.025$ (figure 7). ABC represents the theoretical photometric profile of the edge of the planet, with no effects from the atmosphere or limb darkening. ADE gives a more realistic value of the profile without the atmosphere, but takes into account limb darkening; this has been taken from photometric measurements published in 1957[9]. After computation, an atmosphere having a brightness of $B_a/B_s = 0.025$ gives the resultant profile JFGHI.

The planet is observed with an apparent diameter of approximately 22″ in a refractor of 0.25″ resolution. The profile obliterated by diffraction is computed to be JKLM. The observer, using the double-image micrometer, juxtaposes the opposite edges of the two images given by the instrument in such a way that their blunted part is exactly superposed. Thus, the measured apparent contour corresponds to the point K,

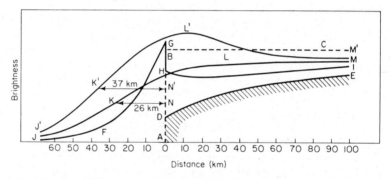

FIGURE 7   The effect of the atmosphere on the brightness distribution of the edge of Mars

for which the brightness is half at L. Therefore, the error of a setting is represented by the length KN = 26 km for an atmosphere of brightness 0.025 times that of the ground at the centre of the disk. An atmospheric layer which is twice as bright as this, as could be the case were the Martian atmosphere laden with clouds, would give a computed profile J′K′L′M′ and the error of the measurements becomes 37 km. It is probable that the Martian atmosphere has a brightness ranging between these limits; we therefore let a correction of approximately 30 km be subtracted from the measured diameters. This correction is to be applied in general to only one of the two limbs, inasmuch as the phase angle is never exactly zero during the observations so that the Martian atmosphere is not illuminated from the limb affected by the residual phase.

In 1956 the atmosphere was slightly veiled by a yellow cloud consisting of very fine dust grains blown up from the soil by the wind[6]. The resulting value of the brightness of the atmosphere of the planet was hence higher than the values given above, and an increase of the measured apparent diameter of the planet could be detected. In fact, the measurements taken in 1956 lead to systematically larger diameters than those taken in 1954 and 1958 and they are larger by approximately 30 km.

By taking into account the results of these corrections to the measurements, we finally adopted the following values for the diameters of Mars: $D_e = 6790$ km, $D_p = 6710$ km. We estimate that these values are accurate to 0.3% which corresponds to ± 20 km.

The volume of the planet is given by the following formula:

$$\frac{4}{3}\pi\frac{D_e \times D_p{}^2}{8} \quad \text{i.e. } 1.620 \times 10^{26} \text{ cm}^3 \pm 1\%$$

Brouwer and Clemence have determined the mass of the planet from a study of the motion of the satellites[1]; they gave a mass ratio of $1/3\,008\,000$ times that of the Sun or 0.1069 times the mass of the Earth, or 6.606×10^{26} g. The corresponding mean density of the globe is, therefore, 4.09.

Apparent Ellipticity of the Globe

$(D_e - D_p)/D_e$, as a result of the previous measurements, is 0.0117; it was obtained with an accuracy of approximately 10%. The difference between the polar and equatorial radii is 40 km. This very strong oblateness is 4 times that of the Earth.

The study of the perturbations in the orbits of the satellites Phobos and Deimos gives a dynamical ellipticity of the order of 0.052, corresponding to an excess of the equatorial radius of only 18 km approximately. The difference between the values of the equatorial radius resulting from the visual observations and dynamical considerations is, therefore, 22 km.

It might be possible to explain this difference by attributing it to atmospheric impurities. If this were the case, it follows that the atmosphere at the poles must always be transparent, and that the atmosphere at the equator is permanently charged with a haze consisting of fine particles; if this is so, the correction adopted in the previous section would be applicable to the equatorial radius only.

In fact, determinations of the brightness of the atmosphere of Mars are obtained from polarimetric measurements. Measurements taken along the equator show that the brightness of the Martian atmosphere varies, by a factor 3, depending on density of aerosols, haze, or veils present; the mean values fall within the above-mentioned values of 0.025 to 0.050 times the brightness of the surface of the centre of the disk. In the best conditions of transparency this ratio may reach as low as the minimum value 0.010 (see Dollfus[7]); accordingly, any residual *permanent* layer of aerosols *at the equator* should contribute only a small fraction to the brightness owing to the additional veils, this leads to the above-mentioned computed correction of 30 km in the diameter.

Unfortunately, a similar determination of the Martian atmospheric brightness near the poles is not easy to achieve by polarimetric techniques; but visual and photographic studies of veils and clouds in the Martian atmosphere show that faint veils occur *at least* as often at the poles as at the equator; it is anticipated, then, that the atmospheric correction for the polar diameter is about the same as that for equatorial diameter.

Furthermore, photograph number 1 taken by the space craft *Mariner IV* shows the limb of the disk near the equator of Mars, and the atmosphere appears to be less bright than the surface, proving that a large correction of the equatorial diameter due to equatorial aerosols cannot apply.

It seems, therefore, that the equatorial bulge should be attributed to the properties of the Martian soil. It could be supposed that the internal mass distribution is that of a heavy core which is covered by a layer of low-density materials that are much thicker at the equator, so that isostatic equilibrium may be maintained. If this is the case, the atmospheric pressure would be higher at the poles than at the equator; the scale height of the Martian atmosphere is $KT/mg = 24$ km, if the composition of the gas is that of terrestrial air. The atmospheric pressure would then be approximately 2·5 times higher at the poles than at the equator of Mars.

References

1. D. Brouwer and G. M. Clemence, in *Planets and Satellites, The Solar System III (Ed.* G. Kuiper), University of Chicago Press, Chicago, 1962.
2. P. Muller, *Bull. Astron.*, **14**, 77 (1949).
3. B. Lyot, see A. Dollfus, *L'Astronomie*, **68**, 337 (1954).
4. A. Dollfus, *Compt. Rend.*, **235**, 1477 (1952).
5. A. Dollfus, *Compt. Rend.*, **255**, 2229 (1962).
6. A. Dollfus, *Ann. Astrophys.*, **28**, 722 (1965).
7. A. Dollfus, *Compt. Rend.*, **262**, 519 (1966).
8. A. Dollfus, *Compt. Rend.*, **232**, 1066 (1951).
9. A. Dollfus, *Compt. Rend.*, **244**, 162 (1957).

3

H. JEFFREYS

St John's College
University of Cambridge
England

Figure and density of the Moon

The mean density of the Moon is close to 3·33 and the diameter 3476 km.

The axis of greatest moment of inertia is nearly normal to the ecliptic, that of least moment towards the Earth. This state is maintained by the Earth's attractions, which produce couples similar to those on the Earth by the Sun and Moon, which produce precession and nutation, but the effects are very different on account of the slowness of the Moon's rotation. Departures of the Moon's motion from a uniform circular motion lead to periodic forced motions that have been observed for about 200 years. One of these is that the axis of greatest moment revolves about the pole of the ecliptic in 18·6 years. In addition there are periodic variations in the Moon's angular velocity about the Earth, with periods 1 sidereal month, 1 year, and half the period of revolution of the perigee with respect to the node. These all lead to periodic oscillations along the ecliptic of the direction of the axis of least moment. The annual one is the largest. Observations are made of the position of a small, bright, and nearly circular crater called Mösting A near the centre of the disk, which is therefore well placed for giving changes of inclination and displacements parallel to the ecliptic separately. If A, B, C are the principal moments of inertia $(C > B > A)$ the relevant quantities are the ratios

$$\alpha = \frac{C - B}{A}, \qquad \beta = \frac{C - A}{B}, \qquad \gamma = \frac{B - A}{C}$$

which satisfy closely

$$\beta = \alpha + \gamma$$

The inclination determines β, apart from a small correction depending on γ; the motions on longitude determine γ. The theory is mostly due to Hayn but I recently[1] found some small corrections that are worth taking into account.

Determinations of inclination by different authors differ by more than their apparent uncertainties will explain, but at the worst we can say that

$$0·000\,621\,2 < \beta < 0·000\,634\,0$$

Until recently estimates of γ were based entirely on the annual period, but Yakovkin detected a term that he attributed to a free vibration. I found[2], however, that it agreed in period and phase with the term in $2(\tilde{\omega} - \Omega)$, where $\tilde{\omega}$ is the longitude of the perigee and Ω that of the node. The importance of this term has been emphasized by Koziel. This term contains the squares of the inclination and eccentricity as factors and consequently the couple due to it is very small; the displacements are inappreciable unless it agrees very closely in period with the free vibration. Consequently, if it is genuine, it gives a very accurate determination of γ. I[1] obtained from this term

$$\gamma = 0.000\,204\,9 \pm 0.000\,000\,9$$

and from various estimates of the annual term[1]

$$\gamma = 0.000\,227\,4 \pm 0.000\,008\,8$$

However, Habibulin[3] seems to have adopted my interpretation of the Yakovkin term, and from several series of observations obtains

$$f = \frac{\beta - \gamma}{\beta} = 0.60 \pm 0.02$$

making

$$\gamma = 0.000\,252 \pm 0.000\,008$$

There are several features in Habibulin's results that I cannot understand. However, $\gamma = \frac{1}{3}\beta = 0.000\,21$ cannot be far wrong.

Laplace pointed out a long time ago that β was inconsistent with the Moon's being in a hydrostatic state. If it was of uniform density, β would be 0.000\,037\,5; if there is any central condensation, β would be less. Also γ should be about $\frac{3}{4}\beta$ instead of $\frac{1}{3}\beta$. Laplace suggested that the differences might be due to deformations arising during solidification. I suggested in 1915 that the Moon might have solidified when much nearer the Earth than it is now, and have retained the form it had then. The discrepancy in γ/β might be due to large oscillations during solidification. I see little to choose between the hypotheses. But it should be pointed out that isostasy is no help. β and γ are summary properties of the whole gravitational field; to account for them with a light outer layer and hydrostatic conditions below, the ellipticity of the visible disk would have to be far more than it is.

The mean density is very close to what appears to be that of the Earth at a depth of 35 km or so. If the materials of the Moon are similar to those of the Earth, this would imply that nearly all the Moon has a composition near that of the Earth's shell, and there is no room for a central iron core. The effect of pressure is small, and it seems that the Moon must be of nearly uniform density except perhaps close to the surface.

Now the differences between the Moon's moment of inertia also react on the orbit; what matter now are the ratios $(C - A)/Ma^2$ and $(B - A)/Ma^2$, where we can take M to be the mass and a the mean radius. If the density is uniform, C/Ma^2 must be near 0.4. The effects on the orbit are increases in the secular motions of the node and perigee. By comparing observation with theory, de Sitter tried to estimate these ratios and found that C/Ma^2 had to be much larger, nearly 0.6. The value for a spherical shell would be $\frac{2}{3}$. In any case the Moon would have to be denser on the outside. Nobody was very happy about the result. But a large part of the uncertainty came from the incompleteness of the calculation of the parts of the secular acceleration due to the Sun. Taking $C/Ma^2 = 0.4$ and allowing for the various uncertainties, I found that theory and observation might agree satisfactorily. Eckert[4], however, has improved the calculation of the solar effects and reinstated de Sitter's difficulty. But if we have to choose between an error in the observed values and a density increasing outwards, the former would reluctantly be preferred.

If the Moon was truly homogeneous the value of $(C - B)/A$ would imply that the visible disk is higher by 0·7 km at the equator than at the pole. The irregularities of the limb much exceed that, and a test would be difficult.

Note added in proof. I find that with Eckert's value the density near the outside would need to be at least 12·5 g/cm^3.

References

1. H. Jeffreys, *Monthly Notices Roy. Astron. Soc.*, **122**, 421–32 (1961).
2. H. Jeffreys, *Monthly Notices Roy. Astron. Soc.*, **117**, 475–7 (1957).
3. Sh. T. Habibulin, 'Lunar physical libration', *Kazan Obs. Izv.*, **1958**, 31.
4. W. J. Eckert, *Astron. J.*, **70** 787–92 (1965).

4

W. J. ECKERT

IBM Watson Laboratory at Columbia University
New York, U.S.A.

The moment of inertia of the Moon determined from its orbital motion

Introduction

For many centuries astronomers have systematically measured and recorded the position of the Moon and have endeavored to develop formulae that will represent all the observations of the past and hopefully predict those of the future. This comparison of observation and theory with ever-increasing accuracy has led to many discoveries including Newton's law of gravitation and the irregular axial rotation of the Earth. The accumulated observations of the position of the Moon constitute perhaps the most precise body of data in all physical science, and thus every discrepancy presents a challenge to the theorist. The aim of this chapter is to discuss a discrepancy between theory and observation that has persisted for more than 50 years.

The Observations

The richest part of the observational data consists of the angular measurements of the Moon's position made during the past two centuries. During this interval of nearly two hundred years, measurements have been made regularly with a nominal accuracy of a single observation of a few tenths of a second of arc (one or two units in the sixth decimal of a radian). The total angular motion of the Moon in a century is $1.7'' \times 10^9$.

The observations are of two types, the meridian observations and the occultations. With the meridian circle the time and altitude of meridian passage of the Moon are measured. The observation of an occultation consists of measuring the time when a star is occulted by the edge of the Moon. In the meridian circle a vertical line at the focus of the instrument is placed tangentially to the edge of the Moon as it crosses the meridian.

Both types of observations are subject to accidental and systematic errors, which in the two methods are largely independent but not completely so. In both cases the measured position is that of a portion of the edge or limb of the Moon and a correction must be applied to reduce it to the center of gravity[1]. These reductions involve the determination of the radius and center of a reference sphere and of the topographical irregularities in the surface. For each observation the orientation of the Moon must be computed and the correction evaluated. Both methods refer the Moon's position to the background system of reference stars (also, each occultation is referred to a particular star). During the two centuries under discussion great progress has been made in reducing the systematic errors.

For any discussion of the observations each observed coordinate is compared with the position computed for the time of observation from the adopted theory. Included in the comparison are all the instrumental and other corrections such as refraction, precession, nutation, aberration, etc. The small differences between theory and observation, or residuals, are then analyzed for corrections to the arbitrary constants of the theory, for systematic errors in the observations, and for significant discrepancies between theory and observation.

A standard part of the analysis of the residuals is the determination of the phase and amplitude of terms with known periods, and of the secular changes in these phases and amplitudes. Of particular interest are the secular changes in the phases of the terms with the periods of the anomalistic and nodical months, i.e. the mean motions of the perigee and node of the Moon's orbit. These motions are large and well determined. They are not arbitrary constants to be determined empirically but they must be deduced from the theory using the adopted fundamental parameters. In view of the high precision with which they can be observed, these motions have long (since the time of the Greeks) been a key to the adequacy of the available theory. The current status of this question is the subject matter of this chapter.

A simple example of the precision of recent observations is the examination of meridian observations made in Washington during the past twelve years (see Klock and Scott[2]). These observations were examined for a correction to the amplitude of a term with argument $2F - 2l$ which has a 3 year period. The probable error of the determination was $0.025''$ and the correction obtained agreed within the probable error with a similar determination from the occultations made at Greenwich.

The definitive discussion of precise observations of the Moon is a very intricate problem involving various types of observational errors and the involved relations between the many parameters. For observations extending over long periods of time the problem is complicated by the changes in method and theory that have been made from time to time. Part of this problem is discussed in section 4 of the paper by Eckert, Walker, and Eckert[3]. For the purpose of this chapter we shall quote the results of Brown and of Spencer-Jones[4]. Brown's expressions for the mean longitude of the perigee and of the node are of the form

$$\text{mean longitude} = a_0 + a_1 T + a_2 T^2 + a_3 T^3$$

The longitudes are for the epoch 1850 and are referred to the mean equinox of date and T is expressed in Julian centuries. Brown obtained these results by discussion of the meridian observations using his theoretical values of a_2 and a_3 and obtaining a_0 and a_1 from the observations. The values of a_1 are the mean motions of the perigee and node; Brown's results and the corresponding ones obtained by Spencer-Jones from the occultations are as follows.

	dπ	dΩ
Brown, meridian	14648559·66″	− 6962918·70″
Spencer-Jones, occultations	14648560·07″	− 6962918·01″
Mean (weights 1, 2)	14648559·93″	− 6962918·24″
Precession	5025·39″	5025·39″
Sidereal motion	14643534·54″	− 6967943·63″

We note the close agreement between the values from the two independent sets of measurements. If we allow for the possibility that the agreement may be partly fortuitous and that the results contain common systematic errors, there seems little doubt that the motions can be measured to better than a second of arc per century, i.e. seven significant figures. The discrepancy in question is of the order of ten seconds.

Until recently, measurement of the Moon's distance was much less accurate than measurement of the angular coordinates, and the distance was used only to correct the observed angular positions for the location of the observer on the Earth. Recent progress with radar and lasers promises precision in measurements of distance greater than that of the angles; in particular the use of lasers with corner reflectors on the Moon promises very exciting results[5]. The use of three reflectors would eliminate many of the limb effects previously discussed. It should be remarked, however, that to get the most from a given type of observation we must have a long series of measurements well distributed in time and made in a uniform manner.

The Theory

The theoretical expressions for the coordinates of the Moon are developed by solving the problem according to Newton's laws and then applying the small corrections for the effects of relativity. The complete solution of the Newtonian problem with the precision of the observations just described is an elaborate process. The first step is to solve the so-called 'main problem' in which the Sun, Earth, and Moon are treated as mass points, and the effects of the planets on the Earth and Moon and of the Moon on the Sun are neglected. The effects of the neglected forces are then treated by variational methods and added to the solution of the main problem. For each part of the theory the differential equations are solved and the adopted numerical values of the parameters of the solution inserted. The solution is expressed as a multi-dimensional harmonic series with secular terms in some of the fundamental parameters[6].

The development of the lunar theory that has been the adopted standard for nearly fifty years is that of Brown[7]. Almost all the parts of the theory have been computed independently by others either before or after Brown and all confirm the high quality of Brown's work.

We shall discuss the various contributions to the motions of the perigee and node under the following headings: the main problem, the planetary perturbations, the distribution of mass in the Earth, the distribution of mass in the Moon, and precession and relativity. Under each heading we shall review the nature of the theory, the assumptions that have been made, and the values of the parameters used. Additional details and references may be found in the paper by Eckert[4].

Table 1 contains the contributions to the motions enumerated above except for those due to the distribution of mass in the Moon. These contributions are of approximately the same size as the differences between theory and observation and will be discussed on p. 105.

TABLE 1   Centennial motions

	$d\pi$	$d\Omega$
Main problem	$+14642652\cdot5''$	$-6967186\cdot6''$
Moon–Sun–Moon	$-1''$	0
Planetary action	$+252\cdot9''$	$-137\cdot0''$
Figure of Earth	$+633\cdot1''$	$-592\cdot1''$
Relativity	$+0\cdot06''$	0
Total	$+14643537\cdot6''$	$-6967915\cdot7''$
Observed	$+14643534\cdot5''$	$-6967943\cdot6''$
O–C (including figure of Moon)	$-3\cdot1''$	$-27\cdot9''$

Motions are per Julian century for the epoch 1850.

The Main Problem

Brown's solution of the main problem left an uncertainty in the motions of the perigee and node of a few seconds per century. For many years it was felt that the source of the trouble was in this area. The new solution of the main problem by Eckert and Smith[8,9] (for preliminary results see Eckert[10]) gives these motions with an increase in accuracy of at least two orders of magnitude beyond Brown's. The method is completely independent of Brown's and it showed the general high quality of his solution. The largest correction to the periodic terms was only $0\cdot07''$ and the corrections to the motions of the perigee and node were $+7\cdot8''$ and $+1\cdot9''$ per century respectively.

The manner in which Brown's basic solution has been applied in practice has recently been reinvestigated. In a recent paper[3] we have investigated the various transformations applied by Brown and the values of the lunar and solar parameters.

The motions of the perigee and node by Eckert and Smith when evaluated for the parameters recommended by the International Astronomical Union (I.A.U.) in 1964[3,4] are given in the first line of table 1.

The Planetary Perturbations

The effects of the planets on the motion of the Moon are of two types called direct and indirect. One recalls that in the main problem it was assumed that the center of gravity of the Earth–Moon system and the Sun moved according to Kepler's laws. The indirect perturbations are those caused by the changes in the elements of the Earth's orbit produced by the other planets.

Brown examined the planetary perturbations twice and compared his results with the previous ones of Radau and of Newcomb[11]. The results of his first computation are given in table 2. The entries in the line 'G.C.' arise from the definition of the Gaussian constant and the astronomical unit.

TABLE 2   Planetary action

Planet	dπ		dΩ	
	Direct	Indirect	Direct	Indirect
Mercury	+4·9″	−4·1″	−1·6″	+1·2″
Venus	+196·6″	−93·4″	−81·9″	+26·7″
Mars	+3·4″	+1·8″	−2·5″	−0·5″
Jupiter	+58·2″	+75·4″	−53·6″	−21·5″
Saturn	+2·6″	+3·6″	−2·5″	−1·0″
G.C.		−1·9″		+0·5″
Total	+265·7″	−18·6″	−142·1″	+5·4″

For his final calculation he gave no details but changed the totals to

$$+269'' \qquad -16'' \qquad -142'' \qquad +5''$$

i.e.

$$d\pi = +253'', \qquad d\Omega = -137''$$

The perturbations for each planet contain the mass of the planet as a linear factor. Table 3 contains the values of the masses used by Brown in table 2 and those presented by Clemence in Joint Discussion F of the I.A.U. in 1964[12]. The last two columns

TABLE 3   Planetary masses

Planet	Brown	Clemence		Correction dπ	dΩ
Mercury	6000000	6110000	±40000	−0·01″	+0·01″
Venus	408000	408539	12	−0·14″	+0·07″
Mars	3093500	3050000		+0·07″	−0·04″
Jupiter	1047·35	1047·41	0·02	−0·01″	0″
Saturn	3501·6	3499·6	0·4	0″	0″
Total				−0·09″	+0·04″

contain the corrections to be applied to Brown's motions to reduce them to Clemence's values of the masses (we have applied −0·1″, 0·0″). From Clemence's discussion of probable future changes in the masses it appears that resulting changes in the motions will probably not exceed 0·01″ except in the case of Mars where changes of 0·2″ in the perigee and 0·1″ in the node would not be surprising.

The Figure of the Earth

The perturbations of the Moon due to the figure of the Earth have been computed independently by Hill and by Brown using completely different methods[4]. Each started with the force function

$$\frac{E+M}{E}\left\{\frac{3}{2}\left(C-\frac{A+B}{2}\right)\frac{\frac{1}{3}-\sin^2\delta}{r^3}-\frac{3}{4}(A-B)\frac{\cos^2\delta}{r^3}\cos 2\alpha\right\}$$

where E and M are the masses of the Earth and Moon, A, B, and C are the moments of inertia, r and δ are the geocentric radius vector and declination of the Moon, and α is the right ascension of the Moon measured from the A axis. The second term was shown to be negligible and the resulting terms contain the linear factor

$$J = \tfrac{3}{2}Eb^2\{C - \tfrac{1}{2}(A + B)\} = \tfrac{3}{2}J_2$$

where b is the equatorial radius of the Earth.

Brown's results for the centennial motions may be stated:

$$d\pi = 389{\cdot}89'' \times 10^3 J, \qquad d\Omega = -364{\cdot}65'' \times 10^3 J$$

We have evaluated them for several values of J as shown in table 4. The value of the reciprocal of the flattening given in the second column was computed from the formula

$$J = \frac{1}{k} - 0{\cdot}0017287$$

Values of k and J in parentheses were used only by implication. The end figure of k in the last line was adjusted slightly to agree with the value adopted by the I.A.U. in 1964.

If we use the I.A.U. 1964 value of the lunar parallax the motions become

$$d\pi = 389{\cdot}83'' \times 10^3 J, \qquad d\Omega = -364{\cdot}60'' \times 10^3 J$$

TABLE 4   Motions as functions of J

$J(10^{-7})$	k	$d\pi$	$d\Omega$	Source
17595	(286·7)	+686·0″	−641·6″	Hill
(16854)	292·9	657·1″	614·6″	Faye-Brown
(16383)	297	638·8″	597·4″	
(16270)	298	634·4″	593·3″	
16240	(298·25)	633·2″	592·2″	I.A.U. 1964

which with the I.A.U. 1964 value of J give the values used in this discussion:

$$d\pi = 633{\cdot}1'', \qquad d\Omega = -592{\cdot}1''$$

Hill's results differed from those of Brown (for the same value of J) by 4″ in the motion of the perigee and by 0·3″ in that of the node.

The Figure of the Moon

In computing the effects of the figure of the Moon on the perigee and node Brown used the force function of the same form as that given in the previous section for the figure of the Earth; in this case, however, he retained both terms. His results may be expressed as follows[4]:

$$d\pi = 1{\cdot}861'' \times 10^9(\mu' - 5{\cdot}269''\mu'')$$

$$d\Omega = -1{\cdot}740'' \times 10^9(\mu' + \mu'')\frac{\sin 2(i + i_1)}{\sin 2i}$$

where i and $-i_1$ are the inclinations to the ecliptic of the Moon's orbit and equator, and

$$a^2\mu' = \frac{3}{2M}\left(C' - \frac{A' + B'}{2}\right)$$

$$a^2\mu'' = \frac{3}{4M}(B' - A')$$

where M is the Moon's mass, a its mean distance, and A', B', C' its moments of inertia. We note that $d\Omega$ contains μ' and μ'' only as their sum.

We shall use the equations in the following form:

$$d\pi = 1 \cdot 861'' \times 10^9\{3 \cdot 134(\mu' - \mu'') - 2 \cdot 134''(\mu' + \mu'')\}$$

$$d\Omega = -1 \cdot 740'' \times 1^9(\mu' + \mu'')\frac{\sin 2(i + i_1)}{\sin 2i}$$

$$\frac{d\pi}{d\Omega} = -3 \cdot 352\left(\frac{\mu' - \mu''}{\mu' + \mu''} - 0 \cdot 6809\right)\frac{\sin 2,}{\sin 2(i + i_1)}$$

$$\mu' + \mu'' = \frac{3C'}{2Mb'^2}\frac{C' - A'}{C'}\left(\frac{b'}{a}\right)^2$$

$$\mu' - \mu'' = \frac{3C'}{2Mb'^2}\frac{C' - B'}{C'}\left(\frac{b'}{a}\right)^2$$

$$\frac{\mu' - \mu''}{\mu' + \mu''} = \frac{C' - B'}{C' - A'}$$

where b' is the Moon's radius. Adopting

$$i = 5° \, 8 \cdot 7', \qquad \frac{b'}{b} = 0 \cdot 2723$$

$$i_1 = 1° \, 32 \cdot 2', \qquad \frac{a}{b} = 60 \cdot 318 \, 54$$

we obtain

$$\frac{\sin 2(i + i_1)}{\sin 2i} = 1 \cdot 294, \qquad \frac{b'}{a} = 0 \cdot 004 \, 514$$

and the motions then involve only the differences between the moments of inertia and the ratio C'/Mb'^2. The discussion of the relations between these quantities and the observations of the libration of the Moon and of the systematic errors involved are beyond the scope of this chapter[13, 14]. We shall, however, accept the value

$$\frac{C' - A'}{C'} = 0 \cdot 000 \, 629$$

determined from the well-known relation between i_1 and $(C' - A')/C'$ based on Cassini's law. The relations then become

$$\mu' + \mu'' = 1\cdot282 \times 10^{-8}g'$$

$$d\pi = (-50\cdot9'' + 74\cdot8''f)g'$$

$$d\Omega = -28\cdot86''g'$$

$$\frac{d\pi}{d\Omega} = -2\cdot591f + 1\cdot764$$

or

$$g' = -0\cdot0346\,d\Omega$$

$$= +0\cdot681 - 0\cdot386\frac{d\pi}{d\Omega}$$

where

$$g' = \frac{3C'}{2Mb'^2}, \qquad f = \frac{C' - B'}{C' - A'}$$

and $d\pi$ and $d\Omega$ are in seconds of arc per century. Table 5 contains the motions computed from these formulae for various values of g' and f.

TABLE 5   Motions as functions of f and g'

				$d\pi$			$d\Omega$
g'	f	0·5	0·6	0·7	0·8	0·9	
0·5		−6·8″	−3·0″	+0·7″	+4·5″	+8·2″	−14·4″
0·6		8·1″	3·6″	0·9″	5·3″	9·8″	17·3″
0·7		9·5″	4·2″	1·0″	6·2″	11·5″	20·2″
0·8		10·8″	4·8″	1·1″	7·1″	13·1″	23·1″
0·9		12·2″	5·4″	1·3″	8·0″	14·8″	26·0″
1·0		−13·5″	−6·0″	+1·4″	+8·9″	+16·4″	−28·9″

To illustrate the implications of various values of g' we may consider models formed by two concentric spheres with different densities inside and outside the inner spherical surface and with mean density equal to that of the Moon. In table 6 the first three lines give, for various values of g' and of the inner density δ, the radius of the inner sphere and the density of the outer shell; the last line gives the limiting value of g'

TABLE 6   Radius, density, and limiting g'

g' \ δ	0·5		1·0		1·5		2·0		2·5		3·0
0·7	0·62	4·3	0·67	4·4	0·73	4·6	0·82	5·1	0·98	18	
0·8	0·81	6·7	0·87	8·1	0·96	17					
0·9	0·95	21									
Limiting value	0·94		0·88		0·82		0·76		0·70		0·65

for each value of δ. The mean density is taken as 3·39. We note that with an outer shell of heavy terrestrial material, in order to produce values of $g' = 0\cdot7, 0\cdot8, 0\cdot9$, the inner density must be in the neighborhood of 2, 1, and 0·5.

Precession and Relativity

The precession used on p. 99 is Newcomb's value with the correction $(+0.75'')$ by Morgan and Watts[4]. Since the precession is an observed value, it contains the geodesic precession and this latter should not be applied as a separate correction as has been done by previous authors. The relativity correction is $0.06''$ in the motion of the perigee, which is given in table 1.

Conclusions

The residuals in the last line of table 1 contain the effects of the figure of the Moon, possible systematic errors in the observations, errors in the theory or adopted para-meters of the various contributions, and possible overlooked or unknown forces. If we assume that the residuals $-3.1''$ and $-27.9''$ are due entirely to the distribution of mass in the Moon, we obtain from the equations on p. 103

$$g' = 0.965, \qquad f = 0.638$$

We can, on the other hand, assume various values of g' and f and obtain the remaining discrepancies between observation and theory. Subtracting the motions in table 5 from the above residuals we obtain table 7. Examination of the last column of the table indicates that any reasonable assumption of the value of g' will leave a large residual in the motion of the node. From consideration of strengths of materials and

TABLE 7   Residuals as functions of f and g'

g' \ f	0·5	0·6	$d\pi$ 0·7	0·8	0·9	$d\Omega$
0·5	$+3.7''$	$-0.1''$	$-3.8''$	$-7.6''$	$-11.3''$	$-13.5''$
0·6	$+5.0''$	$+0.5''$	$-4.0''$	$-8.4''$	$-12.9''$	$-10.6''$
0·7	$+6.4''$	$+1.1''$	$-4.1''$	$-9.3''$	$-14.6''$	$-7.7''$
0·8	$+7.7''$	$+1.7''$	$-4.2''$	$-10.2''$	$-16.2''$	$-4.8''$
0·9	$+9.1''$	$+2.3''$	$-4.4''$	$-11.1''$	$-17.9''$	$-1.9''$
1·0	$+10.4''$	$+2.9''$	$-4.5''$	$-12.0''$	$-19.5''$	$+1.0''$

other factors it is generally believed that g' may be slightly, but not much, greater than 0·6 which leaves an unexplained residual of $10''$ per century. On the other hand, table 6 indicates the difficulty of constructing a model for g' in the neighborhood of 0·9.

The motion of the perigee presents no difficulty. A value of f between 0·60 and 0·65 leaves small residuals for any assumed value of g'. For g' equal to 0·6 and 0·7 the residuals vanish for f equal to 0·611 and 0·622 respectively.

The fact that the large discrepancy is in the motion of the node and not in the perigee is somewhat surprising since for each part of the theory the motion of the node seemed better determined. Thus the theoretical and observed motion agree to 1×10^{-7} in the perigee and 1×10^{-6} in the node.

The effects of higher moments in the figure of the Moon has been suggested as a possible explanation since they have been reported to be of the same magnitude as those of the second order. It must be remembered, however, that these contain two additional powers of the lunar parallax or $1/3600$.

The history of the difficulty here described is not without interest. Brown first encountered it more than half a century ago. He assumed that the radial distribution of mass in the Moon is the same as that in the Earth, i.e. g' slightly greater than $0{\cdot}5$ which with a value of f near $0{\cdot}75$ from Hayn's results gave $-3''$ and $-14''$ for the motions. In order to reconcile the theoretical and observed motions he adopted the value $292{\cdot}9$ for the reciprocal of the Earth's flattening. (The value for the Hayford spheroid of 1909 was 297.) de Sitter[15] examined the moments of inertia of the Earth and Moon and the effects of relativity on the perigee and node. He found a value for the flattening near $1/297$ and pointed out the need for a more accurate solution of the main problem. The discrepancy was brought into still sharper focus by Spencer-Jones' discussion of the occultation which reconciled the motions determined from the meridian observations and the occultations. The determination of the value of J by means of Earth satellites seems to preclude much change in that parameter.

References

1. C. B. Watts, *Astron. Papers, Am. Ephemeris Nautical Almanac, Wash.*, **17** (1963).
2. B. L. Klock and D. K. Scott, *Astron. J.*, **70**, 335 (1965).
3. W. J. Eckert, M. J. Walker, and D. Eckert, *Astron. J.*, **71**, 314 (1966).
4. W. J. Eckert, *Astron. J.*, **70**, 787 (1965).
5. C. O. Alley, P. L. Bender, R. H. Dicke, J. E. Faller, P. A. Franken, H. H. Plotkin, and D. T. Wilkinson, *J. Geophys. Res.*, **70**, 2267 (1965).
6. W. J. Eckert, R. Jones, and H. K. Clark, *Improved Lunar Ephemeris 1952–1959*, U.S. Government Printing Office, Washington, D.C., 1954, p. 283.
7. E. W. Brown, *Mem. Roy. Astron. Soc.*, **59**, 1 (1908).
8. W. J. Eckert and H. F. Smith Jr., *Intern. Astron. Union Symp., 24th, 1964.*
9. W. J. Eckert and H. F. Smith Jr., *Astron. Papers, Am. Ephemeris Nautical Almanac, Wash.*, **19**, to be published.
10. W. J. Eckert, *Trans. Intern. Astron. Union*, **12B**, 113 (1964).
11. E. W. Brown, *Trans. Am. Math. Soc.*, **5**, 286 (1904).
12. G. M. Clemence, *Trans. Intern. Astron. Union*, **12B**, 609 (1964).
13. H. Jeffreys, *The Earth*, 4th ed., Cambridge University Press, London, 1962, Chaps. IV, V.
14. Z. Kopal, *Physics and Astronomy of the Moon*, Academic Press, New York, London, 1962, Chap. 2.
15. W. de Sitter, *Monthly Notices Roy. Astron. Soc.*, **77**, 173 (1916).

III

Radial variation of physical properties in planetary interiors

A. The Earth

    1. New developments in seismology (H. I. S. THIRLAWAY)   109

    2. The mantle as an Einstein solid (D. P. MCKENZIE) .   111

B. The terrestrial planets

    3. Early thermal history of the terrestrial planets (D. L. ANDERSON and R. A. PHINNEY)   113

    4. Models of the internal density in the Earth, Mars, and Venus (K. E. BULLEN)   127

1

H. I. S. THIRLAWAY

U.K. Atomic Energy Authority
Aldermaston, Berkshire, England

New developments in seismology

Abstract

In the last five years, a seismological network of 120 standard six component stations has been established. The frequency responses, acceptance bands, and calibration procedures of each station are identical. Sensitivities are dependent only on ambient (microseismic) noise amplitudes which on the sites concerned vary from 1 to 50 millimicrometres in the short period band, and between 1 to 2 micrometres in the long period band. The U.S.C.G.S. provide microfilm, maintenance, and quality control services.

At the same time arrays of short period seismometers have also come into operation —six in the U.S.A. (including one of 200 km in length containing 525 sensors) and one each in Canada, Scotland, India, and Australia. Microseisms at these sites do not exceed 5 millimicrometres in the 1–2 c/s band.

During this same period, many underground explosions have been fired in several locations. The seismic energy from these sources has been recorded at teleseismic distances. The source function of an explosion is known from close-in observations and the wave form and amplitude of the P signal so generated has been calculated assuming a spherically homogeneous Earth, and allowing for the instrumental response of the short period stations.

The main conclusions which have arisen from records of the standard network and the arrays are the following.

(i) The assumption that the Earth looks spherically homogeneous to a short period P signal is almost true for ranges between 30° and 90°.

(ii) The mechanism of shallow earthquakes must account for the observed large variation in the length and form of the P signal. Two models which qualitatively fit the observations are (a) release of shear strain energy over a time short compared with the maximum length of the P wave train followed by local transformations of S to P, and (b) successive dislocations over a time comparable with the maximum length of the P wave train. The symmetry evidence favours (a).

(iii) The mechanism of deep earthquakes must account for the simple form of the P signal. Model (a) would suffice if no elastic discontinuities are present locally. Evidence from the relative excitation of surface waves by explosions and deep-focus earthquakes does not rule out the mechanism of explosive phase transitions.

(iv) Apart from those limited areas where evidence may be derived from the variation of signal form as a function of source depth, earthquakes are difficult to use as energy sources for detailed studies of the upper mantle and crust. Explosive sources must be a kiloton or more, and where these have been fired, progress has been made using standard stations. A possible case of a second-order discontinuity below the Moho has been observed.

(v) When not using arrays, care must be taken to locate recording stations in areas of low relief and metamorphic basement rocks. Sites with high relief which are associated with well-marked faulting and bedded rocks cause local scattering, refractions, and reflections which seriously interfere with the source generated signal.

References

1. J. Birtill and F. E. Whiteway, 'The application of phased arrays to the analysis of seismic body waves', *Phil. Trans. Roy. Soc. London, Ser. A*, **258**, 421–93 (1965).
2. E. W. Carpenter and E. A. Flinn, 'Attenuation of teleseismic body waves', *Nature*, **207**, 745–6 (1965).
3. E. W. Carpenter, 'A quantitative evaluation of teleseismic explosion records', *Proc. Roy. Soc. (London), Ser. A*, **290**, 396–407 (1966).
4. W. Hutchins, 'A real time seismic array data analyser and its associated event selector', *Radio Electron. Engr.*, **31**, 293–308 (1966).
5. C. G. Keen, J. Montgomery, W. M. H. Mowat, J. E. Mullard, and D. C. Platt, 'British seismometer array recording systems', *Radio Electron. Engr.*, **30**, 297–306 (1965).
6. F. A. Key, 'Locally generated noise at the Eskdalemuir seismometer array station', *Bull. Seismol. Soc. Am.*, in press (1967).
7. P. D. Marshall and E. W. Carpenter, 'Estimates of Q for Rayleigh waves', *Geophys. J.*, **10**, 549–50 (1966).
8. H. I. S. Thirlaway, 'Interpreting array records: explosion and earthquake P wave trains which have traversed the deep mantle', *Proc. Roy. Soc. (London), Ser. A*, **290**, 385–95 (1966).
9. H. I. S. Thirlaway, 'Seismology and fundamental geology', *Discovery*, **27**, 43–8 (1966).
10. H. I. S. Thirlaway, 'Detecting explosions', *Intern. Sci. Technol.*, **1965**, April.
11. F. E. Whiteway, 'The use of arrays for earthquake seismology', *Proc. Roy. Soc. (London), Ser. A*, **290**, 328–42 (1966).
12. F. E. Whiteway, 'The recording and analysis of seismic body waves using linear cross arrays', *Radio Electron. Engr.*, **29**, 33–46 (1965).
13. *The Detection and Recognition of Underground Explosions, U.K. At. Energy Authority Spec. Rept.*, HMSO (1965).

2

D. P. McKENZIE

Department of Geodesy and Geophysics
University of Cambridge
England

The mantle as an Einstein solid

Abstract

The effect of temperature on the seismic velocities is usually calculated from Debye theory. However, it is known from the specific heat measurements that the lattice spectrum of a dense silicate is closer to an Einstein spectrum than a Debye spectrum. An attempt is made to relate a simple Einstein theory of a solid to the bulk modulus of the mantle, and this shows that the temperature effects are smaller than previously believed. Though the results are provisional, the theory, unlike previous treatments, is self consistent and agrees well with the few experiments which have been carried out.

3

D. L. ANDERSON

Division of Geological Sciences
California Institute of Technology
U.S.A.

and

R. A. PHINNEY

Department of Geology
Princeton University
U.S.A.

Early thermal history of the terrestrial planets

Introduction

There is much evidence that the Earth is a chemically differentiated body. If we assume that this was not the original state of affairs, then the differentiation of the original, presumed homogeneous body, into a zoned body consisting of a crust, mantle, and core is one of the most significant events or sequence of events that has occurred in the evolution of the Earth. A favored current hypothesis is that the planets accreted from relatively cold solid particles. The mechanics of the accretion process, the size and temperature of the accreting particles, and the rate of accretion are speculative and this limits our ability to define the initial conditions of the fully accreted planet. Estimates of the initial near-surface temperatures at the end of the major portion of the accretion stage of lunar to Earth-sized objects vary from about 100 to 1000 °K. The temperature profile in a primitive planet will be governed by the rate at which mass and, therefore, gravitational energy is added, the rate at which it can be radiated away from the surface, and the initial temperature of the accreting particles and their change of temperature during the accumulation process.

The subsequent thermal history of a fully accreted body is controlled by the heating caused by the decay of radioactive isotopes and the redistribution of heat internally owing to lattice conductivity, and, at higher temperatures, radiative transfer. In the early stages heat is being generated more rapidly than it is being removed and the body gradually warms up. The onset of partial melting and the subsequent possibility of rapid redistribution of heat and mass by material transport, which we shall call differentiation, signals the end of the stage which we call the 'early thermal history'. The latent heats associated with partial melting, the convective terms in the heat transport equation, convective heating due to material transport, gravitational energy made available in the process of mass redistribution, and the redistribution of radioactive sources must be taken into account in the further thermal history of the planet. We shall consider only the early thermal history of bodies having the composition and mass of the terrestrial-type planets.

Even ignoring the complications of the later thermal history, the uncertainties of the initial conditions, composition, and thermal properties tend to make thermal history calculations suggestive rather than definitive. It is encouraging that previous thermal history calculations are broadly consistent with the known facts about the Earth's interior. The melting point of iron is exceeded at depth in the mantle early in the history of an Earth-sized planet and stays above the melting point at the present time. This is consistent with the formation of a core and at present a liquid core. The eutectic melting point of silicates is reached in the most realistic models, but the latent heat of fusion and the efficient removal of heat by penetrative convection upwards would tend to stabilize the system at a temperature below the complete melting point. Even if the considerable gravitational heating due to core settling causes complete melting, convection and redistribution of radioactivity would occur and it would be difficult to maintain temperatures in the mantle much above the melting point of the minimum melting phase. Although the seismic data indicate that the entire mantle transmits shear waves, this is not inconsistent with partial melting.

Thermal history calculations also show that the upper part of the mantle has the highest geothermal gradient and is closer to the melting points of silicates than other regions of the Earth. This is consistent with the presence of a low seismic velocity zone in the upper mantle and higher seismic attenuation and electrical conductivity.

The astronomical data regarding Mars suggest that it is a relatively homogeneous body having roughly the same composition as the Earth. By homogeneous we mean that the density varies with depth primarily because of self-compression and there is no large concentration of mass toward the center such as exists in the Earth in the form of a heavy core. The presence of a thick atmosphere, volcanism, mountains, and a magnetic field on the Earth are all indirectly related to the fact that the Earth is a differentiated body and similar features are also lacking on Mars. The question arises: can we explain these profound differences between Earth and Mars simply by the difference in size of otherwise initially identical bodies or must we resort to more drastic measures?

Previous thermal history calculations which seemed satisfactory in their predictions regarding partial melting and hence differentiation for the Earth also lead to extensive melting for Mars even for very low initial temperatures[1]. These calculations assumed chondritic compositions for both the Earth and Mars, and MacDonald[1] concluded that these bodies must differ significantly in their radioactive concentrations, a chondritic composition being appropriate for the Earth but not for Mars.

More recent studies suggest that the chondritic analogy is not appropriate for the Earth, particularly in regard to the radioactive abundances. This reopens the question. It is not clear that it will solve it, since the uranium content in the mantle required to give the present observed heat flow in the Earth is about three times the uranium content required in a chondritic Earth. The terrestrial K to U ratio, however, is about one-eighth the chondritic ratio and, because of the shorter half-life of K relative to U and Th, will make the heating up of a planet more uniform in time. Previous thermal history calculations of Earth and Mars are also not directly comparable since the Earth model is already differentiated at the start of the calculation, i.e. a core is already present and the radioactivity is already concentrated toward the surface of the Earth.

Neither an optical nor a dynamic flattening is available for Venus, and thermal calculations provide our only clue regarding conditions in the interior of this planet.

Because of the similarity between the Earth and Venus in mean uncompressed density and total mass, one would expect conditions in the interior to be similar. The thick atmosphere on Venus most probably is evidence for a considerable amount of outgassing of the interior and high internal temperature.

Model Construction

We know the diameters and masses, and hence the mean densities, of most of the planets and satellites in the solar system. We also know the surface temperatures of most of these bodies. For some of these objects we also know the flattening, either from optical or dynamical measurements, and this is related to the internal distribution of mass of the object. Even this limited amount of information is sufficient to make useful comparisons between the internal composition and structure of the various planets. Other information is also available which is not unrelated to the interiors of the planets, for example the presence or absence of an atmosphere, the presence or absence of a magnetic field, the optical properties of the surface, and, in some cases, direct observation of the surface features. This additional information provides clues more than strong constraints. From the study of orbits we can infer the Q, or tidal friction, of some of the planets and satellites.

We know very much more than this about the interior of the Earth. From seismic measurements we have the internal structure. Geology, geophysics, and geochemistry combine to give information relevant to the evolution of the Earth. If we assume that the Earth is a representative planet of the terrestrial type, it seems reasonable to use the Earth as a starting point in discussions of planetary interiors and possible evolutions and to test the known properties of the other planets against predictions made on this basis for planets of corresponding mass. The first step in such a program is to determine the mean densities of Earth-type bodies of different sizes. This calculation requires an equation of state which we can obtain from the Earth by knowing its mass, moment of inertia, and periods of free oscillation[2]. Kovach and Anderson[3], using this equation of state, designed planetary models and obtained the mean density as a function of total mass. They assumed that the transition region in the upper mantle of the Earth was due to pressure-induced phase changes and that the core was an iron-rich alloy, chemically distinct from the material of the mantle. If we knew only the mean densities of the planets, Venus and Mars would survive this first test. In other words both Venus and Mars could be considered smaller versions of the Earth, all having roughly the same composition and structure. The Moon is much lighter and Mercury is much heavier than the corresponding Earth-like bodies and this is most easily interpreted as variations in the iron content. The Moon has a density almost identical with that of the Earth's mantle, decompressed to the appropriate pressure. Although the uncertainties in the radius of Mercury are large it is apparently an iron-rich planet.

The moment of inertia of Mars indicates that it is a much more homogeneous body than the Earth. Although its mean density implies an iron content similar to that of the Earth, it must be more evenly distributed throughout the planet rather than being concentrated at the center in the form of a core. Kovach and Anderson showed that the mass and moment of inertia of Mars could be satisfied by making it a homogeneous self-compressed body having an overall composition similar to the Earth. More recent determinations of the mean density of Mars suggest that it has a slightly smaller density than given by the above procedure. This can be interpreted in the following three ways.

(i) Mars has a slightly lower iron to silicon ratio than the Earth.

(ii) More of the iron in Mars is oxidized than in the Earth, i.e. more of the iron in the Earth has been reduced, either in the process of core formation or as an initial condition of the preplanetary material.

(iii) Mars has retained more light volatiles than the Earth.

Since we do not know the moment of inertia of Venus, a similar test cannot be applied. On the basis of observational data, Venus may or may not have a core.

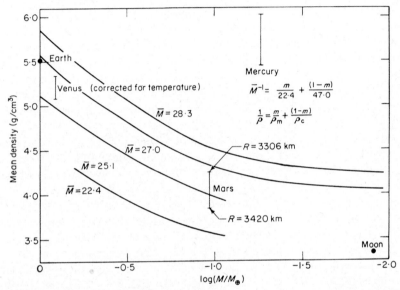

FIGURE 1 Mean density against mass, relative to Earth, for homogeneous self-compressed planets of different mean atomic weight $\bar{M}$. The mean atomic weight of the Earth is about 29·9. These curves represent the density–mass relationship for undifferentiated planets of different composition

However, the presence of a thick atmosphere on Venus is suggestive of outgassing and, therefore, differentiation and a metallic core. This is consistent with thermal history calculations to be presented later. Neither Mars nor Venus seems to have an appreciable magnetic field; this is consistent with the absence of a core on the one hand and a slow rotation rate on the other.

Anderson and Kovach[4] extended their earlier study by calculating the mean densities of different sized homogeneous planets with different compositions (see figure 1). Their index of composition was the mean atomic weight which for the Earth is about 27. The resulting calculation gives the density against depth for various sized bodies of a given composition. Homogeneous bodies constructed in this way will be the starting point of the present computations. These 'protoplanets' can be viewed as homogeneous mixtures of heterogeneous particles, in particular, an intimate mixture of iron and silicate or oxide particles. The present Earth has very rapid increases in physical properties in the depth interval between about 300 and 800 km. These are attributed to phase changes from loose-packed silicates to close-packed silicates or oxides. These pressure-induced phase changes are included in the density–pressure relationship used to construct the photoplanets. The density increases with depth owing to self-compression and, at the appropriate pressure, by solid–solid phase changes.

We now assume that the heat-producing radioactive elements are also homogeneously distributed throughout the initial body. We take the ratios of $K/U = 10^4$ and $Th/U = 3.7$ determined from terrestrial rocks by Wasserburg and others[5]. Arguments have been advanced that these ratios are unaffected by magmatic differentiation. These ratios can be compared with $K/U = 8.15 \times 10^4$ and $Th/U = 4.2$ which are appropriate for chondrites and which have been used in most previous calculations of thermal history. MacDonald[6] has shown that an average U concentration in the mantle between 4 and 5×10^{-8} will give the observed heat flow for an Earth of initial temperature near 1000 °C. We shall assume that the present U content of the crust and mantle is 4.5×10^{-8} and that the present core is free of radioactivity. In the homogeneous protoplanet the average radioactive abundances throughout the planet are reduced from the values given because of dilution by the metallic core which is assumed to be free of radioactive elements. The age of the larger solid objects in the solar system is taken as 4.5×10^9 years. The known half-lives of the long-lived radioisotopes are then used to compute the abundances of the starting protoplanet.

We now have established the rate at which radiogenic energy is released in nominally photoearth-type planets. The rate at which the body will heat up depends also on the specific heat and the mechanism of heat escape to the surface. We follow Lubimova in assuming a lattice conductivity that varies as $T^{-5/4}$ and a radiative conductivity that varies as $\sigma T^3/\varepsilon$, where T is the absolute temperature, σ is the Stefan–Boltzmann constant, and ε is the opacity. The specific heat is taken as 1.2×10^7 erg/g and constant.

We take the initial temperature gradient to be adiabatic, i.e. that due to self-compression alone. We then investigated the subsequent thermal history of various sized bodies with several assumptions regarding the surface temperature, and lattice conductivity. MacDonald[6] presents calculations which show the effect of changing the the opacity.

Initial Temperatures

It is necessary to estimate the initial temperatures in the protoplanets before proceeding with the thermal evolution problem. Recent reviews of this problem are given by Lubimova[7] and MacDonald[8]. According to current ideas, the Earth and terrestrial planets were formed by accretion of particles from a gas-dust protoplanetary cloud. Although the mechanism of accretion remains poorly understood, it is still possible to place crude constraints on the end product. Most discussions, including the present one, assume that accretion required from 10^6 to about 3×10^8 years. Five possible contributions to the initial temperature have been recognized, and are summarized below.

(i) Short-lived radioactivities, with half-lives less than 10^8 years, could have produced substantial heating if the planets formed shortly after nucleosynthesis. The lack of radiogenic ^{129}Xe, due to decay of ^{129}I ($T_{1/2} = 1\cdot6 \times 10^7$ years) on the Earth seems to require an interval greater than about 5×10^7 years between nucleosynthesis and the start of accretion. We can, therefore, eliminate from consideration initial heat from this source.

(ii) Long-lived radioactivities, such as ^{40}K, ^{235}U, ^{238}U, and ^{232}Th, can play a minor part, if the accretion time is sufficiently long.

(iii) Solar radiation leads to equilibrium black-body temperatures in the range 200–600 °K, depending on the planet under discussion and any postulated variations of solar brightness in the past. This gives a probable minimum temperature, unless special assumptions are made about the primitive solar nebula.

(iv) Adiabatic compression of the interior produces a temperature increment which can be reasonably estimated, and which, added to (iii), supplies a minimum starting temperature.

(v) Gravitational energy in the protoplanetary dust cloud must be dissipated or stored in some other form. Impact of accreting matter with the growing planet turns all the energy into heat, most of which is reradiated into space as black-body radiation. The T^4 dependence of black-body radiation ensures a stable situation in which the rate of input of gravitational energy is balanced by the radiation rate:

$$\frac{g(r)M(r)}{r}\frac{\mathrm{d}r}{\mathrm{d}t} = \sigma T^4$$

The gravitational term on the left should be reduced by the amount of energy required to compress the planet and the amount required to heat the incoming material to the equilibrium temperature T. Energy may be stored or released chemically owing to any postulated mineralogical changes occurring on impact. One can easily show that all these effects involve energies small compared with the initial gravitational energy. The above equation is then appropriate to determining the surface temperature at any stage of accretion, and one can then show that the total amount of energy which goes into heating the planet is less than 10% of the gravitational energy of the dust cloud, the remainder being lost by radiation.

If the Earth and Moon accreted at a constant rate in 10^8 years, the equilibrium surface temperatures would be of the order of 250 °K and 73 °K respectively. An Earth which accreted uniformly in 10^9 years would have a temperature of 145 °K. Using Ter Haar's[9] estimates of an accretion rate which accelerates with time, the equilibrium surface temperatures for the Earth, Mars, and the Moon will be, respectively, 1100 °K, 330 °K, and 110 °K.

One can assume some accretion history and estimate the temperature profile due to the input of gravitational energy. Most authors, using similar assumptions, deduce a temperature maximum near the surface. Combining this with the adiaabtic gradient, one can produce an initial temperature which increases in the outer part of the planet and remains roughly isothermal elsewhere[7, 8]. This average temperature is of the order of 1000 °K, 300 °K, and 100 °K for the Earth, Mars, and the Moon, respectively. In this chapter, we study models in which the role of the gravitational energy is minimized, and the more easily estimated adiabatic and solar temperature contributions are taken. An isothermal interior can only be formed by putting in the near-surface maximum due to gravitational energy. We feel that there is some merit in studying the consequences of a distinctly different model without this poorly known contribution. Our starting temperatures are therefore taken as adiabatically increasing with depth. The surface temperature is a parameter of interest, whose value is given by the solar equilibrium temperature plus a contribution due to original heat.

Results of Calculations

Figure 2 gives the development of the internal temperatures for an undifferentiated planet having the mass of the Earth and an initial surface temperature of 330 °K. The calculations were performed for an opacity of 100 cm^{-1} and for two values of the

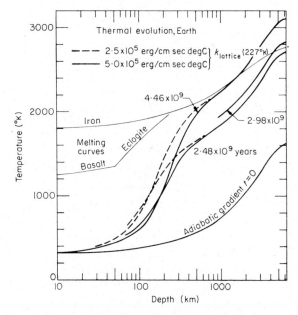

FIGURE 2   Initial temperature and temperatures at three later times for an undifferentiated Earth with a relatively cold origin

lattice conductivity. The lower value is typical of crustal rocks and the higher value is typical of an iron-rich rock which presumably is more representative of the implied early conditions of an undifferentiated planet. The melting curves are from Strong[10], and Yoder and Tilley[11]. The calculations ignore latent heats of fusion and the possibility of heat transport by convection and therefore represent maximum temperatures obtainable under the assumptions stated. The melting temperature of iron is reached at the center of the Earth at about $2 \cdot 7 \times 10^9$ years after formation and is exceeded at the present time, taken as $4 \cdot 46 \times 10^9$ years, below some 1500–1800 km depth. These conclusions are not altered by reasonable variations in the lattice thermal conductivity. This is partially due to the dominance of the radiative term in the deep interior and at high temperatures.

The present depth to the core is 2898 km. The core of the Earth is thought to contain iron, silicon, and nickel, and it presumably contains most of the free iron in the Earth.

Any free iron present below about 1500 km will melt and drain downwards enriching the central region in iron and depleting the region above.

At the onset of melting, however, the latent heats, heat transfer by convection, re-arrangement of radioactivities, and the increase in gravitational energy must all be taken into account in the further thermal evolution. These calculations are only for the purpose of predicting whether or not melting will commence. The conclusion at this point is simply that an initially adiabatic, homogeneous Earth-sized planet, even with a starting surface temperature as low as 330 °K will exceed the melting point of iron and the melting point is first exceeded near the center of the planet. Previous thermal history calculations, using an initially isothermal planet, have indicated that the melting point of iron is first exceeded high in the mantle leading to a molten iron layer which becomes unstable and drops catastrophically toward the center, releasing enough gravitational energy to melt and separate the remaining iron. Our calculations would have the core growing more slowly and the gravitational energy added gradually at least in the earliest stages of core formation. The end result, however, for an initially homogeneous Earth-sized body containing free iron is the same, namely the eventual formation of a central iron-rich molten core. The lighter, lower melting-point silicates, and volatiles would escape toward the surface in the process of core forma-tion. The amount of gravitational energy released by core formation is, of course, independent of the mechanism and the discussion of Birch[12] is relevant in any case.

We consider the existence of a crust, a core, a hydrosphere, and an atmosphere all to be evidence of a differentiated, outgassed planet. Volcanism and tectonism are current manifestations of present differentiation and readjustments to past differentiation.

It should be noted that the melting point of silicates is not reached in the present calculation. In the process of core formation approximately $2 \cdot 5 \times 10^{10}$ erg/g of gravitational energy is transformed to thermal energy and this is equivalent to an average rise of temperature of about 2000 degK (see Birch[13]). The temperature profile in the interior of a planet in the process of differentiation will be approximately that of the lowest melting component, or the minimum eutectic point of the multicompo-nent system. This temperature gradient will presumably be controlled by silicates in the upper mantle and iron in the lower mantle and core. If the starting surface temperature of the Earth is closer to 1000 °K than 300 °K, the process of melting and differentiation will already be under way while the planet is still accumulating material.

We previously estimated that 330 °K is an approximate initial surface temperature for Mars. Figure 3 shows the temperature distribution after $4 \cdot 46 \times 10^9$ years for the Earth and for Mars for this initial temperature.

Although the temperature near the center of the Earth exceeds the melting point of iron, identical assumptions for a Mars-sized body give present-day temperatures that are everywhere below the melting point of iron. Free iron in the interior of Mars will be solid and the process of core formation presumably has not started. However, the temperatures below about 500 km are very close to the melting point, and, if the viscosity of the silicate phase is low enough, a certain amount of separation in the solid phase may be possible. However, this is a much slower process than the separa-tion in the liquid phase. The thermal history calculations are, therefore, consistent with previous calculations regarding the homogeneity of Mars—present-day tempera-tures are too low to cause core formation which presumably is the trigger for the later

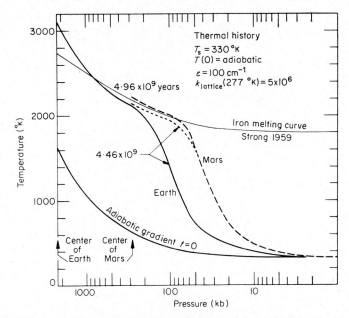

FIGURE 3   Initial and present temperatures for Mars and the Earth having an initial surface temperature of 330 °K and an initially adiabatic thermal gradient. Also shown are temperatures for Mars at $4{\cdot}96 \times 10^9$ years. Note the presence of a liquid core in the Earth and the absence of melting in Mars

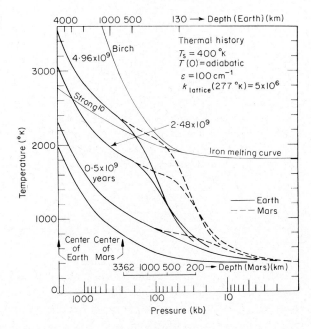

FIGURE 4   Thermal evolution for Mars and Earth for a starting surface temperature of 400 °K

events associated with differentiation. Temperatures in the interior are, however, high enough to be consistent with a certain amount of outgassing. Temperatures are also high enough to suggest that the process of core formation will begin within 0.5×10^9 years.

Figure 4 gives the sequence of events for Mars and Earth for a starting temperature of 400 °K. In this case the melting point of iron is reached at the center of the Earth about 2×10^9 years after planetary formation and the present ($t = 4.46 \times 10^9$ years) temperatures at the center of Mars (not shown) are just about at the melting point of iron. This figure also shows another extrapolation of the melting point of iron which probably represents an upper bound but does indicate another source of uncertainty in the conclusions based on thermal history calculations. The curve of Strong[10] is

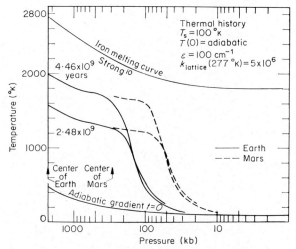

FIGURE 5   Thermal evolution for Mars and Earth for a starting surface temperature
of 100 °K

closer to recent estimates of the melting point of iron and will be the curve shown in subsequent figures.

Figure 5 gives the thermal history calculations for a very low starting surface temperature, 100 °K. In this case, neither Mars nor the Earth will have reached the melting point of iron and both will be undifferentiated planets if they started as homogeneous bodies.

The evolution of Mars with a starting surface temperature of 330 °K and the two different lattice conductivities is given in figure 6. No melting of iron occurs and this conclusion does not depend on the choice of lattice conductivity unless it is much lower than 2.5×10^5 erg/cm sec degc.

So far we have only been comparing Earth and Mars. The conclusion is that it is fairly easy to differentiate an Earth but difficult to differentiate a Mars if our estimates of starting temperatures and radioactive abundances are close to the true conditions.

For any given sized planet there is a critical starting temperature which will give a present central temperature high enough to melt iron (figure 7). Or, put another way, for a given starting surface temperature there is a minimum sized planet which will be able to begin melting its iron in the lifetime of the solar system. For an initial

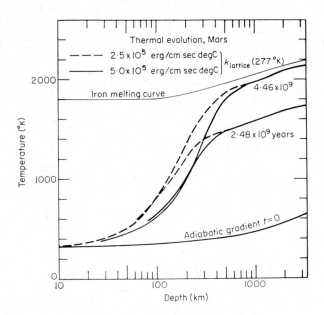

FIGURE 6   Thermal evolution for Mars having a starting surface temperature of 330 °K illustrating the effect of lattice conductivity

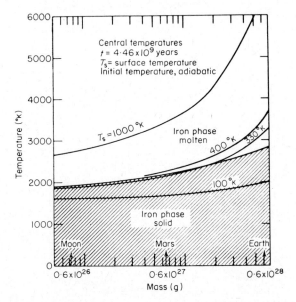

FIGURE 7   Central temperature (also maximum temperature) at $t = 4\cdot46 \times 10^9$ years as a function of planetary mass for various initial surface temperatures. The initial temperature gradient is adiabatic and the planets all have the same composition as the present Earth. The hatched region represents planets that are completely solid, assuming that iron is the minimum melting phase. The boundary between the hatched and unhatched regions represents the melting point of iron at the pressure at the center of the planet. The label 'Iron phase molten' refers to conditions near the center of the planet. In general, the isothermals are not loci of physically realizable planets

temperature of 330 °K this critical sized planet falls between the masses of Mars and the Earth, roughly about 2×10^{27} g. If the initial temperature is related to mass approximately as discussed in the previous section, then the Earth is represented by a point at $T_s = 1000$ °K, and Mars by a point near $T_s = 330$ °K. Hypothetical intermediate planets would be represented by a continuous curve between these points. Mars then appears to have such a mass that its center is now about at the melting point of iron. Venus, with a mass of 0.5×10^{28} g, must have melted its iron, given the postulates of our model. This is, of course, compatible with the inference that Venus is differentiated, based on the existence and composition of its thick atmosphere.

A Moon-sized body with the same composition as the Earth is below critical mass and will not differentiate. However, the density of the Moon alone tells us that it is not the same composition as the Earth and is probably deficient in iron relative to the Earth as a whole. The average concentration of radioactive elements in the Moon is probably like that in the Earth's mantle. The uncompressed density of the Moon is remarkably close to the uncompressed density of the Earth's mantle. The simplest explanation is that the Fe to Si ratios are the same for the Moon and the mantle and quite different from the Fe to Si ratio of Mars, Venus, and the Earth taken as a whole. Urey has argued that the Fe to Si ratio of the Sun is similar to that of the Moon and, therefore, the Moon may represent primordial matter.

If one starts with an isothermal interior, then our principal conclusions are unaffected. The iron will begin melting in a shell instead of at the center. The conclusions follow basically from our relation between mass and average initial temperatures and from the radioactive concentrations obtained by mixing iron into mantle material to form a protoplanet.

Temperatures in the Moon

It is obvious from figure 1 that the mean density of the Moon is much lower than the other terrestrial planets. It is, in fact, very close to the density of a material having a mean atomic weight of about 22·4 which is the mean atomic weight of the mantle[13,14]. The most reasonable inference is that the composition of the Moon and the Earth's mantle are very similar, at least in the major elements. In the absence of information to the contrary, it is reasonable to assume that the concentration of radioactive elements in the Moon is also similar to that in the mantle rather than that in the Earth as a whole. An alternate assumption is that the radioactivity of the Moon is similar to chondritic meteorites. Thermal history calculations for both assumptions are shown in figure 8. In both cases the melting point of silicates is exceeded early in the history of the Moon. In these calculations the initial temperature is taken as 273 °K and constant and the opacity is 100 cm^{-1}.

In the chondritic model melting commences at about 2.1×10^9 years after formation at a depth of 300 km and proceeds rapidly inwards. Latent heat of melting and heat transfer by differentiation, ignored in these calculations, will keep the interior from being totally fluid. If heat removal by fluid convection is not allowed, a temperature in excess by about 300 degK of the melting curve implies total melting and this is achieved throughout most of the interior of the Moon for both assumptions regarding the radioactive content. A 200 km thick solid crust is also implied. If the interior of

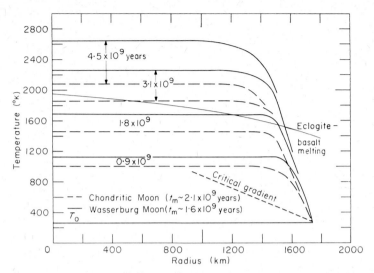

FIGURE 8   Variation of temperature with radius and time for Moons with chondritic and terrestrial (Wasserburg and others[5]) radioactive abundances. t_m is estimated time of initial melting of the silicate phase. Thermal gradients greater than *critical gradient* imply density decreasing with depth

the Moon is to stabilize at or below the melting point of silicates, extensive volcanism is required to remove the excess heat and this will commence after about $2 \cdot 1 \times 10^9$ years for a chondritic Moon and $1 \cdot 6 \times 10^9$ years for a Moon having terrestrial (mantle) abundances of radioactivities

The broken line labeled 'critical gradient' represents the thermal gradient in the Moon that will lead to constant density with depth. The temperature rise in the interior of the Moon which is implied by the thermal history calculations gives supercritical gradients near the surface and this in turn implies a density that decreases with depth.

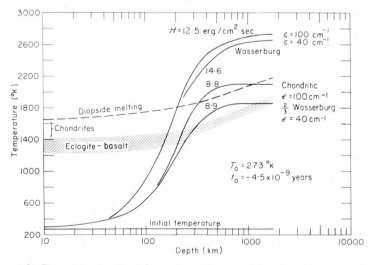

FIGURE 9   Present temperatures for various Moon models. The parameter H is the present heat flow predicted for these models

M.E.—5*

Figure 9 shows the 'present' temperatures for various Moon models ignoring latent heats and convective transfer. The radioactive abundances must be reduced below $\frac{2}{3}$ of the terrestrial mantle abundances if melting is to be avoided. It is difficult to avoid having a 'hot' Moon without having extensive volcanism in the past. An alternate way to achieve a 'cold' Moon is to have its formation antedate that of the Earth by several billion years.

Near each curve is the value for H, the present heat flow, ignoring convection. This is obviously an important quantity to measure on the Moon and, along with measured radioactivities, will place useful constraints on further thermal history calculations and discussions of the composition and evolution of the Moon.

The present calculations suggest that the Moon is a differentiated body, presumably basalt over something like pyrolite. We should expect surface concentrations of uranium more like that of basalt, $\sim 6 \times 10^{-7}$ g/g, than that of ultrabasic rocks, ~ 0.01 to 2.5×10^{-7} g/g.

Acknowledgements

This research was initiated and concluded during summer meetings of the TYCHO Study Group under the National Aeronautics and Space Administration Contract No. NSR-24-005-047 with the University of Minnesota.

The senior author would like to acknowledge support during the intervening period by the Sloan Foundation. Calculations reported herein were performed at the University of Colorado, Princeton University, and the California Institute of Technology.

This study represents contribution 1419, Division of Geological Sciences, California Institute of Technology.

References

1. G. J. F. MacDonald, *J. Geophys. Res.*, **67**, 2945 (1962).
2. D. L. Anderson, *Trans. Am. Geophys. Union*, **45**, 101 (1964).
3. R. L. Kovach and D. L. Anderson, *J. Geophys. Res.*, **70**, 2873 (1965).
4. D. L. Anderson and R. L. Kovach, to be published (1966).
5. G. J. Wasserburg, G. J. F. MacDonald, F. Hoyle, and W. A. Fowler, *Science*, **143**, 465 (1964).
6. G. J. F. MacDonald, *J. Geophys. Res.*, **69**, 2933 (1964).
7. H. Lubimova, *Geophys. J.*, **1**, 115 (1958).
8. G. J. F. MacDonald, *J. Geophys. Res.*, **64**, 1967 (1959).
9. D. Ter Haar, *Kgl. Danske Videnskab. Selskab., Mat. Fys. Medd.*, **25**, 3 (1948).
10. H. M. Strong, *J. Geophys. Res.*, **64**, 653 (1959).
11. H. S. Yoder and C. E. Tilley, *J. Petrol.*, **3**, 342 (1962).
12. F. Birch, *Geol. Soc. Am., Spec. Papers*, **76**, 133 (1965).
13. F. Birch, *Geophys. J.*, **4**, 295 (1961).
14. D. L. Anderson, 'Latest information from seismic observations', in *The Earth's Mantle* (Ed. H. Gaskell), Academic Press, New York, London, in press, 1966.

4

K. E. BULLEN
University of Sydney
Australia

Models of the internal density in the Earth, Mars, and Venus

Introduction

The chapter is principally concerned with the distribution of the density ρ, incompressibility k, and pressure p inside certain of the planets. Thermal influences are ignored because of their uncertainty and because they are likely to be small in relation to the effects here discussed. The planets considered will be mainly the Earth and Mars, with occasional references to Venus. For ease of exposition, crustal complications will be ignored.

Spherical symmetry will be assumed except where the ellipticity of figure of a planet is used to provide evidence on moments of inertia. Except where stated, hydrostatic stress will be assumed.

Reference will be made to equations of state for particular planets, or particular zones in planets, but these will frequently be of the form of numerical tables rather than formal equations. The equations of state for the Earth will be mostly taken from specific Earth models and will provide the basis for model representations in other planets. The equations considered will mostly be equivalent to the form (1).

$$\rho = f(p) \tag{1}$$

Let g be the gravitational intensity at distance r from the centre of a planet, m the mass inside the sphere of radius r, and G the constant of gravitation. Where density calculations are involved, use will be made of the relations (2) and (3). The auxiliary equations (4) and (5) enable masses and moments of inertia to be computed.

$$dp/dr = -g\rho \tag{2}$$

$$g = Gm/r^2 \tag{3}$$

$$dm = 4\pi r^2 \rho \, dr \tag{4}$$

$$dI = (8\pi/3)r^4 \rho \, dr \tag{5}$$

The chapter will attempt to summarize the essential results of a number of early and recent model calculations and will refer at the end to some current work. The spirit in the presentation will be 'if p, then q', rather than 'because p, therefore q'. The view is taken that the well-determined observational data in this field are still so meagre that more than usual precautions are necessary against the semblance of dogmatic conclusion. The need for prudence is all the greater in that, before I die, it is possible that seismographs on some of the planets may be providing definitive evidence on matters where at present we are only groping.

Observational Evidence

The observational evidence to be used consists of evidence from the Earth's interior, together with a highly limited number of astronomical observations on the planets. The consideration of evidence from sources such as geochemistry, meteorite observations, and theories of the origin of the solar system will be considered in other chapters in this book.

Evidence from the Earth

In most of this chapter, the Earth will be represented in terms of one or other of the author's Earth models A and B (see Bullen[1]). The author's previous calculations have been based on these models, and most other authors have used either them or fairly small deviants from them. Between them, the two models appear to indicate sufficiently the principal possibilities.

The author's earlier work[2-5] showed that the choice of the particular Earth model has a non-negligible effect on the planetary calculations. The effect in the case of Venus is, of course, not as great as with Mars. At the same time, this author does not agree with the view, oft-repeated during the last decade, that 'Venus is so similar to the Earth that it can be made to fit any theory that accounts for the Earth' (see below).

Where Mars is concerned, special attention has to be paid to uncertainties in seismological and other data for the Earth's upper mantle. The pressure at the centre of Mars, about 3×10^5 atm, is reached at about 800 km depth in the Earth. The pressure range in Mars thus corresponds to that part of the Earth where the uncertainties in ρ and k are substantially greater than the average.

At the present time, there are quite a number of sources of uncertainty on the seismic P and S velocities in the Earth's upper mantle. These include uncertainties about possible low velocity layers—their existence, degree, and possible ranges of depth, questions connected with the 20° discontinuity or whatever should replace it, and questions as to how far significant lateral deviations extend downward in depth. Further complications arise from the substantially revised value of the Earth's moment of inertia due to recent artificial-satellite observations, evidence from the Earth's long-period oscillations leading Landisman and others[6], for example, to contemplate a markedly smaller density variation than usual in the lower mantle, and suggestions by Sacks[7] and others that the assessed radius of the core may need a significant increase.

The boundary associated with the 20° discontinuity was originally placed at a depth exceeding 400 km. Subsequent work by Jeffreys[8], Lehmann[9], Gutenberg[10], and Bullen[11] indicated that the principal changes associated with the discontinuity may set in at a depth of 200 km, or even less. This has been followed by recent work which suggests that the whole region between 200 and 800 km may be one of abnormally high velocity gradients. Hence the need for special care in drawing inferences on Mars.

The difficulties should not, however, be overstated. Values of k/ρ continue to be fairly well determined in the outer mantle. It is with the gradients that the uncertainties are specially large, and there are some special problems on the separation of ρ and k. The differences between the Earth models A and B happen to be of such character that the models, between them, still appear broadly to cover the possibilities. By considering both models, one can get an idea of the degree of precision to be attached to inferences based on them.

In the range of depth in the Earth of chief relevance to Mars, i.e. down to 800 km depth, both the Earth models A and B contain (essentially) two zones, zone I and zone II, say. In view of some recent work on Mars, it is desirable to stress important differences in these zones for the two models.

(i) In model A, ρ is continuous throughout the whole range of depth occupied by zones I and II. In model B, on the other hand, the two zones are separated by a first-order discontinuity in ρ at a depth of 80 km.

(ii) In model A, zone II (which extends down to 400 km depth) is a zone of continuous change of chemical composition and/or phase. In model B, both zones are roughly compatible with chemical homogeneity.

One immediate consequence is that it is invalid to assume equation (6) in zone II of model A. Planetary comparisons which involve (6) have to be treated with special

$$\frac{d\rho}{dp} = \frac{\rho}{k} \tag{6}$$

care (see below).

The mass and radius of Mars

A central question is the degree of precision to be attached to observations of the masses and radii of the planets considered. Here the case of Mars will be discussed.

In previous calculations, the author has usually taken the mass M of Mars as $6\cdot442 \times 10^{26}$ g. The preferred value now appears to be that of Brouwer and Clemence[12], namely $(6\cdot434 \pm 0\cdot006) \times 10^{26}$ g, but the difference is unimportant for present purposes. However, Lyttleton[13] mentions studies by Marsden[14] which lead him to suggest that the estimate of M could be in error by $2\cdot5\%$.

Whatever the case with M, there does appear to be substantial uncertainty over the mean radius R of Mars. At the time when the author first wrote on the subject, values near 3400 km were commonly assumed. Strong preference was later expressed for Trumpler's value of 3310 ± 12 km, and in 1957 the present author used 3330 km after a number of consultations on the best value to take. Since then, de Vaucouleurs[15] has given 3362 ± 10 km, which is close to an earlier value 3360 ± 10 km of Camichel[16] (see also the footnote on page 133).

The author's calculations have mainly used values near 3400 or 3330 km, and this range appears sufficient to indicate most of the possibilities.

The moment of inertia of Mars

The observational data relating to the moment of inertia, zMR^2 say, of Mars come from estimates of the surface ellipticity e. Most of the values that have been used centre around the estimate $e^{-1} = 191\cdot8$ made by Woolard[17] from studies of the motions of Phobos and Deimos.

Woolard gave a result equivalent to (7), where A and C are the moments of inertia

$$J_2 = \frac{C - A}{MR^2} = 0.001\,95 \qquad (7)$$

of Mars about the polar and equatorial areas. MacDonald[18] later gave 0.002 03, taking Trumpler's estimate of R.

The ratio q of the centrifugal and gravitational forces at the equator of Mars is given by (8), where Ω is the axial angular velocity. The usual hydrostatic theory gives (9)

$$q = \Omega^2 R^3 / GM \qquad (8)$$

$$J_2 = \tfrac{1}{3}(2e - q) \qquad (9)$$

to the first order in e, so that a value of e can be obtained when J_2 and q are known. It needs to be noted that e as thus estimated depends on the assumed values of M and R.

A first necessity is to estimate the uncertainty in the inferred value of e. The largest uncertainty is likely to come from deviations from the hydrostatic state in Mars. Let a_1 and a_3 be the equatorial and polar radii of Mars, and let $\theta \, (= 2\cdot6)$ be the ratio between surface gravity on the Earth and Mars. A departure, y say, from the value of $a_1 - a_3$ given on the hydrostatic theory would be consistent with a difference $y/\theta, = x$ say, between the extreme equatorial radii of the Earth. Early estimates of x by Jeffreys[19] were of the order of 0.7 km, but were later reduced by different authors to values between 0.3 and 0.1 km. The corresponding y would lie between 0.8 and 0.25 km, and would alter e^{-1} by amounts between 9 and 3 units. Hence[20], the estimate of e^{-1} must be regarded as uncertain by at least 3 units and possibly by 9 units or so. Thus one cannot rule out any calue of e^{-1} lying between about 183 and 201.

An independent calculation by MacDonald[18] made some years later gave the range of acceptable values of e^{-1} as 182 to 200, which is essentially the same result.

Additional uncertainty connected with the dependence of the computed value of e on the assumed values of M and R might extend the range of uncertainty 2 or 3 units further on either side.

The value of z is derived from e using the Radau approximation. In terms of η, where $\eta = (r/e)\, de/dr$, the Radau theory gives (10) and (11). It is to be noted that the

$$1\cdot5z = 1 - 0\cdot4(1 + \eta)^{1/2} \qquad (10)$$

$$2\eta = 5q/e - 4 \qquad (11)$$

values of η and z, when deduced through e/q, also depend on the assumed values of M and R.

Some Early Calculations

The author's first calculations[2] on planetary interiors were based on a provisional density–pressure model for the Earth[21]. The equation of state for mantles was assumed to be common to the terrestrial planets, and similarly for cores, but the mantles and cores were assumed to be chemically distinct. The results gave different mantle–core mass ratios for the Earth, Venus, and Mars (for numerical detail, see

Jeffreys[19]). It was thence concluded at the time that the overall compositions of the three planets are markedly different.

The result for Venus is interesting, the implied mantle–core mass ratio being 3·6, as against 2·1 for the Earth. The difference is large enough to involve a significant difference between the compositions of Venus and the Earth—in contrast with certain later procedures which have involved a common composition. This illustrates the point that evidence from Venus can assist in discriminating between different theories on planetary interiors.

A new train of thinking started when Kuhn and Rittman[22] proposed a predominantly hydrogen composition for the Earth's core. This idea was soon shown to be highly implausible on several grounds. But it led to some useful investigations, including the calculation of Kronig and others[23] that, at $0·7 \times 10^6$ atm, the pressure reached about two-thirds of the way down in the Earth's mantle, hydrogen would change to a metallic form, with an accompanying density jump from about 0·4 to 0·8 g/cm^3.

Then Ramsey[24] and Bullen[3] independently proposed a compromise theory which, to a first approximation, would take the Earth's core to be composed, not of hydrogen, but of the same ingredients as the mantle. The changes at the mantle–core boundary would thus be principally a pressure effect, rather than due to a change of composition. The formal consequences of assuming this theory will now be considered.

Ramsey's approach was partly through considerations of high-pressure physics; Bullen's approach was severely empirical. Both authors saw that the theory would act in the direction of permitting a common overall composition for the Earth, Venus, and Mars. Instead of having two separate equations of state for these planets, one for the mantles and one for the cores, there would now (to a first approximation) be a single equation of the form (1) right through. Obviously, the smaller the planet, the larger would now be the mantle–core mass ratio. In a planet as small as Mars, there would be no zone corresponding to the Earth's outer core.

Ramsey started by taking the (p, ρ) relation of Bullen's Earth model A, but obtained a mean density of Mars too low by some 10% to fit the observed M and R. He sought to rectify this discrepancy by an *ad hoc* continuous change of composition. His was the first of a number of *ad hoc* devices that have been used to improve the agreement between theory and observation in this field. An essential conclusion from Ramsey's work is that, when the model A equation of state is used, the phase-transformation theory is roughly compatible with a common overall composition for the Earth and Mars, but that an *ad hoc* device has to be resorted to in order to obtain really close agreement.

The use of *ad hoc* devices involves in effect the introduction of one or more adjustable parameters. The number of *ad hoc* devices on planetary interiors that have been produced since Ramsey's paper shows that there is quite a variety of ways in which the adjustments can be made. Not all authors who have used *ad hoc* devices appear to have appreciated how far their particular theory is from being thereby established.

Bullen also used model A to begin with, and had obtained numerical results essentially similar to those of Ramsey when Ramsey's first paper appeared. Model B[25] was being constructed at the time and was seen to differ from model A in a direction towards removing the discrepancies with the observational data for both Venus and Mars. The essential point is that the density in the upper mantle is appreciably greater in model B than in model A. Between 80 and 500 km depth, the density ranges from 3·9 to 4·1 g/cm^3 in model B, as against 3·4 to 3·9 g/cm^3 in model A.

In the author's 1949 calculations, the model B equation of state gave precise agreement with the values

$$M = 6·442 \times 10^{26} \text{ g}, \qquad R = 3410 \text{ km}$$

for Mars. The preferred observational value for R at the time was 3396 ± 8 km, so that the agreement appeared to be fairly good.

When it was assumed that the Earth's inner core is chemically distinct from the outside regions, the agreement was better still; this involved putting in a small 'inner' core in Mars in appropriate proportion. With the same mass, the result for R was now 3391 km. (Incidentally, it remains probable that the representative atomic number for the Earth's inner core is significantly higher than for the outer core.)

The values deduced for the moment of inertia of Mars also appeared to be fully satisfactory. With the use of (10) and (11), they gave e^{-1} = 188, 183, according as Mars was or was not assumed to contain a small inner core. The moment of inertia results were little different whether model A or model B was used. In both cases the results slightly favoured presence of a small core in Mars.

The agreement of the theory with the observational mass and radius of Venus was also very satisfactory when model B was used. Thus it appeared at the time (1949–50) that the assumptions that the Earth, Venus, and Mars have the same overall composition and that the Earth's outer core is a phase modification of the mantle material agree closely with all the pertinent astronomical observations.

Another result of interest is that the theory implied a much smaller fluid 'outer core' in Venus than the Earth, the depth ranging from 4020 to 4940 km in Venus, as against 2900 to 4980 km in the Earth. Thus if seismographs on Venus should be able in due course to delineate the fluid zone in Venus, a very crucial test will have been provided of a number of theories. This again emphasizes the value of Venus as a test planet for certain purposes. Incidentally, the smallness of the implied fluid zone in Venus would be compatible with the failure so far to detect a sizable magnetic field around Venus, though other factors such as the small rate of rotation could also apply.

The foregoing calculations are now past history, but it is useful to bear in mind the essential numerical detail and the possibilities that were opened up, when other theories are being examined.

Effect of Changes in the Astronomical Data

Shortly after the above work was completed, the observational assessments of the radii of Mars and Venus came to be reduced by amounts substantially greater than the previously assigned probable errors. In consequence, a set of revised calculations was carried out[20].

The value of M was kept unchanged at 6·442 × 10^{26} g, while (see page 129) R was now assumed to be 3330 km. With the model B equation of state for the Mars mantle, it was formally necessary to have a Mars core of radius 1225 km to fit the changed value of R. The moment of inertia of the Mars model incorporating these features gave e^{-1} = 211, which is rather beyond the plausible range.

This set of calculations therefore implied that, if $R \leq 3330$ km, the densities in the Mars mantle must be somewhat greater than in the corresponding part of the Earth model B. The calculations were formally compatible with the view of Urey[26] that Mars is less differentiated than the Earth.

At the same time, although acceptance of the reduced value of R would remove the previous remarkably close fit with the astronomical data, the discrepancies would not be so great as to rule out the phase-transformation theory as a possibly useful first approximation to the actual state of affairs. Should R need to be increased above 3330 km, as more recent observations suggest, then the discrepancies are reduced. The phase-transformation theory has of course been opposed on other grounds, and the present author's attitude since 1957 has been to await the emergence of further evidence before pursuing further implications of the theory*. The purpose of the present chapter is to show the results of certain formal calculations rather than to press any particular theory.

The author's 1957 paper[20] included some further model calculations which deviated from his earlier procedure by taking the density in the Mars mantle to be $(1 + \delta)$ times the model B values. Table 1 shows representative results for different assigned values of δ, the radius of the Mars core being denoted by R_c.

TABLE 1   Values of R_c, z, and e^{-1} for Mars for assigned
values of δ

δ	R_c (km)	z	e^{-1}
0·000	1225	0·365	211
0·045	900	0·378	201
0·064	600	0·385	196
0·071	300	0·388	194
0·073	0	0·388	194

If the radius of Mars does not exceed 3330 km, table 1 would indicate that the radius of any core in Mars is not likely to exceed about 900 km, the value which gives $e^{-1} = 201$. All the cases give values of e^{-1} in excess of Woolard's figure and therefore appear to involve some departure from hydrostatic stress. Table 1 also shows that, until direct seismic observations become available on Mars, it is unlikely that it will be possible to discriminate between the absence of a core and the presence of one up to several hundred kilometres radius. For $0 < R_c < 700$ km, the range of variation of the inferred e^{-1} is only 3 units.

The least departure in table 1 from Woolard's value of e^{-1} occurs when there is no core. This case would require the material of Mars to be about 7% denser than the

---

* At the NATO Symposium, a discussion of Dr. E. A. Gaugler's paper (section VIII, chapter 4 of this book) on the *Mariner IV* observations brought to light the provisional information that the observations had indicated a value of M for Mars equal to $322·7 \times 10^{-9}$ times the mass M_S of the Sun, and a value for R between 3390 and 3400 km. Taking $M_S = 1·989 \times 10^{33}$ g (Allen[27]) gives $M = 6·418 \times 10^{26}$ g. The new value of R, if substantiated, constitutes a reversion to a value in agreement with detail in the present author's work of seventeen years ago. Also of interest are values of the major and minor axes of Mars given by Dr. A. Dollfus in connection with his estimate of e by optical means; these values give $R \simeq 3380$ km. (See also Bullen[30].)

material of the Earth's upper mantle, when model B is used. The factor of 7% is compatible with a Mars mantle containing about 15% of uncombined iron. (This value corrects certain results in the author's 1957 paper which has an arithmetical error in the estimate of iron content.) With calculations based on model A, the percentage of iron would be somewhat higher. Thus, subject to certain reservations, the calculations are compatible with inferences made by Urey on the composition of Mars. Included in the reservations are that the percentage of iron needed would be lowered either by an upward shift in R, or by the presence of a small core which, it seems, cannot yet be precluded.

The upward changes in measurements of R since 1957 (see also the footnote on page 133) now suggest that the proportion of uncombined iron in Mars is appreciably less than in Urey's 1952 estimate. Further, if the newest data are substantiated, the remarkable agreement given by the phase-transformation theory would appear to be restored.

Recent Work of Other Authors

Calculations of MacDonald

MacDonald[18] used a different form of representation for the Earth in making comparisons with Mars. For the mantle, he assumed equations of state of the form (12), where $\phi = k/\rho$, selecting the value of ϕ_0 (usually taken by him as $5 \cdot 1 \times 10^{11}$ c.g.s.)

$$\phi/\phi_0 = (\rho/\rho_0)^3 \tag{12}$$

from data for the Earth. He assumed the presence of a core in Mars, and considered two classes of core models with densities $7 \cdot 2$, $7 \cdot 8$ g/cm³ at zero pressure, respectively.

He assumed $M = 6 \cdot 453 \times 10^{26}$ g, postulated a series of values of R ranging from 3319 to 3453 km, and derived curves showing values of the Mars core radius and surface density against e.

On his procedure, and assuming $e^{-1} = 192$, he concluded that R had to be about 3450 km to give agreement with an olivine composition of the Mars mantle. On the author's procedure, it is sufficient to have R less than this figure by nearly 60 km when model B is used. The author's procedure gives results closer to MacDonald's when model A is used. Numerical differences between MacDonald's results and the author's again illustrate the degree of dependence of conclusions on the assumed Earth model.

MacDonald also concluded that, for $R = 3313$ km, Mars would have to be of nearly uniform composition throughout.

Calculations of Kovach and Anderson

Kovach and Anderson[28] investigated the possibility of securing agreement with a common overall composition for the Earth and Mars by another type of procedure. Starting from the notion of a chemically distinct, iron-rich core in the Earth, they evaluated planetary models in which parts of the Earth core material are mixed into the mantle, and vice versa. Their basic Earth model was slightly different from model A, and they assumed $M = 6 \cdot 434 \times 10^{26}$ g for Mars. One of their Mars models, with 80% of Earth core material mixed into the mantle, gives $R = 3306$ km and $e^{-1} = 205$;

a model with 90% gives 3305 km and 202. The model they regarded as best for the purpose has 97% of Earth mantle material mixed into the core and gives $R = 3309$ km, $e^{-1} = 200$. They appear to have found difficulty in reducing e^{-1} below 200 without reducing R to still lower values.

As might be expected from the calculations quoted above, their best models are not far from chemical homogeneity when a radius near 3310 km is taken for Mars.

Kovach and Anderson also concluded that, if the Earth and Mars have a common overall composition, and the Earth's core is chemically distinct from the mantle, then the Mars radius must not be much more than 3310 km.

An approach of Lyttleton

Lyttleton[13] applied an Emden equation approach to the problem of the internal constitution of Mars.

An Emden equation is derived on combining (2), (3), and (4) with the relations (6) and (13), where a and b are constants. The result is (14), where A is constant. The

$$d\rho/dp = \rho/k \qquad (6)$$

$$k = a + bp \qquad (13)$$

$$\frac{d}{dr}\left(r^2 \rho^{b-2} \frac{d\rho}{dr}\right) = -A^2 r^2 \rho \qquad (14)$$

corresponding equation of state is of the form (15). It is to be noticed that (14)

$$p = \frac{a}{b}\left\{\left(\frac{\rho}{\rho_0}\right)^b - 1\right\} \qquad (15)$$

involves, through (6) and (13), additional assumptions.

Let q_i and n_i be parameters representing the phase and chemical composition. Then inside a planetary zone one can write (16), where the first term on the right-hand side

$$d\rho = \frac{\partial \rho}{\partial p} dp + \sum \frac{\partial \rho}{\partial q_i} dq_i + \sum \frac{\partial \rho}{\partial n_i} dn_i \qquad (16)$$

relates to the effect of changing p without taking account of any possible consequent phase changes. More generally than (6), k is connected with ρ by (17).

$$\frac{\partial \rho}{\partial p} = \frac{\rho}{k} \qquad (17)$$

For a zone that is chemically homogeneous and also devoid of phase changes, dq_i and dn_i are of course zero, and (17) reduces to (6).

Where $dn_i = 0$ but $dq_i \neq 0$, i.e. where there are phase but not composition changes, it is permissible to treat ρ as a function of p alone in respect of a planet's equilibrium state (i.e. apart from short-lived disturbances as in seismic wave transmission). But (6) has now to be replaced by (18).

$$\frac{d\rho}{dp} = \frac{\rho}{k} + \sum \frac{\partial \rho}{\partial q_i} \frac{dq_i}{dp} \qquad (18)$$

In some contexts, the use of (6) can lead to serious error. It has been shown by the author, for example, that in certain more general conditions the Williamson–Adams equation (19), which depends on (6), requires the additional factor η on the right,

$$\frac{d\rho}{dr} = -\frac{Gm\rho}{r^2(k/\rho)} \tag{19}$$

where η is given by (20). On the Jeffreys P velocity distribution for a certain range of

$$\eta = \frac{dk}{dp} + g^{-1}\frac{d(k/\rho)}{dr} \tag{20}$$

depth inside the Earth's core, this factor exceeds 30 units.

Thus, because of its dependence on (6), the Emden equation approach is unsatisfactorily more restricted than the older approaches which start from a (p, ρ) relation, and can be very unreliable in contexts where dq_i and dn_i are not negligible. The relevance of the assumption (13) also needs some examination in the Mars context.

Some other points in Lyttleton's procedure need comment. The starting point was an Earth model essentially equivalent to model A, and a phase transformation was assumed at the mantle–core boundary. For the relevant range of depth in the Earth (0–800 km), Lyttleton took two zones in each of which the form (13) was assumed. In so doing, he made, however, some significant departures from model A. These included a sizable discontinuity at the boundary between zone I and zone II, and absence of phase or composition changes throughout the lower zone II. The Emden equation procedure forced these departures.

Thus the comparison was really not with model A but with a model nearer the type of model B. A further *ad hoc* device was selecting the level of the boundary between the two zones in Mars to best advantage. Lyttleton was able to achieve apparent agreement with a common overall composition for the Earth and Mars, but this was because the enforced deviations from model A accidentally put the needed quantity of extra mass into the upper mantle. When the deviations are all allowed for and various corrections made, the results do not appear to differ significantly from the essential results of Ramsey and the writer. The calculations are discussed at greater length elsewhere[29].

Work in Progress

In view of the tendency among authors to introduce more and more *ad hoc* devices to fit favoured theories, and of the limitations of the observational data available for testing, Haddon and Bullen have embarked on a series of formal calculations not closely tied to theories. As a first step, they are constructing families of Mars models with assumed equations of state of the form (21). Using (2), (3), and (4), but not the

$$\rho = A + Bp - Cp^2 \tag{21}$$

homogeneity relation (6), they then derive a second-order differential equation in ρ which, with the help of a digital computer, yields a density distribution when $A, B, C,$ and certain other requirements are assigned.

The intention is to present the results in a form which will show at a glance the types of models of the form (21) that are permissible when values of M, R, and e are given. The work is not quite complete. Examples of approximate results so far obtained are given (in c.g.s. units for ρ and p) in table 2.

TABLE 2   Approximate results from the calculations of Haddon and Bullen

ρ	e^{-1}
$M = 6.442 \times 10^{26}$ g, $R = 3330$ km	
$3.30 + 0.70 \times 10^{-11}p + 0.40 \times 10^{-23}p^2$	205.6
$3.60 + 0.64 \times 10^{-11}p - 0.80 \times 10^{-23}p^2$	195.8
$3.80 + 0.34 \times 10^{-11}p$	192.8
$3.80 + 0.20 \times 10^{-11}p + 0.80 \times 10^{-23}p^2$	194.7
$M = 6.442 \times 10^{26}$ g, $R = 3370$ km	
$3.30 + 0.60 \times 10^{-11}p + 0.77 \times 10^{-23}p^2$	196.0
$3.60 + 0.46 \times 10^{-11}p - 0.40 \times 10^{-23}p^2$	186.7
$M = 6.442 \times 10^{26}$ g, $R = 3410$ km	
$3.30 + 0.60 \times 10^{-11}p - 0.15 \times 10^{-23}p^2$	184.8
$3.30 + 0.20 \times 10^{-11}p + 2.5 \times 10^{-23}p^2$	190.2

Should the need arise, classes of models less simple than (21) may later be considered, for example models with cores. But the calculations based on (21) are already serviceable in showing a number of important properties of the models. For example they show how altering R and altering the density gradient affects e and the surface density.

Finally, attention is drawn to the density distribution (22) derived by the author[20]

$$\rho = 4.68 - 0.86(r/R)^2 \tag{22}$$

as a Mars model fitting $M = 6.442 \times 10^{26}$ g, $R = 3330$ km, and $e^{-1} = 191.8$ precisely. This model is compatible with chemical homogeneity throughout Mars, and gives $k = 1.1 \times 10^{12}$ dyn/cm² at the surface, in fair agreement with the value just below the Earth's crust.

Haddon has shown that the model (22) corresponds almost exactly to (23).

$$\rho = 3.82 + 0.32 \times 10^{-11}p - 0.10 \times 10^{-23}p^2 \tag{23}$$

The surface density in this model is, however, 3.82 g/cm³, and so is much higher than the usually assumed value of 3.3 for the Earth's upper mantle. This raises the piquant point that, if a density of 3.8 g/cm³ were reached in the Earth at a level rather higher than is generally believed at present, there would be no difficulty in getting agreement, on the earlier theory of Ramsey and the author, with a Mars radius of 3330 km. On the other hand, if the *Mariner IV* results are substantiated, there is no need for a surface density higher than 3.3 g/cm³.

Acknowledgements

The author wishes to thank his colleague Mr. R. A. Haddon for helpful comments on several points in this chapter.

References

1. K. E. Bullen, *Introduction to the Theory of Seismology*, 3rd ed., Cambridge University Press, Cambridge, 1963.
2. K. E. Bullen, *Rept. 23rd Australian New Zealand Assoc. Advan. Sci. Meeting*, XXIII, 25 (1937).
3. K. E. Bullen, *Monthly Notices Roy. Astron. Soc.*, **109**, 457, 688 (1949).
4. K. E. Bullen, *Monthly Notices Roy. Astron. Soc.*, **110**, 256 (1950).
5. K. E. Bullen and A. H. Low, *Monthly Notices Roy. Astron. Soc.*, **112**, 637 (1952).
6. M. Landisman, Y. Satô, and J. Nafe, *Geophys. J.*, **9**, 439 (1965).
7. I. S. Sacks, *Carnegie Inst. Wash. Yearbook*, **64**, 275 (1965).
8. H. Jeffreys, *Geophys. J.*, **1**, 191 (1958).
9. I. Lehmann, *Ann. Geophys.*, **15**, 93 (1959).
10. B. Gutenberg, *Physics of the Earth's Interior*, Academic Press, New York, 1959, p. 84.
11. K. E. Bullen, *Publ. Bur. Centr. Séismol. Intern.*, Ser. *A*, **21**, 7 (1961).
12. D. Brouwer and G. M. Clemence, *Planets and Satellites*, University of Chicago Press, Chicago, 1961, p. 69.
13. R. A. Lyttleton, *Monthly. Notices Roy. Astron. Soc.*, **129**, 21 (1965).
14. B. G. Marsden, *Intern. Astron. Union Symp.*, *21st*, *1963*.
15. G. de Vaucouleurs (1962), quoted in reference 13.
16. H. Camichel, *Bull. Astron.*, **10**, 97 (1954).
17. E. W. Woolard, *Astron. J.*, **51**, 33 (1944).
18. G. J. F. MacDonald, *J. Geophys. Res.*, **67**, 2945 (1962).
19. H. Jeffreys, *Monthly Notices Roy. Astron. Soc.*, *Geophys. Suppl.*, **4**, 62 (1937).
20. K. E. Bullen, *Monthly Notices Roy. Astron. Soc.*, *Geophys. Suppl.*, **7**, 272 (1957).
21. K. E. Bullen, *Monthly Notices Roy. Astron. Soc.*, *Geophys. Suppl.*, **3**, 395 (1936).
22. W. Kuhn and A. Rittmann, *Geol. Rundschau*, **32**, 215 (1941).
23. R. Kronig, J. de Boer, and J. Korringa, *Physica*, **12**, 245 (1946).
24. W. H. Ramsey, *Monthly Notices Roy. Astron. Soc.*, **108**, 406 (1948).
25. K. E. Bullen, *Monthly Notices Roy. Astron. Soc.*, *Geophys. Suppl.*, **6**, 50 (1950).
26. H. C. Urey, *The Planets, their Origin and Development*, Princeton University Press, Princeton, New Jersey, 1952.
27. C. W. Allen, *Astrophysical Quantities*, 3rd ed., Athlone Press, London, 1963.
28. R. L. Kovach and D. L. Anderson, *J. Geophys. Res.*, **70**, 2873 (1965).
29. K. E. Bullen, 'On the constitution of Mars, III', *Monthly Notices Roy. Astron. Soc.*, **133**, 229 (1966).
30. K. E. Bullen, 'Implications of the revised Mars radius', *Nature*, **211**, 396 (1966).

IV

Physical evidence for non-hydrostatic conditions in the planets

A. The Earth

1. Determination of the geopotential from satellite observations (R. R. ALLAN) 141

2. Determination of the Earth's geoid by satellite observations (R. J. ANDERLE) 151

3. Travel-time anomalies of elastic waves reflected at the core–mantle boundary (A. VOGEL) . . 163

B. The Moon

4. The figure of the Moon (S. K. RUNCORN and B. GRAY) 165

5. The accuracy of the information on absolute heights on the Moon, and the problem of its figure (J. HOPMANN) 175

6. Determination of the shape of the Moon by the terminator method (O. CALAME) 183

1

R. R. ALLAN

Royal Aircraft Establishment
Farnborough, Hampshire, England

Determination of the geopotential from satellite observations

Introduction

Since the first artificial satellite was launched in 1957, much progress has been made, and still is being made, in determining the gravitational potential of the Earth. The particular power of the method is that a satellite samples all longitudes and a range of latitudes in the course of time as the Earth rotates underneath its orbit. Moreover, if the satellite is visible in the twilight hours, the long-term changes in its orbit can be found to high accuracy simply by timing its passage through the star background.

Expansion of the Gravitational Potential

In principle, if the acceleration suffered by a satellite over a small arc of its orbit could be measured with sufficient precision, the gravitational potential could be determined. The accuracy that can be obtained, however, falls short of this ideal, and instead we must use the cumulative effects built up over at least a small number of orbits. The first requirement is to assume some suitable general form for the potential, with disposable parameters, and to solve the direct problem: given the potential, what is the motion of the satellite? Since the potential satisfies Laplace's equation where there is no mass, it can be expanded in a series of spherical harmonics in the form (1) where r, θ, ϕ are spherical polar coordinates relative to the centre of mass

$$U(\mathbf{r}) = \frac{\mu}{r}\left\{1 - \sum_{l=2}^{\infty} J_l \left(\frac{R}{r}\right)^l P_l(\cos \theta) \right.$$

$$\left. + \sum_{l=2}^{\infty} \sum_{m=1}^{l} J_{lm} \left(\frac{R}{r}\right)^l P_l^m (\cos \theta) \cos m(\phi - \phi_{lm})\right\} \tag{1}$$

of the Earth as origin, and the axis of rotation is taken as the pole of coordinates. In (1), μ is G times the mass of the Earth, and R is conventionally taken as the mean equatorial radius. The functions involved are the Legendre polynomials and the associated Legendre functions and are defined in the appendix. Having chosen the centre of mass as origin, there are no terms in (1) with $l = 1$. Also the coefficient $J_{2,1}$ must be very small, since the rotation axis must very nearly coincide with a principal axis of inertia.

Our final objective is now that of finding the coefficients J_l of the zonal harmonics, and the coefficients J_{lm} and the phase angles ϕ_{lm} of the tesseral harmonics. These are in fact determined piecemeal, since the different types of term have different cumulative effects. It is worth pointing out that the coefficient J_2, which corresponds to the oblateness of the Earth, is rather special; its magnitude is approximately 10^{-3}, and it arises almost entirely because the Earth is a rotating fluid mass. All the other zonal harmonic terms (apart from a significant contribution to J_4 from the rotation), and all the longitude-dependent parts, arise from variations in the distribution of mass somewhere within the Earth. If the spherical harmonic functions were properly normalized, which has not been done in (1), all these coefficients would be roughly comparable (at least those of relatively low order) with a magnitude of approximately 10^{-6}, and

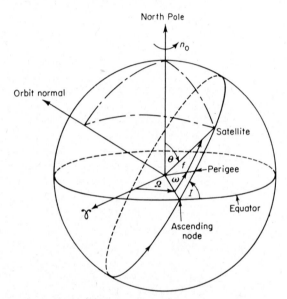

FIGURE 1   Projection of a satellite orbit on a unit sphere

fall off only slowly with increasing l. They would give roughly comparable forces on close satellites, and would correspond to comparable deviations in the geoid.

The last part of the potential in (1) depends on the longitude relative to the Earth and, since the Earth is rotating, it will average out to zero in approximately one day. Hence it will give rise only to short-period effects, except in the special circumstance that the motion of the satellite is commensurable with the rotation of the Earth in such a way that the path of the satellite very nearly repeats relative to the Earth. On the other hand, the axially symmetric part of the potential in (1) is unaffected by the rotation, and will give long-period and secular effects. Thus the zonal harmonic coefficients are easier to determine and were found first.

To describe the motion of the satellite it is simplest to use slowly varying quantities. If the Earth were a point mass, the orbit would be a fixed ellipse with the attracting centre at one focus, and this ellipse could be defined by the parameters a, e, I, Ω, ω, and χ^* (the solution of the equation of motion in three dimensions involves six arbitrary constants). The semimajor axis a and the eccentricity e give the size and shape of the ellipse. The orientation of the plane is defined by Ω, the right ascension of the ascending node measured in the equatorial plane from the first point of Aries, and the inclination I of the orbital plane to the equatorial plane, as shown in figure 1. The orientation of the ellipse within its plane is given by ω, the argument of perigee, measured in the orbital plane from the ascending node. From the usual formulae for elliptic motion, equation (2) holds, where f and E are the true and eccentric anoma-

$$r = \frac{a(1 - e^2)}{1 + e \cos f} = a(1 - e \cos E) \tag{2}$$

lies both measured from perigee, and the mean anomaly M is given by Kepler's equation, (3). The last element χ^* is then defined in general by (4), where n, the

$$M = E - e \sin E \tag{3}$$

$$M = \int n \, dt + \chi^* \tag{4}$$

mean motion, is given by $n^2 a^3 = \mu$.

The six elements which have been defined would be constants of the motion for the Kepler problem, and will therefore vary only slowly in the presence of small perturbations. The instantaneous or osculating elements at any instant of time are defined as the elements of the fixed ellipse in which the satellite would move if all the perturbing terms were switched off at that instant so that the potential reverted to μ/r. It is now possible to solve the direct problem of finding the motion of the satellite by the standard methods of celestial mechanics. The potential is first expressed in terms of the six elements, and the rates of change of these elements are found from Lagrange's planetary equations (see Brouwer and Clemence[1]). Since the development of the disturbing function is rather a technical matter, this has been described in the appendix.

The remaining question of how the basic observations are reduced to a manageable form is even more involved, since the observations may be of a number of different types. Optical observations, either visual or using Baker–Nunn cameras, and radio interferometer (Minitrack) observations all give directions; radio Doppler observations give range rate; radar observations can give all six components of position and velocity. Usually an orbit determination programme is used to produce a set of orbital elements at a particular time from a group of observations over perhaps a few days. The elements used, however, are not usually the osculating elements described here, but have been modified in various ways according to the analyses of Kozai[2], Brouwer[3], or Merson[4], so as to avoid the short-period variations which occur with the osculating elements due to oblateness.

Determination of the Longitude-independent Part

The coefficients of the even zonal harmonics

It can be shown from the development of the disturbing function given in the appendix that there is a nearly steady secular change in Ω given by (5). The even zonal

$$d\Omega/dt = \sum A_{2k}J_{2k} + e \sin \omega \sum A_{2k+1}J_{2k+1} + O(e^2)$$
$$+ \text{ short-period terms} + \text{other effects} \tag{5}$$

harmonics give secular terms, and the odd zonal harmonics give long-period terms of order e which oscillate with the position of perigee. If we crudely picture the oblateness of the Earth as an extra ring of mass around the equator, it is clear that it exerts a torque on the orbit attempting to pull it towards the equatorial plane, but by the usual rules of gyroscopic motion the orbit instead precesses at constant inclination about the Earth's axis. The other even zonal harmonics, which are also symmetric about the equator, produce torques in the same way, and contribute to the precession; but the odd zonal harmonics, being antisymmetric about the equator, give a net torque only in so far as the orbit is eccentric. There is a similar but slightly more complicated secular change in ω, which is also sometimes used to evaluate the even zonal harmonic coefficients. The position of perigee, however, cannot be determined with the same accuracy as the position of the node, so that changes in ω are rather less useful in finding the gravity coefficients.

To determine the even harmonic coefficients, one chooses a number of suitable satellites for which accurate orbits are known, covering at least one revolution of perigee so that the effects of the odd harmonics in (5) can be averaged out to zero. Ill-conditioned equations are avoided if the satellites are well spaced in inclination, since the factors A_{2k} in (5) depend strongly on inclination, as well as rather weakly on semimajor axis and eccentricity. After correcting for lunisolar effects, which also change Ω, there remain N linear equations which can be solved for the m coefficients $J_2, J_4, \ldots, J_{2m}$ ($m \leq N$) if the higher coefficients J_{2m+2}, J_{2m+4}, etc., are assumed to be zero. Indeed the main difficulty is in deciding how many coefficients should be included, and table 1 shows the results of three recent analyses by King-Hele and Cook[5], Kozai[6], and Smith[7]. The values of J_2, J_4, and J_6 in table 1 are in very good agreement,

TABLE 1   Three recent evaluations of even zonal harmonic coefficients

Source	King-Hele and Cook[5]				Kozai[6]		Smith[7]
Number of coefficients	3	4	5	6	6	7	7
$10^6 J_2$	1082·70	1082·64	1082·62	1082·68	1082·63	1082·64	1082·64
$10^6 J_4$	−1·58	−1·52	−1·48	−1·61	−1·63	−1·65	−1·70
$10^6 J_6$	0·59	0·57	0·48	0·71	0·59	0·65	0·73
$10^6 J_8$		0·44	0·46	0·13	−0·15	−0·27	−0·46
$10^6 J_{10}$			−0·19	0·09	−0·16	−0·05	−0·17
$10^6 J_{12}$				−0·31	−0·29	−0·36	−0·22
$10^6 J_{14}$						0·18	0·19

[From table 1 of King-Hele, Cook, and Scott[9].]

although the authors have used different satellites, have adopted different methods of solution, and have solved for different numbers of coefficients. The significance to be attached to the values of J_8, J_{10}, etc., however, is rather problematical, since the largest source of error is the neglected higher coefficients. Cook[8] considers that the coefficients beyond J_6 cannot be adequately evaluated as yet; one is merely fitting the potential by more or fewer coefficients. As shown by King-Hele, Cook, and Scott[9], the potentials given by the different determinations are in very good agreement over the range of inclination, say 30° to 90°, for which satellites are available; the potentials diverge below 30°, and the differences are more associated with the number of coefficients being evaluated than with the different authors.

The coefficients of the odd zonal harmonics

These are probably best found from the long-period oscillation in eccentricity which, from the development of the disturbing function in the appendix, is given by (6).

$$de/dt = \cos \omega \sum B_{2k+1} J_{2k+1} + e \sin 2\omega \sum B_{2k} J_{2k} + O(e^2)$$
$$+ \text{ short-period terms } + \text{ other effects} \tag{6}$$

There is a corresponding variation in I which is also sometimes used, although the changes in inclination are not so well-determined as the changes in eccentricity. In fact the two variations are related since $(1 - e^2) \cos^2 I$ is constant, which arises from the condition that the component of angular momentum along the axis of symmetry is invariant for motion in an axisymmetric field. The periodic parts of the variations in Ω and ω are also sometimes used in evaluating the odd harmonics.

Provided the observations cover at least half a cycle, and preferably a complete cycle, of the rotation of perigee, the coefficient of $\cos \omega$ in (6) can be evaluated after correcting for all the other effects, air drag, lunisolar forces, and radiation pressure, which can change the eccentricity. The even harmonics are sufficiently well known to be subtracted out. The evaluation of the gravity coefficients then follows as before, since the factors B_{2k+1} depend strongly on the inclination. Table 2 shows results obtained by Smith[10], King-Hele, Cook, and Scott[11], Guier and Newton[12], and

TABLE 2   Recent evaluations of odd zonal harmonic coefficients

Source	Smith[10]	King-Hele, Cook, and Scott[11]			Guier and Newton[12]	Kozai[6]
Number of coefficients	3	3	4	5	4	5
$10^6 J_3$	−2·44	−2·54	−2·56	−2·73	−2·69	−2·56
$10^6 J_5$	−0·18	−0·21	−0·15	0·17	−0·01	−0·18
$10^6 J_7$	−0·30	−0·32	−0·44	−0·94	−0·63	−0·38
$10^6 J_9$			0·12	0·53	0·21	0·04
$10^6 J_{11}$				−0·68		0·30

[From table 9 of King-Hele, Cook, and Scott[11].]

Kozai[6]. Once again the various authors have used different satellites, different methods, and evaluated different numbers of coefficients. When the sets of coefficients are translated into the amplitudes of the oscillations in eccentricity and inclination, however, King-Hele, Cook, and Scott[11] show that the different determinations are in very good agreement over the range of inclination actually used (approximately

30° to 90°), and that the only significant discrepancies are below 30° where no suitable satellite is available.

Since the axially symmetric part of the geopotential alone determines the long-period and secular effects on Earth satellites (except when there is a resonance), a geoid based on zonal harmonics alone is of considerable interest, even though it may

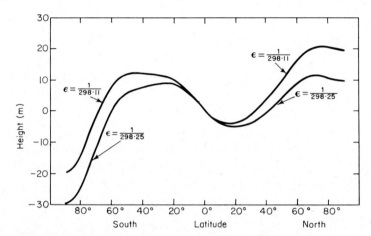

FIGURE 2   Height of the geoid relative to spheroids of flattening $\varepsilon = 1/298\cdot25$ and $\varepsilon = 1/298\cdot11$. [After King-Hele, Cook, and Scott[11]]

appear to be a somewhat artificial concept to the geophysicist. Figure 2 shows the geoid based on the four-coefficient solutions of King-Hele and coworkers in tables 1 and 2; the height of the geoid is shown against a spheroid of flattening $1/298\cdot25$ as adopted by the International Astronomical Union, and also against a spheroid of flattening $1/298\cdot11$ as derived by King-Hele and Cook[5].

Determination of the Longitude-dependent Part

The tesseral harmonics are rather more difficult to determine, since they produce no long-period or secular effects in the way that the zonal harmonics do. Instead the (l, m)th tesseral harmonic would be expected to produce (*inter alia*) variations in a satellite's position with a period of approximately $1/m$ of a day, since the harmonic function resumes its original appearance when the Earth rotates through the angle $2\pi/m$. To show the complexity of the problem, the variation in position, which can be derived from (18) of the appendix, can be written in the form (7), where n_0 is the

$$\delta\mathbf{r} = \mathcal{R} \sum_{l,m} J_{lm} \sum_{p,q} \mathbf{C}_{lmpq}(a, e, I)$$

$$\times \exp\left[i\{(l - 2p)\omega + (l - 2p + q)M + m(\Omega - n_0 t - \phi_{lm})\}\right] \qquad (7)$$

angular velocity of the Earth, and the summations extend over $2 \leqq l \leqq \infty$, $1 \leqq m \leqq l$, $0 \leqq p \leqq l$, $-\infty \leqq q \leqq \infty$. The expected variations with period approximately $1/m$ of a day are given by $l - 2p + q = 0$, but some of the short-period terms may be of comparable or larger amplitude since $\mathbf{C}_{lmpq}$ is of order $e^{|q|}$.

The coefficients C in (7) also depend strongly on the inclination, so that the effects of gravity coefficients with the same m but different l can be separated by using observations of a number of satellites well-spaced in inclination. All satellites used ought to be relatively high, say above 700–850 km, so that they are little affected by air drag; a nearly constant drag would be irrelevant, but variations in drag would simulate the effects we are looking for. The observations must be corrected for short-period variations due to the zonal harmonics (mainly oblateness), and for lunisolar effects. Given a sufficient number of observations, perhaps some thousands, it is then possible to determine the J_{lm} and ϕ_{lm} up to some chosen limit by a least-squares fit. Orbital parameters and corrections to the positions of the observing sites also have to be found from the observations, and it appears to be highly desirable to make the least-squares fit to all the parameters simultaneously rather than in sequence.

At least two different types of observation are sufficiently accurate to allow a solution to be made; Kaula[13] and Izsak[14] have used optical data, while Anderle[15] and Guier and Newton[12] have used radio Doppler shift measurements. The optical data are provided by the network of twelve Baker–Nunn cameras operated by the Smithsonian Institution. These are accurate to a few seconds of arc and will give the position of a satellite at 1000 km to an accuracy of about 10 m; the variations we are looking for are of the order of some tens to some hundreds of metres. Observations are restricted to the twilight hours by the visibility of the satellite. There are slightly more Doppler sites, and the observations are not restricted to the twilight hours (see section IV, part A, chapter 2 of this book).

It is probably fair to say that the determination of the individual longitude-dependent gravity parameters has not reached the same stage as for the zonal harmonic coefficients. The different determinations are now beginning to converge, however, and further rapid progress will without doubt be made; Anderle reports the latest results by Doppler methods (in section IV, part A, chapter 2 of this book). It must be emphasized that the gravity parameters so far found are more significant when taken as a complete set rather than individually. When translated into geoid maps, the different determinations are in much better agreement than might appear from a comparison of individual parameters; this suggests that the amount of data used, massive though it is, is not yet sufficient to resolve the individual gravity parameters properly.

In their gravity analysis, Guier and Newton[12] found that the residuals, after the least-squares solution had been made, were not as small as expected, particularly for the nearly polar satellites. Moreover, the residuals revealed oscillations with periods of the order of a few days and amplitudes of the order of 100 m. Yionoulis suggested that this was due to resonance with higher-order harmonics, and the periods were indeed found to correspond (see Guier and Newton[12]). If the changes in ω and Ω are ignored, the argument of the general term in (7) will be slowly varying if equation (8) holds true. Since n/n_0 is approximately 12, 13, or 14 for the relatively close satellites

$$(l - 2p + q)n \simeq mn_0 \qquad (8)$$

used, there is a near resonance for all terms for which m is the nearest integer to n/n_0, and $l - 2p + q = 1$. In fact all satellites must show a resonant oscillation with a period of at least two days, but the amplitudes will tend to be larger for the higher inclinations. Yionoulis[16,17] has given a discussion of these resonance effects, and

Anderle[15], Guier and Newton[12], and Yionoulis[18] have found values for the harmonics (13, 13), (15, 13), and (15, 14).

The behaviour of nearly synchronous satellites, analysed by Allan[19], is also an instance of resonance effects. Such a satellite is moving very slowly in longitude relative to the Earth, and is subject to a longitudinal force which produces a drift acceleration. Although this is very small, its cumulative effects are easily detectable. Because of the great distance, about 6·6 Earth radii, the dominant effect must be due to the harmonic of lowest l value, namely $J_{2,2}$, which corresponds to the ellipticity of the equator. The satellite can oscillate about one or other of two stable positions which lie on the minor axis of the Earth's equatorial section. The ellipticity of the equator can be crudely pictured as arising from two small extra masses lying at opposite ends of an equatorial diameter, so that the problem is related to the restricted three-body problem; instead of moving under their mutual gravitation, the two small masses are carried by the Earth, and the stable points at synchronous height correspond to the stable Lagrange points. It should be possible to determine the parameters for the dominant (2, 2) harmonic with some accuracy from the drift motions of existing synchronous satellites, and Wagner[20, 21] and Allan and Piggott[22] have derived values for $J_{2,2}$ and $\phi_{2,2}$ (together with more doubtful values for some other low-order even tesseral harmonics) which are in very good agreement with the Doppler results of Anderle[15] and Guier and Newton[12].

Appendix. Development of the Disturbing Function

The associated Legendre functions used in (1) are here defined by (9), where $P_l(z)$

$$P_l^m(z) = |1 - z^2|^{m/2} \frac{d^m P_l(z)}{dz^m}, \qquad 0 \leq m \leq l \tag{9}$$

is the Legendre polynomial given by $(1/2^l l!)d^l(z^2 - 1)^l/dz^l$. To express the general axisymmetric term in the potential in terms of the orbital elements, it is simplest to use the addition theorem for Legendre polynomials[23] which is as follows: if equation (10) holds, then so does equation (11). If the normal to the orbital plane is taken as the

$$\cos \gamma = \cos \theta \cos \theta' + \sin \theta \sin \theta' \cos (\phi - \phi') \tag{10}$$

$$P_l(\cos \gamma) = \sum_{p=-l}^{+l} \frac{(l - |p|)!}{(l + |p|)!} P_l^{|p|} (\cos \theta) P_l^{|p|} (\cos \theta') \cos p(\phi - \phi') \tag{11}$$

new pole (see figure 1), then the polar angles of the Earth's axis and the direction to the satellite can be taken as $(I, \frac{1}{2}\pi)$ and $(\frac{1}{2}\pi, \omega + f)$ with respect to the new pole, and γ in (10) and (11) is the original colatitude θ. The disturbing function still contains products of the form $(r/a)^{-l-1} \exp(ipf)$, where f is the true anomaly, but these may be expanded[24] in terms of e and M in the form (12), where the Hansen coefficient

$$(r/a)^l \exp(ipf) = \sum_{q=-\infty}^{\infty} X_q^{l,p}(e) \exp(iqM) \tag{12}$$

$X_q^{l,p}(e)$ is of order $e^{|p-q|}$. Thus the general lth zonal harmonic term in (1) is expressed in terms of the orbital elements as in (13). This contains only terms with $l - p$ even,

$$-\left(\frac{\mu}{R}\right)J_l\left(\frac{R}{a}\right)^{l+1}\sum_{p=-l}^{+l}\sum_{q=-\infty}^{+\infty}\frac{(l-|p|)!}{(l+|p|)!}(-i)^p P_l^{|p|}(0)P_l^{|p|}(\cos I)$$

$$\times X_q^{-l-1,p}(e)\exp{(ip\omega + iqM)} \quad (13)$$

since otherwise $P_l^{|p|}(0)$ vanishes. All terms with $q \neq 0$ contain the mean anomaly and are of short period. Thus for long-period terms we require $q = 0$, and for secular terms (also independent of ω), we also require $p = 0$; in consequence only the even zonal harmonics contain secular parts. For long-period terms, the relevant Hansen coefficients reduce to a closed form, for the definition (12) leads to (14), where the

$$X_0^{-l-1,p}(e) = (1-e^2)^{-l+\frac{1}{2}}(2\pi)^{-1}\int_0^{2\pi}(1+e\cos f)^{l-1}\exp{(ipf)}\,\mathrm{d}f \quad (14)$$

integral gives a polynomial in e. Alternatively, as pointed out by Garfinkel and McAllister[25], by using the Laplace integrals for the associated Legendre functions[23] these coefficients can be written as in (15), where the definition (9) applies.

$$X_0^{-l-1,p}(e) = (1-e^2)^{1/2}\frac{(l-1)!}{(l-1+p)!}P_{l-1}^p\{(1-e^2)^{-1/2}\} \quad (15)$$

The longitude-dependent part of the potential, which contains the tesseral harmonics $P_l^m(\cos\theta)\exp{(im\phi)}$, $1 \leq m \leq l$, requires rather more sophisticated methods to effect a neat development of the general (l, m)th harmonic in terms of the orbital elements. It involves a transformation from the polar coordinates θ, ϕ which are referred to a coordinate system rotating with the Earth, to a coordinate system effectively defined by the orbital plane. This can be regarded as a rotation through the angle $\Omega - n_0 t$ about the Earth's axis (where $n_0 t$ is the current sidereal time at Greenwich), followed by a further rotation I about the line of nodes. As pointed out by Izsak[14], this induces a linear transformation of the lth-degree spherical harmonics; if the coordinates θ, ϕ transform to θ', ϕ' in the rotated coordinate system, $P_l^m(\cos\theta)\exp{(im\phi)}$ must be expressible as a linear combination of the harmonics $P_l^{m'}(\cos\theta')\exp{(im'\phi')}$ with the same value of l but all values of m' (with some suitable definition of the associated Legendre functions for $m' < 0$). Since the pole of the new coordinate system is the normal to the orbit, $\theta' \equiv \frac{1}{2}\pi$, and the $P_l^{m'}(\cos\theta')$ reduce to constants, in fact to zero when $l - m'$ is odd. The required formula may be derived from texts on the applications of group theory in quantum mechanics such as Wigner[26] or Rose[27], and Allan[19] writes the explicit result as (16), where f is the true

$$P_l^m(\cos\theta)\exp{(im\phi)} \equiv \sum_{p=0}^{l} F_{lmp}(I)\exp{[i\{(l-2p)(\omega+f)+m(\Omega-n_0 t)\}]} \quad (16)$$

anomaly, and $F_{lmp}(I)$ is given by (17), where the summation is over all permissible

$$F_{lmp}(I) = i^{l-m}\frac{(l+m)!}{2^l p!(l-p)!}\sum_k (-)^k\binom{2l-2p}{k}\binom{2p}{l-m-k}c^{3l-m-2p-2k}s^{m-l+2p+2k}$$

$$(17)$$

values of k, i.e. from $k=\text{maximum}\,(0, l-m-2p)$ to $k=\text{minimum}\,(l-m, 2l-2p)$. In (17), $c \equiv \cos\frac{1}{2}I$ and $s \equiv \sin\frac{1}{2}I$. Other ways of handling this transformation have also been given by Garfinkel[28] and Jeffreys[29]. On using (12) and (17), the general (l, m)th tesseral harmonic term in (1) becomes (18). In (18), G_{lpq} is the Hansen coeffi-

$$\left(\frac{\mu}{R}\right)J_{lm}\left(\frac{R}{a}\right)^{l+1}\mathcal{R}\sum_{p=0}^{l}\sum_{q=-\infty}^{\infty}F_{lmp}(I)G_{lpq}(e)$$

$$\times \exp\left[i\{(l-2p)\omega + (l-2p+q)M + m(\Omega - n_0 t - \phi_{lm})\}\right] \quad (18)$$

cient $X_{l-2p+q}^{-l-1,l-2p}$ and is of order $e^{|q|}$. This notation has been chosen to correspond closely with that of Kaula[30]; thus G_{lpq} is identical with the quantity used by Kaula, while $F_{lmp}(I)$ is identical for $l - m$ even but contains an extra factor $-i$ for $l - m$ odd (although the form is apparently considerably different).

Acknowledgements

This chapter is crown copyright, reproduced with the permission of the Controller, Her Majesty's Stationery Office.

References

1. D. Brouwer and G. M. Clemence, *Methods of Celestial Mechanics*, Academic Press, New York, 1961, Chap. 11, pp. 273–307.
2. Y. Kozai, *Astron. J.*, **64**, 367 (1959).
3. D. Brouwer, *Astron. J.*, **64**, 378 (1959).
4. R. H. Merson, *Geophys. J.*, **4**, 17 (1961).
5. D. G. King-Hele and G. E. Cook, *Geophys. J.*, **10**, 17 (1965).
6. Y. Kozai, *Publ. Astron. Soc. Japan*, **16**, 264 (1964).
7. D. E. Smith, *Planetary Space Sci.*, **13**, 1151 (1965).
8. A. H. Cook, *Geophys. J.*, **10**, 181 (1965).
9. D. G. King-Hele, G. E. Cook, and D. W. Scott, *Planetary Space Sci.*, **14**, 49 (1966).
10. D. E. Smith, *Planetary Space Sci.*, **11**, 789 (1963).
11. D. G. King-Hele, G. E. Cook, and D. W. Scott, *Planetary Space Sci.*, **13**, 1213 (1965).
12. W. H. Guier and R. R. Newton, *J. Geophys. Res.*, **70**, 4613 (1965).
13. W. M. Kaula, *J. Geophys. Res.*, **68**, 5183 (1963).
14. I. G. Izsak, *J. Geophys. Res.*, **69**, 2621 (1964).
15. R. J. Anderle, *J. Geophys. Res.*, **70**, 2453 (1965).
16. S. M. Yionoulis, *J. Geophys. Res.*, **70**, 5991 (1965).
17. S. M. Yionoulis, *J. Geophys. Res.*, **71**, 1289 (1966).
18. S. M. Yionoulis, *J. Geophys. Res.*, **71**, 1768 (1966).
19. R. R. Allan, *Proc. Roy. Soc. (London), Ser. A*, **288**, 60 (1965).
20. C. A. Wagner, *J. Geophys. Res.*, **70**, 1566 (1965).
21. C. A. Wagner, *J. Geophys. Res.*, **71**, 1703 (1966).
22. R. R. Allan and B. A. M. Piggott, *Proc. Intern. Symp. on Use of Artificial Satellites for Geodesy, 2nd, Athens, 1965*, to be published.
23. E. T. Whittaker and G. N. Watson, *A Course of Modern Analysis*, 4th ed., Cambridge University Press, Cambridge, 1927, p. 326.
24. H. C. Plummer, *An Introductory Treatise on Dynamical Astronomy*, Cambridge University Press, London, 1918, Dover Publications, New York, 1960, pp. 44–6.
25. B. Garfinkel and G. T. McAllister, *Astron. J.*, **69**, 453 (1964).
26. E. P. Wigner, *Group Theory*, Academic Press, New York, 1959, Chap. 15.
27. M. E. Rose, *Elementary Theory of Angular Momentum*, Wiley, New York, 1957, Chap. 4.
28. B. Garfinkel, *Astron. J.*, **69**, 567 (1964).
29. B. Jeffreys, *Geophys. J.*, **10**, 141 (1965).
30. W. M. Kaula, *Geophys. J.*, **5**, 104 (1961).

2

R. J. ANDERLE
U.S. Naval Weapons Laboratory
U.S.A.

Determination of the Earth's geoid by satellite observations

Introduction

Geoid heights determined by various scientists on the basis of careful analysis of satellite observations have produced results which differ by 40 m or more in some geographic locations[1]. Since studies of the mantle of the Earth often involve comparison of the geoid determined by satellite observations with other physical measurements, a study of the variations in the computed geoid was undertaken. There are many differences in the methods used by the various authors to determine the geoid, which are outlined in the next section. Finally, quantitative results obtained from systematic tests of some of these differences are reported.

Sources of Differences in Solutions for Geoid Heights Based on Satellite Observations

Observations

Geodetic solutions reported to date have been based upon observations made by the Baker–Nunn camera network of the Smithsonian Astrophysical Observatory[2,3] or the Doppler satellite tracking system of the U.S. Navy[4,5]. The camera observations are available for many satellites for time periods of several years. While daily observations have not been made by the complete Doppler system for such time spans, because of failures which ultimately occur in the satellite power system or circuitry, only a few of the data which have been obtained have been used in geodetic solutions made to date. The all-weather capability and the somewhat larger number of stations in the Doppler network have permitted the extraction of a large amount of information from short time periods of observation. The Baker–Nunn network is shown in figure 1. Since the observations must be referenced to a star background, the stations observe only on relatively clear nights. Since few satellites are actively illuminated, observation times are further limited to times near sunrise and sunset when the Sun and satellite are in favorable positions to permit the camera to record a reflection of the Sun off the satellite. Up to 1966, the Doppler equipment, consisting of thirteen relatively fixed stations and five mobile vans, has obtained data from the sites shown in figure 2 for time periods of six weeks to six years. The equipment has provided reliable data more than 90% of the time that a satellite is scheduled for observation. Thus data

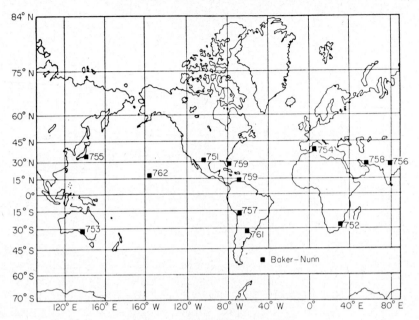

FIGURE 1   Baker–Nunn camera sites

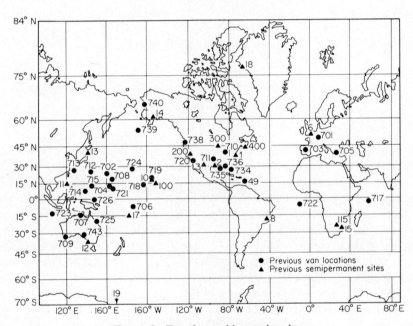

FIGURE 2   Doppler tracking station sites

during four or more passes, depending on the satellite altitude, are obtained each day for each satellite with a stable oscillator unless another such satellite with a higher priority is above the radio horizon of the station during the pass. Other types of observations have not played a role in determining the complete specifications for the gravity field either owing to lack of precision of the equipment or owing to scarcity of observations. However, the Minitrack system of the National Aeronautics and Space Administration provided the first information on the latitude variation of the gravity field[6,7] and is still contributing to the refinement of this information[8,9] through the determination of the direction to actively transmitting satellites. The direction is found by comparison of phase of the incoming signal on pairs of antenna systems. Another important contribution to the verification of the geoid has been made by the analysis of observations[10] of synchronous satellites, which yields information on some of the gravity coefficients.

Parameters

The geoid is found by determining the coordinates for which the potential, defined by the following or some similar expression, is equal to a selected constant:

$$V = \frac{\mu}{r} \sum \left(\frac{R}{r}\right)^n P_n^m (\phi)\{C_{nm} \cos (m\lambda) + S_{nm} \sin (m\lambda)\}$$

where ϕ, λ, r are the polar coordinates of a point on the geoid, $P_n^m (\phi)$ are the associated Legendre polynomials of degree and order (n, m), R is a nominal Earth's radius which scales the coefficients $C_{n,m}$, $S_{n,m}$ which are to be determined, and μ is the product of the Earth's mass and the universal gravitational constant. The potential may be evaluated for a constant which minimizes the differences between the geoid and a reference ellipsoid, although a different choice may be made as in the last section of this chapter as a computational expedient. Although attempts have been made to evaluate the coefficient μ from Doppler observations alone[1] and from optical observations together with a scale provided by survey[11], the most reliable estimate to date has been obtained from the analysis of observations of lunar probes[12,13]. The geoids determined from satellite solutions have involved increasingly larger numbers of coefficients ranging from fourth to eighth degree and order. Coefficients of thirteenth and fourteenth order have also been obtained[14,15]; while these higher-order coefficients do not directly influence the geoid by more than a meter, they do influence the satellite motion significantly and therefore could bias the determination of the lower coefficients if their effects are ignored. Other parameters which affect the observational data and must therefore be considered in the solution for the gravity coefficients include the coordinates of the observing stations, the orbital constants of the satellites, atmospheric drag and solar radiation parameters, and instrument biases. The strength of the solution for station coordinates may be improved in various ways. Constraints may be imposed on the solution, such as fixing the longitude of one of the observing stations at an arbitrary value, or holding the relative coordinates of the stations within a datum to the positions found by survey. Rather than imposing survey constraints, the positions of the stations are sometimes introduced into the solution as additional observational data with weights corresponding to the estimated accuracy of the assumed positions. The six orbit constants for each span of data used in the solution are defined differently in accordance with the theory used, as discussed in the next section. The drag and radiation parameters modify physical models of varying levels of complexity. The most complex models include a parameter to scale external measures of time, latitude, longitude, and altitude variations in density and radiation.

Simpler models include parameters to scale functions which vary only with altitude, while, in still other models, extra parameters are introduced to account for the dominant effects of drag on satellite motion, without the use of a specific atmospheric model. Instrument biases are introduced only to take account of variations in the Doppler signals owing to variations in the oscillator frequencies of the satellite or observing station. Either a frequency parameter, or both frequency and frequency drift parameters, are introduced for each pass of each satellite over each station.

Orbit theory

The orbit constants are the six constants of integration of the satellite orbit which best fit the observations. The orbit is computed either by numerical integration of the equations of motion from these initial conditions or by general perturbation methods, wherein the quadratures are completed analytically after appropriate transformations and approximations are made. Since partial derivatives of the observations with respect to the orbit constants, gravity parameters, and other constants in the equations of motion are required in the least-squares solution, the partial derivatives of satellite position with respect to these parameters are also obtained either by numerical integration or by general perturbation methods. In some cases, some or all of the partial derivatives are found by general perturbation methods while the satellite orbit is found by numerical integration. Although the methods differ in their accuracy, the differences are not sufficient to account for the differences in the solutions for the geoid.

Statistical representation

Since the distribution of the observing stations on the Earth is not uniform, some attempts have been made to compensate by introducing weights which tend to equalize the strength of the data from different geographic areas. Some experiments have also been performed in which the component of the optical sight line, which is along the direction of motion of the satellite, was given a lower weight in order to compensate for variable atmospheric drag effects. The various methods of aggregating the 300 or so Doppler observations obtained on each satellite pass include a special form[16] of averaging groups of eight points, polynomial fitting to the pass, and transformation of the raw data to measurements of frequency, slant range, and the equivalent of the time of closest approach for the pass. All representations of the data assume the observations are uncorrelated whether in the raw or in the transformed state.

Method of solution

Each solution for the geoid involves the formation of the normal equations arising from imposing the condition that the values of the parameters shall minimize the sums of squares of the residuals of observation. These equations are sometimes solved simultaneously, while in other cases subsets of the equations are solved for subsets of the parameters. It is expected that converged solutions obtained by either method would be equivalent, although statistical estimates of the accuracy of the solution are normally obtained only when the parameters are obtained from the simultaneous solution of the equations.

Sensitivity of Solutions to Variations in Observations and Parameters Used

Solution NWL-5E

The most complete solution for the geoid obtained by the Naval Weapons Laboratory on the basis of Doppler observations is called NWL-5E. This parameter set was

TABLE 1   Number of satellite passes used in solution NWL-5E

Station	1961 $a\eta1$	1962 $\beta\mu1$	1961 01	Polar[a]	Total
Maryland	64	228	160	449	901
Texas	71	259	130	100	560
North Mexico	87	314	195	446	1042
England	—	48	119	332	499
Brazil	84	193	—	312	589
Hawaii	78	—	—	354	432
Philippines	66	203	—	353	622
Australia 12	44	164	—	197	405
Australia 709	—	—	—	145	145
Alaska	—	157	156	900	1213
South Africa 15	76	160	—	—	236
South Africa 115	—	—	—	331	331
Samoa	—	170	—	348	518
Greenland	—	—	—	707	707
Oahu	—	271	21	285	577
California 200	—	202	—	296	498
California 720	—	—	—	295	295
Minnesota	—	—	33	334	367
Maine	—	—	34	381	415
Marcus	—	116	—	—	116
Japan	75	214	—	419	708
Indiana	—	68	—	—	68
Oklahoma	—	77	—	—	77
Iwo Jima	—	50	—	—	50
Okinawa	—	96	—	112	208
Yap	—	—	—	49	49
Guam	—	—	—	35	35
Johnston	—	—	—	127	127
Kauii	—	—	—	212	212
Total passes	645	2990	848	7519	12002
No. of weeks of data	5	7	10	15	37
Orbital inclination	32°	50°	67°	90°	

1963 38B, 1963 38C, or 1963 49B.

obtained as a simultaneous solution for the gravity coefficients to seventh degree and sixth order, the coordinates of the observing stations, the orbit parameters and a drag parameter for each span of data used, and a frequency and frequency drift parameter for each satellite pass over each station. The extent and distribution of the observational data upon which this solution is based is shown in table 1. The NWL-5E gravity parameters obtained in the solution are listed in table 2, while the geoid contours

TABLE 2   NWL-5E normalized gravity coefficients[a]

n	m	$\bar{C}_{nm}$	$\bar{S}_{nm}$	n	m	$\bar{C}_{nm}$	$\bar{S}_{nm}$
2	0	−484·194		6	1	−0·085	0·192
3	0	0·984		6	2	0·129	−0·457
4	0	0·507		6	3	−0·020	−0·134
5	0	0·045		6	4	−0·193	−0·316
6	0	−0·219		6	5	−0·093	−0·786
7	0	0·105		6	6	−0·324	−0·360
2	1	0·016	0·062	7	1	0·331	0·083
2	2	2·446	−1·519	7	2	0·350	−0·195
3	1	2·148	0·274	7	3	0·323	0·045
3	2	0·978	−0·906	7	4	−0·467	−0·244
3	3	0·585	1·625	7	5	0·055	0·021
4	1	−0·495	−0·575	7	6	−0·477	−0·244
4	2	0·274	0·671				
4	3	1·030	−0·247				
4	4	−0·413	0·336				
5	1	0·032	−0·119				
5	2	0·637	−0·328				
5	3	−0·389	−0·124				
5	4	−0·549	0·148				
5	5	0·215	−0·594				

$$V = \mu \Sigma \left\{ R^n C_{nm} \frac{P_n^m (z/r)}{r^{n+1}} \cos (m\lambda) + R^n S_{nm} \frac{P_n^m (z/r)}{r^{n+1}} \sin (m\lambda) \right\}$$

$$\bar{C}_{n,m} = \left\{ \frac{(n-m)!(2n+1)K}{(n+m)!} \right\}^{-1/2} C_{nm}$$

where $K = 1$ when $m = 0$, $K = 2$ when $m \neq 0$, and where P_n^m is the associated Legendre polynomial, R is the Earth's radius, μ is the Earth's gravity constant, λ is the longitude with respect to Greenwich, and z and r are the distances above the equatorial plane and from the center of the Earth, respectively.
[a] All coefficients should be multiplied by 10^{-6}. $\mu = 398\ 605\cdot42$ km^3/sec^2.

obtained from these coefficients are shown in figure 3. As a computational expedient, each geoid given in this chapter was defined to be the equipotential surface equivalent to the gravity coefficients, which passes through a geocentric reference ellipsoid at zero degrees latitude and longitude. The next sections describe the sensitivity of this solution for the geoid to variations in the number of gravity parameters in the solution, to the number and distribution of observations on satellites having different orbital

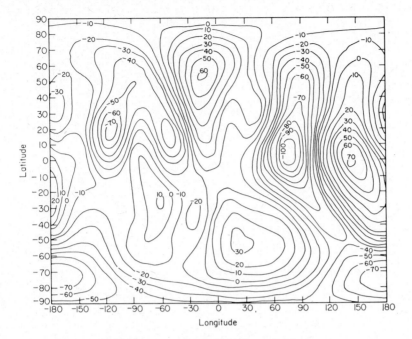

FIGURE 3 Geoid heights for NWL–5E solution

inclinations, and to the number of observing stations. It is believed that these are the principal sources of variations in the solutions for the geoid obtained to date.

Effect of reducing number of parameters

The NWL-5E observational data were used to conduct a series of tests to determine the influence of the number of gravity parameters on the solution for the geoid. First, the solution was truncated from seventh degree to fourth degree by simply discarding the higher-degree coefficients. Some of the features of the geoid were lost, and many of the other features were reduced in depth as may be seen by comparing the first two columns of table 3. The set of coefficients to fourth degree and order obtained in a solution which did not include higher-order coefficients as parameters was termed the 'best (4, 4) solution'. The features of this solution, shown in the third column of table 3, are similar to the truncated (4, 4) solution. Another method of reducing the number of gravity parameters in the solution involves a transformation to the space in which the gravity parameters are decoupled and reduction of the number of gravity parameters in this 'Q' space[1]. Solutions for the 40 and 50 most significant parameters in Q space, based on the same observational data used in the NWL-5E solution, are given in the last two columns of table 3. It can be seen that the solution for the 40 most significant gravity parameters is inferior to the (4, 4) solution, although the latter involves a smaller number of parameters. However, this does not indicate that solutions in Q space are without application. The transformation was designed to obtain a solution in cases where the full parameter set is indeterminate, which was not the case in this example.

M.E.—6*

TABLE 3   Effect of number of gravity coefficients on geoid

Location		NWL-5E	(4, 4) truncation	(4, 4) best fit	'Top 40' solution	'Top 50' solution
England	latitude	55° N	45° N	40° N	50° N	55° N
	longitude	340° E	0°	355° E	335° E	345° E
	height	61 m	57 m	59 m	36 m	62 m
South Africa		50° S	50° S	50° S	50° S	45° S
		20° E	35° E	40° E	40° E	15° E
		33 m	48 m	37 m	19 m	35 m
India		5° N	10° N	20° N	15° N	5° N
		75° E	75° E	75° E	75° E	75° E
		−110 m	−84 m	−91 m	−108 m	−100 m
Japan		0°	0°	10° N	5° N	5° N
		145° E	145° E	150° E	155° E	150° E
		71 m	68 m	57 m	47 m	66 m
north Pacific		35° N	—	—	35° N	35° N
		185° E	—	—	185° E	185° E
		−36 m	(−13 m)[a]	(−5 m)[a]	−54 m	−42 m
east Pacific		20° N	30° N	30° N	30° N	15° N
		245° E	265° E	265° E	275° E	245° E
		−72 m	−45 m	−60 m	−81 m	−57 m
west Atlantic		15° N	—	—	—	20° N
		305° E	—	—	—	305° E
		−56 m	(−19 m)[a]	(−23 m)[a]	(−50 m)[a]	−46 m
South America		25° S	25° S	30° S	15° S	20° S
		295° E	285° E	280° E	285° E	295° E
		11 m	16 m	9 m	12 m	14 m
south Pacific		75° S	70° S	70° S	75° S	75° S
		180° E	195° E	185° E	180° E	185° E
		−77 m	−52 m	−52 m	−74 m	−68 m

[a] Geoid height at location given under NWL–5E solution.

Effect of satellite orbital inclination

The NWL-5E solution was based upon observations of satellites having four different orbital inclinations. Solutions were also obtained omitting data from each of the
four inclinations in turn. A summary of the geoid features for each of these solutions
is given in table 4. Omission of the data observed on the satellite with an orbital
inclination of 32° resulted in the largest disturbance of the solution. However, the
geoid heights generally agree to 15 m.

Effect of number of observations and number of stations

In order to test the influence of the number of observations and the number of
observing stations on the solution, solutions were made using data obtained during

TABLE 4   Effect of satellite inclination on solution for geoid

Location		NWL-5E solution	Solution omitting following orbital inclination:			
			32°	50°	67°	90°
England	latitude	55° N	60° N	60° N	55° N	50° N
	longitude	340° E	340° E	345° E	345° E	345° E
	height	61 m	73 m	89 m	63 m	54 m
South Africa		50° S	35° S	30° S	55° S	45° S
		20° E	15° E	15° E	50° E	50° E
		33 m	49 m	46 m	36 m	22 m
India		5° N	5° N	5° N	5° N	5° N
		75° E	70° E	75° E	75° E	75° E
		−110 m	−95 m	−90 m	−110 m	−125 m
Japan		0°	0°	10° N	0°	10° S
		145° E	145° E	145° E	145° E	160° E
		71 m	106 m	79 m	73 m	68 m
north Pacific		35° N	30° N	35° N	35° N	35° N
		185° E	180° E	185° E	185° E	200° E
		−36 m	−34 m	−39 m	−39 m	−63 m
east Pacific		20° N	20° N	20° N	20° N	20° N
		245° E	240° E	240° E	245° E	250° E
		−72 m	−56 m	−63 m	−73 m	−46 m
west Atlantic		15° N	10° N	15° N	20° N	20° N
		305° E	305° E	305° E	305° E	305° E
		−56 m	−38 m	−57 m	−54 m	−74 m
South America		25° S	25° S	25° S	30° S	10° S
		295° E	295° E	295° E	300° E	285° E
		11 m	32 m	36 m	11 m	3 m
south Pacific		75° S	75° S	75° S	75° S	70° S
		180° E	180° E	185° E	185° E	195° E
		−77 m	−67 m	−88 m	−85 m	−85 m

one week for each of three satellites. In the first of three solutions summarized in table 5, data from all observing stations were used to determine gravity coefficients to the seventh degree and sixth order. A second test, which limited the number of observing stations to eight, resulted in gross distortions of the computed geoid. However, adding three pairs of thirteenth- and fourteenth-order gravity coefficients as parameters of the solution resulted in a computed geoid close to that obtained with more extensive observations. The number of passes used in these last two solutions, which was only 1/40 of the number used in the NWL-5E solution, were distributed as shown in table 6.

TABLE 5   Effect of number of observations and stations on solution for geoid

Location		NWL-5E solution	Solutions based on three weeks of data		
			All stations without resonant parameters	8 stations without resonant parameters	8 stations with resonant parameters
England	latitude	55° N	40° N	30° N	50° N
	longitude	340° E	340° E	335° E	345° E
	height	61 m	77 m	273 m	65 m
South Africa		50° S	40° S	30° S	50° S
		20° E	15° E	345° E	15° E
		33 m	63 m	220 m	18 m
India		5° N	10° N	30° N	10° N
		75° E	75° E	90° E	75° E
		−110 m	−101 m	−37 m	−129 m
Japan		0°	0°	0°	30° N
		145° E	145° E	140° E	150° E
		71 m	81 m	237 m	46 m
north Pacific		35° N	30° N	—	45° N
		185° E	180° E	—	190° E
		−36 m	−16 m	—	−59 m
east Pacific		20° N	10° N	20° N	50° N
		245° E	245° E	230° E	280° E
		−72 m	−65 m	−26 m	−88 m
west Atlantic		15° N	5° N	0°	10° N
		305° E	315° E	310° E	300° E
		−56 m	−37 m	−21 m	−88 m
South America		25° S	40° S	30° S	30° S
		295° E	260° E	270° E	295° E
		11 m	33 m	174 m	−7 m
south Pacific		75° S	70° S	75° S	65° S
		180° E	190° E	165° E	175° E
		−77 m	−59 m	2 m	−91 m

Summary

While differences in various published solutions for the geoid based on satellite data were not tested under controlled conditions, the differences do not appear to be unreasonable in view of the effects of variations in the number of parameters on the solution (table 3) and of the effects of biases under conditions where the data density is limited (table 6). The latter tests show that the principal geoid features can be

TABLE 6   Number of satellite passes used in 3 arc solution

Station	1962 $\beta\mu1$	Satellite 1961 01	Polar	Total
Maryland	19	22	—	41
New Mexico	30	20	28	78
England	6	26	16	48
Brazil	8	—	26	34
Australia	22	—	11	33
South Africa	14	—	—	14
Samoa	15	—	25	40
Hawaii	29	—	—	29
Total	143	68	106	317

obtained on the basis of data obtained from a small number of stations during a short time period, provided that all significant parameters are considered in the solution. The sensitivity of the solution to the satellite inclinations considered (table 4) tends to indicate that the recent solutions based on the Doppler system, which yields the highest data density, provides geoid undulations to an accuracy of about 20 m. Considering that future solutions will include three times the number of gravity coefficients and three times the number of satellite inclinations[15], it seems reasonable to expect that an accuracy of 10 m will be obtained in the geoid features in the future.

References

1. R. J. Anderle, 'Computational methods employed in deriving geodetic results from doppler observations of artificial earth satellites', *Symp. on Trajectories of Artificial Celestial Bodies as Determined from Observations, Paris, 1965.*
2. I. G. Izsak, 'A new determination of tesseral harmonics by satellites', *Symp. on Trajectories of Artificial Celestial Bodies as Determined from Observations, Paris, 1965.*
3. W. M. Kaula, 'Improved geodetic results from camera observations of satellites', *J. Geophys. Res.*, **68**, 5183–90 (1963).
4. W. H. Guier and R. R. Newton, 'The Earth's gravity field as deduced from the Doppler tracking of five satellites', *J. Geophys. Res.*, **70**, 4613–26 (1965).
5. R. J. Anderle, 'Geodetic parameter set NWL–5E–6 based on Doppler satellite observations', *Intern. Symp. on Use of Artificial Satellites for Geodesy, 2nd, Athens, 1965,* to be published.
6. J. A. O'Keefe, A. Eckels, and R. K. Squires, 'The gravitational field of the Earth', *Astron. J.*, **64**, 245–53 (1959).
7. C. J. Cohen and R. J. Anderle, 'Verification of Earth's "pear shape" gravitational harmonic', *Science*, **132**, 807 (1960).
8. Y. Kozai, 'New determination of zonal harmonics coefficients of the Earth's gravitational potential', *Publ. Astron. Soc. Japan*, **16**, 263–84 (1964).
9. D. G. King-Hele and G. E. Cook, 'The even zonal harmonics of the Earth's gravitational potential', *Geophys. J.*, **10**, 17–29 (1965).
10. R. R. Allen, 'Even tesseral harmonics in the geopotential derived from *Syncom 2*', *Intern. Symp. on Use of Artificial Satellites for Geodesy, 2nd, Athens, 1965,* to be published.

11. G. Veiss, 'The deflection of the vertical of major geodetic datums and the semimajor axis of the Earth's ellipsoid as obtained from satellite observations', *Bull. Geodesique No.* 75, 13–45 (1965).
12. W. R. Wollenhaupt and others, '*Ranger VII* flight path and its determination from tracking data', *Jet Propulsion Lab. Tech. Rept. No.* 32-694 (1964).
13. W. M. Kaula, 'Comparison and combination of satellite with other results for geodetic parameters', *Intern. Symp. on Use of Artificial Satellites for Geodesy, 2nd, Athens, 1965,* to be published.
14. S. M. Yionoulis, 'A study of resonance effects due to the Earth's potential function', *J. Geophys. Res.,* **70**, 5991–6 (1965).
15. R. J. Anderle, 'Use of Doppler observations on satellites in geodesy', *Proc. Inst. Elec. Electron. Engrs. Intern. Space Electron. Symp., 1965.*
16. R. J. Anderle, 'Doppler observations on the *Anna 1B* satellite', *Trans. Am. Geophys. Union,* **46**, *No.* 2 (1965).

3

A. VOGEL

Geophysical Laboratory
University of Uppsala
Husbyborg, Uppsala, Sweden

Travel-time anomalies of elastic waves reflected at the core–mantle boundary

Abstract

The result of a World-wide investigation on elastic waves reflected at the Earth's core–mantle boundary shows certain deviations between theoretical and observed travel times depending on the position of focus and station. The possible sources of these regional travel-time anomalies are discussed and their relations to other geophysical phenomena are investigated. The publications of Vogel[1–4] were reviewed.

References

1. A. Vogel, 'Über Unregelmässigkeiten der äusseren Begrenzung des Erdkerns auf Grund von am Erdkern reflektierten Erdbebenwellen', *Beitr. Geophysik*, **69**, 150 (1960).
2. A. Vogel, 'Laufzeitanomalien von am äusseren Erdkern reflektierten Erdbebenwellen und deren Korrelation zum Schwerkraft- und Nicht-Dipol-Magnetfeld der Erde', *Z. Geophysik*, **26**, 273 (1960).
3. A. Vogel, 'Secular variations in the lower harmonics of the Earth's gravity field due to convection currents in the Earth's core', *Medd. Geodet. Inst. Uppsala Univ. No. 7* (1963).
4. A. Vogel, 'Theoretical aspects on secular changes in the Earth's gravity field', *Bur. Gravimetrique Intern., Bull. Inform. No. 12* (1966).

4

S. K. RUNCORN
and
B. M. GRAY*

Department of Geophysics and Planetary Physics
School of Physics
University of Newcastle upon Tyne
England

The figure of the Moon

As a result of the observations of the orbits of artificial satellites, it has recently become clear that the Earth's figure departs from that of hydrostatic equilibrium over thousands of kilometres. There also appears to be a discrepancy between the optical and dynamical ellipticities of Mars. The new rotation periods of Mercury and Venus can be explained if non-hydrostatic figures are postulated for these planets also. It is interesting to note, by contrast, that the non-hydrostatic figure of the Moon has been known for two centuries.

From the dynamical behaviour of the Moon, it is possible to determine the differences between its moments of inertia. It is usual to call C the moment of inertia about the polar axis, A the moment of inertia about the axis directed towards the Earth, and B the third axis in the plane of the sky. There are three important observational laws concerning the Moon's motion discovered by Cassini. The first is that the orbital period of the Moon is equal to its period of rotation. The second law is that the Moon's axis of rotation, or polar axis, is inclined at an invariable angle with the pole of the ecliptic, which is found to be $1° 32'$. The third law is that the axis of rotation, the pole of the ecliptic, and the pole of the Moon's orbit lie in a plane in the order stated. As the pole of the Moon's orbit precesses around the pole of the ecliptic once in 18·6 years, the axis of rotation of the Moon also precesses about a cone, the axis of which is the pole of the ecliptic. For the Moon's axis of rotation to move in space, there must be a torque on it and this can only arise if the Moon departs from a uniform sphere. This is most simply thought of by supposing the existence of bulges towards and away from the Earth. In fact the existence of bulges along the Earth–Moon line was also postulated to explain the fact that the Moon always presents the same face to the Earth, that is, to explain Cassini's first law.

The Earth considered as a point mass is attracting these two bulges but with different force and so the Moon's axis will precess in the way indicated in figure 1. As the second harmonic of the gravitational field of any body is really a measure of the difference between its moments of intertia, the Cassini laws give the fractional difference between the moments of intertia C and A. It is found that the value of this is about 0·00063.

* Now at Computing Centre, University of East Anglia, Norwich, England.

Now the theoretical shape of the Moon, if it were in hydrostatic equilibrium, would be very close to a sphere, to within about 20 to 60 m. For all practical purposes the theoretical shape of the Moon should be a sphere. The observed value of $(C - A)/C$ has usually been interpreted, assuming the Moon is uniform and distorted. Then it would be an ellipsoid with a bulge of 1 km towards the Earth. This means that the Moon is very far out of hydrostatic equilibrium.

It is possible by a rather more complicated dynamical argument to obtain $(C - B)/(C - A)$ and, as this equals about 0·64, the Moon is a triaxial ellipsoid.

When the determination of the surface shape of the Moon is attempted, great observational difficulties are found. The method used is to measure plates of the Moon taken at two different librations. Owing to the inclination of the Moon's orbit and its equator the north and south polar regions are seen preferentially at half-month intervals: all points on the Moon's surface appear to move in latitude, an effect

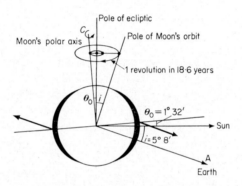

FIGURE 1   Diagrammatic representation of the Moon's motion

known as the libration in latitude. There is also a libration in longitude, in which the east and west limbs are seen preferentially at half-month intervals: thus, all points appear to move in longitude. This libration occurs because of the eccentricity of the Moon's orbit, for the uniform rotation of the Moon about its polar axis and its non-uniform rotation about the Earth cannot be exactly in step except on the average over a month. Thus points on the Moon's surface appear to move owing to these two geometrical librations, and therefore it is possible to determine the distance of a point on the lunar surface from the centre of mass of the Moon. The observations of the radii of the surface were always held to indicate that the radius of the Moon in the centre of the disk was greater than at the limb. It was therefore thought that there was a bulge towards the Earth of roughly the order expected on the hypothesis of a uniform and strained Moon, although the estimates varied very considerably. Baldwin[1] made an important advance in this discussion by plotting the distances between points on the Moon's surface and its centre of mass against distance from the centre of the disk of the Moon separately for points on the maria and on the uplands.

By separating the points on the uplands from the points on the maria, Baldwin obtained two separate sets of data for analysis. Recognizing that both sets of observations were very scattered, he fitted a parabolic arc to each by the least-squares method.

The points are considerably scattered for the following reasons:

(i) The roughness of the Moon's surface.

(ii) The Rayleigh limit for telescopes used in this study imposes a fundamental uncertainty of about $\frac{1}{2}$ km in the measured height of any point.

(iii) Owing to the variation of lighting, images do not remain fixed and the accuracy of determining the position of any point is impaired.

He showed that the ellipticities of the surface of the Moon determined from the points on the uplands and points on the maria were rather close. On the assumption that the total error in each point due to the various causes is about 1 km, then with 100 points it is possible to determine the height of the bulge to an accuracy of about $\frac{1}{10}$ km. Baldwin's method of analysis has shown that the Moon has a bulge which is about 2 km high, twice the dynamically determined one.

This work of Baldwin has come under criticism. Kopal[2] believes that the scatter of these points precludes a decision concerning the presence or absence of the bulge indicated by the dynamical method. Goudas has made spherical harmonic analyses of the points on the Moon's surface arguing that the surface of the Moon cannot be very well represented by a simple ellipsoid. By fitting the heights on the Moon's surface, determined from the geometrical librations, to a series of spherical harmonics, it is found that the second harmonic is on the whole less important than the fourth harmonic.

Now obviously the method of spherical harmonic analysis is a legitimate method of describing any observations given over a spherical surface, in this case the departures from a sphere. The question whether the surface of the Moon determined in this way is really the surface one ought to be considering when making a comparison with the dynamical method of determining the non-equilibrium state of the Moon must, however, be asked. The Earth's solid surface, for example, deviates by a few kilometres from the shape of a hydrostatic rotating Earth—an order of magnitude more than the actual deviations of the geoid from the theoretical figure. This is, of course, due to variations of chemical composition of the Earth's crust, particularly the difference between the continental blocks and the ocean floor.

It is therefore desirable to reinvestigate the question of the Moon's bulge by an analysis of the ACIC (Aeronautical Chart and Information Center of the U.S. Air Force) heights on the lunar surface[3]. If the readings are represented by a histogram, a broad spread of about 4 or 5 km in the heights is obtained. If Baldwin's procedure of dividing the points between those from the uplands and those from the maria is followed, then there is a very definite difference between the histograms for the uplands and the maria (see figure 2). The significance of this is best illustrated by reference to the Earth. A similar analysis of the heights of the Earth could conveniently be displayed by two histograms, one for the ocean floors and one for continents, the peaks of which are displaced by 5 km. Now let us suppose that one is trying to use this method to determine whether or not the Earth has an equatorial bulge, and suppose for a moment the equatorial bulge due to its rotation is 2 km rather than 20 km; then a spherical harmonic analysis of the heights would show that the second harmonic due to the equatorial bulge is lost among the harmonics essentially describing the distribution of continents and oceans. It therefore seems that, if one is to analyse the shape of the surface of the Moon with the aim of examining the existence of a bulge suggested by the value of $(C - A)/C$, one ought to follow Baldwin's procedure of separating the points on the maria and the points on the uplands. The assumption which lies behind this procedure of course is that the uplands and the maria are at different heights, possibly because of some kind of isostatic equilibrium or because separate physical processes are responsible for their formation.

The data listed by Meyer and Ruffin[3] at the ACIC are given as both the Cartesian and the spherical coordinates of 196 control features on the Moon, referred to seleno-centric axes with the y axis defined as the zero libration axis. The data were obtained from separate plates (groups I and II). They were divided into two sets, all points in the dark areas being assigned to the maria, and all points in the bright areas being assigned to the uplands (see figures 3(*a*) and 3(*b*)). Histograms of these two sets showed reasonable goodness of fit to normal error curves and gave a mean difference between the peaks of 0.85 ± 0.25 km. The means of the maria and uplands points are 1737·61 km and 1738·45 km respectively, and the standard deviations 1·20 km and 1·29 km respectively. The standard deviation of the difference is 0·12 km, much less than the actual difference in heights.

Triaxial ellipsoids were fitted to the Cartesian coordinates of each set of data by

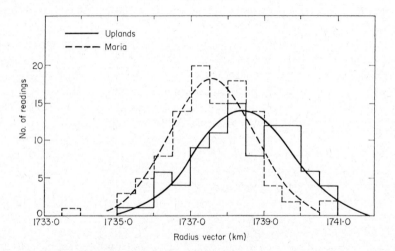

FIGURE 2   Histogram of heights on lunar surfaces—points on uplands and on maria shown separately

the method of least squares. An approximate formula for the distance between any point i and the ellipsoid was used for the error (see Gray[4]):

$$e_i = \frac{x_i^2/a^2 + y_i^2/b^2 + z_i^2/c^2 - 1}{(x_i^2/a^4 + y_i^2/b^4 + z_i^2/c^4)^{1/2}}$$

The standard deviation σ_e of the errors was found:

$$\sigma_e = \frac{\{\sum(e_i - \bar{e})^2\}^{1/2}}{n}$$

If any point was found to have an error $e_i > 3\sigma_e$, the point was discarded and the ellipsoid refitted. In practice not more than three points were discarded from any one set. The error in the final fit was taken as

$$E = \frac{(\sum e_i^2)^{1/2}}{2n}$$

To test the assumption that the ellipsoid was displaced from the Earth-aligned axis, the calculations were repeated every ten degrees through a quarter revolution of the equatorial axis about the polar axis. The best fit was chosen to be that containing the greatest number of data points with the smallest error in the final fit (see figure 4). It is satisfactory that for both the maria and the uplands points E is least when the axis is within 10° of the Earth-directed one.

Maria

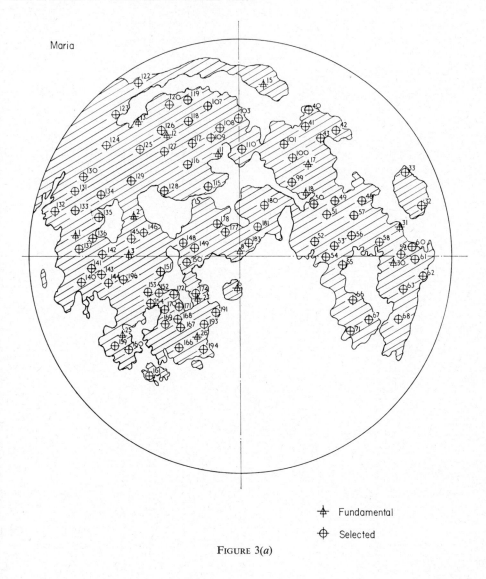

+ Fundamental

⊕ Selected

FIGURE 3(*a*)

TABLE 1   Results of calculations

	Uplands		Maria		Differences	
	Baldwin	Runcorn and Gray	Baldwin	Runcorn and Gray	Baldwin	Runcorn and Gray
ζ	1·000815	1·001239	0·998846	1·000871		
ξ	0·999767	0·999524	0·998176	0·998804		
η	0·999418	0·999236	0·998826	0·998321		
c	1741·82 km	1739·63 km	1738·40 km	1738·99 km	3·42 km	0·64 km
a	1740·00 km	1736·65 km	1737·23 km	1735·40 km	2·77 km	1·25 km
b	1739·40 km	1736·15 km	1738·36 km	1734·56 km	1·04 km	1·59 km
e		0·12 km		0·075 km		
					Mean	Mean
					2·41 ± 1·37 km	1·16 ± 0·43 km
$c - a$	1·82 km	2·98 km	1·17 km	3·59 km		
$c - \frac{1}{2}(a + b)$	2·13 km	3·23 km	0·6 km	4·01 km		

ζ, ξ, η are selenocentric coordinates such that $\zeta^2 + \xi^2 + \eta^2 = 3$. ζ is the polar or zero libration coordinate corresponding to semiaxis a. η is the Earth-directed coordinate corresponding to semiaxis c. ξ is the equatorial coordinate corresponding to semiaxis b. e is the standard deviation of the mean of the two sets of data.

Baldwin's values of $\zeta, \xi,$ and η were originally expressed with respect to an equivalent sphere of radius 1·000 535. We have reduced them to correspond with a sphere of unit radius for comparison with our semiaxes.

The results are displayed in table 1. For the uplands, where a is the equatorial semi-axis, b the polar or zero libration semiaxis, and c the Earth-aligned semiaxis, we find the mean radius of the Moon in the plane of the sky to be 1736·40 km and the bulge of the Moon towards the Earth to be 3·23 ± 0·24 km, lying along the Earth-aligned axis. Baldwin[5] found a value of 2·13 km.

For the maria, the mean radius is 1734·98 km and the bulge is 4·01 ± 0·15 km. The best fit from which these figures are taken seem to indicate that the bulge lies some five degrees east of the Earth-aligned axis. Baldwin's value for the maria bulge is 0·6 km. Following Baldwin's note that very few data points are available in the polar regions for the maria, we can discard the values for the b axis and define the bulge using only the c and a axes. These give a value of 1·16 km for Baldwin's work and a value 3·50 ± 0·15 km for these calculations. We may take a mean value for the bulge of 3·37 ± 0·39 km.

The two ellipsoids fitted to the uplands and the maria were of common selenocentric origin. By differencing the values of a, b, and c, we find a mean distance between the ellipsoids of 1·15 ± 0·43 km in reasonable agreement with the value 0·85 ± 0·25 km obtained from the histograms of the radii. If we derive an analytic expression for the mean distance between the ellipsoids $\overline{r_1 - r}$, where r_1 and r are the radial coordinates of the two ellipsoids, we have

$$\overline{r_1 - r} = a_1(1 - 0.75d_1 - 0.5e_1) - a(1 - 0.75d - 0.5e)$$

where $d = 1 - c/a$, $e = 1 - b/a$. Then $\overline{r_1 - r} = 0.97 \pm 0.59$ km. It should be noted that

$$\overline{r_1 - r} = \int_0^{\pi/2} \int_0^{\pi/2} (r_1 - r)\, d\theta\, d\phi \Big/ \int_0^{\pi/2} \int_0^{\pi/2} d\theta\, d\phi$$

where

$$r^2 \sin^2 \theta \sin^2 \phi + \frac{r^2 \cos^2 \theta \sin^2 \phi}{(1 - e)^2} + \frac{r^2 \cos^2 \phi}{(1 - d)^2} = a^2$$

If, for the moment, the height of the bulge obtained from Baldwin's procedure on his own measures or on the ACIC points is regarded as the real ellipticity of the boundary of the Moon's interior, then certain important consequences follow. A model of uniform density having $(C - A)/C = 0.0006$ and $(C - B)/(C - A) = 0.6$ would have the a axis pointing towards the Earth 1·1 km longer than the average radius in the plane of the sky. The polar radius would also be shorter than the equatorial radius by 0·7 km. The above results give values of these quantities between two and three times greater. The ACIC results seem much more consistent than those derived from the plates Baldwin used. That the former data are likely to be the best to use has been established by Goudas[6,7].

The spherical harmonic analysis of the heights completed by Goudas[8] shows that the fourth harmonic exceeds the second by about 30%. The second harmonic gives a bulge of just over 1·5 km, that is the excess of the a axis over the average in the plane of the sky. However, it has been shown above that this figure is not necessarily the value of the bulge either of the mean surface through the uplands or through the maria. Thus this figure does not in any way contradict the higher values for the bulge above. It would of course be interesting to test whether higher harmonics, such as the fourth, are appreciable in the spherical harmonic expansion of these two surfaces analysed separately. It seems doubtful if the data are sufficient yet to be able to do this meaningfully.

Uplands

$-\!\!\!\!\!\!\!\!+\!\!-$ Fundamental

$\oplus$ Selected

FIGURE 3(*b*)

Runcorn[9] concludes that the analysis discussed above argues in favour of the existence within the Moon of a convection pattern of second degree. The mean ellipsoidal surfaces determined for the uplands and maria separately are of clear physical significance, because roughly the same ellipticities are obtained. One may conclude by analogy with the Earth that the maria and uplands have a systematically different density which accounts for the difference in height between the two. If some type of isostatic balance is present within the Moon, then the ellipticity of the surfaces obtained above is also the ellipticity of the surface below the rigid lunar crust, below which long-term flow by diffusive or other types of creep is possible. It is then necessary to explain the reason for the ellipticity of this surface which is greater, by more than an order of magnitude, than that corresponding to hydrostatic equilibrium. Runcorn shows that this can arise through hydrodynamic motions within the Moon, most plausibly the result of thermal instability.

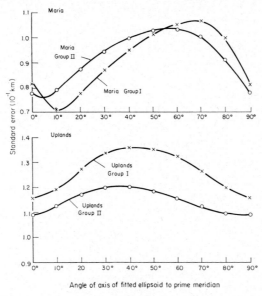

FIGURE 4

References

1. R. B. Baldwin, *The Face of the Moon*, University of Chicago Press, Chicago, 1958.
2. Z. Kopal, *Proc. Roy. Soc.* (*London*), *Ser. A*, **296**, 254–65 (1967).
3. D. L. Meyer and B. W. Ruffin, *Icarus*, **4**, 513–27 (1965).
4. P. Gray, unpublished.
5. R. B. Baldwin, *The Measure of the Moon*, University of Chicago Press, Chicago, 1963.
6. C. L. Goudas, 'Note on the gravitational field of the Moon', *Icarus*, **3**, 273–6 (1964).
7. C. L. Goudas, 'Moments of inertia and gravity field of the Moon', *Icarus*, **3**, 375–409 (1964).
8. C. L. Goudas, 'The selenodetic control system of the Aeronautical Chart and Information Center of the U.S. Air Force', *Icarus*, **4**, 527–43 (1965).
9. S. K. Runcorn, *Proc. Roy. Soc.* (*London*), *Ser. A*, **296**, 270–84 (1967).

5

J. HOPMANN

University Observatory
Wien, Austria

The accuracy of the information on absolute heights on the Moon, and the problem of its figure*

Observational Material

All the contemporary valid lunar coordinates are still ultimately based on the measurements of the Mösting A crater and 8 points close to its edge, which were carried out about 70 years ago in Königsberg by Franz using the Fraunhofer heliometer (built in 1835)[2], and on the almost simultaneous observations of Hayn on four further craters using a 10-in. refractor and position micrometer in Leipzig[3,4]. The lack of details and calculations prompted Schrutka of Vienna (at the suggestion of the author) to reexamine this question[5,6], and as a result he obtained the rectangular coordinates ξ, η, ζ and the polar coordinates λ, β, h for Mösting A as a first-order trigonometrical position, and for eleven other second-order positions.

In 1900 Franz, using the full Moon photographs from Lick Observatory with various and strong librations (by way of a sort of provisional solution), connected about 60 craters with his 9 craters, and calculated their heights with respect to a defined sphere through the Moon's limb, using the stereo effect produced by the libration[7]. His contour map already showed, as later measurements have more or less confirmed, that there were lowlands in the northeast quadrant (Mare Imbrium) opposite bright 'continents' in the southwest (astronomical and not astronautical designations will be used throughout this chapter).

Later in Breslau, Franz extended the measurements on the same five Lick photographs to 150 objects and accordingly measured third-order points, but he only related the coordinates calculated from these measurements to a sphere[8]. Further developments led Franz, Saunders, and others to derive the ξ, η or λ, β coordinates for more than 2000 precisely measured points. However, this does not belong to the main topic of this chapter.

Since Franz[8] had given the rough values in detail, Schrutka was in a position in 1958 to recalculate them completely[9] in connection with his own paper[5,6]. A catalogue was thus made of 150 coordinates, in particular of the absolute heights. These

* The author did not receive the important work of the Aeronautical Chart and Information Center of the U.S. Air Force (ACIC)[1] in time to deal with it fully during the report and subsequent discussion at Newcastle. However, since returning to Vienna, the author has taken up the matter and considered several other propositions. This chapter therefore gives more extensive results than those given at Newcastle.

form the basis of four other similar catalogues which are available, to the author's knowledge, at present.

In 1963 Baldwin, using Schrutka's results, published a catalogue of the absolute heights of 696 objects based on the measurements of copies of five newer Lick photographs in his book *The Measure of the Moon*[10]. In a similar way the U.S. Army Map Service in 1964 published a catalogue of the coordinates of 256 points[11].

Schrutka was able to conclude his measurements on twelve copies of Lick photographs with 140 points in 1966. The plates were measured by Haidrich and 23 points from Schrutka's 1958 results[9] were used in addition as references. Four of the photographs were taken at full Moon and eight in pairs at equal phase but with widely different librations[12].

Another catalogue, the work of Meyer and Ruffin[1] from the Aeronautical Chart and Information Center of the U.S. Air Force (ACIC), concerns ten photographs which were taken in the Pic du Midi. 31 objects from Schrutka's 1958 results[9] were also included and the catalogue deals with a total of 196 objects. (A comparison of this catalogue with the four others was somewhat difficult at first, since the objects were not designated by their International Astronomical Union (I.A.U.) number[13] or ξ, η, but by λ and β. As can be seen from their picture 3 the order is also somewhat different.)

Comparison of the Five Catalogues

It has been indicated by Hopmann[14] and several other authors that, even with the focal length of the Lick refractor, the determination of absolute heights by the libration effect is just within the limits of measurement. Even with a strong libration, a difference of height of $\pm 1 \cdot 0$ km at the middle of the lunar disk only corresponds to $\pm 0 \cdot 050''$ of arc. This, however, is the lower limit of practically useful star parallaxes, based on an average measurement of twenty photographs per star. In recent times fifty to a hundred plates have been desirable. Photographs of stars, on the other hand, are much better defined than many of the objects on the Moon, where mean errors of 1 to 2 km may be expected.

The quoted mean errors for individual craters in the various publications are meaningless, although their average values are of significance. For example, in the paper by Meyer and Ruffin[1], the quoted mean errors in height $\pm 0 \cdot 003$ and $\pm 1 \cdot 12$ km of numbers 18 and 20, respectively, only show that a few plates have more or less fortuitously agreed at some instant. There is, in fact, no reason to suppose that any given height is more accurate than any other.

It is shown below that an individual set of observations has an accuracy of $\pm 1 \cdot 5$ km. Certain of the quoted height values (and their mean errors) in metres have been derived by computer to several decimal places, which of course are largely meaningless. The same also holds for coordinate data which are quoted as $\pm 0 \cdot 001° = \pm 30$ m.

The mean errors calculated in the normal way from a comparison between plates, etc., only gives the internal accuracy of the individual set. The true external accuracy is only found by comparing several independent parameters. Examples of these are atomic weights, the speed of light, the wavelengths of spectral lines, the star parallaxes, radial velocities, etc. The quantities in the five catalogues are then accurate in this sense, and the absolutely necessary comparison is carried out in the following way.

The first three columns of table 1 repeat the above data, and the other quantities will be explained below. For each crater, the I.A.U. number, the name, the approximate ξ and η, and the values of height according to the five sources were recorded on a

TABLE 1 Various quantities for the five catalogues

	(1)	(2)	(3)	(4)	(5)
I	5	150	$\pm 1{\cdot}17$	$0{\cdot}0$	$\pm 1{\cdot}78$
II	12	140	$\pm 1{\cdot}78$	$+1{\cdot}3$	$\pm 1{\cdot}98$
AM	15	256	$\pm 2{\cdot}02$	$-2{\cdot}0$	$\pm 2{\cdot}16$
B	5	696	$\pm 1{\cdot}79$	$+0{\cdot}4$	$\pm 1{\cdot}88$
ACIC	10	196	$\pm 1{\cdot}13$	$+0{\cdot}1$	$\pm 1{\cdot}20$

I, Schrutka's 1958 results[9]; II, Schrutka's 1966 results[12]; AM, the results of the U.S. Army Map Service[11]; B, Baldwin's results[10]; ACIC, Meyer and Ruffin's results[1].
Column (1), No. of plates; column (2), No. of objects; column (3), mean error (km); column (4), reduction (km); column (5), scatter (km).

card index. Many objects, especially in Baldwin's book[10], have only one value of height, others two or three, and a fairly small number four or five.

A comparison table was then drawn up of the ten possible pair combinations, in order to calculate the scatter and the linear correlation coefficients, etc., at $1{\cdot}0$ km intervals (table 2, column (1)). Earlier investigations[14] had shown that smaller intervals were meaningless because of the strong scatter. Column (2) gives the number n of objects common to the two sets of measurements, which is surprisingly small in some cases. Apart from the objects in Schrutka's 1958 results[9], each author has made his own choice. In fact at the Bagnères conference[15] Weimer listed 140 objects as future third-order fixed points, in which the larger craters of Schrutka's results were replaced by smaller more well-defined craters. It is only in Schrutka's later results[12], however, that these have been utilized. The catalogue by Meyer and Ruffin[1] in particular contains many very small objects which have not been measured elsewhere.

In constructing the distribution tables, two factors are immediately evident: the strong scatter and the occurrence of zero-point differences. It is surprising to learn that

TABLE 2 Comparison of the ten possible pair combinations

(1)	(2)	(3)	(4)	(5)
II, I	60	$+0{\cdot}15 \pm 0{\cdot}13$	$\pm 2{\cdot}27$	$-1{\cdot}36$
AM, I	58	$+0{\cdot}31 \pm 0{\cdot}12$	$\pm 2{\cdot}09$	$+1{\cdot}98$
AM, II	64	$+0{\cdot}05 \pm 0{\cdot}12$	$\pm 2{\cdot}91$	$+3{\cdot}98$
B, I	60	$+0{\cdot}00 \pm 0{\cdot}13$	$\pm 2{\cdot}27$	$-0{\cdot}36$
B, II	73	$+0{\cdot}31 \pm 0{\cdot}11$	$\pm 2{\cdot}13$	$+0{\cdot}68$
B, AM	106	$+0{\cdot}09 \pm 0{\cdot}10$	$\pm 2{\cdot}75$	$-2{\cdot}00$
ACIC, I	39	$+0{\cdot}76 \pm 0{\cdot}07$	$\pm 1{\cdot}12$	$-0{\cdot}21$
ACIC, II	29	$+0{\cdot}20 \pm 0{\cdot}11$	$\pm 1{\cdot}79$	$+0{\cdot}82$
ACIC, AM	31	$+0{\cdot}28 \pm 0{\cdot}16$	$\pm 1{\cdot}83$	$-1{\cdot}58$
ACIC, B	80	$+0{\cdot}48 \pm 0{\cdot}06$	$\pm 2{\cdot}05$	$+0{\cdot}25$

Column (1), pair combination; column (2), number n of objects common to the two sets of measurements; column (3), linear correlation coefficients r and their mean error; column (4), mean difference (km); column (5), difference in heights.

discrepancies of 4 and 5 km in the heights of the same craters were quite common, and that some even went as far as 9 km without any indication as to which value was 'false'. Table 3 gives, as an example, the frequency distribution of Schrutka's results[9,12]

TABLE 3   The frequency distribution
of Schrutka's results

Difference	Number
0·0 to 0·9 km	8
1·0 to 1·9 km	23
2·0 to 2·9 km	15
3·0 to 3·9 km	6
4·0 to 4·9 km	4
5·0 to 5·9 km	2
6·0 to 6·9 km	1
7·0 to 7·9 km	1
Total	60

(after making a systematic zero-point correction of 1 km). According to this, the mean difference amounts to $\pm 2 \cdot 27$ km. In a similar way the values for the nine other comparisons were calculated (table 2, column (4)).

It is now possible to deduce from these values the true accuracies of the five sets. By way of illustration let us suppose that we have three arbitrary sets A, B, and C with true mean errors $x = 3$, $y = 4$, and $z = 4$ units. The squares of the mean differences $A - B$, $A - C$, and $B - C$ are then given by

$$\overline{(A - B)}^2 = x^2 + y^2 = 9 + 16 = 25 \quad \text{i.e.} \quad \pm\overline{(A - B)} = \pm 5 \cdot 0$$

$$\overline{(A - C)}^2 = x^2 + z^2 = 9 + 25 = 34 \quad \text{i.e.} \quad \pm\overline{(A - C)} = \pm 5 \cdot 8$$

$$\overline{(B - C)}^2 = y^2 + z^2 = 16 + 25 = 41 \quad \text{i.e.} \quad \pm\overline{(B - C)} = \pm 6 \cdot 4$$

The reverse is also true and one can obtain x, y, and z from a 'comparison in a triangle'.

In our case we are considering ten comparisons from the five sets, i.e. the true accuracies must be derived from the ten mean differences by the method of least squares. The values of the column (4) in table 1 were derived in this way, and they themselves are each subject to an uncertainty of $\pm 0 \cdot 25$ km.

Obviously Schrutka's results[9] and Meyer and Ruffin's results[1] are far more accurate than the other three. On the average the mean errors amount to $\pm 1 \cdot 15$ and $1 \cdot 86$ km which corresponds to a weight proportion of 2·6 to 1—by taking into consideration the proposed later summary of all five works (see below).

It is not really possible to establish where these differences in accuracy arise. It is worth noting, however, that copies were always used by Schrutka[12], Baldwin[10], and the U.S. Army Map Service[11]. With the Lick refractor $\pm 1 \cdot 0$ km corresponds to $\pm 4 \cdot 4$ μm, and nearer the edge to an even smaller value. It is probably sufficient to suppose that additional photographic inaccuracies on the copy slides of a few micrometres could explain the larger uncertainty in the height values derived from them.

From the distribution tables one can obtain four values of the scatter of the heights themselves (around their actual mean) for each of the four sets. The mean of this scatter is shown in column (5) of table 1. The scatter in heights is much smaller in the most accurate set[1] than in the four others. One might conclude from this that *all* the measured heights are simply an expression of the uncertainty in measurement and that the Moon is actually a sphere. This would be the case if the positive and negative heights were completely randomly distributed over the face of the Moon. All previous observations, however, have shown that there are more or less pronounced features including only high- or low-lying regions.

This is confirmed from the linear correlation coefficients r and their mean errors (table 2, column (3)) derived from the distribution tables. They are all positive, i.e. in each of the five sets all the heights (depths) have been recognized as such and, except in one case, all the r are very small so that the mean errors are almost as large as the average r. It is only in the comparison (ACIC, I) that the heights are not excessively different but more closely correlated than usual. Column (4) of table 1 shows that these are the two best series.

As explained above, column (5) of table 1 gives the amounts by which it is necessary to reduce all the sets to obtain the fundamental system due to Schrutka[9]. In view of the conditions of meridian circles, stellar parallaxes, proper motions, etc., it is hardly surprising that such differences should arise. The large value in the results of the U.S. Army Map Service is essentially due to the fact that at the definition level only the one point Mösting A, or its height (given by Schrutka[9]), was taken. The large deviation of Schrutka's later results[12] probably has two causes: eight of the twelve plates were taken at more or less strong phase, so that errors could possibly arise in measuring through the shadows, and, moreover, there are fewer reference points originating from his earlier results[9] on the phase plates. Also, systematic errors may arise in measuring the copy slides.

Suggestions for Further Work

The above critical remarks lead one to conclude that the geometrical shape of the Moon, and in particular the supposedly rigid tidal bulge, should be explained by using the information from more than one of the above five catalogues. If this is not done the result is just as uncertain as the various contour maps published by Franz[7], Schrutka and Hopmann[16], Baldwin[10], and the U.S. Army Map Service[11]. The same also holds for the mathematical interpolation of the heights calculated in the individual catalogues by three-dimensional trigonometric series[17].

Actually one should repeat, using modern photographic techniques, the heliometric measurements of Franz[2] carried out over 70 years ago. The same 200-point network (e.g. those of the ACIC or other institutes), with plates from various refractors (Lick, Pic du Midi, Yerkes, etc.), should then be *uniformly* revised into a general catalogue. This network would then provide—with the same or other plates— the reference points for selenographic details.

We have an exact parallel in the history of astronomy. By repeating the *Zonenunternehmen der Internationalen Astronomischen Gesellschaft* (the precisely determined positions of over 100 000 stars) made by the Astronomische Rechen-Institut in Berlin, Dahlem was able to produce in 1925 the so-called third fundamental catalogue of 1500 stars—this used the results of numerous observatories which had carried out absolute meridian circle observations for one century. The positions of about 17 000 reference stars for photographic work were then observed with seven different meridian circles from 1928 to 1932. It was felt that each star should be observed at least six times and that if possible at three different observatories. Moreover, in Babelsberg, Bergedorf, and Bonn, 1200 of these 17 000 stars distributed in the northern hemisphere of the sky were measured, every attempt being made to minimize unavoidable systematic sources of error. This produced empirically more precise results than if the individual stars had been fixed six times with the same meridian circle. The Astronomische Rechen-Institut later combined the results of the seven observatories into a general catalogue.

As suggested above, the same reasoning should also apply to selenographic data. Since more than 10 years would certainly be needed to carry this out—because of the long libration periods—it would be good enough to combine the material which is at present to hand from our five sets.

The most correct procedure would be to relate the measured values of ξ, η for the individual works (and not the derived values from λ, ϕ in Schrutka's earlier results) by computing the A, B, C, D in the equation

$$\xi_{II} - \xi_I = A\xi_I + B\eta_I + C\xi_I + D$$

for the common craters by the least-squares method. (The subscripts I and II refer to Schrutka's 1958 and 1966 results, respectively.) Then the same procedure should be applied to the other craters in Schrutka's 1966 results. The same relation holds for $\eta_{II} - \eta_I$, $\xi_{II} - \xi_I$, and for the three remaining comparisons of the other works.

A general catalogue of ξ, η, ζ and subsequently λ, β, h obtained in this way should provide a very useful basis for studying the shape of the Moon.

The author hopes to be able to produce in the near future—in a much simplified form—a preliminary general catalogue of absolute heights on the Moon. This will be based on the above results for about 400 objects and will certainly be more precise than the five individual catalogues.

The Problem of the Shape of the Moon

The idea of a rigid tidal bulge on the Moon goes back to Laplace (1800), who explained the equal periods of rotation and revolution of our satellite in terms of the difference in the three principal moments of inertia of the Moon, or the difference in the three axes of a homogeneous ellipsoid extended towards the Earth. In a long since superseded work, Hansen proposed in 1860 that this bulge could be 60 km high. The 19th- and 20th-century observations were used by Schrutka[5] to show that the ratio of the three moments A, B, and C, was $1:1\cdot000\,235\,3:1\cdot000\,627\,3$, or for an internally homogeneous Moon that the differences in the principal axes of rotation were $A - C = 1\cdot09$ km, $B - C = 0\cdot41$ km. This then would be the dynamic figure of the Moon.

On the other hand, it would be possible to derive the geometrical form to a first approximation from an absolute height catalogue by computation of the constants of a triaxial ellipsoid with the equation

$$A\xi^2 + B\eta^2 + C\zeta^2 + D\xi\eta + E\zeta\xi + F\eta\zeta + G\xi + H\eta + I\zeta - 1 = 0$$

using the least-squares method. In this formula A, B, C are the lengths of the semiaxes, D, E, F their direction cosines, and G, H, I the coordinates of the centre, which should not coincide with that of a sphere drawn through the limb of the Moon. The origin of the rectangular coordinate system is ξ, η; ζ is the centre of this sphere; the ζ axis points towards the Earth, the η axis towards the north, and the ξ axis towards the west.

In 1953 the author[18] used the rough values from Franz's[8] measurements on 150 craters to derive an approximation formula for absolute heights. This gave an ellipsoid with a major axis 6·8 km longer than the average value, directed towards a point in the southwest quadrant. The constants G, H, I were not derived in this case.

Schrutka[16] then recalculated Franz's data and deduced all nine constants. They gave $C - 1 = -3\cdot8 \pm 2\cdot5$ km and $I = 5\cdot1 \pm 2\cdot0$ km which, as the mean errors show, are unreliable, and they effectively cancel one another out. A second computation without G, H, I was then carried out, from which the values of the coefficients A to F all lay within their mean errors. This shows that the Moon can be taken as a sphere to an accuracy of $\pm0\cdot5$ km and a tidal bulge would not be detectable.

However, the most significant result of these calculations is that they do not include a 2–3 km high 'swell' near the centre of the Moon, which according to the contours has sharp boundaries (see below). Schrutka also considered this[9] and, bearing in mind Hayn's edge profile[3,4], obtained $a = 1738\cdot9 \pm 0\cdot4$ km, $b = 1738\cdot6 \pm 0\cdot4$ km, and $c = 1737\cdot6 \pm 0\cdot5$ km which within the limits of mean error again constitutes a sphere.

One can, of course, calculate a similar ellipsoid for each of the five sets as, for example, was done by Runcorn and Gray (see section IV, chapter 4 of this book) using the ACIC data for both uplands and maria. The same ACIC material was used by Potter[19] (Leningrad) to derive an ellipsoid with axes $a = 1739\cdot23$, $b = 1735\cdot44$, and $c = 1736\cdot04$ km. If the proposed preliminary general catalogue were to hand, this could also be done. By this method are not the many irregularities of the Moon unnecessarily levelled, and the nature of them unnecessarily stressed?

We cannot go into the details of the somewhat different approach of Goudas[17] at this stage, but basically he represents the measured heights by higher-order spherical harmonics, taking into consideration the edge profile maps of Watts[20]. Amongst others he has stated 'if it is assumed that the Moon is a homogeneous body, then the elliptical component of its limb at zero libration must be $r = r_0 + 0\cdot18''\cos 2\beta$. This result is in complete contradiction with all expressions for the limb obtained from observations so far. The obvious conclusion is that the Moon is not homogeneous, at least in its marginal zone, although it is very unlikely that is not true for the entire lunar body'. Massevich[21] also reported that there had been very little perturbation in the orbit of *Luna 10* near the Moon, which also indicates a fair degree of homogeneity.

The approach of Goudas lies somewhere between the rigid binding to an ellipsoid idea and the author's proposal that the Moon is a sphere with 'swells' and 'basins' here and there. The above data indicate that, apart from the swell near the centre of the lunar disk, there are apparently similar swells near Eudoxus, the Taurus Range, between Mare Crisium and Mare Serenitatis, south of Fracastor, and near Tycho. Other basins are the Mare Crisium, Imbrium, Humorum, and Nubium. Not all the maria are deep lying, so that the Mare Tranquillitatis is at the level of the mean sphere, whereas the Mare Vaporum is even higher and belongs to the swell around the Sinus

Medii. This had already been indicated earlier[18], on the basis of Hayn's profile map[3,4]. Swells and basins are also clearly visible in Watt's map, especially in the figure on p. 949 of his work.

After preparing the preliminary general catalogue a contour map should be drawn, in which, for example, the shape of the abrupt break-off at the maria should be taken into account.

It should be pointed out, in addition, that only about 50% of the nearer side of the Moon is covered by the 150 points of Schrutka's earlier results[9]. The ACIC catalogue covers a larger region. In calculating this the points were recorded on a map with a Lambert's projection. The central swell only covers 2·6% of the nearer side.

As regards the edge profile, a large portion of the marginal zone is still *terra incognita* as far as absolute heights are concerned. Perhaps this gap in our knowledge could be filled—since the stereo effect is absent here—by using the 'point light boundary' technique proposed by the author[14]. About a hundred such measurements are available, but they have yet to be worked out. It is somewhat similar to the method proposed by Calame (see section IV, chapter 6 of this book).

Note added in proof. In June 1966 a Selenodetic Conference was held in Manchester (the proceedings of this will be published by the Astronomical Department of the University of Manchester). At this conference the problems of this chapter were thoroughly discussed. By extending his material from five to seven series of observations, the author confirmed all the conclusions contained in this chapter. He is now preparing a general catalogue of absolute heights on the Moon, with about 1000 points and a new 'contour map'.

References

1. D. L. Meyer and B. W. Ruffin, *Icarus*, **4**, 513 (1965).
2. J. Franz, *Astron. Beobachtungen Kgl. Univ. Sternwarte Königsberg*, **38** (1899).
3. F. Hayn, *Abhandl. Kgl. Saechs. Ges. (Akad.) Wiss., Math. Physik. Kl.*, **29** (1904).
4. F. Hayn, *Abhandl. Kgl. Saechs. Ges. (Akad.) Wiss., Math. Physik. Kl.*, **33** (1914).
5. G. Schrutka, *Mitt. Univ. Sternwarte, Wien*, **8**, 151 (1956).
6. G. Schrutka, *Mitt. Univ. Sternwarte, Wien*, **9**, 97 (1958).
7. J. Franz, *Astron. Beobachtungen Kgl. Univ. Sternwarte Königsberg*, **38**, No. 5 (1899).
8. J. Franz, *Mitt. Sternwarte Univ. Breslau*, **1** (1901).
9. G. Schrutka, *Mitt. Univ. Sternwarte, Wien*, **9**, 251 (1958).
10. R. B. Baldwin, *The Measure of the Moon*, University of Chicago Press, Chicago, 1963.
11. U.S. Army Map Service, *Tech. Rept. No. 29* (1964).
12. G. Schrutka, *Ann. Univ. Sternwarte Wien*, **26**, 6 (1966).
13. M. A. Blagg and K. Müller, *Proc. Gen. Assembly Intern. Astron. Union, Paris, 1935*.
14. J. Hopmann, *Mitt. Univ. Sternwarte, Wien*, **12**, 8 (1964).
15. Th. Weimer, *Astron. Contrib., Univ. Manchester, Ser. III, No. 90* (1960).
16. G. Schrutka und J. Hopmann, *Mitt. Univ. Sternwarte, Wien*, **10**, 15 (1959).
17. C. L. Goudas, *Icarus*, **4**, 528 (1965).
18. J. Hopmann, *Mitt. Univ. Sternwarte, Wien*, **6**, 13 (1954).
19. H. J. Potter, *Space Research VII, Proc. Intern. Space Sci. Symp., Vienna, 1966*, to be published.
20. E. B. Watts, *Astron. Obs., Am. Ephemeris Nautical Almanac, Wash.*, **17** (1963).
21. A. Massevich, *Space Research VII, Proc. Intern. Space Sci. Symp., Vienna, 1966*, to be published.

6

O. CALAME
Observatoire du Pic du Midi
Bagnères de Bigorre, Hautes-Pyréneés, France

The determination of the shape of the Moon by the terminator method

Principle of the Method

This method, aimed at constructing contour maps mainly for the central regions of the lunar disk, was proposed by Ritter[1] in 1934. It is based upon the fact that the position of the true terminator depends upon the shape of the selenoid.

The tangency points of the Sun's rays on a hypothetically spherical Moon would be situated on a circle which would be seen from the Earth as an ellipse. Thus, deviations of the true terminator from such an ellipse, computed from Brown's theory of lunar motion, can be used to derive the elevation of the observed points above (or below) the reference sphere.

Relation between the Altitude and the Inclination of Lunar Surface

In fact, the elevation h of a point of the true terminator above (or below) the reference sphere is not the only parameter involved; one must also take into account the inclination i of the surface element, surrounding this point, on the lunar horizontal plane, i.e. the angle i between the normal at the lunar surface, at this point, and the vector radius.

The shape of the Moon is not very different from a sphere, so that h^2 can be neglected with respect to the measured quantities (if we assume the observation errors).

The chosen reference system (M, ξ, η, ζ) is as follows: the origin is the center of gravity of the Moon, M; Mζ is directed towards the observer, Mξ towards the projection of the Sun on the plane normal to Mζ (figure 1). Each observed point P is in a plane passing through the Sun and intersecting the line of cusps in ω (figure 2).

Let ϕ be the topocentric phase of the Moon and $\Delta\xi$ the difference $\xi - \xi_c$ (ξ is a measured coordinate of a point P of the true terminator and ξ_c the computed coordinate of the corresponding point P' on the reference sphere). Equation (1) can then be

$$h = \frac{\Delta\xi(1 - \eta^2)^{1/2}}{\cos(\alpha + \phi - i)} + (1 - \eta^2)\left\{\frac{\cos\phi}{\cos(\alpha + \phi - i)} - 1\right\} \tag{1}$$

readily established (the length unit being the mean lunar radius), with

$$(1 - \eta^2)^{1/2}/(\eta^2 + D^2)^{1/2} = \alpha$$

and $D = MS$ (the Moon–Sun distance). α will be neglected as long as the observing and measuring errors are larger than its maximum value; one cannot derive absolute

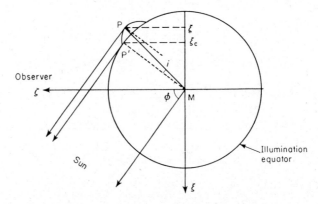

FIGURE 1   The chosen reference system (M, ξ, η, ζ)

heights through equation (1) because it contains two unknown quantities h and i. But using the approximation (2), then the system of equations (1) and (2) can be solved

$$dh = \tan i \, d(\phi - i) \tag{2}$$

by numerical integration.

For this purpose, an approximate value h_0 of h is derived from ϕ; then, equation (1)

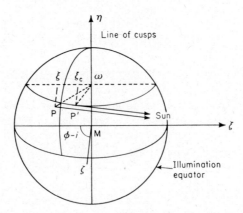

FIGURE 2   Diagram showing observed points P

gives a value i_0 for i and dh is computed by numerical integration of the differential equation (3).

$$dh \left\{ \frac{z}{1 - \eta^2 + h} - \frac{(1 - \eta^2 + h) \sin(\phi - i)}{(1 - \eta^2)^{1/2}} \frac{}{\tan i} \right\} = dz \tag{3}$$

This gives a better value $h_0 + dh$ of h; the final values of h and i are obtained by trial and error until dh is smaller than the estimated errors.

Observations and Measurements

The instrument used is a refractor, of 6 m focal length, and of 38 cm aperture; the photographic plates are preexposed to overcome the threshold of sensitivity; thus, the position of the true terminator does not depend upon exposure time. The orientation of the plate is given by a star trail.

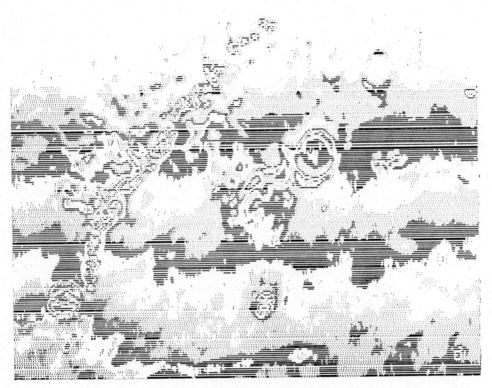

FIGURE 3 Isophotal curves on a region of the terminator

The reduction is conducted in the following way.

(i) An isodensitracer is used to draw isophotal curves on the regions close to the terminator (figure 3).

(ii) The small craters, which rise on this surface, are then located, with respect to the 196 reference points of the Aeronautical Chart and Information Center of U.S. Air Force (ACIC), with a comparator (micrometer) giving the rectangular coordinates for each point with an error of about some micrometers. In fact, these are the coordinates of the oblique projection of the point on the apparent disk.

The main difficulties lie in the fact that the measurements of distances are made with two different procedures and that the reference points are not entirely known.

This method is not reliable for regions close to the central meridian, where the stereo method, on the contrary, yields good results. Both methods thus complement one another.

References

1. H. Ritter, 'Versuch einer Bestimmung von Schichten linien auf dem Monde', *Astron. Nach.*, **252**, 157 (1934).

V

Planetary rotation

1. The radar method for the determination of the rotation rates
   of planets (J. H. THOMSON). 189

2. The planet Mercury: its rotation and atmosphere (S. I.
   RASOOL) 191

3. Theory of the axial rotations of Mercury and Venus (E. BEL-
   LOMO, G. COLOMBO, and I. I. SHAPIRO) . . . 193

4. Rotation of planets (H. ALFVÉN) 213

5. Spin–orbit coupling in the solar system (P. GOLDREICH and
   S. PEALE) 219

6. The history of the lunar orbit (P. GOLDREICH) . . 221

1

J. H. THOMSON
University of Manchester
England

The radar method for the determination of the rotation rates of planets

Abstract

Since 1961 pulse and continuous wave radar systems have been used in the U.S.S.R., the U.S.A., and the U.K. to study the three inner planets. Measurements of delay and Doppler shift allow range and line of sight velocity to be computed, whilst the spread of returned pulses in time and of continuous wave returned signals in frequency can be interpreted in terms of the physical characteristics and rotation of the planet. By interpreting such data taken throughout a close approach it is possible to determine the rotation rate and sense, together with the orientation of the rotation axis of a planet. This method has been applied to Venus and Mercury with the result that Venus rotates in the retrograde sense in 250 days, and Mercury in the direct sense in 57 days.

References

1. J. H. Thomson, *Sci. J.*, **1**, 53 (1965).
2. J. H. Thomson, *Quart. J. Roy. Astron. Soc.*, **4**, 347 (1963).
3. G. H. Pettengill, *Radio Sci.*, **69D**, 1617 (1965).

2

S. I. RASOOL

Institute for Space Studies
Goddard Space Flight Center, NASA
New York, New York, U.S.A.

The planet Mercury:
its rotation and atmosphere

Abstract*

A number of drawings of Mercury have been analyzed to derive various possible rotation periods for the planet. Combining these values with the range of uncertainty allowed by radar measurements (59 $\pm$ 5 days), we obtain an improved value for the rotation period of Mercury, namely 58·65 $\pm$ 0·1 days.

The possibility of the existence of a small amount of atmosphere on Mercury is examined. A theoretical investigation of the exospheric temperatures for different model atmospheres indicates that (i) a pure argon atmosphere cannot be stable against gravitational escape and will therefore be lost quickly from the planet, and (ii) if, however, a small amount of CO_2 is present in the atmosphere of Mercury (as has been observed by Moroz), then the exosphere is 'cooled' to ~ 1000 °K, and the escape of heavy gases becomes inefficient. The presence of CO_2 therefore seems to be an essential condition for any substantial amount of atmosphere to exist on the planet.

* The full paper is published in *Space Science Reviews*, **5**, 565–84 (1966).

3

E. BELLOMO

University of Padua
Italy
and
Consiglio Nazionale delle Richerche
Italy

and

I. I. SHAPIRO

Lincoln Laboratory*
Massachusetts Institute of Technology
Lexington, Massachusetts, U.S.A.

G. COLOMBO

Smithsonian Astrophysical Observatory
Cambridge, Massachusetts, U.S.A.
and
University of Padua
Italy

Theory of the axial rotations of Mercury and Venus†

Introduction

Radar observations have disclosed that Mercury's axial rotation has a sidereal period of 59 ± 3 days (see Pettengill and Dyce[1], Dyce, Pettengill, and Shapiro[2]), rather than the previously accepted value of 88 days (see for example Dollfus[3]). Peale and Gold[4] attempted to explain this new result exclusively in terms of solar tidal torques. They pointed out that for a noncircular orbit the tidal torque could change sign during an orbital revolution and therefore could have a zero average over this interval if its axial angular velocity were to lie between the mean orbital angular velocity and the angular velocity at perihelion (which corresponds to a spin period of about 56 days). However, Colombo[5] noticed that the observed spin period P_s was nearly two-thirds of the 88-day orbital period P_o and suggested that the axial rotation might well be 'locked' to the orbital motion in a three-halves resonance state by the additional solar torque exerted on an axial asymmetry in Mercury's inertia ellipsoid. Colombo and Shapiro[6,7] examined a two-dimensional model of the Sun–Mercury interactions, introducing both a frictional tidal torque T_t and a torque T_p attributable to a permanent axial asymmetry in the inertia ellipsoid. This analysis, carried to the second order in orbital eccentricity, showed that a torque balance was possible and that periodic rotational motion could exist with $P_s = (2/k)P_o$ $(k = 1 \rightarrow 4)$ provided that the ratio of the average magnitude of T_t to that of T_p was sufficiently small. Here the stability conditions are studied in full detail, the analysis being applicable to the rotational motion of any celestial object that interacts with the primary about which it orbits. We show that two periodic solutions exist for integral k $(k_{min} \leq k \leq k_{max})$ with the limiting

* Operated with support from the U.S. Air Force.
† This work was supported in part by grant No. NsG87-60 from the National Aeronautics and Space Administration.

values depending upon the relative magnitude of $\mathbf{T}_t$ and $\mathbf{T}_p$. One of these solutions is always unstable whereas the asymptotic stability of the other depends, at least in the linear analysis, on the sign of the derivative with respect to the spin angular velocity of the average value of $\mathbf{T}_t$. (A negative sign signifies stability when the positive direction of a torque is that of the orbital angular momentum vector.)

In addition to studying the rotational motion analytically in the neighborhood of the resonance states, we also consider the long-term evolution of Mercury's spin. If one assumes that initially Mercury was spinning much faster in either a direct or a retrograde sense, then it had to avoid being captured into either the $k = 4$ resonance state or the synchronous ($k = 2$) state, respectively, to have reached its present rotation. A first-order analysis of our simplified model indicates that, for the orbital eccentricity less than 0.3, the $k = 4$ resonance state is not asymptotically stable. Although the $k = 2$ state is stable, there exist conditions under which this barrier may be passed, implying that Mercury may have evolved to its present spin state from an initially retrograde axial rotation.

Radar measurements have also revealed that Venus rotates in a retrograde direction with a period of 247 ± 5 days (see Carpenter[8], Goldstein[9], Shapiro[10]). The more accurate of these radar data consist of delay-Doppler maps of the planet's surface[11] and seem to be beyond question, especially since observations at widely different frequencies yield substantially the same result. This value for the rotation period is not inconsistent with a period of 243.15 days which would ensure that Venus makes exactly four rotations between inferior conjunctions, as seen by an Earth observer. The spin of Venus may therefore be controlled by the Earth. A sidereal period of 250.5 days (retrograde) would imply that Venus presents the same 'face' to Jupiter at every close approach of these two planets. The average gravitational torques exerted by Jupiter on Venus are, however, about an order of magnitude smaller than those exerted by the Earth and hence Jupiter is less likely to be the controlling influence. (Mercury, whose view of Venus would repeat at alternate close approaches for a 238-day spin period, exerts an even smaller average torque.)

A satisfactory theoretical description of the anomalous rotation of Venus must provide answers to two questions: (i) how did the axial rotation evolve to the neighborhood of its present state, and (ii) is a spin state that is 'locked' to the relative orbital motion of the Earth and Venus (Earth–Venus resonance rotation) asymptotically stable? We examine both questions below. Assuming the primordial rotation to have been rapid and retrograde, we find it possible that Venus, after being slowed sufficiently by the solar tidal torque, was captured into the $k = -2$ resonance state (see above). This capture requires that the tidal torque should have a viscous component and that the orbital eccentricity should not be too low. When either condition is violated the spin state can escape from the resonance lock and the slowing down can continue. The next resonance encountered would then be the one between the spin and the relative orbital motion of the Earth and Venus in which the sidereal rotation period is 243.15 days. If the original rotation were rapid and direct and the orbital eccentricity sufficiently small (as it is at present), we could envisage Venus being slowed by tidal torques until its orbital and spin motions were synchronous ($k = 2$ resonance). Although we have considered a wide variety of different possible continuously acting torques, none appears to be nearly of sufficient strength to destabilize the synchronous rotation. The angular momentum transferred to Venus during a collision with a 200-km diameter asteroid could, however, have been sufficient to cause Venus to rotate in a retrograde direction with a period in the neighborhood of 247 days.

The dynamics of the rotation in the vicinity of the Earth–Venus resonance value is complex and our study incomplete. Nonetheless, from an analysis of the equations of motion we may conclude that for the rotation with a period of 243·15 days to be asymptotically stable, the fractional difference in its principal equatorial moments of inertia must be relatively large—greater than about 10^{-3}. (The corresponding difference for the Moon is 2×10^{-4}.) If the other necessary conditions are considered as well, it is clear that the existence of a stable Earth–Venus resonance rotation would indeed be a surprising phenomenon. A stable Jupiter–Venus resonance rotation would be even more surprising.

Rotation of Mercury

Mercury's physical constitution and shape are too poorly known to allow the formulation of an accurate model of the solar interactions that affect its rotational motion. We therefore confine our analysis to a simple two-dimensional model in which the total torque exerted on Mercury by the Sun is composed of two parts: a tidal torque $\mathbf{T}_t$ and a torque $\mathbf{T}_p$ attributable to the lack of axial symmetry of Mercury's inertia ellipsoid. This model leads to the equation of rotational motion (1)[6,7], where the

$$\frac{d^2\theta}{dt^2} = -\left\{ \frac{\alpha'}{r^6} \operatorname{sgn}\left(\frac{d\theta}{dt} - \frac{dv}{dt} \right) + \frac{\beta'}{r^3} \sin 2(\theta - v) \right\} \tag{1}$$

first term on the right side represents the effect of $\mathbf{T}_t$ and the second term that of $\mathbf{T}_p$. The angle θ between the planet's equatorial principal axis of minimum moment of inertia and the line from the Sun to perihelion is measured positively for a rotation in the direct sense. The true anomaly of the planet's orbital position is denoted by v and the distance of the planet from the Sun by r. The constant β' is given by (2),

$$\beta' = \frac{3\mu}{2} \frac{B - A}{C} \tag{2}$$

where μ represents the product of the gravitational constant and the mass of the Sun, and $A < B < C$ denote the three principal moments of inertia of the planet. (Of course, C is assumed to be the moment about an axis normal to the orbital plane.) The constant α' also depends on μ and on more subtle physical characteristics of the planet. In fact, the specific functional form chosen for $\mathbf{T}_t$ is a rather simplified one; it implies, for example, that the magnitude of the tidal torque is independent of the frequency of rotation. We could easily generalize the form of $\mathbf{T}_t$ in an *ad hoc* manner; some reasonable variations can alter the results significantly, as discussed below.

Introducing the mean anomaly M and expressing r in terms of v and the orbital eccentricity e, we obtain (3), where we have chosen units in which the orbital period

$$\frac{d^2\theta}{dM^2} = -\left\{ \alpha \left(\frac{1 + e \cos v}{1 - e^2} \right)^6 \operatorname{sgn}\left(\frac{d\theta}{dM} - \frac{dv}{dM} \right) \right.$$
$$\left. + \beta \left(\frac{1 + e \cos v}{1 - e^2} \right)^3 \sin 2(\theta - v) \right\} \tag{3}$$

and semimajor axis are unity; hence $\alpha = \alpha'/4\pi^2$ and $\beta = \beta'/4\pi^2$.

Stability analysis

To discuss the stability of the solution in the neighborhood of a resonance, we shall develop only the first-order solution to equation (3) which may be written as (4), with (5) and (6) representing the initial conditions. The integer l has been inserted to

$$\theta(M) = \omega_0'M + \theta_0' + \alpha\theta_{1\alpha}(M) + \beta\theta_{1\beta}(M) - l\pi \tag{4}$$

$$\theta(0) = \theta_0', \qquad \frac{d\theta}{dM}\bigg|_{M=0} = \frac{1}{2\pi}\frac{d\theta}{dt}\bigg|_{t=0} = \omega_0' \tag{5}$$

$$\theta_{1\alpha,\beta}(0) = \frac{d\theta_{1\alpha,\beta}}{dM}\bigg|_{M=0} = \omega_{1\alpha,\beta}(0) = 0 \tag{6}$$

restrict θ to the interval $(-\tfrac{1}{2}\pi, \tfrac{1}{2}\pi)$, since the inertia ellipsoid is symmetric with respect to reflections through a plane determined by two of its principal axes.

In terms of the Fourier series developments (7) and (8), the first-order solution to

$$-\left(\frac{1 + e\cos v}{1 - e^2}\right)^6 \text{sgn}\left(\omega_0' - \frac{dv}{dM}\right) \equiv T(e, \omega_0', M) = T(e, \omega_0', - M)$$

$$= \sum_{j=0}^{\infty} T_j(e, \omega_0')\cos jM \tag{7}$$

$$-\left(\frac{1 + e\cos v}{1 - e^2}\right)^3 \sin 2(\omega_0'M + \theta_0' - v) \equiv P(e, \theta_0' + \omega_0'M, M)$$

$$= \sum_{j=-\infty}^{\infty} P_j(e)\sin\{(j - 2\omega_0')M - 2\theta_0'\} \tag{8}$$

equation (3) that obeys the initial conditions (5) and (6) can, after one orbital revolution, be expressed as (9) and (10), where both $\theta_{1\beta}$ and $\omega_{1\beta}$ are continuous functions

$$\left.\begin{array}{l} \theta_{1\alpha}(2\pi) = 2\pi^2 T_0(e, \omega_0') \\[4pt] \omega_{1\alpha}(2\pi) = 2\pi T_0(e, \omega_0') \end{array}\right\} \tag{9}$$

$$\left.\begin{array}{l} \theta_{1\beta}(2\pi) = \sum_{j=-\infty}^{\infty} P_j(e)\left\{\dfrac{2\pi\cos 2\theta_0'}{j - 2\omega_0'} + \dfrac{\sin(2\theta_0' + 4\pi\omega_0') - \sin 2\theta_0'}{(j - 2\omega_0')^2}\right\} \\[14pt] \omega_{1\beta}(2\pi) = -\sum_{j=-\infty}^{\infty} \dfrac{P_j(e)}{j - 2\omega_0'}\{\cos(2\theta_0' + 4\pi\omega_0') - \cos 2\theta_0'\} \end{array}\right\} \tag{10}$$

of $\omega_0'(-\infty \leq \omega_0' \leq \infty)$. Explicit expressions for all of the T_j and P_j coefficients are given by Bellomo, Colombo, and Shapiro[12, 13]; $T_0(e, \omega)$, derived previously by Colombo and Shapiro[6, 7], is given by (11), where (12) applies. For $\omega < (1 - e)^{1/2}/(1 + e)^{3/2}$

$$T_0(e, \omega) = -(1 - e^2)^{-9/2}(2\pi)^{-1}[2(\pi - 2v_c) - 16e\sin v_c$$

$$+ 6e^2(\pi - 2v_c - \sin 2v_c) - \tfrac{16}{3}e^3(3\sin v_c - \sin^3 v_c)$$

$$+ \tfrac{1}{8}e^4\{6(\pi - 2v_c) - 8\sin 2v_c - \sin 4v_c\}] \tag{11}$$

$$\cos v_c = e^{-1}\{(1 - e^2)^{3/4}\omega^{1/2} - 1\}, \qquad 0 \leq v_c \leq \pi \tag{12}$$

or $\omega > (1 + e)^{1/2}/(1 - e)^{3/2}$, $T_0(e, \omega)$ equals $(1 - e^2)^{-9/2}(1 + 3e^2 + \frac{3}{8}e^4)$ or $-(1 - e^2)^{-9/2}(1 + 3e^2 + \frac{3}{8}e^4)$, respectively. The coefficients $P_j(e)$ for $j = -3$ to 7 are given in table 1 for convenience.

TABLE 1   Coefficients in the Fourier expansion of the solar torque as power series in the eccentricity up to e^5

j	$(1 - e^2)^3 P_j(e)$	
7	$59{\cdot}4653e^5$	
6	$33{\cdot}3125e^4$	
5	$17{\cdot}6041e^3$	$- 95{\cdot}1627e^5$
4	$8{\cdot}5e^2$	$- 44{\cdot}6667e^4$
3	$3{\cdot}5e$	$- 18{\cdot}1875e^3 + 37{\cdot}3828e^5$
2	1	$- 5{\cdot}5e^2 \quad + 11{\cdot}3125e^4$
1	$-0{\cdot}5e$	$+ 1{\cdot}5625e^3 - 1{\cdot}7005e^5$
0	0	
-1	$0{\cdot}020834e^3 - 0{\cdot}4818e^5$	
-2	$0{\cdot}041666e^4$	
-3	$0{\cdot}06328e^5$	

If we assume that ω_0' is near a resonance value (i.e. $|k - 2\omega_0'| \ll 1$ for some k), then we may expand equations (10) retaining terms only of first order in $k - 2\omega_0'$ and obtain (13), where $Q_k(e)$ and $R_k(e)$ are given by (14). Equations (13), together with

$$
\begin{aligned}
\theta_{1\beta}(2\pi) &= 2\pi[Q_k(e) \cos 2\theta_0' - \pi P_k(e) \sin 2\theta_0' \\
&\quad + 2(k - 2\omega_0')\{\tfrac{1}{3}\pi^2 P_k(e) - \tfrac{1}{2}R_k(e)\} \cos 2\theta_0'] \\
\omega_{1\beta}(2\pi) &= -2\pi[P_k(e) \sin 2\theta_0' + (k - 2\omega_0')\{Q_k(e) \sin 2\theta_0' \\
&\quad - \pi P_k(e) \cos 2\theta_0'\}]
\end{aligned}
\right\} \tag{13}
$$

$$
\begin{aligned}
Q_k(e) &\equiv \sum_{\substack{j=-\infty \\ j \neq k}}^{\infty} \frac{P_j(e)}{j - k} \\
R_k(e) &\equiv \sum_{\substack{j=-\infty \\ j \neq k}}^{\infty} \frac{P_j(e)}{(j - k)^2}
\end{aligned}
\right\} \tag{14}
$$

equations (4) and (9), yield a good approximation of the values of θ and ω ($\equiv d\theta/dM$) after one orbital revolution in terms of the initial values (θ_0', ω_0'), when the latter are near a resonance value.

The initial conditions (θ_p, ω_p) corresponding in this approximation to a periodic solution are determined from (15), with $\theta(2\pi)$, $\omega(2\pi)$ given by equations (4), (9), and

$$
\begin{aligned}
\theta(2\pi) &= \theta(0) \equiv \theta_p \\
\omega(2\pi) &= \omega(0) \equiv \omega_p
\end{aligned}
\right\} \tag{15}
$$

(13). Solving equations (15) we obtain (16) and (17). The ratio γ/γ^* is, in effect, the

$$
\left.
\begin{aligned}
\sin 2\theta_p &= \frac{\gamma}{\gamma^*} \\[2mm]
\omega_p - \tfrac{1}{2}k &= -\beta Q_k(e) \cos 2\theta_p
\end{aligned}
\right\} \tag{16}
$$

$$
\gamma \equiv \frac{\alpha}{\beta}, \qquad \gamma^*(k, e) \equiv \frac{P_k(e)}{T_0(e, \tfrac{1}{2}k)} \tag{17}
$$

ratio of the tidal torque to that exerted on the permanent axial asymmetry of the planet. It is clear that, for given values k and e, there will be two real solutions for θ_p provided that γ is sufficiently small. The corresponding values of ω_p must be close to $\tfrac{1}{2}k$ since we have assumed throughout that β is small. Under these conditions there are two periodic rotational motions for each value of k. The solution with $|\theta_p| < \tfrac{1}{4}\pi$ has the axis of minimum moment of inertia forming at perihelion an angle smaller than $\tfrac{1}{4}\pi$ with the radius vector from the Sun to the planet.

If Mercury is in fact in a resonance state, the orientation of the inertia ellipsoid can be used to estimate γ, whereas knowledge of the deviation of the instantaneous angular velocity from its average value will allow β to be determined. The experimental determinations are far too crude for any meaningful deductions to be made at present.

To investigate the stability of the above solutions, we consider initial conditions (θ_0', ω_0') that deviate slightly from (θ_p, ω_p). Introducing the notation (18), we find

$$
\left.
\begin{aligned}
\Delta\theta &\equiv \theta_0' - \theta_p \\[2mm]
\Delta\omega &\equiv \omega_0' - \omega_p
\end{aligned}
\right\} \tag{18}
$$

from equations (4), (9), and (13) that after one orbital revolution the differences $(\delta\theta, \delta\omega)$ between the values $(\theta(2\pi), \omega(2\pi))$ and (θ_0', ω_0') are given by (19) and (20),

$$
\begin{aligned}
\delta\theta \equiv \theta(2\pi) - \theta_0' &= 2\pi\Delta\omega - 4\pi\beta[\Delta\theta\{Q_k(e)\sin 2\theta_p + \pi P_k(e)\cos 2\theta_p\} \\
&\quad + \Delta\omega \cos 2\theta_p\{\tfrac{2}{3}\pi^2 P_k(e) - R_k(e)\}] \\
&\quad + 2\pi^2\alpha\Delta\omega T_0'(e, \tfrac{1}{2}k) + O(2)
\end{aligned} \tag{19}
$$

$$
\begin{aligned}
\delta\omega \equiv \omega(2\pi) - \omega_0' &= -4\pi\beta[\Delta\theta P_k(e)\cos 2\theta_p + \Delta\omega\{-Q_k(e)\sin 2\theta_p \\
&\quad + \pi P_k(e)\cos 2\theta_p\}] + 2\pi\alpha\Delta\omega T_0'(e, \tfrac{1}{2}k) \\
&\quad + (\Delta\omega)^2 O(1) + O(2)
\end{aligned} \tag{20}
$$

where $O(i)$ denotes terms of order i in either α or β and $T_0'(e, \tfrac{1}{2}k)$ is given by (21).

$$
T_0'(e, \tfrac{1}{2}k) \equiv \left.\frac{\partial T_0(e, \omega)}{\partial \omega}\right|_{\omega=k/2} = -\left.\frac{\omega^{3/2}}{\pi e(1 - e^2)^{3/4} \sin v_c}\right|_{\omega=k/2} \tag{21}
$$

These difference equations can be solved in the standard manner. The values of $\Delta\theta$ and $\Delta\omega$ for which (22) hold true lead to the second-order secular equation for λ

$$
\left.
\begin{aligned}
\delta\theta &= \lambda\Delta\theta \\[2mm]
\delta\omega &= \lambda\Delta\omega
\end{aligned}
\right\} \tag{22}
$$

whose roots λ_1 and λ_2 satisfy the relations (23) and (24) if we omit the higher-order

$$\lambda_1 + \lambda_2 \equiv s = -8\pi^2\beta P_k(e)\cos 2\theta_p + 2\pi\alpha T_0'(e, \tfrac{1}{2}k) \tag{23}$$

$$\lambda_1\lambda_2 \equiv p = 8\pi^2\beta P_k(e)\cos 2\theta_p \tag{24}$$

terms from equations (19) and (20). Denoting the differences between (θ, ω) and (θ_p, ω_p) after m orbital revolutions by $(\Delta\theta^{(m)}, \Delta\omega^{(m)})$, we find (25) by iteration. This

$$\left.\begin{array}{l} \Delta\theta^{(m)} = (1 + \lambda)^m \Delta\theta^{(0)} \\[1mm] \Delta\omega^{(m)} = (1 + \lambda)^m \Delta\omega^{(0)} \end{array}\right\} \tag{25}$$

rotational motion will converge asymptotically to the periodic solution condition of asymptotic stability) if (26) is true. When (27) applies, the corresponding periodic

$$|1 + \lambda_i| < 1, \qquad i = 1, 2 \tag{26}$$

$$P_k(e)\cos 2\theta_p < 0 \tag{27}$$

rotation motion is unstable since $\lambda_1\lambda_2$ being negative (see equation (24)) implies that both λ_1 and λ_2 are real and hence that one of them is positive for which inequality (26) would be violated. Further analysis[12,13] shows that the necessary and sufficient conditions for inequality (26) to be satisfied are

$$T_0'(e, \tfrac{1}{2}k) < 0$$

and

$$\pi\{2\pi\beta P_k(e)\cos 2\theta_p - \alpha T_0'(e, \tfrac{1}{2}k)\} < 1$$

The second condition will of course hold for all cases of interest, since our entire analysis assumes that both α and β are small. By the same token it is clear that the roots λ_i will be restricted to complex values ($s^2 < 4p$). Our analysis also assumes that the physical characteristics of the planet and its orbit remain unchanged, conditions which are certainly not strictly valid over geologic time intervals.

Rewriting the solution (25) in terms of the sum and product of the (complex) roots λ_i yields, for example, equation (28). When the conditions for asymptotic

$$\Delta\theta^{(m)} = \Delta\theta^{(0)}\{1 + s + p + O(2)\}^{m/2}\sin[\{p^{1/2} + O(\tfrac{3}{2})\}m + \phi] \tag{28}$$

stability are satisfied, this relation illustrates how the orientation of the axis of minimum moment of inertia at successive perihelion passages exhibits damped oscillations around the value corresponding to the stable periodic rotation described by equations (16). Each of these oscillations obviously requires a number N of orbital revolutions given by (29). In this approximation no damping takes place if $p + s = 0$ which will

$$N = \frac{2\pi}{p^{1/2}} = (2\beta)^{-1/2}\{P_k^2(e) - \gamma^2 T_0^2(e, \tfrac{1}{2}k)\}^{-1/4} \tag{29}$$

occur if $T_0'(e, \tfrac{1}{2}k) = 0$. On the other hand, if $T_0'(e, \tfrac{1}{2}k) < 0$, then there will be damping and the relative decrease δ in the amplitude after one oscillation will be given by (30); that is, after N orbital revolutions, the amplitude of the oscillation has been

$$\delta = -\tfrac{1}{2}(p + s)N$$

$$= -\frac{\pi\alpha}{(2\beta)^{1/2}}\frac{T_0'(e, \tfrac{1}{2}k)}{\{P_k^2(e) - \gamma^2 T_0^2(e, \tfrac{1}{2}k)\}^{1/4}} \tag{30}$$

reduced from $\Delta\theta^{(0)}$ to $(1 - \delta)\Delta\theta^{(0)}$. Provided that θ_p remains small ($\ll 1$), we see from equations (29) and (30) that both N and δ are inversely proportional to $\beta^{1/2}$. In table 2 we present some numerical values for N and δ for various values of α and β assuming conditions appropriate for the present state of Mercury ($k = 3$, $e \simeq 0.2$).

TABLE 2   The number of orbital revolutions N per libration period and the fractional decrease δ in the libration amplitude as functions of α and β for $e = 0.2$, $k = 3$, and $\alpha \ll \beta$

β	N	δ
10^{-5}	297	$8.2 \times 10^3 \alpha$
3.16×10^{-5}	167	$4.6 \times 10^3 \alpha$
10^{-4}	94	$2.6 \times 10^3 \alpha$
3.16×10^{-4}	53	$1.45 \times 10^3 \alpha$
10^{-3}	29.7	$8.2 \times 10^2 \alpha$
3.16×10^{-3}	16.7	$4.6 \times 10^2 \alpha$
10^{-2}	9.4	$2.6 \times 10^2 \alpha$

In studying the behavior of the rotational motion in the vicinity of a stable periodic solution, it is important to note that a very poor approximation will result from changing equations (19) and (20) into differential equations by considering the number m of orbital revolutions to be a continuous variable. To show the necessity for maintaining m as a variable taking on only integer values, let us compare the solutions of the differential and difference equations. With m considered to be a continuous variable, we can show[12, 13] that (31) holds true, where q is given by (32). Even if $\alpha = 0$,

$$\Delta\theta(m) = \Delta\theta(0)e^{(s/2)m} \sin(p^{1/2}m + \phi)$$

$$\left. \begin{array}{l} \Delta\psi(m) \equiv \dfrac{2\pi}{p^{1/2}}\Delta\omega(m) = \Delta\theta(0)e^{(s/2)m}\Big\{\cos(p^{1/2}m + \phi) \\[3mm] \qquad\qquad + \dfrac{\frac{1}{2}s - q}{p^{1/2}} \sin(p^{1/2}m + \phi)\Big\} \end{array} \right\} \qquad (31)$$

$$q \equiv -4\pi\beta\{Q_k(e)\sin 2\theta_p + \pi P_k(e)\cos 2\theta_p\} \qquad (32)$$

equation (31) predicts that the modulus in the $(\Delta\theta, \Delta\psi)$ plane will decrease to zero exponentially for $P_k(e) > 0$. In other words, the differential equations predict asymptotic stability in this case, whereas the corresponding linearized difference equations do not lead to this conclusion.

It is also instructive to study from a geometric point of view the differences in the solutions that are present after one orbital revolution in the limit of small β. Let P_1 in figure 1 be the position corresponding after one orbital revolution to the exact solution to equation (3), let P_2 represent the solution given in equations (19) and (20), and let P_3 correspond to the solution (31). With γ held constant and β allowed to approach zero the distance P_1P_2 decreases as $\beta^{3/2}$ (note the β dependence of the higher-order terms in equations (19) and (20)), whereas the distance PP_2 decreases as $\beta^{1/2}$ and the ratio P_1P_2 to PP_1 as β. The approximate solution given in equations

(19) and (20) therefore approaches the exact solution as β tends to zero. On the other hand, the distance P_2P_3 (and, hence, P_1P_3) decreases only as β. Since the arc length PP_3 and the tangent PP_2 both tend to $p^{1/2}$ whereas the radius of curvature tends to CP, simple geometry shows that P_2P_3/CP_2 tends to $\frac{1}{2}p$ which proves that P_2P_3 decreases only as β and that $CP_2 = CP_3(1 + \frac{1}{2}p)$ in agreement with our analytical results.

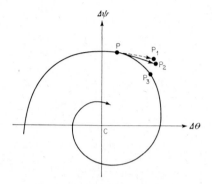

FIGURE 1 Contrast in the phase-plane behavior of the solutions to the differential and difference equations (see text)

Motion near a periodic solution

We now discuss qualitatively the time dependence of the rotational motion when the angular velocity is close to the value corresponding to a periodic solution. For convenience, we adopt the angular velocity variable ψ defined by (33), where the

$$\psi \equiv \frac{2\pi}{p^{1/2}}\{\omega - \omega_p(\theta)\} \tag{33}$$

dependence of ω_p on θ is as given in the second of equations (16), and follow the behavior of (θ, ψ) in the phase plane at successive perihelion passages. Periodic solutions correspond to points $(\theta_p, 0)$; for reasons discussed previously, points with the same value of ψ but with θ's differing by an integral multiple of π are to be considered equivalent. By either a forward or backward iteration of the first-order solution developed earlier, we trace out a set of points in the phase plane corresponding to the state of rotation at successive perihelion passages. For the sake of simplicity in the following figures, continuous lines instead of points are drawn to represent the motion in the phase plane. In general there can be no proper connection among all points. But by considering only lines defined by sets having as a point of accumulation the point representing the unstable periodic rotation there will be no ambiguity. (The trajectories in phase space governed by differential equations never intersect; however, sets of points determined by difference equations may interleave.) By restricting the lines to be drawn in the above-described manner, we may also define with no difficulty the intersection of such a line with the θ axis.

In the absence of a tidal torque ($\alpha = 0$), equations (16) and (17) show that $\theta_p = 0$ for the stable periodic solution and $\theta_p = \frac{1}{2}\pi$ for the unstable one. The latter corresponds to a saddle point in the phase plane (λ_i real, $\lambda_1 \lambda_2$ negative). Here the rotational motion does not slow down and we do not have asymptotic stability. The phase-plane motion in this case is represented schematically in figure 2, where C_1 and C_2 correspond

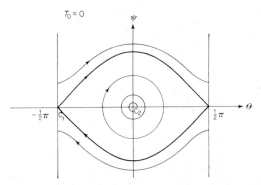

FIGURE 2   Illustration of the phase-plane behavior of the spin state at successive perihelion passages in the absence of a tidal torque. For convenience, continuous curves are drawn instead of sets of points

to the unstable and stable periodic solutions, respectively. With the presence of a constant tidal torque tending to slow down the rotational motion in the vicinity of a periodic solution ($T_0 < 0, T_0' = 0$), we have the phase-plane motion illustrated in

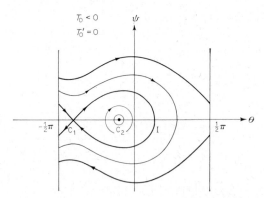

FIGURE 3   Same as for figure 2, except that here a constant tidal torque is assumed to be present

figure 3. We note the gradual decrease in ψ along the trajectory relative to the corresponding behavior in figure 2. In view of equations (16) and (17), the points C_1 and C_2 move to the right and left, respectively, by equal amounts. Since $T_0' = 0$, the trajectories starting from, and arriving at, C_1 intersect the $\psi = 0$ axis at the same point I ($\equiv I_1, I_2$). Here we do not obtain asymptotic stability. For $T_0 < 0$ but $T_0' > 0$, then we again have slowing down; however, no stability for the periodic solutions is possible. This motion is presented schematically in figure 4. Since $T_0' > 0$ the states with smaller values of ψ will be influenced most by the tidal torque, causing the point

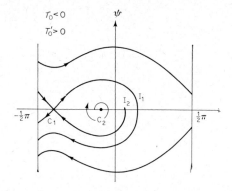

FIGURE 4   Same as for figure 3, except that the tidal torque is assumed to have a positive
derivative with respect to the spin angular velocity

I_2 to be driven to the left of I_1 as shown. On the other hand, with $T_0' < 0$, we may have
asymptotic stability. The shaded zones in figure 5 represent the rotational states of
motion at perihelion that will slow down and 'lock into' the stable periodic solution.
Here the rotational states with larger values of ψ will be slowed down more effectively
by T_0; hence point I_1 is driven to the left of I_2.

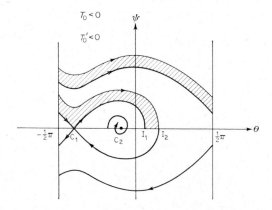

FIGURE 5   Same as for figure 4, except that the sign of the derivative is assumed to be
negative

From the analytical development above, we see that along the path from either
C_1 to I_1 or I_2 to C_1, the magnitude of ψ is of the order of unity (i.e.

$$|\omega - \omega_p| < p^{1/2}/2\pi \ll 1$$

if β is small). Since the actual tidal torque cannot be expected to exhibit rapid oscillations as a function of ψ (or ω), we should anticipate that T_0' does not change its sign
along either of the two paths. Hence, permanent combination oscillations, as shown in
figure 6, could not be expected to take place around a periodic solution.

If $T_0' < 0$ and T_0 changes sign as a function of ψ along the path C_1 to I_1 or I_2 to
C_1, then the motion in the phase plane could resemble that shown in figure 7. Here we

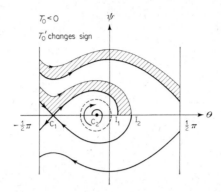

FIGURE 6   Same as for figure 3, except that the tidal torque is assumed to vary with spin angular velocity in such a manner as to produce combination oscillations

have a situation in which T_0 causes a decrease in the rotational speed for positive ψ but an increase for negative ψ. 'Locking-in' will then certainly be achieved. For other cases, the planet's rotational motion may not be captured into a stable periodic state, but may pass through the resonance when being decelerated by the tidal torque.

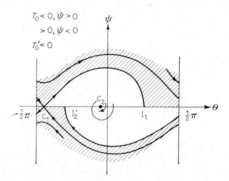

FIGURE 7   Same as for figure 5, with the addition that the tidal torque is assumed to change sign near the spin angular velocity corresponding to a periodic solution

Discussion

The actual behavior of θ and ω as a function of time depends in our simple model on five parameters: the initial conditions θ_0', ω_0', the orbital eccentricity e, and the coefficients α, β of the contributing torques. As was mentioned previously by Colombo and Shapiro[6,7], planetary eccentricities and arguments of perihelia change with time in a quasiperiodic manner, whereas the coefficients α and β may undergo secular changes. The effect of a constant advance of the argument of perihelion on the rotational motion can be treated easily by introducing a reference system rotating uniformly with the angular velocity of the apsidal line. Centrifugal forces will not affect the rotational motion and one need only use the anomalistic period as the orbital period. On the other hand, a nonconstant advance requires a less trivial modification. Whether or not capture into a stable periodic rotational state takes place depends more importantly on the variation in eccentricity. If the eccentricity undergoes a long-period oscillation of several hundred thousand years between the values of 0·11 and

0·24 (see Brouwer and Clemence[14]), then some (perhaps, weighted) average of the eccentricity should be used in our model, since the time scale for capture is probably far greater than the eccentricity oscillation period. As for α and β, it is not yet possible to determine their present values let alone any variations that may have occurred.

Even by restricting the parameter values to be time independent, the determination of the conditions for capture into the various possible periodic rotational states might seem a large task. Nonetheless, certain important results are easily deduced. For $k \geq 4$ the eccentricity would have to exceed 0·31 in order to satisfy the condition $T_0'(e, \frac{1}{2}k) < 0$ required for asymptotic stability. It therefore appears as if Mercury's rotational state could easily have evolved from an initially rapid, direct rotation to its present $k = 3$ resonance state. However, asymptotic stability follows from our model for $k = 3$ only if the average value of e exceeds 0·19 which is just slightly below its present value. One might be tempted to conclude that Mercury will therefore only remain temporarily in its present resonance rotational state. Before such a conclusion could be made reliably, two factors must be investigated: (i) the actual contribution of a viscous component to the tidal torque which may have a stabilizing influence ($T_0' < 0$) for $k = 3$, and even, say, for $k = 4$ (this component is discussed in more detail in the following section), and (ii) the effects on our analytic solution of second-order terms in β. If Mercury were as asymmetric as the Moon, we might expect $\beta \simeq 2 \times 10^{-4}$, whereas for α we should expect a value in the vicinity of 5×10^{-9} (see Colombo and Shapiro[6,7]). Therefore second-order β terms may be as important as first-order α terms in determining the conditions for asymptotic stability. We have already completed a second-order analytical solution[12,13], but the corresponding stability analysis remains to be carried out.

The conditions for the penetration of the $k = 2$ resonance barrier that would lead to capture in the $k = 3$ state are also difficult to establish. Our preliminary and incomplete results[12,13], obtained partly with the aid of a computer, indicate that this barrier, too, can be penetrated although the conditions are somewhat severe. We can therefore not yet rule out the possibility that Mercury's rotational motion was originally retrograde.

Rotation of Venus

As mentioned earlier, radar observations have demonstrated that Venus rotates in a retrograde direction with a period of about 247 ± 5 days. This determination is consistent with the axial motion being in resonance with the relative orbital motion of the Earth and Venus for which a period of 243·15 days is required. Our theoretical discussion will therefore be divided into two sections. In the first we consider the conditions that could have allowed the axial rotation to evolve to the neighborhood of its present state; in the second we examine for a simplified model the equation of motion governing the rotation near an Earth–Venus resonance state.

Evolution

If we were to assume that Venus initially rotated rapidly in a direct sense, then we could postulate the existence at least in the past of solar tidal torques of sufficient magnitude to have caused the axial and orbital motion to become synchronous. (The orbital eccentricity would, of course, have had to be small enough for the higher resonances to have been passed; in view of its present value, this restriction on the eccentricity does not appear to be severe.) What torques could disrupt such a synchronous rotation? We have examined the gravitational torques exerted by the Sun and planets on body tidal distortions and on atmospheric tides, induced either gravitationally or thermally. We have also considered possible torques exerted by sunlight pressure. None appears to possess the qualities necessary to convert the synchronous, direct rotation into a retrograde rotation. An asteroid 200 km in diameter could, however, transfer the necessary angular momentum as the result of a collision with Venus. Analyzing such a collision in detail is not feasible, but one might expect the

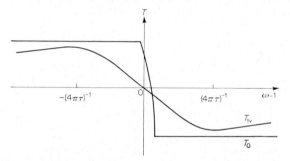

FIGURE 8   Illustration of the dependence of a viscous tidal torque on the spin angular
velocity. For comparison the purely frictional tidal torque $T_0(e \simeq 0.2, \omega)$ is shown

surface to exhibit traces of such a monumental impact. Although most probably unrelated, a large region on the surface of Venus does have anomalous backscattering characteristics[15,16].

Considering the rather primitive state of the theories of the origin of planets, we may assume, alternatively, that the rotation of Venus was originally rapid but retrograde. Tidal torques of not unreasonable magnitude can be postulated to have slowed down the rotation. Let us then consider the possibility that Venus' rotational motion became locked to its orbital motion in the resonance state $k = -2$, corresponding to a retrograde rotation with a period of 224.7 days. According to equation (16), a periodic rotation would have been possible with $P_{-2}(e)$ as given in table 1, only if (34)

$$|\alpha T_0| \leqq 0.0417\beta(1 - e^2)^{-3}e^4 \tag{34}$$

applies at the time of capture. If the tidal torque were of the same type as assumed on p. 195, then stability would not have been possible (at least to first order in α and β) no matter how large the eccentricity since $T_0'(e, -1) = 0$. If, on the other hand, the tidal torque had a viscous component $\mathbf{T}_{tv}$ the periodic solution with $k = -2$ could have been stable provided that the contribution to $T_0'(e, -1)$ of this component had been negative. Bellomo, Colombo, and Shapiro[12,13] have developed a simple model of such a viscous torque for which $\mathbf{T}_{tv}$ will vanish when $\omega = 1$ (in the units adopted earlier), will reach a positive maximum at $\omega = 1 - (4\pi\tau)^{-1}$, and will reach a negative maximum at $\omega = 1 + (4\pi\tau)^{-1}$, where τ is the characteristic relaxation time governing the return to equilibrium following a deformation. The behavior of T_{tv} is indicated schematically in figure 8 along with the expression for $T_0(e \simeq 0.2, \omega)$. The derivative of T_{tv} will have the proper sign for stabilization in the vicinity of the kth resonance provided that $\tau < (2\pi|k - 2|)^{-1}$, i.e. for $\tau \lesssim 10$ days with $k = -2$. This inequality could hold if the viscous component were due mainly to a liquid or gaseous tide.

Inequality (34) could have been satisfied if, for example, $\alpha T_0 \lesssim 10^{-9}, \beta \gtrsim 2\cdot5 \times 10^{-4}$, and $e \gtrsim 0\cdot1$. The value of α required is below the magnitude necessary to have slowed Venus from an initially rapid rotation; the value of β required in this example is comparable with that for the Moon. For this model we must therefore assume that α had decreased before capture into the $k = -2$ state took place, and that Venus had a relatively large equatorial asymmetry. Inequality (34) could also have been satisfied if the tidal torque were primarily viscous and τ sufficiently small[12, 13]. The analysis of this capture process of course is equally applicable to conditions following a hypothetical Venus–asteroid collision that disrupted a $k = 2$ resonance and placed the rotational state near the $k = -2$ resonance.

Escape from the $k = -2$ resonance state could have occurred either if inequality (34) ceased to be satisfied or if the viscous component ceased to be effective (e.g. if τ had increased sufficiently). With the rotation of Venus continuing to slow down after escape, the first Earth–Venus resonance state that is encountered is that with a period of 243·15 days (see below).

Planetary resonances

We shall now consider the effect on the rotational motion of the torques exerted by other planets and, in particular, the resonances that occur between the relative Venus–planet orbital motions and the axial rotation of Venus. As with Mercury, the shape of the inertia ellipsoid and the elastic properties of Venus are virtually unknown. We therefore cannot hope to formulate an accurate equation of motion for the axial rotation and must restrict ourselves to simple models. Only the planar aspects will be considered, primarily for simplicity and, secondarily, because the radar observations show Venus' rotation axis to be nearly perpendicular to its orbital plane[10].

Analysis shows that the effects of planetary torques exerted on a solar-induced body tidal bulge may be neglected in comparison with the corresponding torque exerted by the Sun; similarly, the solar and planetary torques exerted on a planet-induced body tidal bulge may be neglected[12, 13]. Atmospheric tides (both thermal and gravitational) also appear to be of little significance. The torque $T_p^{(S)}$ exerted by the Sun on the permanent equatorial asymmetry of the inertia ellipsoid has the form given on p. 195. The corresponding torque $T_p^{(p)}$ exerted by a planet can be expressed as (35), where (36), (37), and (38) apply and where μ_p is the product of the perturbing

$$T_p^{(p)} = -\frac{\beta_p'}{R_p^3} C \sin 2(\eta + \theta - v) \tag{35}$$

$$\beta_p' = \frac{3}{2}\mu_p \frac{B - A}{C} \tag{36}$$

$$R_p^2 = r_p^2 + r^2 - 2r_p r \cos(v - v_p) \tag{37}$$

$$\left.\begin{array}{l} R_p \sin \eta = r_p \sin(v - v_p) \\ R_p \cos \eta = r_p \cos(v - v_p) - r \end{array}\right\} \tag{38}$$

planet's mass and the gravitational constant, R_p is the Venus–planet distance, η is the angle between the Venus–planet line and the Sun–Venus line, r_p and v_p are the orbital radius and true anomaly of the perturbing planet, respectively, and the other quantities are defined as on p. 195. With the inclusion of $T_t^{(S)}$, $T_p^{(S)}$, and $T_p^{(p)}$ for one perturbing planet, the equation of motion becomes (39), where $\gamma_p = r/r_p$. The effects

$$\frac{d^2\theta}{dt^2} = -\frac{\alpha'}{r^6}\,\text{sgn}\left(\frac{d\theta}{dt} - \frac{dv}{dt}\right) - \frac{\beta'}{r^3}\sin 2(\theta - v)$$

$$-\frac{\beta_p'\sin 2(\theta - v_p) + \gamma_p^2\sin 2(\theta - v) - 2\gamma_p\sin(2\theta - v_p - v)}{r_p^3\{1 + \gamma_p^2 - 2\gamma_p\cos(v_p - v)\}^{5/2}} \tag{39}$$

of additional planets could be added in an obvious manner. As before, a first-order solution in α', β', and β_p' can be found and a stability analysis performed; however, numerical as well as analytical techniques are needed.

At first glance, one notes that $\beta' \gg \beta_p'$ and so questions the importance of $T_p^{(p)}$. But in the limit of circular orbits it is clear that to first order, at least, the effect of $T_p^{(S)}$ will cancel out. Furthermore, even for $e \neq 0$, the effect will tend to cancel in first order. Although realizing that second-order effects of $T_p^{(S)}$ must be considered before a reliable conclusion can be drawn, we may nevertheless consider the motion as influenced only by $T_p^{(p)}$ and $T_t^{(S)}$. It is clear that there will be resonances involving the planetary torque. These occur for spin periods such that a principal equatorial moment of inertia axis makes the same angle with the Venus–planet line at successive close approaches. Since dynamically one cannot distinguish between one or the other 'end' of the principal axis pointing in a given direction, this resonance condition can be phrased as follows. From the time of one close approach of Venus and a planet to the time of the next, Venus must rotate through an angle $\Delta v\,(0 \leq \Delta v < 2\pi)$ plus an integral number of half revolutions, where Δv represents the difference (modulo 2π) between the true anomaly of Venus at the beginning and at the end of this (synodic) time interval P_{sn}. Thus, (40) is true, where in general the negative values of m correspond to

$$\theta(P_{sn}) - \theta(0) = 2\pi\omega P_{sn} = m\pi + \Delta v, \qquad m = \ldots, -2, -1, 0, 1, 2, \ldots \tag{40}$$

resonances for retrograde rotation ($\omega < 0$). As before, we employ units in which the period and semimajor axis of the orbit of Venus are both unity and we measure the spin angular velocity ω in radians per radian. The difference in true anomaly is given by (41), where, for example, $q = 0, 2$, and 1 for Mercury, Earth, and Jupiter, respect-

$$\Delta v = 2\pi(P_{sn} - q) \tag{41}$$

ively. Since $P_{sn} = |1 - n_p|^{-1}$, where n_p is the ratio of the mean motion of the planet to that of Venus, the conditions for resonance are met if ω satisfies (42).

$$\omega = 1 + (\tfrac{1}{2}m - q)|1 - n_p| \tag{42}$$

Assuming the orbits to be circular and expressing $T_p^{(p)}$ in terms of m, we find, for example, that with the Earth as the perturbing planet the average torque over a synodic period can be expressed as (43), where θ_0 is the inclination of the principal axis of

$$\langle T_p^{(E)} \rangle = -\frac{\beta_E'}{a_E^3}\int_0^{2\pi}\frac{dx}{2\pi}$$

$$\times \frac{\sin\{2\theta_0 + (m-2)x\} + \gamma_E^2\sin\{2\theta_0 + (m-4)x\} - 2\gamma_E\sin\{2\theta_0 + (m-3)x\}}{\{1 + \gamma_E^2 - 2\gamma_E\cos x\}^{5/2}} \tag{43}$$

minimum moment of inertia to the Venus–Earth line at inferior conjunction. Similar expressions are obtained for Jupiter and Mercury. To illustrate the relative importance of the various resonances, we show in figures 9 to 11 the average values of $T_p^{(p)}$ as a function of m with $\theta_0 = \frac{1}{4}\pi$ for Earth, Jupiter, and Mercury, respectively. We note that $\langle T_p^{(E)} \rangle$ has its maximum at $\omega = 2n_E - 1$, corresponding to $m = 0$, and that the subsidiary peaks fall off rather gradually. The retrograde rotation with period 243·15 days corresponds to $\omega = -4 + 5n_E$ (i.e. to $m = -6$)* and appears rather undistinguished relative to the neighboring resonances. The maximum value

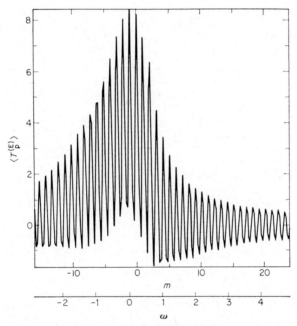

FIGURE 9   Average torque exerted by the Earth on Venus as a function of the spin angular velocity (the ordinate unit is arbitrary)

of $\langle T_p^{(J)} \rangle$ occurs for $\omega = n_J$ ($m = 0$) and the secondary peaks fall off rather precipitously. The retrograde rotation with a period of 250·5 days corresponds to $\omega = -1 + 2n_J$ ($m = -2$); in comparison with the neighboring Earth resonance, we find that $\langle T_p^{(J)} \rangle$ is an order of magnitude smaller. (The ordinate units though arbitrary are consistent throughout the three figures.) For $T_p^{(M)}$ there is no value of m which corresponds to a period in the neighborhood of 247 days; however, if Venus had a retrograde rotation with a period of 238 days, it would present the same face to Mercury at every other inferior conjunction. In any event $\langle T_p^{(M)} \rangle$ is considerably smaller than the relevant values for the Earth and Jupiter. In all cases, of course, the higher-order resonances lead to little enhancement of the average torque, since the rapid variations of $\cos(mx)$ cancel out the effects of the denominator of the integrand which does not vary appreciably during the interval $0 \leq mx \leq \pi$.

* This value of m corresponds to Venus making four complete revolutions during a synodic period as viewed by an Earth observer.

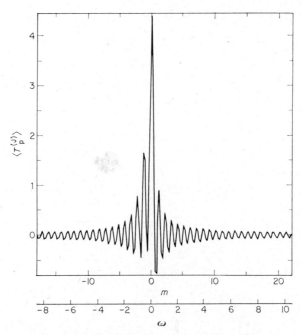

FIGURE 10   Average torque exerted by Jupiter on Venus as a function of the spin angular velocity (the ordinate unit is consistent with figure 9)

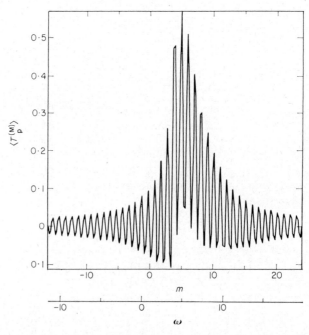

FIGURE 11   Average torque exerted by Mercury on Venus as a function of the spin angular velocity (the ordinate unit is consistent with figure 9)

A necessary condition for the retrograde rotational motion of Venus to be stable with a period nearly 243·15 days is (44). For the model we assumed for the tidal torque,

$$|\langle T_p^{(E)} \rangle| > |T_t^{(S)}| \tag{44}$$

this condition is equivalent to demanding that

$$\frac{B - A}{C} > 10^{-3}$$

if we assume $\alpha' \simeq 2 \times 10^{-7}$. Explaining the origin and persistence of such an equatorial asymmetry which would be about five times the lunar value might prove somewhat difficult; its existence would certainly be surprising. On the other hand, it is perhaps conceivable that α' is substantially smaller, having decreased appreciably during geologic times.

Note added in proof. Some similar ideas on the rotation of Venus were discussed independently and almost simultaneously by Goldreich and Peale[17,18].

References

1. G. H. Pettengill and R. B. Dyce, *Nature*, **206**, 1240 (1965).
2. R. B. Dyce, G. H. Pettengill, and I. I. Shapiro, *Astron. J.*, **71**, in press (1966).
3. A. Dollfus, *Bull. Soc. Astron. France*, **67**, 61 (1953).
4. S. J. Peale and T. Gold, *Nature*, **206**, 1240 (1965).
5. G. Colombo, *Nature*, **208**, 575 (1965).
6. G. Colombo and I. I. Shapiro, *Smithsonian Astrophys. Obs. Spec. Rept.*, **188R**, 1 (1965).
7. G. Colombo and I. I. Shapiro, *Astrophys. J.*, **145**, 296 (1966).
8. R. L. Carpenter, *Astron. J.*, **69**, 2 (1964).
9. R. M. Goldstein, *Astron. J.*, **69**, 12 (1964).
10. I. I. Shapiro, *Proc. Gen. Assembly Intern. Astron. Union, 12th, 1964*, Joint Discussion F.
11. G. H. Pettengill and I. I. Shapiro, *Ann. Rev. Astron. Astrophys.*, **3**, 377 (1965).
12. E. Bellomo, G. Colombo, and I. I. Shapiro, *Smithsonian Astrophys. Obs. Spec. Rept.*, in press (1967).
13. I. I. Shapiro, G. Colombo, and E. Bellomo, to be published.
14. D. Brouwer and G. M. Clemence, in *The Solar System III* (Eds. G. P. Kuiper and B. M. Middlehurst), University of Chicago Press, Chicago, 1961.
15. R. M. Goldstein, *J. Res. Nat. Bur. Std.*, *D*, **69**, 1623 (1965).
16. I. I. Shapiro, *J. Res. Nat. Bur. Std.*, *D*, **69**, 1632 (1965).
17. P. Goldreich and S. J. Peale, *Nature*, **209**, 1117 (1966).
18. P. Goldreich and S. J. Peale, *Astron. J.*, **71**, in press (1966).

H. ALFVÉN

Royal Institute of Technology
Stockholm, Sweden

Rotation of planets

The Period of Axial Rotation

Photometric registrations of asteroids show intensity variations which must be interpreted as produced by rotation of a body whose albedo is a function of its longitude. Several investigators have measured the periods of axial rotation of 27 asteroids. As has been pointed out elsewhere[1], the periods show no systematic dependence on the magnitudes of the asteroids. In fact, as is shown in figure 1, almost all asteroids have

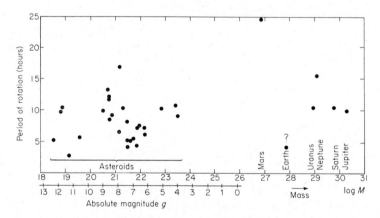

FIGURE 1   Periods of axial rotation for the asteroids in relation to their masses. To the right are included the periods of the ordinary planets

periods which deviate by less than 50% from an average of 8 or 9 hours. (It appears that this result is not due to observational selection.) If we consider the planets, we find that the same holds for the giant planets and also for the Earth before the capture of the Moon (according to Gerstenkorn[2]). Hence we find the very remarkable fact that the axial period is the *same* for a number of bodies with *very different masses*. In fact, when the mass varies by a factor of more than 10^{11}—from less than 10^{19} g (for small asteroids) up to more than 10^{30} g (for Jupiter)—the axial period varies by less than a factor 2.

This *law of isochronic rotation* of the celestial bodies obviously cannot be applied to bodies whose rotation is regulated by tidal action. Most satellites are probably examples of such bodies, because their axial periods are made equal to the orbital periods by the tides produced by their mother planets. The axial period of Mercury is $\frac{2}{3}$ of the orbital period, which according to Bellomo, Colombo, and Shapiro (see section V, chapter 3 of this book) is due to a tidal resonance. It is believed that also Venus is influenced by solar tides (as suggested by Bellomo, Colombo, and Shapiro). Hence the only remarkable exception to the isochronic law seems to be Mars (period 25 hours).

Conclusions from the Equality of the Periods

Concerning the mechanism producing the equality of the axial periods the following conclusions can be drawn.

(i) The equality of the periods cannot be produced by any factor acting today. For example, we cannot expect that the rotation of Jupiter is affected very much by forces acting now.

(ii) The equality of the periods cannot have anything to do with the rotational stability of the bodies. The giant planets, for example, are today very far from rotational instability. It is unlikely that one could find a mechanism by which the present isochronism can be connected with rotational instability during the prehistory of bodies as different as a small asteroid and a giant planet.

(iii) Hence the isochronism must be of cosmogonic origin. All the bodies must have been agglomerated by a process which has the characteristic feature that it makes their axial periods about equal, no matter how much mass they acquire. A two-step process for agglomeration, which has this property, has been suggested[3].

(iv) The braking of the axial rotation of the bodies has not been very significant since their agglomeration. A braking produced by a surrounding viscous medium should lengthen the period of a small body much more than the period of a larger body. The fact that asteroids as small as some ten kilometres rotate with the same periods as the largest planets indicates that not even such small bodies have been braked very much since they were formed. In essential respects the solar system seems to be in the same state now as when it was formed. This makes it reasonable that cosmogonically important results can be obtained from detailed analysis of the present state of the solar system, a view which is the background of the analysis by Alfvén[4] (chapters VI and VII).

(v) The isochronism shows further that the asteroids cannot derive from a broken-up planet. If a planet explodes (or is disrupted in some other way) we should expect an equipartition of the rotational energies of the parts. This means that the periods of axial rotation of the smallest asteroids should be much smaller than those of the larger asteroids. This is in conflict with observations. Other arguments against the broken-up planet theory have earlier been forwarded (see, for example, Alfvén[4], chapter VII).

Formation of Celestial Bodies in the Solar System

The general process of the formation of secondary bodies around a planet or around the Sun is the following:

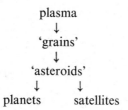

The first process is an accumulation of plasma at certain distances from the central body. This determines the general mass distribution in the system of secondary bodies. The central body transfers angular momentum to the plasma and this angular momentum is later found as orbital momentum of the secondary bodies.

The second process is a condensation of part of the plasma into 'grains', by which we may mean microscopic bodies or bodies of considerable size. The grains agglomerate to larger bodies, of the size of ordinary asteroids, and later to satellites or planets. This process has been discussed by Alfvén[4-6] in *Origin of the Solar System* (chapters V–VIII) and by Alfvén and Wilcox[7].

Both processes may proceed at the same time. It is the second process which is of interest to us in this connection. This process must be of such a character that it affects a build-up of larger and larger bodies, all of which have the same period of rotation.

Theory of Agglomeration

A two-step process of condensation has been proposed[3] which produces celestial bodies whose rotational periods are independent of both the mass of the body and of the rotational velocity of the plasma from which the condensation takes place. In this way it seems possible to account for the isochronism which has been found from observations.

The process consists of a condensation from a magnetized plasma, resulting in the formation of a number of small 'grains' which thereafter move only under the action of gravitation. A celestial body increases its mass by collecting such grains which move in Kepler orbits in its neighbourhood. Because the body collects only those grains whose orbits intersect the surface of the body, the growth of its mass and of its rotational momentum obeys such a law that isochronism is produced. The theory results in the relation

$$T\sqrt{\theta} = \left(\frac{3\pi}{2G}\right)^{1/2} \frac{25\alpha}{9C}$$

where T is the period of axial rotation, θ the density of the body (supposed to be homogeneous), G the constant of gravitation, and $\sqrt{\alpha}$ the radius of gyration divided by the radius of the sphere ($\alpha = 0\cdot4$). C is a numerical constant, which for the simplified case treated here is equal to $0\cdot46$. Under the simplifying assumptions the numerical value is

$$T\sqrt{\theta} = 5\cdot8 \text{ hours g}^{1/2}/\text{cm}^{3/2}$$

The value is independent of both the mass of the body and of the rotation of the plasma cloud from which the condensation takes place, and these are the properties we require in order to explain the isochronism. However, its absolute magnitude is too low by a factor of about 2, possibly because of oversimplification of the model.

Correction of the Internal Structure of the Bodies

In our theoretical model it has been assumed that the density of the body was homogeneous. This is probably a good approximation for the asteroids, but it is not true for the major planets, in which the density is much higher in the core than in the outer layers. In order to calculate the rotational period of a body with inhomogeneous density it is necessary to know not only the present density distribution within the body but also how the density has changed during the whole process of formation of the body. This is unknown.

However, we could use the following simplified, but still somewhat more realistic, model. We assume that during the formation the density was constant and had the present mean value, which means that $T\sqrt{\theta}$ should be constant during the formation. After the body was formed, there was a redistribution of matter inside the body so that the present distribution was produced. During this process the value of α changed from the value $\alpha_h = 0.4$, which characterizes a homogeneous sphere, to the present value of α, which is known from observations. This produces a decrease in the period of rotation by a factor of α/α_h.

This means that we expect

$$T \times A = \text{constant}$$

where A is a factor given by the internal density distribution so that

$$A = \sqrt{\theta}\,\alpha_h/\alpha$$

Comparison with Observations

Table 1 gives the observational values of the mean density θ, the relative moment of inertia α, the axial rotation period T, and the value of $T \times A$.

TABLE 1   Observational values of θ, α, T, and TA

Planet	θ	α	$A = 0.4\sqrt{\theta/\alpha}$	T (hours)	TA
Earth	5·52	0·33	2·9	<4·8	<14
Mars	3·97	0·39	2·0	24·6	50
Jupiter	1·33	0·25	1·8	9·8	18
Saturn	0·68	0·22	1·5	10·2	15
Uranus	1·60	0·23	2·2	10·8	24
Neptune	2·25	0·29	2·1	15	31
asteroids	3·5	0·40	1·9	8·2	16

The numerical values are taken from Allen[8]. The value for the Earth should refer to the state before the Moon was captured. According to Gerstenkorn[2] the value of the period of the Earth when the Moon was at the Roche limit was 4·8 hours. The period of the Earth before that time is uncertain because the original Moon may have broken up when it was at the Roche limit. The listed period for the asteroids is an average over all the known asteroid periods.

Table 1 shows that A does not vary very much, so the earlier results (figure 1) are not changed very much by taking account of the density and internal structure of the planets. The value of TA for Mars is abnormally high, but all the other bodies have about the same value ($TA \simeq 20$). The value for Neptune should be somewhat smaller because it has transferred some of its angular momentum to Triton, but the effect is probably not very large. The asteroids and Jupiter, representing the smallest and the largest of the bodies, have almost the same value of TA.

Hence the law of isochronic rotation is confirmed.

Formation of Celestial Bodies from a 'Contracting Nebula'

Since the time of Laplace many theories of the origin of the solar system have started from the concept of a 'contracting nebula', but the picture of this nebula has often been very vague.

In reality the general problem we encounter is how the following celestial bodies are formed: (i) stars, (ii) planets, (iii) satellites, and (iv) asteroids. The isochronism of planets and asteroids indicate that they probably are built up in the same way.

In a series of papers a number of arguments have been given for the view that both the satellite systems and the planetary system should be regarded as results of a general process of formation of secondary bodies around a central body. Very few people deny explicitly that the formation of satellites around a planet must be a process of the same kind as the formation of planets around the Sun. However, in spite of this a number of theories of the formation of the planets are proposed which obviously cannot be applied to the formation of the satellite systems.

Leaving such theories aside we may state that planets, satellites, and asteroids are likely to be built up by the same type of process.

From this follows that also the satellites originally should have obeyed the law of isochronism. However, tidal action from their mother planets has a very strong braking action and at least the innermost satellites are likely to have been braked so that their present axial period coincides with their orbital period. It may be worth while to investigate whether some of the outermost satellites have axial periods which differ from their orbital periods.

Having thus concluded that a build-up process of the general type discussed on p. 215 is likely to be responsible for the production of asteroids, satellites, and planets, we may ask whether also the stars could be formed in a similar way. Of course, in this case the 'grains' must be very large, but the size of the 'grains' forming planets must likewise be much larger than those forming the smallest satellites or asteroids.

It should first be noted that, although stars are likely to be produced from interstellar clouds, the simple model of a 'contracting nebula' does not work. This has been shown by Spitzer and others who demonstrate that there are two major difficulties: the angular momentum of the original cloud is far too large to allow a condensation, and also a frozen-in magnetic field may prohibit a contraction.

A two-step process of the kind we have discussed should therefore be considered as a possibility also for star formation.

McCrea[9] has suggested a process by which the stars are formed of 'floccules', which are sort of secondary condensations in a nebula, and which coalesce into stars when they collide. This is an interesting possibility of avoiding the Spitzer difficulties and is somewhat related to our mechanism. However, McCrea does not take into account any electromagnetic forces when treating the dynamics of cosmic clouds. Further, his theory of the formation of planets probably runs into difficulties when applied to the formation of satellites.

References

1. H. Alfvén, 'On the origin of the asteroids', *Icarus*, **3**, 52 (1964).
2. H. Gerstenkorn, 'Über die Gezeitenreibung beim Zweikörperproblem', *Z. Astrophys.*, **36**, 245 (1955).
3. H. Alfvén, 'On the formation of celestial bodies', *Icarus*, **3**, 57 (1954).
4. H. Alfvén, *On the Origin of the Solar System*, Clarendon Press, Oxford, 1954.
5. H. Alfvén, 'On the mass distribution in the solar system', *Astrophys. J.*, **136**, 1005 (1962).
6. H. Alfvén, 'On the early history of the Sun and the formation of the solar system', *Astrophys. J.*, **137**, 981 (1963).
7. H. Alfvén and J. M. Wilcox, 'On the origin of the satellites and the planets', *Astrophys. J.*, **136**, 1016 (1962).
8. C. W. Allen, *Astrophysical Quantities*, Athlone Press, London, 1963.
9. W. H. McCrea, 'The origin of the solar system', *Proc. Roy. Soc. (London), Ser. A*, **256**, 245 (1960).

5

P. GOLDREICH

and

S. PEALE

Department of Astronomy and Institute of Geophysics and Planetary Physics
University of California at Los Angeles
U.S.A.

Spin–orbit coupling in the solar system

Abstract*

Two possible types of resonant spin rates for planets and satellites are investigated. The first occurs in eccentric orbits at rotation rates which are commensurate with the orbital mean motion. A resonant spin state exists at each half-integer multiple of the mean motion, the simplest case being the well-known synchronous rotation. The second class of resonant spins involves the presence of another planet or satellite. A planet (or satellite) with such a resonant spin always aligns the same axis toward the second planet (or satellite) at each conjunction.

Averaged equations of motion are derived, and stability criteria are formulated for both types of resonance. Probabilities of capturing a planet (or satellite) into one of the commensurate rotation states as it is being despun by tidal friction are calculated.

Application of the results to Mercury reveals that the very small value of $(B - A)/C$ $(\times 10^{-8})$ would suffice to stabilize Mercury's rotation period at $\frac{2}{3}$ of its orbital period. The probability that Mercury would be captured at this resonance is calculated for several assumed forms of tidal torques. Venus may be in a resonant spin state of the second kind. A sidereal rotation period of 243·16 days retrograde would be commensurate with its synodic motion. However, a large value of $(B - A)/C \, (\gtrsim 10^{-4})$ seems to be required to stabilize this rotation. In addition, the capture probability at this resonance appears to be small.

* The full paper is published in *Astronomical Journal*, **71** (1966).

6

P. GOLDREICH

Department of Astronomy and Institute of Geophysics and Planetary Physics
University of California at Los Angeles
U.S.A.

The history of the lunar orbit

Abstract

A method of calculating the past states of the Earth–Moon system is developed. The method is based on the existence of three distinct time scales for dynamical change. The short time scale is determined by the revolution periods of the Sun and Moon about the Earth or, equivalently, by the year and current month. The intermediate time scale is set by the precessional motions of the lunar orbit plane and the Earth's equator plane. The rate at which tidal friction alters the state of the Earth–Moon system defines the long time scale. The equations of motion which govern the Earth–Moon system are successively averaged over the short, and then the intermediate, time scales. These averaged equations are then integrated back a short interval on the long time scale. The equations of motion appropriate to this new state of the Earth–Moon system are then reaveraged on the short and intermediate time scales, and once again the averaged equations are stepped back on the tidal time scale. The first step in this procedure (i.e. averaging on the short time scale) is performed analytically, whereas the calculations on the intermediate and long time scales require the use of a large computer.

At present, the inclination of the lunar orbit plane to the ecliptic remains nearly constant during the precessional motion. On the other hand, if the Moon's semimajor axis were ever less than $10R_{\oplus}$, the inclination of the lunar orbit plane would have maintained a fixed value with respect to the Earth's equator plane. The current investigation shows that this inclination could never have been less than $10°$ and, therefore, that the Moon could never have moved in an equatorial orbit. This result contradicts theories which postulate fission of the Earth to form the Moon and also those which propose that the Moon formed by accretion within $10R_{\oplus}$.

VI

The origin of the Moon

1. A palaeontological measurement of the rate of retreat of the
   Moon from the Earth (S. K. RUNCORN)   .   .   .   225

2. The model of the so-called 'weak' tidal friction and the
   limits of its applicability (H. GERSTENKORN)   .   .   229

3. The origin of the Moon I (H. ALFVÉN)   235

4. The origin of the Moon II (H. P. BERLAGE)   .   .   .   241

5. The origin of the Moon III (H. C. UREY)   .   .   .   251

6. The origin of the Moon IV (K. E. BULLEN)   .   .   .   261

1

S. K. RUNCORN

Department of Geophysics and Planetary Physics
School of Physics
University of Newcastle upon Tyne
England

A palaeontological measurement of the rate of retreat of the Moon from the Earth

The measurement of lunar tidal friction, and the secular deceleration of the Earth's rotation which it causes, has until recently been the concern of the astronomer. Halley[1] was the first to suggest that there was an unexplained acceleration in the Moon's mean longitude and he drew this inference from studies of the ancient eclipses recorded in classical literature. The value he obtained for the acceleration of the Moon in longitude was ten seconds per century per century. Naturally, attempts were made to explain this acceleration in terms of the perturbations caused by other bodies on the Moon. Finally the problem was set as a competition by the French Academy, a prize to be awarded for the discovery of the cause of this anomaly. Laplace won the prize with an essay in which he demonstrated that the Sun's action caused a change in the eccentricity of the Moon's orbit of very long period. This perturbation in the Moon's motion could be approximated by an acceleration in the Moon's longitude, which he found to be about ten seconds of arc per century per century. So it appeared at first that there was a satisfactory solution to the problem.

Later on Adams[2] of Cambridge reexamined these calculations, and found that Laplace had made a mistake; in fact by gravitational theory only about half the observed acceleration could be explained. So there was therefore an unknown term in the motion of the Moon, of about five seconds of arc per century per century, which had no gravitational explanation. The first person to suggest a possible solution was Kant[3], the German philosopher, who suggested that this acceleration of the Moon arose from lunar tidal friction. He argued that the tides raised by the Moon on the Earth dissipated its rotational energy. This implies that the tidal bulges lead on the Earth–Moon line owing to the Earth's rotation. It is now known that this lead angle is of the order of a degree. A torque results through the difference in the attraction of the Moon on the two tidal bulges. The resultant slowing down of the Earth's rotation lengthens the unit of time used by the astronomers. Therefore, as well as the acceleration of the Moon, accelerations of the Sun, Venus, and Mercury in longitude were predicted, for the positions of these bodies at various times would only have agreed with those worked out on gravitational theory, if the unit of time used in the observations had been invariable. Lunar tidal friction thus lengthens the unit of time and so gives rise to apparent accelerations of the longitudes of these bodies. These much smaller accelerations were eventually discovered. However, the angular momentum lost by the Earth through lunar tidal friction is transferred to the Moon. This alters the Moon's angular velocity around the Earth. Thus the observed secular acceleration of the Moon's longitude is the difference of two effects: an apparent acceleration due to the lengthening of the unit of time, and a real deceleration due to a gradual change in the Moon's orbit.

Now meridian telescopes at observatories have yielded exact measurements of the differences between the calculated position of the Moon on gravitational theory and the observed position over the last three or four hundred years. The results which have been obtained show that, in addition to the deceleration giving a parabolic term in the difference between the calculated and observed longitudes, there is a fluctuating discrepancy. Various attempts were made to explain it until finally Spencer-Jones[4] demonstrated that it arose from an irregular fluctuation in the length of the day, a phenomena different from the secular slowing down of the Earth's axial rotation. This has now been explained as an irregular coupling of the liquid core of the Earth with the mantle by the geomagnetic secular variation field. To calculate exactly the value of the deceleration of the Earth due to lunar tidal friction over the last few hundred years, these changes in the Earth's rotation due to internal motions in the Earth's fluid core must be eliminated. Spencer-Jones proved that the irregular fluctuations in the Moon's mean longitude were the result of changes in the rotation of the Earth and were not due to defects in the gravitational theory of the Moon's motion, by comparing the discrepancies in the Moon's longitude with those in the longitudes of the Sun, Mercury, and Venus. He made the motions comparable, by multiplying each by the ratio of the Moon's mean motion, with that of the other bodies. Spencer-Jones was able to show that, if the real acceleration of the Moon about the Earth is eliminated, the remainder is due to changes in the Earth's rotation or in the unit of time, for the errors or anomalies between calculations and theory in the longitudes of the Sun, Venus, and Mercury agree with those of the Moon. As the Sun's motion against the fixed stars is only 1/13·4 times that of the Moon, the Moon is the best object from the point of view of measuring the irregular fluctuations in the rate of rotation of the Earth.

Munk and MacDonald[5] have produced a useful method of examining the data. They suppose that the discrepancies in the longitude of the Sun, Venus, and Mercury, which are reasonably in agreement, give the changes of the unit of time, that is the changes in the Earth's rotation. They then can make use of these changes in the rotation of the Earth to remove from the Moon's motion the effects of this change in the length of the day. They demonstrated that the differences in the Moon's longitude so obtained lie along a parabola. This shows that the Moon has a real acceleration in longitude which, if the conservation of angular momentum of the Earth–Moon system is to be satisfied, can only be due to a deceleration of the Earth through lunar tidal friction. Thus the effects on the Earth's rotation which arise from inside the Earth have been eliminated and the value of the real acceleration of the Moon due to lunar tidal friction can be obtained by fitting a parabola to these measurements referred to above. The value so obtained for the lunar tidal frictional torque over the last few centuries is reasonably accurate and equals $3·9 \times 10^{23}$ dyn cm.

That based on the eclipse data is larger and it has not been possible to decide whether the reliability of this figure is good enough to conclude that lunar tidal friction has changed. The latter depends on records from 2000 years ago of the places from which lunar and solar eclipses were seen. An approximate knowledge of the data of the eclipse enables the eclipse to be identified. A discrepancy between the modern determination of the lunar tidal frictional torque on the basis of astronomical observations over the last few hundred years and that based on the ancient eclipses which span 2000 years is not unlikely. From the work of Jeffreys[6] and Taylor[7] we know that tidal friction occurs largely in shallow seas, because the tidal currents and particularly their gradients are greater there. It is possible that changes in sea level and in the coast lines could alter the value of the lunar tidal frictional torque quite considerably in the course of thousands or tens of thousands of years, especially in view of the changes of sea level which have occurred since the last Ice Age. On the other hand, these changes could merely alter the location of the frictional dissipation without altering the total amount.

If the value is supposed constant throughout geological time, Slichter[8] demonstrated that difficulties arise. The effect of a loss of angular momentum by the Earth is to increase the Moon's distance from the Earth. If T is the length of the month and R the Earth–Moon distance, then from Kepler's laws, neglecting the small eccentricity of the Moon's orbit, we find that G^2T is proportional to the cube of the Moon's orbital angular momentum L and GR is proportional to the square, where G is the gravitational constant. Thus, if the Earth as the result of tidal friction loses angular momentum to the Moon, L increases and so R increases. This fact, that the Moon is retreating from the Earth, was first pointed out by Darwin[9], who first appreciated its significance in the discussion of the origin of the Moon. Now the value of the lunar tidal frictional torque depends, of course, on the Earth–Moon distance. The height of the equilibrium tide depends on $1/R^3$. The difference in the attraction of the Moon on the two tidal bulges depends on the gravitational field gradient of the Moon which is again proportional to $1/R^3$. Thus, if other parameters are constant, the lunar tidal friction torque varies as $1/R^6$. If we look back in time, the change in the torque and therefore in the Earth–Moon distance was once catastrophic and the Moon rushes towards the Earth. Though this was known a long time ago, it had been thought that the critical time was equal to, or greater than, the Earth's age. Slichter pointed out that, as a result of certain recalculations of the lunar tidal frictional torque and owing to the fact that the age of the Earth is now about $4\frac{1}{2}$ billion years, a real problem exists because the critical time is about two thousand million years ago.

This supposed difficulty in the early history of the Earth–Moon system has not perhaps been taken too seriously, because it was thought that lunar tidal friction was very unlikely to have been constant. The difficulty was easily avoided by supposing that the present value of lunar tidal friction is greater than that typical for geological time. The parameter in the discussion could then be adjusted to avoid the critical time being so relatively recent as the last thousand or two thousand million years. However, as the result of a new way of determining the rotation of the Earth in the geological past, it has become possible to determine the value of lunar tidal friction over a really long period of geological time, and this has given a new dimension to this discussion.

Wells[10] suggested that on well-preserved epitheca of Devonian rugose corals the tiny lines or ridges 1/20 mm thick are daily increments of growth. It had previously been argued particularly by Ma[11] that the much broader bands also seen are annual growth increments. Thus Wells, by counting the number of the tiny ridges in each band, obtained a value for the number of days in the Devonian year. If we suppose that the year was constant, then the length of the day is obtained. Wells, by a simple count, found 400 days in the Devonian year. This was at once seen to be an encouraging result. If one extrapolates back the present effect of tidal friction in lengthening the day by two milliseconds per century, one finds that in the middle Devonian Period, about 370 million years ago, the length of the day was shorter by about 2 hours and this is what Wells found. However, every theory of the Earth's evolution predicts that the moment of inertia of the Earth has changed. The theory of growth of the Earth's core, for example, predicts a decreasing moment of inertia and will therefore alter the rotation of the Earth in the opposite sense to tidal friction. This idea originated with Urey[12] who argued that the Earth had formed by accretion and that originally the iron was distributed throughout the mantle and had only gradually collected to form a core. Wells' observations were not sufficiently accurate, nor can the theoretical value of lunar tidal friction be calculated with sufficient confidence for past times, to separate internal effects from those of the Moon in changing the Earth's rotation. The count of the number of days in the year only is not sufficient.

However, Scrutton[13] has identified, on the epitheca of Devonian corals, other bands which, as he found each band contained 30·6 days, he concludes are monthly. We know that the tides do affect marine life in various ways and so from Scrutton's work a value can be obtained for the number of days in the month. Therefore, the length of the month is obtained as a fraction of the year by dividing Scrutton's count (s) by Wells' count (w). Runcorn[14] shows that, if both the length of the month and the length of the day are known for any geological time, the changes in the Earth's rotation due to the lunar tidal frictional torque can be separated from those due to other causes. The lunar tidal friction will alter the length of the month so that any change in the Earth's rotation due to a change in the Earth's moment of inertia can be separately determined, if an allowance is made for the effect of solar tidal friction. Thus the mean value of the lunar tidal frictional torque since the Devonian Period can be found from Wells' and Scrutton's counts and it works out to be $3·9 \times 10^{23}$ dyn cm. It does now appear that the dilemma first posed by Slichter is one which must be faced in all theories of the origin of the Moon.

References

1. E. Halley, *Phil. Trans. Roy. Soc. London, Ser. A*, **19**, 174 (1695).
2. J. C. Adams, *Phil. Trans. Roy. Soc. London, Ser. A*, **143**, 397 (1853).
3. E. Kant, quoted in *Handbuch Phys., Geophys.* 1, **1956**, 3.
4. H. Spencer-Jones, *Monthly Notices Roy. Astron. Soc.*, **99**, 541 (1939).
5. W. H. Munk and G. J. F. MacDonald, *The Rotation of the Earth—a Geophysical Discussion*, Cambridge University Press, London, 1960.
6. H. Jeffreys, *The Earth*, Cambridge University Press, London, 1952.
7. G. I. Taylor, *Phil. Trans. Roy. Soc. London, Ser. A*, **220**, 1 (1919).
8. L. B. Slichter, *J. Geophys. Res.*, **68**, 4281–8 (1963).
9. G. H. Darwin, *Scientific Papers*, Vol. II, Cambridge University Press, Cambridge, 1908, p. 368.
10. J. W. Wells, *Nature*, **197**, 948 (1963).
11. T. Y. H. Ma, *Research on the Past Climate and Continental Drift*, Taiwan, **XIV** (1958).
12. H. C. Urey, *Geochim. Cosmochim. Acta*, **1**, 209 (1951).
13. C. T. Scrutton, *Palaeontology*, **7**, 552 (1964).
14. S. K. Runcorn, *Nature*, **204**, 823–5 (1964).

2

H. GERSTENKORN

Hannover
Western Germany

The model of the so-called 'weak' tidal friction and the limits of its applicability

When talking about tidal friction, one is normally thinking of two tidal bulges; these bulges are carried over the surface of the Earth. Usually one envisages the bulges as real differences in the level of the ocean. But often one connects with the conception of two bulges the image of a deformation of the Earth as a whole to an ellipsoid with rotational symmetry. The axis of this ellipsoid forms a small angle φ with the line joining the centres of Earth and Moon. The ellipsoid originates under the influence of the gravitation of the Moon as an equipotential surface. The angle φ is caused in the last resort by the dissipation of energy, connected with the tidal movements of matter, either in the seas or in the body of the Earth. Further, the image is as follows. The Moon, considered as a point, exerts a retarding couple on these tidal bulges. On the one hand, the couple chiefly retards the rotation of the planet; on the other, it changes the distance Earth–Moon and the eccentricity of its orbit in accordance with the law of invariance of the total angular momentum. If the Moon does not travel in the equator of the Earth, it is usual to retain this image with the two bulges; then changes of the obliquity of the orbit are the inevitable consequence.

It does not seem to be generally known that this simple image does not always satisfy the real conditions, even if the tidal friction is 'weak'. The failure of the model is caused by the fact that the tidal potential is not characterized by only one single frequency. As harmonical analysis shows, the potential is given generally by a sum of periodic terms with many different frequencies. Each term corresponds to a partial deformation of the body of the planet. The phase angles of these deformations may be dependent on the frequency. This depends on the assumptions concerning the physical properties of the matter participating in the tidal movements. Only under definite assumptions about these properties is the deformed surface of the Earth the result of simply turning the equipotential surface by a small angle. The model with the two bulges outlined above, however, is based just on this image. In an investigation of this problem in 1954 the author[1-3] showed that the model holds true absolutely if we consider the Earth as a viscous liquid of small viscosity, as Darwin[4] did in his detailed investigations of this problem in the last century. Thus, if dissipation of energy takes place mainly in the mantle of the Earth, and if the temperatures there are high enough, this procedure is allowed. But, if the loss of energy is caused by other reasons, for example by tides in flat seas or by events in the crust, then the question as to applicability of the simple model cannot be principally answered in the affirmative.

Nevertheless, let us first outline the main results of the 1954 calculations, based on this model. The torque of the tidal friction today increases the angular momentum of the Moon's orbit and decreases the angular momentum of the Earth's rotation. In this model, by forming the mean over the period of the revolution, the torque has two components, $\frac{1}{2}h\omega_E \sin \varepsilon$ and $h(\omega_E \cos \varepsilon - \omega)$, in the directions transverse to the node of the orbit and to the normal of the orbit, respectively. Essentially the factor h increases reciprocally with the sixth power of the Earth–Moon distance. The component transverse to the node changes the direction of the angular momentum of the orbit; the other component changes the amount of this angular momentum. The ratio of the two components is of great importance in the relation between the radius and the obliquity of the orbit. This ratio is independent of the factor h, the value of which is rather uncertain; also the factor one-half is valid only for this model. Beyond this, only for the model of 'weak' tidal friction are the components of the torque given by two such simple terms. We shall discuss this below.

The model gives, as a main result, a minimum of the orbital angular momentum and, therefore, also of the Earth–Moon distance for $r = 2.89R$ (Roche limit) for a time in the past; before this time, the Moon was, however, more distant. Simultaneously, the obliquity of its orbit increased towards large values. These were for the distance minimum about 45°; still further back in time, values of more than 90° resulted, and thereby it was possible that the Moon had a formerly retrograde revolution. The length of a day at that time was approximately only 5 hours. But the expected increase of the eccentricity of the orbit towards the value 1, near the minimum of distance, did not follow. Only far beyond the minimum did the transition into a parabolic orbit take place. From these considerations, obvious deficiencies in this model become apparent. These can be caused by not allowing for the so-called 'radial' tides in the Earth and more importantly in the Moon. They are tides with a period of revolution in an eccentric orbit, in which a dissipation of energy, but no exchange of angular momentum, takes place. But the reason for these deficiencies may be seen just as well in the assumptions concerning the physical mechanism of the dissipation of energy in a homogeneous liquid of small viscosity. The course of eccentricity obviously depends on the assumptions about this dissipation, and thereby about the model used; this is easily seen by forming the equation for the change in time of the eccentricity. This restriction does not seem to be valid to this extent for the obliquity of the orbit, and even less for the distance Earth–Moon.

Nevertheless the question arises as to what extent treating the problem by means of the model outlined above is justified. Till now, an answer is hardly possible because of the lack of profound knowledge of the physical conditions in the bodies of Earth and Moon. The reaction by periodic forces in different zones in the depth for small frequencies of $10^{-4} \sec^{-1}$ is not known very exactly.

To obtain a survey, a simple model for the matter of the Earth is needed. But this model should be more extensive than the model of a simple viscous liquid. The liquid model should be contained in the new model as a limiting case. Therefore, in the following, the Earth is treated as a so-called 'Maxwell body' with the well-known relation between strain and stress:

$$\frac{dP}{dt} + \frac{P}{\tau} = 2\mu \frac{d\varepsilon}{dt}$$

P is the stress, ε the strain, μ the rigidity, and τ the relaxation time. For a periodic process, the tensor between the components of strain and stress has the same form as in the case of a body with perfect elasticity; however, the rigidity μ must be substituted for by a complex one $\tilde{\mu}$, which is related to the relaxation time and the frequency by

$$\frac{1}{\tilde{\mu}} = \frac{1}{\mu}\left(1 + \frac{1}{i\omega\tau}\right)$$

i is the unit imaginary number. The incompressibility K keeps its former numerical value as a second parameter. The Earth is considered as being homogeneous; therefore, it is necessary to substitute for K and μ suitable mean values over the mantle. Then, such a mean value is also needed for the relaxation time. This body is exposed to a periodic external perturbation; the potential has the form of a spherical harmonic of the nth order; the case $n = 2$ is especially studied in more detail. Periodic shifts of the masses result, and generate on their part an additional periodic potential of gravitation; this ought to be taken into consideration. The expression for the resulting deformation is given by

$$s_j = \left\{\frac{\partial}{\partial x_j}(Fr^n Y_n) + x_j Gr^n Y_n\right\} \exp(i\omega t)$$

If the condition $|\sigma\omega^2/\tilde{\mu}| \ll 4n + 6$ is fulfilled, the so-called terms of inertia can be neglected in the differential equations. Then the function G is, to a good approximation, a complex constant independent of the distance r from the centre, and F is given by an expression $F = F_0 + cr^2$, to the second order in r. Furthermore, surface conditions ought to be fulfilled for tangential and radial components. Then it is possible to find the complete solution of the problem by voluminous, but elementary, calculations. For the order $n = 2$ and for the case of an incompressible Earth especially, the deviation of the surface in the radial direction is given by

$$\frac{s}{R} = \frac{5\tau_2}{19\tilde{\mu} + 2\sigma g R}$$

τ_2 is a constant of the perturbing potential (in this case $\tau_2 = fm\sigma/r^3$). This result is transformed for $\tilde{\mu} = \mu$ (a body with perfect elasticity) into the well-known relation for an ideal Earth. Then, the ratio $z = 2\sigma g R/19\mu$ has a value ~ 0.3. For an Earth with finite compressibility, one obtains a more complicated expression. Furthermore, we obtain expressions for the phase angles and the amount of dissipation of energy.

As is known, the Maxwell body reacts to different frequencies in very different ways. For $\omega\tau \ll z$, it behaves nearly like a liquid of small viscosity. In the other limiting case $\omega\tau \gg 1$, it behaves nearly like an ideal solid body. Both cases are characterized by small phases φ. It is of general interest that, for an incompressible Earth, the dissipation of energy per second in the interior of a sphere with radius $r < R$ depends in both cases, and in the interval between them, in the same way on this radius, namely

$$\dot{E} \sim 6r^7 - 16r^5 R^2 \quad \text{for} \quad n = 2$$

It means that in this homogeneous model one-half of the dissipation takes place in the uppermost zone; the thickness of it is approximately one-sixth of the Earth's radius.

For the case of a compressible Earth, we need not expect greater deviations from this result. In the mantle of the Earth K is $m\mu$, with the parameter m within the narrow limits $1.9 < m < 2.2$. If we calculate the phase $\sin\varphi$ as a function of $\omega\tau$, we obtain a curve which behaves as though it nearly coincides with that which is valid for the case m

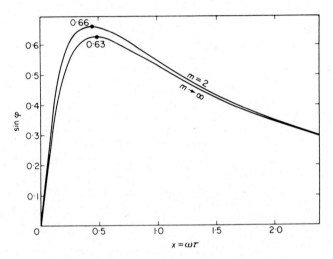

FIGURE 1   The phase φ is shown as a function of frequency

tending to infinity, i.e. the limiting case of incompressibility. The differences in the ordinates are small (see figure 1):

$$\tan\varphi = \frac{10x}{3 + 13x^2}, \qquad \tan\varphi = \frac{(4.08 + 4.32x^2)x}{1 + 6.31x^2 + 5.55x^4}, \qquad x = \omega\tau$$

The maximal values of φ, $\varphi = 39°$ and $\varphi = 42°$, are for $\omega\tau = 0.48$ and 0.43, respectively. Therefore it seems a good approximation to use the simple formulae for incompressibility. The left-hand side of the curve shows a nearly linear increase of φ with $\omega\tau$; here the body behaves like a liquid. Then a transition zone follows with a maximum. On the right-hand side, we find $\varphi \sim 1/\omega\tau$; the body behaves like a solid. Large phases are existent only in the transition zone near the maximum $\omega\tau \simeq \frac{1}{2}$. In this region we also find the maximum of the loss of energy per second, if we consider this loss as a function of the relaxation time τ for a given frequency. In both outer parts of the curve, on the left and also on the right, the phases are small. But only for Darwin's[4] case of a viscous liquid (on the left-hand side) may we speak of 'weak' tidal friction in the proper sense; for this case only is φ proportional to $\omega\tau$. This condition is of great importance for the harmonical analysis of the tidal movements and enables us to make the decisive simplifications of Darwin's model.

Strictly speaking, the above-mentioned is valid only for the special case of homogeneity. How far this calculated model fulfils the conditions in the real inhomogeneous Earth must be left undecided. Indeed, by substituting appropriate mean values for μ, K, and density σ, we probably are not making any serious mistakes. But if we use the relaxation time in a similar way, we get into difficulties. For, as is known, the value of the relaxation time τ varies from 10^{10} sec for the crust to 10 sec or less near the boundary of the core. Therefore, $\omega\tau \gg 1$ is valid for the crust and $\omega\tau \ll 1$ for the deeper zones of the mantle, for the usual tidal frequencies $\omega \simeq 10^{-4}$ sec^{-1}. The main difficulty is to find a good mean value for the relaxation time.

In accordance with the preceding, each frequency ω is correlated with a phase φ. If this correlation is known, it is in principle possible to calculate the total deformation of the Earth's body at any given point for a given time. We can develop the tidal potential into a series of Legendre functions of the distance from the zenith; each of them is written as a sum of spherical surface harmonics multiplied by a sum of periodic time functions. An example for such a partial term is

$$V_n^m = Y_n^m \sum_i \{a_i \cos(\omega_i t) + b_i \sin(\omega_i t)\}$$

$$Y_n^m = P_n^m \cos(m\phi) \quad \text{or} \quad P_n^m \sin(m\phi)$$

P_n^m are Legendre associated functions of the first kind. The tidal wave is given as the sum of all partial waves $s = \Sigma_n s_n$. The deviation of the term written above is given by

$$s_n^m = Y_n^m \sum_i \{a_i' \cos(\omega_i t - \varphi_i) + b' \sin(\omega_i t - \varphi_i)\}$$

The amplitudes and phases are dependent on the frequency. For the homogeneous case, the phase φ is shown as a function of the frequency in figure 1. But the structure of the term forming the partial deviation s_n is not changed considerably, even if we account for the inhomogeneity of the interior of the Earth, or if we use another relation between strain and stress. However, if the condition $\varphi = \omega_i T \ll 1$ is fulfilled with $T = \tau/z$ (which is independent of the frequency), only in the single case is the simple relation valid for all terms

$$s_n = cV(t - T)$$

In this case only can the surface of the Earth be considered as a tidal equipotential surface for an earlier time $t - T$, that is the tidal figure of the order n is simply turned by a small angle. But that is just the same as the above-mentioned model with the tidal bulges, which is easy to calculate. The condition for its applicability is $\omega\tau \ll z$, that is the case of a Darwin liquid with small viscosity. Here we are dealing with a 'weak' tidal friction in the proper sense. The other condition $\varphi \ll 1$ alone is not sufficient for this; what is decisive is the proportionality between φ and ω. In all other cases, the image of a tidal figure, deviated by a small angle from equilibrium, is not really justified, but at best it is a more or less rough approximation. For a Maxwell body, this is also true for the limiting case of a solid body with $\omega\tau \gg 1$, though the phases φ are much less than 1; the partial tide has a form other than the level of the corresponding generating potential. This statement holds true also for MacDonald's[5,6] assumption, φ is a constant, which is independent of the frequency ω. Therefore, unfortunately, harmonical analysis is unavoidable. This fact is apparently overlooked by Mac-Donald[5,6]. His tidal figure originates simply by turning the potential surface by a small angle in contradiction to the consequences of his own assumption that φ is constant. This would be true only if the Moon travels in a circular orbit around the equator and if, in addition, the order is $n = 2$. Even for $n = 3$, two different frequencies appear in the equations, namely $\omega_E - \omega$ and $3(\omega_E - \omega)$; consequently, there are also two different phases. Therefore MacDonald's calculation will be more correct the smaller the obliquity ε of the Moon's orbit. For large values of ε, it is difficult to estimate the error of his approximation. As can be seen, outside the limits of validity of the case of 'weak' tidal friction, there are enormous difficulties in using the required harmonical analysis. For example, if we compute the two components of the torque mentioned above, instead of a single term we obtain 5 or 7 terms, respectively, with just as many phases φ. Moreover, for the above-mentioned reasons these angles are not definitely known. At best, numerical methods by means of a computer show some promise in obtaining results. It would be of some interest, for example, to know the differences that will result compared with the calculations using Darwin's model (both calculated for a circular orbit, for example). We expect primarily slightly changed values for the obliquity.

In fact, it would be necessary before beginning such a calculation to study the behaviour of an inhomogeneous Earth under the influence of a periodic potential. The case of an Earth, in which the relaxation time varies with depth, is especially of interest. Unfortunately, we fall into great mathematical difficulties; these are added to by insufficient knowledge of the law between relaxation time and depth. Indeed, it is formally possible to give solutions of the problem for special assumptions for the complex rigidity as a function of the distance r of the considered point from the centre of the Earth; but the phases and the dissipation of energy in different zones of depth cannot be found without some numerical work. This is even more relevant to the question of the total amount of dissipation in the Earth and to its dependence on the frequency.

We can presume, however, that the phase and dissipation are large at a depth where the condition $\omega\tau \simeq 1$ is nearly fulfilled. The greater the frequency, the deeper lies the corresponding zone. For tidal frequencies $\omega \simeq 10^{-4}\ \sec^{-1}$, we may estimate it to be at a depth of almost 2000 km; for the greater frequencies of earthquakes it is about 1000 km deeper. If the frequency is slightly changed (for example from ω_E to $\omega_E \pm \omega$), we may expect only a corresponding slight displacement of this zone, which responds maximally to the external forces, and thus we expect a relative slight change of the total dissipation in the Earth as a whole. It is in such a way that we can possibly interpret MacDonald's assumption of a constant value for the phase φ, which he derives from the empirical data.

By this example of a Maxwell body it is shown, it is hoped, that the physical mechanism of the energy dissipation of tidal events is of great importance (whenever we leave the limits of the model of the so-called 'weak' tidal friction in Darwin's meaning) to the methods and results of a calculation back in time for the Earth–Moon system. At present we cannot say with certainty whether our problem of the Earth–Moon system using Darwin's model is sufficient, or whether we have to leave the limits of this model to obtain more correct results.

References

1. H. Gerstenkorn, *Z. Astrophys.*, **36**, 245 (1955).
2. H. Gerstenkorn, *Z. Astrophys.*, **42**, 137 (1957).
3. H. Alfvén, *Icarus*, **1**, 357 (1963).
4. G. H. Darwin, *Scientific Papers*, Vol. II (*Tidal Friction*), Cambridge University Press, Cambridge, 1906.
5. G. J. F. MacDonald, *Science*, **145**, 881 (1964).
6. G. J. F. MacDonald, *Rev. Geophys.*, **2**, 467 (1964).

3

H. ALFVÉN
Royal Institute of Technology
Stockholm, Sweden

The origin of the Moon I

The Moon Compared with Other Satellites

The Earth–Moon system is so different from most other planet–satellite systems that we must count the Moon as an 'abnormal' satellite, which is not generated in the same way as the 'normal' satellites.

As typical examples of 'normal' satellites we could take the Galilean satellites of Jupiter, the inner satellites of Saturn, and the five satellites of Uranus. All these bodies move in the same sense as the planet rotates; their orbits are almost circular ($e < 0.03$) and are situated very close to the equatorial planes of the planets ($i < 2°$). The mass of a normal satellite is very small compared with the planet (less than 3×10^{-4}).

Besides the normal satellites there are a number of very small satellites which must be classified as 'abnormal', viz. the four outermost satellites of Jupiter, and the outermost satellite (Phoebe) of Saturn. They move in a retrograde sense and their orbits have high eccentricities and inclinations. Their masses are less than 10^{-6} of that of the planet. They are usually considered to be captured asteroids.

We shall not here enter into a detailed classification of all the known satellites[1,2,3], but we shall direct our attention to the Earth–Moon system, and also to the Neptune–Triton system which in some respects is similar to the former. The Moon–Earth mass ratio is 1.2×10^{-2} and the Triton–Neptune ratio is 1.3×10^{-3}. Hence in both cases the satellites are considerably larger than normal satellites. The orbital distance of Triton is comparable with the distances of the Uranian satellites, but as it moves in a retrograde sense its origin must be different.

General Laws for the Formation of Celestial Bodies

The problem of how the Moon originated is, of course, part of the general problem of how the celestial bodies in our solar system were formed. A theory of the formation of the solar system has been developed in a number of papers[1-8], and the general features of this theory are as follows.

(i) The interest is centred more on the satellite systems than on the planetary system. The reason is that we have three well-developed satellite systems, but only one planetary system; so the satellites provide us with more empirical data with which to compare a theory. Moreover, a number of hypotheses, which may seem reasonable for the formation of planets around the Sun, are not acceptable when applied to the formation of satellite systems. The theory which is developed is a general theory of formation of small bodies around a central body, and it turns out that the theory can be applied not only to the satellite systems, but also to the planetary system.

(ii) Secondary bodies cannot be produced by ejection of matter from the central body. They must originate from matter falling in towards the central body.

(iii) At the formation of the satellite systems the mother planets were in a state which is rather similar to the present state. A study of the rotation of the planets which is discussed elsewhere in this book (section V, chapter 4) (see also Alfvén[6, 7]) excludes the possibility that the planets earlier contained much more mass than now. Theories in which 'protoplanets' have properties that are much different from the present planets are not acceptable.

(iv) The general cosmogonic process is the following:

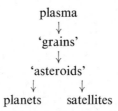

Out of a plasma surrounding the central body there is a condensation to what we may call 'grains', moving in Kepler orbits with relatively small eccentricities. The grains later coalesce into larger asteroid-like bodies, which finally combine to form satellites (or planets).

(v) The mass distribution in a satellite system, or in the planetary system, is determined by the process through which plasma is collected at different distances from the central body.

(vi) The production of secondary bodies is centred on the problem of how, in principle, mass could be accumulated near a planet like the Earth, within its magnetosphere. It is obvious that under the present conditions, when the magnetosphere is situated in an interplanetary plasma wind, no appreciable accumulation of matter can take place. However, if, instead, jets of neutral gas were falling down into the magnetosphere, these would not be affected by the magnetic field and would not be stopped until the gases became ionized. This should take place when the gas velocity reaches a certain value v_c, called the 'critical velocity', which is approximately given by the relation $\frac{1}{2}mv_c^2 = eV_{ion}$ (m is the atomic mass and eV_{ion} is the ionization energy). This phenomenon has been the subject of extensive experimental studies with modern plasma research techniques[9, 10].

(vii) It is likely that a group of bodies (two to five bodies) will be formed in the region where the critical velocity is reached. The critical velocities belonging to the different groups of bodies agree with the values for the most common elements in the cosmos. However, there is no simple relation between these elements and the chemical constitutions of the bodies produced by the different resulting clouds, because the process of condensation is very complicated.

(viii) All the planets and the normal satellites can be classified by two parameters: (i) the gravitational energy in relation to the central body, and (ii) the ratio between the orbital period and the axial rotation period of the central body (see figure 1).

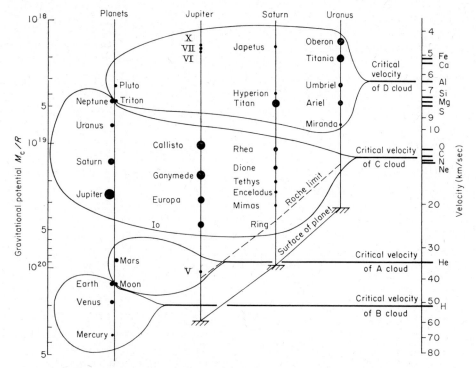

FIGURE 1   Gravitational potential diagram of the planetary system and of the satellite systems of Jupiter, Saturn, and Uranus. The vertical scale on the left, M_c/R, is a measure of the gravitational energy per gramme of the indicated body in the field of its corresponding central body (M_c is the mass of central body and R is the orbital radius of indicated body about its corresponding central body).

The diagram shows that the giant planets have about the same gravitational energy per unit mass in the field of the Sun as the Galilean satellites have in the field of Jupiter and the inner Saturnian satellites have in the field of Saturn, and hence all these bodies may have been produced from similar clouds of in-falling material. However, it is not expected that Uranus has satellites with the same gravitational potential, because the corresponding value is reached too close to the surface of the planet. For the same reason one would not expect to find satellites analogous to the Mercury–Venus–Earth group. The fifth Jovian satellite may have an origin similar to the Moon–Mars group. The top of the diagram shows that the Uranian satellites, the Saturnian outer satellites, and the Jovian satellites VI, VII, and X have similar values of gravitational potential. It is likely that Pluto and Triton belong to the same group. According to the diagram there is an overlap between adjacent groups in two cases, represented by the 'double planets' Earth–Moon and Neptune–Triton

Formation of Double Planets

With this as a general background we can state that there should be an overlap of orbits between adjacent groups of bodies only in two cases: one is associated with the Earth–Moon system, and the other with the Neptune–Triton system. In both cases we could imagine that the formation process has produced two groups of planets so close to each other that one member of one group moves in an orbit very close to that of one member of the other group. Under certain conditions a capture is possible.

In this connection it is of interest to note that Dole[11] has calculated possible orbits for small bodies which originally move in circular Kepler orbits around the Sun, but reach the vicinity of a planet which is also assumed to move in a circular orbit. In the neighbourhood of the planet the small bodies may move in orbits which are extremely complicated. In some cases the small bodies spend rather a long time in the close neighbourhood of the planet, looping it either in a direct, or in a retrograde, sense.

Under the idealized initial conditions which Dole assumes (zero mass of small body, the planet moves in a circular orbit, etc.), no capture is possible (except by impact). The small body will be deflected and after the encounter move in a new heliocentric Kepler orbit. The new orbit has the property that sooner or later a new encounter will take place (or in any case has a high probability of taking place). Hence, if the two bodies have passed close to each other once, there may be a great number of encounters during the lapse of time.

If we admit more complicated (and realistic) assumptions, we conclude that one of these encounters may lead to a capture. In the case of the Moon, as well as Triton, the bodies are so large that tidal effects are of importance. The effect of the tides which a satellite produces on a planet is that the orbital distance of the satellite will usually increase if it moves in a direct sense, but decrease if its motion is retrograde. Hence, if a body is captured into a direct-sense orbit, tidal effects will loosen the binding so that it may be ejected again. On the other hand, after a capture into a retrograde orbit, tidal effects will strengthen the binding, bringing the captured body closer to the planet.

Thus, if the small body is so large that tidal effects are of importance, these will have a destabilizing effect on a direct orbit capture, but a stabilizing effect on a retrograde orbit capture. From this we conclude that the final result—possibly after a large number of encounters—is likely to be a capture in a retrograde orbit.

Hence from our general principles we can understand the formation of 'double planets' both in the Earth–Moon case and the Neptune–Triton case. However, we should expect that not only Triton but also the Moon should be captured in a retrograde orbit. The direct sense of the Moon's present orbit previously constituted a serious difficulty in our cosmogonic theory.

This difficulty has been removed by Gerstenkorn[12] who has shown that the present orbit of the Moon is reconcilable with a capture in a retrograde orbit. Together with the general theory of the formation of planets, Gerstenkorn's calculations make it possible to understand the whole prehistory of the Moon. Only the time scale of the development is not known, because we cannot make an accurate estimate of the phase angle of the tidal effects.

Recently McCord[13] has calculated the prehistory of the Neptune–Triton system, and shown that this may derive from a capture. Also in this case the time scale is uncertain because the viscosity of the bodies is not known.

The Moon at the Roche Limit

An interesting result which Gerstenkorn has obtained is that the minimum distance of the Moon was very close to the Roche limit. This indicates that the Moon may have been broken up by tidal action. Later calculations by MacDonald[14] seem to give a slightly different value of the minimum distance of the Moon. These differences are probably not very important because the limiting distance, at which a satellite breaks up, is well defined only for a liquid body with constant density. A very detailed study is necessary in order to decide what may have happened to the Moon near the Roche limit. In principle we could speculate along three different lines.

(*a*) There was no considerable break-up.

(*b*) Part of the Moon was disrupted, but only some rather small parts of it fell down on the Earth.

(*c*) A large fraction, perhaps half the original Moon or more, fell down on the Earth.

It is of interest to see whether one can connect this picture with geological evidence. In all three cases the effect on the Earth would be enormous tidal waves with a height of several kilometres. An intense heating would also result, but a quantitative estimate has not yet been made, and seems to be rather difficult.

It has been suggested by Donahoe[15] that the Earth originally had an atmosphere of the same kind as Venus, but that at the Gerstenkorn event a large part of it evaporated.

In case (*c*) part of the Earth's crust should derive from the break-up of the Moon. If a mass, equal to the present mass of the Moon, has fallen down on the Earth, a layer with an average thickness of about 20 km would derive from the Moon. If so it is possible that the crust above the Moho discontinuity derives from the Moon, so that the Moho represents the original surface of the Earth.

In case (*b*) one would only expect to find some minor regions on the Earth deriving from the broken-up Moon.

In case (*a*) the Moon did not lose any matter when it was close to the Roche limit; so it would now be in about the same state as when it was a sister planet of Mars. A certain similarity between the surface of the Moon and that of Mars would then be expected.

Different authors have tried to draw cosmogonic conclusions from the different densities of the celestial bodies. Such conclusions are very uncertain for two reasons. Firstly, the interior structure of the celestial bodies is not known with any certainty. Secondly, conclusions from a cosmogonic theory about the chemical constitution of the generated bodies are also uncertain, because the chemical processes during their formation are very complicated.

Acknowledgements

The author would like to thank T. Giuli for his kind help.

Note added in proof. In a recent paper Ruskol[16] compares the calculations of the history of the Earth–Moon system by several authors and concludes that the calculations of the inclination of the Moon's orbit by Gerstenkorn are inaccurate. However, the values attributed to MacDonald and Sorokin in Ruskol's table 1 are not consistent with $\omega_M = \omega_E\cos\varepsilon$ at the minimum distance. So far there seems to be no reason to doubt Gerstenkorn's calculations.

A paper by Gerstenkorn[17], which will shortly be available, seems to clarify the problem.

The first attempt to find geological evidence for the Gerstenkorn event has been made by Olson[18].

References

1. H. Alfvén, *On the Origin of the Solar System*, Clarendon Press, Oxford, 1954.
2. H. Alfvén and J. M. Wilcox, 'On the origin of the satellites and the planets', *Astrophys. J.*, **136**, 1016 (1962).
3. H. Alfvén, 'On the mass distribution in the solar system', *Astrophys. J.*, **136**, 1005 (1962).

4. H. Alfvén, 'On the early history of the Sun and the formation of the solar system', *Astrophys J.*, **137**, 981 (1963).
5. H. Alfvén, 'The early history of the Moon and the Earth', *Icarus*, **1**, 357 (1963).
6. H. Alfvén, 'On the origin of the asteroids', *Icarus*, **3**, 52 (1964).
7. H. Alfvén, 'On the formation of celestial bodies', *Icarus*, **3**, 57 (1964).
8. H. Alfvén, 'Origin of the Moon', *Science*, **148**, 476 (1965).
9. B. Angerth, L. Block, U. Fahleson, and K. Soop, 'Experiments with partly ionized rotating plasmas', *Nucl. Fusion, Suppl.*, Part 1 (1962).
10. J. Eninger, 'Experimental investigation of an ionizing wave in crossed electric and magnetic fields', *Proc. Intern. Conf. Ionization Phenomena Gases, 7th, Belgrade, 1965*, to be published.
11. S. H. Dole, 'The gravitational concentration of particles in space near the Earth', *Planetary Space Sci.*, **9**, 541 (1962).
12. H. Gerstenkorn, 'Über die Gezeitenreibung beim Zweikörperproblem', *Z. Astrophys.*, **36**, 245 (1955).
13. T. McCord, private communication.
14. G. J. F. MacDonald, 'Earth and Moon: past and future', *Science*, **145**, 881 (1964).
15. F. J. Donahoe, 'On the abundance of Earth-like planets', *Icarus*, in press (1966).
16. E. L. Ruskol, 'On the past history of the Earth–Moon system', *Icarus*, **5**, 221 (1966).
17. H. Gestenkorn, *Icarus*, to be published.
18. W. S. Olson, *Am. Scientist*, **54**, No. 4 (1966).

4

H. P. BERLAGE
Rijksuniversiteit te Utrecht
The Netherlands

The origin of the Moon II

The problem of the origin of the Moon has a long history and we are still in the dark about it. Let us first consider the two current opposite theories. One is the expulsion theory; the other is the capture theory.

The Pacific Ocean Basin, 600 metres deeper than the Atlantic and Indian Ocean Basins and surrounded by a chain of deep sea troughs and earthquake epicentres, suggests that the Moon was a part of the Earth's crust which had broken away. A simple fission of the primitive Earth is highly improbable, because the angular momentum can never have reached the required value. Disruption might have been promoted by resonance, but Jeffreys pointed out that forces and deformations are not in a linear relation. This excludes the significant contribution of resonance to the Moon's birth. However, some kind of propulsion of the Moon is not excluded. Several possibilities have been suggested by Wise[1] and others, but there is one serious objection. The Moon can hardly have been propelled into a closed orbit around the Earth. Moreover, the Moon should have been launched beyond Roche's limit in order to survive. It is possible to state, in our space age, that launching the Moon is an operation so complicated as to be plainly impossible. We can discard this idea.

Let us therefore consider the other alternative, the capture of the Moon by the Earth. It has gained many supporters. The major point is that the ratio of the Moon's mass to the Earth's mass is exceptionally high, $1:81$. The only ratio which is anywhere near it is the one of Triton's mass to Neptune's mass. Yet this latter ratio is only $1:800$.

These two cases are abnormal and the consequences are well known. The systems are both subject to tidal interaction. The Moon has been deflected outwards by the Earth. Triton is a retrograde satellite and must have approached Neptune. As a matter of fact, these two structures, the simplest among satellite systems, are the most puzzling ones.

Darwin was the first to tackle the problem of the evolution of the system, Earth–Moon, theoretically and with great care. The Moon causes tides which in the open ocean are one-half metre high. These tidal bulges are forced to move around our globe in one day, that is quicker than a natural ocean wave would do. In particular, the tidal currents through shallow seas and narrow straits cause the tidal friction which decelerates the Earth's rotation and accelerates the Moon's orbital motion. At the present time the length of the day increases about one second in 100·000 years.

It is not permissible to extrapolate present time conditions into the past, but one thing is certain—if we disregard the solar tides, the Earth–Moon system is closed and angular momentum is conserved. It is, in particular, a problem of duration. One investigator may conclude that 2000 million years, another that 6000 million years, separate us from zero hour, the birth of our Moon, but the initial circumstances remain much the same.

Darwin's calculations have recently been revised by Gerstenkorn[2] and Mac-Donald[3] with the aid of modern computers. These two investigators respectively concluded that at the critical zero hour the Moon circulated at a distance 2·89 or 2·72 Earth radii from the centre.

How did the Moon arrive there? Gerstenkorn and MacDonald both suggest that the Moon was captured by the Earth. After having been captured, the Moon moved round the Earth in the retrograde sense. Consequently, the Moon approached the Earth by tidal interaction and spiralled inwards towards the critical distance that Roche indicated. Because the average density of the Earth is 5·52 and the average density of the Moon is 3·34, Roche's limit is about 2·9 Earth radii.

According to both Gerstenkorn and MacDonald, during the time of closest approach the inclination of the lunar orbit and the obliquity of the Earth's equator changed rapidly. The Moon's orbital plane passed over the poles, and the Moon's orbital motion changed from retrograde to direct. Gerstenkorn readily assumes that in the course of this operation several small parts of the primitive Moon were detached. Some of these may even have fallen on Earth. Alfvén[4] and Kopal[5] are inclined to follow this view and explain the characteristic features of the lunar hemisphere facing the Earth by its disruption while violating Roche's limit.

After all, the present Moon should have emerged safely from the danger zone. Since this happened, as first described by Darwin, the Moon receded from the Earth. It is now at a distance of 60 Earth radii.

How far back dare we go? Apparently as far as Gerstenkorn and MacDonald, but then, it is feared, we should be prepared to find the Moon completely destroyed, resolved into dust, as a ring like Saturn's ring, of average radius 2·8 Earth radii, spinning just inside Roche's limit round the Earth in the direct sense.

Now, the question is why we should assume catastrophes, such as an expulsion or a capture of the Moon by the Earth (this question is almost certainly supported by Ruskol[6, 7], Öpik[8], and Whipple[9]). Why do we not assume that our Moon originated as all satellites and planets did? They must be the agglomeration products of concentric rings of gas, dust, and planetesimals, spinning round their primaries.

The Sun was initially surrounded by a gaseous nebula in quasi-steady motion. The average molecular weight of the gas probably decreased from the centre to the periphery in agreement with the average densities of the planets. If the total mass of the nebula is equal to the total mass of the planets, an axial section through the nebula looks like the upper part of figure 1[10]. The nebula does not show the lenticular shape which one might have expected; it presents a torus-like structure and is not strictly limited. It has a great likeness to a Cartesian vortex in the interstellar medium. The nebula is subjected to internal friction and the upper part of figure 1 presents the form adopted by the nebula when obeying the rule that the loss of energy by viscosity is minimum. However, internal friction remains active and it can be shown that the nebula changes from a disk into a set of concentric rings. The result is shown by the lower part of figure 1.

With reference to Poincaré's way of proving the existence of pear-shaped figures of

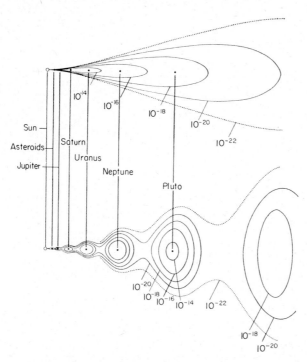

FIGURE 1   Section through initial disk surrounding the Sun showing lines of equal density of the gas. Upper half, in quasi-steady motion; lower half, transformation into set of concentric rings

rotating fluid masses in equilibrium, Berlage[10] pointed out that the tendency of a gaseous or dust disk (spinning round a massive centre) towards reformation into concentric rings rests upon the fact that this reformation may be associated with an increase of kinetic energy at the cost of potential energy.

In the steadiest state of the disk, the density of the gas in the equatorial plane, ρ_e, depends on the distance from the centre, r, in the manner shown in equation (1) (see

$$\rho_e = \rho_0 \exp\left(-ar^{3/2}\right) \tag{1}$$

von Weizsäcker[11], Lüst[12], Berlage[13]). ρ_0 is the central density, and a is a constant.

Now, let us suppose that an arbitrary density wave of the type (figure 2) given by equation (2) is superimposed on the exponential decrease of the density from the centre

$$\varepsilon \cos\left(p \log \frac{r}{r_m}\right) \tag{2}$$

to the periphery as in (3). p is an arbitrary constant and r_m a given distance from the

$$\rho_e = \rho_0 \exp\left\{-ar^{3/2} + \varepsilon \cos\left(p \log \frac{r}{r_m}\right)\right\} \tag{3}$$

centre where the density reaches a maximum. Then, for certain combinations of p and r_m the deformation, while mass and angular momentum remain constant, is associated with a decrease of potential energy and an equal increase of kinetic energy.

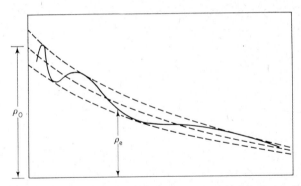

FIGURE 2   Superposition of density fluctuation on exponential decrease of density from
centre to periphery

As this is the natural course of every disequilibrium, the dust disk is obliged to follow
it. In this case the radii of the rings follow the terms of a geometric series. The possible
deviations from this rule[13] will not be considered here.

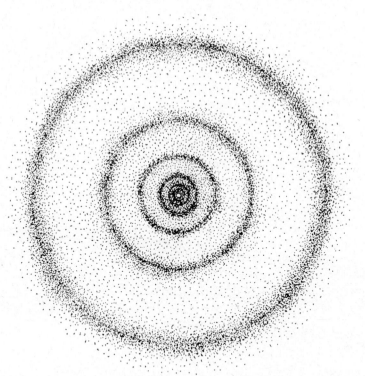

FIGURE 3   Conglomeration of dust rings spinning around a central mass by 'accretional
instability'

The gas rings as such (figure 3) have not got the density required for condensation.
Further evolution is stimulated by the agglomeration of molecules of the gaseous
constituents to grains, meteorites, and planetesimals. The grains collide; these
collisions are not perfectly elastic. The solar field of gravitation keeps all materials

within a limited space. Hence the grains continue to collide and to agglomerate. The matter experiences 'accretional instability'[13]. The rings are flattened and become gradually narrower. Finally, further condensations are achieved by 'gravitational instability'. Each ring is divided into planetesimals, growing bodies, viz. asteroids, moving in nearly one and the same circular orbit.

These bodies will pick up each other. Figure 4 shows that only when the initial radii of the orbits of two parts differed by more than Δ will the resulting body start rotating in the retrograde sense. The central and major part of a 'protoplanet' will tend to rotate in the direct sense. Finally, a primitive planet will again be surrounded

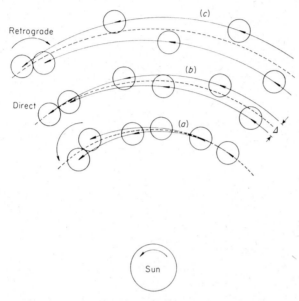

FIGURE 4 Protoplanets and protosatellites will tend to rotate in the direct sense, except their peripheral parts

by a dust disk. The secondary dusk disks are reformed to sets of concentric rings and then to satellites. Only the outermost satellites may become retrograde, their speed checked by friction in the outer regions of the dust disks. The proof lies in the systems of Jupiter and Saturn. Neptune's Triton is probably the main one of this kind[14,15].

The Earth is an agglomeration of one of the dust rings rotating round the Sun. The Earth obtained a dust disk spinning around it in the direct sense. The only abnormal property of the Earth's disk, when compared with the initial dust disks of the other planets, was its large mass. This amounted to roughly 0·03 Earth mass. What happened to our terrestrial disk?

Figure 5 shows a graph of the two opposite possibilities: energy transformations are associated with those specific density undulations, following formula (3), which limit the number of major satellites to one or two[10]. Attention should be given to the surface of the black parts relative to the surface of the white parts in the two figures. The natural course of evolution is indicated by the condition that the sum of the white surfaces exceeds the sum of the black surfaces. This condition is realized in case (*a*) and not realized in case (*b*). Consequently the creation of a system of two satellites is the most probable event, and a system of only one satellite the most improbable event, that occurs.

Mars with its two small satellites, Phobos and Deimos, has operated with the greatest efficiency. The Earth with only one satellite is to be regarded with suspicion. This, in a sense, was done by all those proposing some catastrophe, in particular, a capture of the Moon by the Earth. When reviewing the arguments there is also this point to consider. The Earth, of average density 5·52, must contain iron and nickel in a much greater percentage than the Moon, of average density 3·34. If the Earth and

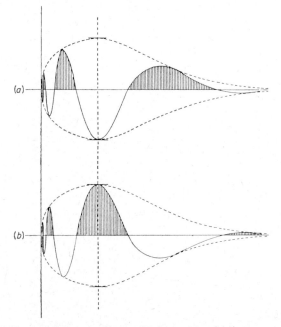

FIGURE 5   Density undulations leading to the formation of (*a*) a system of two major
satellites and (*b*) a system of only one major satellite

Moon were built up out of the same substances in the same proportions, how could such a difference be explained? The answer to this vexing question is probably as follows.

The innermost planet, Mercury, has a density of 5·46. It is a very small planet, its mass being 0·0543 Earth mass, and it could never have reached this density if it did not contain iron and nickel in a higher percentage than the Earth. Evidently the normal development of a dust disk, spinning round a massive primary body, is associated with a concentration of the heaviest materials towards the centre. This would explain the high density of the Earth relative to the low density of the Moon. The substances contained in the Moon are similar to those contained in the Earth's mantle.

Now, returning to the evolution of satellites, we have to concede that two satellites of significant mass is the smallest number of satellites a planet can produce. This number is easily duplicated. For this reason we meet four major satellites in the systems of Jupiter and Uranus. Moreover, in the solar system we meet four large planets and four terrestrial planets of significant mass. Apparently the primary system was created in two phases.

Consequently the Earth must have endeavoured to produce two major satellites. At what distances are these from the centre? These are clearly indicated. Figure 6 represents the basic scheme of any planetary and satellite system, developed by Berlage[16]. This scheme depends upon the theory of the transformation of a dust disk into a set of concentric rings, of which a summary was just given. The curves show the logarithms of r_m, where r_m is the distance of satellite m from the centre of its system, as a function of the factor p which was introduced in formula (2). The radius of every planet is included in the scheme of satellite distances and the remarkable fact is that these radii are logically situated. The same is true for the average densities

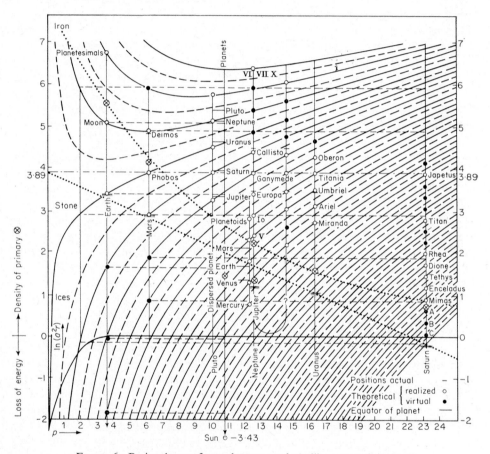

FIGURE 6   Basic scheme of any planetary and satellite system (corrected)

of the planets. Evidently the Bode factor increases with the average density of the planet.

We are not free to place the Earth and its system wherever we wish in our basic scheme. It finds its natural place. The Moon originated at a distance of 5·8 Earth radii from the centre. The Moon's heavy colleague originated close to the Earth's equator, and a third satellite originated at a distance of $5·8^2$ or roughly 34 Earth radii.

As regards the masses of the three satellites, Berlage[16] obtained the relations $m_2/m_1 = 0.76$ and $m_3/m_2 = 0.00058$. Hence a satellite of about 1·3 times the Moon's mass was united with the Earth. The third satellite was very small and can only have existed as a ring of meteorite bodies. These planetesimals are likely to have bombarded the Moon, creating its prominent maria and impact craters, when the Moon, during its recession, passed the distance of 34 Earth radii.

Urey[17] estimated the diameter of the planetesimal (the largest of all), which created the Mare Imbrium, as 230 km. The diameter of the Moon is 3476 km. If the density of this planetesimal is assumed to be equal to the density of the Moon, the ratio of the masses of the two bodies is 0·00048. This particular mass is in excellent agreement with the total mass of planetesimals which is given above. That this strong bombardment and change of surface of the Moon should have occurred in this way roughly 2000 million years ago may be of importance from many points of view.

At least a significant part of the Moon's life must have elapsed before it crossed the distance of 34 Earth radii and, according to Fielder[18] and Hartmann[19], even the majority of the lunar craters seem to have been formed previous to the maria. Moreover, the puzzling lunar moments of inertia may have been determined largely by the fall of the heaviest planetesimals, and the structure and consistence of the maria caused by them. Even if the strongest impacts occurred mostly on the Moon's hemisphere which was projected in the direction of the Moon's orbital motion, it may explain the singular morphology of the Moon's hemisphere which is facing the Earth at the present time, because tidal interaction may well have turned the Moon through 90° since its critical passage through the belt of planetesimals.

We now come to the conclusion that the inner satellite, of roughly 0·016 Earth mass, can only have existed as a dust ring within Roche's limit. This satellite covered the Earth's mantle with a crust of average thickness 65 km and of typical satellite material in a relatively late stage of development. There is every reason to assume that several geologists, van Bemmelen[20], and Donn, Donn, and Valentine[21] will welcome this 'gift from heaven', to quote Dietz[22], because they have great difficulty in explaining the segregation of a sialic crust from the Earth's mantle.

Berlage[16] showed that the Earth may have received its total amount of angular momentum from the inner moon. This suggests that the Earth did not rotate before this satellite was powdered down. Probably the Earth, by tidal interaction with the Sun, has been in the position still held by Mercury and Venus. On the other hand, why should Mars have been free to start rotating? Apparently the Earth must have been in a rather fluid state when its iron and nickel sunk down and formed the Earth's core. It is possible that this did not happen to the much smaller Mars. Mars, moreover, circulates at a much greater distance from the Sun than the Earth, and tidal forces decrease with the third power of this distance. Finally, are we quite sure that the rotation of Mars was *not* retarded by solar tidal forces? In fact, Phobos moves around Mars in a time shorter than the planet's period of rotation.

The Earth, after receiving its thick cover, rotated in 6·5 hours, whereas the month lasted 19·4 hours. Starting from this situation the Moon spiralled away.

The Moon's internal evolution is elucidated by figure 7, a graph of the average density of all members of the solar system whose density is known[23]. We have the logarithm of mass as abscissa. There are, on the left-hand side, three categories for common materials, the 'ices', the stone meteorites, and the iron meteorites. From this diagram we see that compression causes a density increase in proportion to the mass of the body.

The Moon, of average density 3·3, has left the stage of Jupiter's Callisto and Ganymede, of average densities 2·0 and 2·4, but has not yet reached the stage of Jupiter's Europa and Io, of average densities 3·7 and 4·0. Callisto and Ganymede evidently contain all the ice they gathered, whereas Europa and Io have lost it completely. The Moon has apparently lost the greater part of its water content, but may still contain a small amount.

In figure 7 Mars is situated close to Europa, Io, and the Moon. Now, the *Mariner VI* photographs of Mars show a striking resemblance to the Moon. Evidently Mars

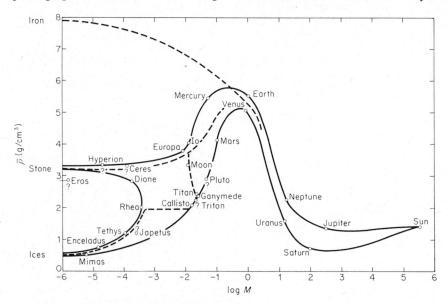

FIGURE 7   Graph of the average densities of the bodies of the solar system as a function of the logarithm of their masses

and the Moon went through a parallel evolution, largely dependent on the similarity of their masses.

One point should still be touched on. Evidence has accumulated about the origin of the tektites from the Moon. Most probably, jets of tektites are propelled from the Moon when it is hit by rather heavy normal meteorites. If this is true, we receive with a tektite a sample of the Moon's crust, and this cannot be much different chemically from the Earth's crust, because it is also satellitic. We need not be surprised therefore to find that, because of such similarity between tektites and terrestrial superficial materials, many geologists have been induced to support the terrestrial origin of the tektites.

References

1. D. U. Wise, *J. Geophys. Res.*, **68**, 1547–54 (1963).
2. H. Gerstenkorn, *Z. Astrophys.*, **36**, 245–74 (1955).
3. G. J. F. MacDonald, *Rev. Geophys.*, **2**, 467–541 (1964).
4. H. Alfvén, *Science*, **148**, 476–77 (1965).

5. Z. Kopal, *Boeing Sci. Res. Lab.*, D1-82-0425 (1965).
6. E. L. Ruskol, *Astron. Zh.*, **40**, 288 (1963).
7. E. L. Ruskol, *Icarus*, **5**, 221–7 (1966).
8. F. L. Whipple, *Proc. Natl. Acad. Sci. U.S.*, **52**, 565–94 (1964).
9. E. J. Öpik, *Space Sci.*, **10**, 2–7 (1961).
10. H. P. Berlage, *Koninkl. Ned. Akad. Wetenschap., Proc.*, **51**, 796, 965 (1948).
11. C. F. von Weizsäcker, *Z. Naturforsch.*, **3a**, 524–39 (1948).
12. R. Lüst, *Z. Naturforsch.*, **7a**, 87–98 (1952).
13. H. P. Berlage, *Koninkl. Ned. Akad. Wetenschap., Proc., Ser. B*, **65**, 199, 211 (1962).
14. G. P. Kuiper, *Astrophys. J.*, **110**, 93 (1949).
15. H. P. Berlage, *Koninkl. Ned. Akad. Wetenschap., Proc., Ser. B*, **57**, 452 (1954).
16. H. P. Berlage, *Koninkl. Ned. Akad. Wetenschap., Proc., Ser. B*, **62**, 63 (1959).
17. H. C. Urey, *Geochim. Cosmochim. Acta*, **1**, 209 (1951).
18. G. Fielder, *Nature*, **198**, 1256–60 (1960).
19. W. K. Hartmann, *Icarus*, **4**, 157–65 (1965).
20. R. W. van Bemmelen, *Tectonophysics*, **3**, 83–127 (1966).
21. W. C. Donn, B. D. Donn, and W. G. Valentine, *Bull. Geol. Soc. Am.*, **76**, 287–306 (1965).
22. R. S. Dietz, *Tectonophysics*, **2**, 515–20 (1965).
23. H. P. Berlage, *Koninkl. Ned. Akad. Wetenschap., Proc., Ser. B*, **56**, 45, 56 (1952).

5

H. C. UREY
University of California
San Diego, La Jolla, California, U.S.A.

The origin of the Moon III

The origin of the terrestrial Moon has been the subject of serious discussion for many years because it is an exceptional object, being very large as compared with its primary. In the later years of the 19th century, Darwin suggested that the Moon escaped from the Earth owing to tidal action of the Sun. This hypothesis was carefully investigated by Moulton and by Jeffrey, during the early years of this century. Both concluded that it was very improbable that the Moon could have separated from the Earth. The problem has been reopened by Wise[1] and by Cameron[2]. Wise suggested that the Moon separated from a single body by an elongation of the primitive Earth into a pear-shaped Poincaré figure. He assumed that the Earth was rotating with a velocity that was almost unstable and that the formation of the core by melting of iron draining to the center was responsible for the separation. This assumes a very nearly unstable figure for the primitive Earth. Cameron also assumes a very nearly unstable Earth, but assumes that it flattened into a spheroid that was unstable as the core formed and that particles were thrown off at the equator and accumulated into the Moon. Both these hypotheses account for a Moon of low density as compared with the Earth. MacDonald[3] and, in greater detail, Goldreich[4] have studied the history of the Moon starting from the present Moon and tracing its history back in time, trying to take into account very carefully all the tidal effects, and it seems that Goldreich has been particularly successful in this calculation. He concludes that the Moon could not have originated in the plane of the equator of the Earth and hence that all separation schemes are impossible. His work seems to be particularly reliable and conclusive. Gerstenkorn[5] has studied the history of the Moon in the past and postulated that it was captured in a retrograde orbit and attained its present position owing to tidal action. His work, though not as conclusive as Goldreich's, appears not to be in contradiction with it.

If the escape mechanism of Wise occurred, the material of the Moon must have been at a high temperature, for otherwise the metallic iron–nickel of the Earth's core could not have separated from the lunar material. In this case very extensive melting of the Moon should have occurred and a high concentration of radioactive elements, K, U, and Th, at the lunar surface should have occurred. If Cameron's mechanism were correct, one would expect some concentration of radioactive elements at the Earth's surface as the core formed, and again an increased concentration of these elements in the lunar material should have occurred and extensive melting of the Moon would be expected. The recent observations on the content of these elements in the lunar surface from *Luna 10* indicate very slight, or only moderate, concentrations of these elements in the lunar surface.

It appears that we must conclude again that the Moon could not have escaped from the Earth.

It has also been proposed that the Moon accumulated in the neighborhood of the Earth as a double planet. In this case we must account for the difference in composition of the Moon. The Moon contains approximately 10–15% of a heavy element, presumably iron, whereas the Earth is estimated to contain 30% or more of iron. It seems difficult to accomplish this. Also, the process of accumulation must have been very special in order to permit the Earth and the Moon to grow in size in precisely the correct amount of angular momentum in the course of growth so that the Moon would neither collide with the Earth nor separate from the Earth*.

The third mechanism that has been considered is capture of the Moon by the Earth. Various studies have been made on the mechanism of capture, most recently by Lyttleton[6], who finds that the Earth and the Moon moving in very special orbits would result in the Moon being held by the Earth for rather short periods of time, after which it would be very likely to escape unless some dissipative mechanism was present. This may have been the presence of many objects moving in the neighborhood of the Earth during the accumulation of the Earth from solid objects. Collisions of such objects with the surface of the Moon would probably have the effect of permitting capture and permitting the rounding up of the orbit. Of course, close approach of objects to the Moon would be effective since the Moon has a substantial gravitational field. In fact, as MacDonald has argued, small moons might be thrown out of the Earth–Moon system resulting in a loss of energy from the Moon. It should be noted that capture in a nearly circular orbit should be an exceedingly improbable process, in fact, much more improbable than capture by collision with the Earth, and this would not be a likely mechanism unless many moons were about in the neighborhood of the Earth during the terminal stage of the formation of the Earth.

The present tidal effects have been studied by MacDonald who has shown that extrapolating the now observed tidal effects back in time leads to the conclusion that the Moon should have been very near the Earth some 1·5 to 2 eons of time ago (one eon $= 10^9$ years). This raises the difficult question as to where the Moon was in the first $2\frac{1}{2}$ or 3 eons of the history of the solar system. The calculations of Öpik[7, 8] and of Arnold[9, 10] show that objects moving in the solar system in the neighborhood of the Earth's orbit should be captured by the Earth or by other planets in the course of some tens of millions of years. There seems to be just no possibility of the Moon having remained as a separate body in the solar system from the time of the origin of the solar system some 4·5 or 4·6 eons ago up to a time of 1·5 to 2 eons ago.

This remains a rather puzzling situation. But it seems to the present author that possibly the tidal effects in the past were not as important as they are today, and the

---

* At a recent meeting in New York these arguments were advanced and someone in the audience pointed out that possibly metallic iron objects would move preferentially towards the Earth in an accumulation process owing to collisions between massive iron metal objects and less massive silicate objects. Equipartition of energy would act in such a way as to slow down the translational motion of the more massive particles and hence cause them to move towards the center of gravitation which would be the Earth. This possibility must be considered in connection with this possible accumulation of the Earth as a double planet.

explanation of the problem resides somewhere in this possibility. It will be very interesting indeed to study the dates of rocks of the Moon to see whether any light can be
thrown on this problem as a result of such studies. For the present it will be assumed
that the Moon originated during the terminal stage of the formation of the Earth,
and it will be assumed that the Moon was indeed captured, and that it was captured
because of collisions and close approaches with objects moving in the neighborhood
of the Earth during the terminal stage of the formation of the Earth.

It has been the present author's point of view for quite a number of years that the
Moon was indeed captured by the Earth. In this case it is not only necessary to account
for the mode of capture but also to account for the differing compositions of the
Moon and Earth. The mechanism of capture is very difficult to discuss if indeed collisions were an important part of the mechanism of capture, for it is difficult to set out a
dynamical model in this case. The chemical composition of the Moon is interesting
from the standpoint of the problem of the composition of the terrestrial planets in
general and the composition of the Sun and meteorites. Table 1 gives a list of the
estimated ratios of iron to silicon in the meteorites, the Sun, Moon, and the terrestrial

TABLE 1   Ratios of iron to silicon

	Fe/Si
Achondrites	~0·0–0·3
Sun (uncorrected)	0·13
Sun (corrected)	0·22
Moon	0·3
L chondrites	0·59
Mars	~0·6
H chondrites	0·81
Type I carbonaceous chondrites	0·89
Earth	1·0
Venus	~1·0
Enstatite chondrites	0·5–1·1
Mercury	~3

planets. In making this calculation we assume that the different densities of the Moon
and planets are indeed due to the different proportions of the element iron, but that
the chemical composition otherwise does not deviate markedly from the composition
of the silicate fraction of the chondritic meteorites. This composition is indeed fairly
constant and not unreasonable as compared with what we know of the composition
of the Earth's mantle. The composition of the Sun is taken from the studies of Aller
and his associates, but two values are listed, assuming that it may be that the silicon
ratio in the Sun is indeed incorrect by a factor of 2. The argument that this is the case
is not an unreasonable one. In the meteorites, magnesium and silicon are of an
approximately equal abundance and, if we assume that silicon is less abundant
relative to other elements than is indicated by the astronomical data, better agreement
between the abundances of silicon and magnesium and some other elements that are
well determined in the Sun and in the meteorites is secured.

Table 2 gives a list of the logarithmic abundances in the Sun as estimated by Aller
using data from other workers[11–16], and in the meteorites using particularly the

TABLE 2   Logarithmic abundances in the Sun and in meteorites

Element	Solar abundances H = 12·00	Estimated error in solar values	Orgueil meteorite abundances Si = 6·00	Difference in abundances
Na	6·27	0·1	4·81	1·46
Mg	7·40	<0·1	6·02	1·38
Al	6·22	<0·15	4·93	1·29
Si	7·50	0·3	6·00	1·50
P	5·40		4·04	1·36
S	7·35	>0·3	5·70	1·65
K	4·82		3·55	1·27
Ca	6·04	0·1	4·87	1·17
Sc	2·80	0·3	1·54	1·26
Ti	4·58	0·1	3·36	1·22
V	4·12	0·1	2·47	1·65
Cr	4·90	0·15	4·08	0·82
Mn	4·80	0·15	3·93	0·87
Fe	6·59	0·1	5·95	0·64
Co	4·70	0·1	3·37	1·33
Ni	5·69	0·15	4·69	1·00
			Average	1·24

The solar abundances are taken from Aller's summaries of his own and others' data [11-16]. The sodium value given by Aller is very doubtful and a revised value of his colleague O'Mara is used. This is reported to be much superior to previous values. The meteoritic abundances have been taken from the paper by Ringwood[16]. Neither his values for astronomical abundances nor his estimated errors for these quantities are generally accepted.

Orgueil meteorite. This is one of the carbonaceous meteorites that contains many of the elements in approximately correct abundances for primitive solar material derived partly from meteorites and partly from theoretical considerations. The solar abundances are referred to hydrogen with an abundance of 12·00, while meteoritic abundances have been given on the assumption that silicon can be assigned the value 10^6, i.e. its logarithm equal to 6. In the third column we give the approximate error as estimated by Aller for the solar abundances. No errors are given for the meteoritic abundances. Errors in the meteoritic abundances are due to some unknown chemical fractionation process to which the meteorite was subjected in the past, but the errors are not due to experimental errors of analysis. A column is given showing the differences in the logarithms of the abundances of the solar and meteoritic data. When this is averaged, it is found that there is a systematic difference between the two sets of abundances of about 1·24 in the logarithm. This indicates that silicon in the Sun has been estimated too high by a factor of 1·8, i.e. the antilogarithm of 0·26, since the mean difference is 1·24, while the difference for silicon is 1·5. If we assume that its correct solar abundance is 7·24, the ratio of iron to silicon in the Sun is 0·22, while this ratio, if no correction of the solar value is made, is 0·13. This argument accounts for the two solar values shown in table 1*. If we take the estimated error in the

* In a recent paper Ringwood[17] has estimated the astronomical errors in solar abundances as factors of 2 or 3. With such errors it is possible to come to quite different conclusions. However, estimates of errors should be taken from well-known scientists who have studied the problems of solar abundances for years. These estimated errors are as given in table 2.

abundance of iron seriously, as it is by specialists in this field, then we must conclude that there is a discrepancy between the abundance of iron in the Sun and in the meteorites, or else that a systematic error exists in the solar abundance data covering many elements and very many spectrum lines of these elements. This seems improbable and is not accepted by astronomical students of solar abundances.

A glance at table 2 shows that the composition of the Moon is about the same then as the composition of the Sun, with possibly somewhat more of the element iron in the Moon, though the data are not precise enough to come definitely to such a conclusion. We conclude that a fractionation process has occurred during the origin of the solar system producing terrestrial planets and meteorites and the Moon of different chemical composition. It should be noted that the problem is more general than just the composition of the Sun, Moon, and Earth. It involves explaining considerable variation in the composition of meteorites and the composition of Mars, Earth, Venus, and Mercury.

There is of course the problem of the accumulation of the Moon out of this solar material. The proposed mechanism was advanced some years ago by the present author on the basis of gravitational instability in the solar nebula. This was discussed some 10 years ago and has been reviewed again in recent papers[18,19]. We assume that a gaseous nebula existed in the plane of the ecliptic of the solar system, and that gravitational instability developed in this gaseous nebula and resulted in the separation of gaseous masses with solid material suspended within them. If we neglect the presence of the solid matter, formulae have been developed which determine the size of the critical mass:

$$m = 2\left(\frac{RT}{G\mu}\right)^{3/2}\left(\frac{2\pi}{\rho_0}\right)^{1/2}\frac{\gamma}{1 - 2\Omega^2/\pi G\rho_0}$$

Using formulae of this kind we must ask what the temperature and density are. We shall take the density ρ_0, in the median plane of the solar nebula, as that given by the Roche density, which is

$$\rho_0 = \frac{M_\odot}{2\pi R^3 \times 0.04503}$$

and, if we assume that it is necessary to produce lunar-sized objects, we could now make a calculation of the temperature. Such temperatures have been calculated and are listed in table 3.

TABLE 3   Temperatures for formation of lunar-sized objects
$(m = 2.2 \times 10^{28}$ and $3.7 \times 10^{28})$ at various distances from the Sun

Distance	T (°K)	
	$m = 2.2 \times 10^{28}$	$m = 3.7 \times 10^{28}$
Mercury	106.0	150.0
Earth	41.3	58.2
Ceres	14.0	21.0
Jupiter	7.9	11.2
Neptune	1.37	1.94
Pluto	1.05	1.47

$\gamma = \frac{5}{3}, \rho_0 = 2.1 \times 10^{-6}/c^3$.

It is seen that the temperatures are rather remarkably low, probably too low. On the other hand, it would appear that solids suspended in a gas would always be unstable, providing energy is dissipated to the gas from the solid objects. Of course in this case much higher temperatures would be permitted in order to produce the same size of objects. Probably in natural circumstances something intermediate in temperature would be required in order to produce objects of the kind under discussion. It should also be noted that there is no reason to expect that all objects would be of the same size. Some may have been rather small and others of fairly massive character. One can hardly expect that instability in a gaseous nebula would necessarily be complete. Possibly all matter did not arrive in the gaseous masses, and collisions between such objects should be taking place in probably a very confusing manner. But our object at present is to see whether a lunar-type object could evolve and what sort of object it might be.

Taking an isolated gas sphere of this kind, it would be expected to radiate energy to space, the gases would contract, and temperatures would rise in the interior. A gravitational field would be present and settling of solid objects to the interior would be expected. If this settling took place when the temperatures were low, then condensed solid substances such as water, ammonia, and carbonaceous material would be expected to settle out. As temperatures rose the water would be volatilized and carbonaceous material should be present mostly as methane, according to thermodynamic calculations. If the suspended solid particles were of micrometre size, very slow settling would be expected, but if objects were of macroscopic size, very rapid settling would occur. It would be expected that the energy of accumulation would of course be transferred to the very large mass of gaseous material, principally hydrogen and helium, and the object collecting at the center might very well accumulate at very moderate temperatures. There may of course have been some volatile substances absorbed on the solid material. As time progressed and further contraction occurred, the surface of the accumulated object could have been raised to a high temperature. Melting would occur and iron would be reduced to the metallic state and would collect in pockets below the surface. This sort of development has been proposed in connection with the origin of the solar system and the meteorites in the papers to which reference is made. The pressures and temperatures may have been such as to have produced diamonds, as is shown by the approximate calculations of Ostic[20]. Since the equations of state of hydrogen and helium are not well known at very high pressures, very definite calculations cannot be made.

At some stage the gases of the solar nebula must have been dissipated, for they would have been retained in large quantities by the terrestrial planets, particularly those of high atomic weight, for example xenon, which is certainly not true of the Earth, and probably not true of the other planets. This dissipation of gases must have occurred before the accumulation of objects with fields such as those of the terrestrial planets, particularly Venus and the Earth. Of course, as the gas of an object such as our Moon was dissipated in space, the surface would cool off. But considerably high temperatures would exist somewhat below the surface and would remain high for a considerable length of time. Objects of this kind would interact with each other and an equipartition of energy would occur to some extent. The collision of such objects was discussed at the Leningrad Symposium on the Moon some years ago. It is very difficult to be certain that collisions and destruction of such objects would indeed occur in a reasonable time scale but this did not seem to be impossible. It was assumed that break-up of the objects would occur in this collisional process with silicates being broken into much smaller particles than the iron–nickel masses. The silicate particles were preferentially dissipated into space relative to more massive metallic objects, thus producing the higher iron content of the Earth and other terrestrial planets.

At the time that these events are postulated to have occurred, the Earth would have been accumulating, and presumably the Moon was one of those objects moving about the Sun during the time of formation of the Earth and would be subject to bombardment by objects of the chemical composition of terrestrial matter. The bombardment of the Moon by material of this kind should have produced a layer on the surface having an increased concentration of iron relative to the original solar material and to the main body of the Moon.

It is well to review briefly the predicted structure of the Moon which is a complicated one. The interior of the Moon on this model is supposed to have approximately solar composition with respect to the nonvolatile elements, though some gaseous materials may have been retained in small amounts. The outer layer of the Moon should have the composition of mean terrestrial material, which is approximately the same as that of the chondritic meteorites, with respect to iron particularly. This outer layer of course would be unstable with respect to the lunar interior, and it may have sunk to the interior of the Moon, partly or totally. It is very difficult to estimate the probabilities in regard to a problem of this kind. It is the author's preference to think that at least a considerable amount of this outer layer of the Moon would remain mixed with the other materials of the lunar surface. The model provides for the presence on the exterior of the Moon of types of material, like the achondritic meteorites, having little metallic iron and perhaps approximately a basaltic composition, material of the chondritic type, and even substantial masses of metallic iron.

Many people postulate lava flows for the surface of the Moon but it has been the author's argument for years that one can hardly expect to have as extensive a volcano history on small planetary objects as those that exist on larger ones such as the Earth, simply because the amount of radioactive heating is proportional to the volume, whereas the loss of heat should depend upon the surface of the object. Hence smaller objects are subject to greater cooling proportionately. However, there are indications that some melting may be characteristic of the outer parts of the Moon. Thus, Shoemaker[21] has pointed out a smooth area in Mare Imbrium and describes this smooth area as a lava flow; this argument is not at all unreasonable. Also, the crater Wargentin is filled to the brim with something that looks as though it should have been liquid at one time, and the argument that this was a lava flow is also not unreasonable. The great difficulty with postulating high temperatures for the outer part of the Moon resides in the irregular shape of the Moon. If isostatic equilibrium is established and the effective viscosity of the Moon is the same as that of the Earth, then such irregularities in elevation as exist on the Moon and the irregular shape of the Moon seem improbable. Runcorn[22] argues that there is a high temperature on the interior of the Moon and that convection with rising currents towards, and away from, the Earth and sinking currents around the limb of the Moon account for this irregular shape, but this does not explain the great differences in elevation between some mountainous areas and neighboring depressions which also argue for a cool Moon.

Collisions of massive objects, either during the capture of the Moon in its early history, or in the time since then, should have mixed up the various layers of the original surface structure with each other and with the material arriving on the surface to produce an exterior of the Moon similar in composition to the mean composition of the Earth. At the same time some material may well have been thrown off the Moon into space and would not in general return to the Moon but would be more probably captured by the Earth or other planets. Of course, if material is thrown from the surface of the Moon by such collisions, then material from the entire surface of the Moon has to a certain extent been distributed to all other parts of the surface of the Moon. One would expect that a net transfer probably from the higher regions to the lower regions would occur. In addition to this, the larger collisions that produced the circular maria, for example, may have penetrated through the outer regions of the Moon to the interior where gas pressures may have been produced by radioactive heating. In this case ash flows, similar in physical character to those observed on the Earth but of quite different chemical composition, could be expected. Terrestrial ash flows have approximately a granitic structure mostly, while one would expect the corresponding ash flows on the Moon to have something approaching solar composition with respect to the nonvolatile solar fraction. Materials of this kind may have contributed to the formation of the maria of the Moon and to the smooth filling of craters and covering other parts of the Moon with a smooth layer. From these general considerations one could predict that the outer parts of the Moon are indeed fine dust or sandy or gravelly material, or perhaps these materials admixed with coarser fragments. Of course at the same time limited lava flows might reasonably be expected. Quite regardless of what the original material of the surface of the Moon was, after $4\frac{1}{2}$ billion years of bombardment with macrometeorites and micrometeorites and the effects of particle bombardment and light, a layer of some depth of finely divided material might be expected.

The chemical composition of the surface to be expected might thus be somewhat like the chondritic meteorites. Whether collisional effects of the kind described could have produced chondrules or not is a question about which there is great controversy, and the present author has no feeling of certainty with regard to it.

If we turn to the *Ranger* and *Surveyor* pictures, it seems that there is considerable evidence for a fragmented layer of some thickness on the lunar surface. The *Ranger* pictures, according to the author's interpretation[23,24], seem to present evidence indicating that fragmental material of at least some tens of meters thickness is present on the lunar surface. The *Surveyor 1* pictures indicate with much greater certainty that there is a conglomerate layer of material on the Moon in which the particles vary from those of small size to those of perhaps meters in size, with most of the material being of the finer sort. It is also possible from these pictures to deduce that water may have played a part in the smoothing of the surface of the Moon for very short periods of time, and there seems to be no way to exclude the possibility that water is rising from the interior of the Moon and producing a permafrost layer, as has been particularly emphasized by Gold[25]. Physically, the surface of the Moon, as indicated by the *Ranger* pictures and by *Surveyor 1*, is not in contradiction to the ideas expressed here in regard to the surface of the maria.

The *Luna 9* pictures gave rise to contradictory interpretations of the lunar surface, some maintaining again that the surface consisted of lava flows with no fragmented material, and others maintaining a fragmental structure. It appears, in the author's opinion, that the *Surveyor 1* pictures definitely show a layer of fragmented material covering the surface of the maria.

The *Luna 10* experiments, in which the gamma spectrum of the Moon was investigated, have been reported very briefly in the press. Reports indicate that the potassium concentration is lower than that of the ordinary basalts, but exact figures have not been reported. One is tempted to conclude, in view of the lack of definitely conclusive statements, that the detection of potassium may be marginal, and hence that the results may be uncertain. In this case one would probably conclude that there might be some local lava flows which would average into a general chondritic background. The theory proposed in this chapter would predict that maria and land areas should have a very similar potassium concentration and it should probably be expected that uranium and thorium could not be detected. The *Luna 10* reports would seem to indicate that, contrary to popular ideas, tektites cannot come from the Moon, which is certainly in accord with the model for the origin of the Moon proposed here.

Hapke[26] has studied the reflective properties of the Moon and various terrestrial materials, and definitely comes to the conclusion that materials of meteoritic composition containing metallic iron are not in accord with the materials observed on the lunar surface; this seems to be definitely in disagreement with the surface of the Moon as predicted here. There is, however, the difficulty that collisional processes, such as we believe have occurred on the lunar surface, may well result in producing a thin surface layer of the Moon consisting of the silicate materials rather than the metallic materials which may be present and, since the light-reflecting properties of the Moon record only the thinnest layer of the surface, his results may not be decisive. Some of the *Surveyor 1* pictures showing the surface disturbed by the landing pads indicate that the subsurface material may have quite different optical reflecting properties from the exposed surface layer. Thus Hapke's results may not be applicable because of factors other than those that he considered. The possible presence of dark carbonaceous material resulting from the ash flows coming from the deep lunar interior may play an important role in the optical properties of the lunar surface*.

The reported observation from *Luna 10* that the K, U, and Th concentrations are the same for maria and terrae, indicating that the maria are not lava flows or at least are not any more definitely lava flows than the terrae, raises the question of the origin of the albedo differences. Possibly ash flows due to the great collisions as suggested above[27] provides an acceptable answer. For some reason this material may have contained carbonaceous matter which provides a dark color and which is vaporized by particle bombardment, giving a lighter exposed surface relative to freshly exposed materials.

---

* *Note added in proof.* C. E. Ken Knight, D. L. Rosenberg, and G. K. Wehner have recently reported results on the optical properties of various silicate materials after bombardment by a simulated solar wind[28] (talk at the Los Angeles meeting of the American Geophysical Union on September 9, 1966[29]) The data on the Holbrook meteorite agreed best with those of the Moon. The higher iron content of the meteorite is the most obvious difference between it and the other silicate materials. The authors hesitate to stress the importance of this finding, which disagrees with Hapke's observations, citing a small, but uncontrolled, carbon contamination in their simulation and citing the importance of simulating the effects of the flight of sputtered atoms in the lunar atmosphere. They point out that a significant flux of carbon is expected in the solar wind. If the simulation of the solar wind by this group was more realistic than that by Hapke, their findings may indicate that the lunar surface has a high iron content.

If the Moon accumulated from fragmented material as a sister planet to the Earth with higher density material concentrating in some way in the Earth as compared with the Moon, the Moon may have accumulated slowly at low temperatures, and no increase in radioactive elements at the surface is required. In this case no high iron content at the surface is required.

It is the conclusion of this chapter that a high iron content at the lunar surface, such as that of the chondritic meteorites, will show that the Moon was captured by the Earth during the terminal stages of the accumulation of the Earth. On the other hand, if a low iron content in the lunar surface exists, then most probably the Moon accumulated as a sister planet of the Earth and metallic objects by some nondefined process accumulated preferentially in the Earth, thus accounting for the differing densities of the Moon and Earth.

Acknowledgements

Support for this research from the AEC is gratefully acknowledged (the contents of this chapter is contained in *AEC Rept. No.* UCSD-34P43-5).

References

1. D. U. Wise, *J. Geophys. Res.*, **68**, 1547 (1963).
2. A. G. W. Cameron, *Icarus*, **2**, 249 (1963).
3. G. J. F. MacDonald, *Rev. Geophys.*, **2**, 467 (1964).
4. P. Goldreich, preprint (1966).
5. H. Gerstenkorn, *Z. Astrophys.*, **26**, 245 (1955).
6. R. Lyttleton, private communication (1966).
7. E. Öpik, *Proc. Roy. Irish Acad.*, **54**, 165 (1951).
8. E. Öpik, *Advan. Astron. Astrophys.*, **2**, 220 (1963).
9. J. R. Arnold, *Isotopic and Cosmic Chemistry*, North-Holland, Amsterdam, 1964, p. 347.
10. J. R. Arnold, *Astrophys. J.*, **141**, 1536, 1548 (1965).
11. L. H. Aller, *Advan. Astron. Astrophys.*, **3**, 1 (1965).
12. L. G. Goldberg, E. A. Müller, and L. H. Aller, *Astrophys. J.*, *Suppl.*, **5**, 1 (1960).
13. L. H. Aller, B. J. O'Mara, and S. Little, *Proc. Natl. Acad. Sci. U.S.*, **51**, 1238 (1964).
14. L. H. Aller, *Phys. Chem. Earth*, **4**, 1–26 (1961).
15. E. A. Müller and J. P. Mutschlecner, *Astrophys. J.*, *Suppl.*, **9**, 1 (1964).
16. A. E. Ringwood, *Rev. Geophys.*, **4**, 124 (1966).
17. A. E. Ringwood, *Geochim. Cosmochim. Acta*, **30**, 41 (1966).
18. H. C. Urey, *Proc. Chem. Soc.*, **1958**, 67.
19. H. C. Urey, *Monthly Notices Roy. Astron. Soc.*, **131**, 199 (1966).
20. R. G. Ostic, *Monthly Notices Roy. Astron. Soc.*, **131**, 191 (1965).
21. E. M. Shoemaker, private communication.
22. S. K. Runcorn, *Nature*, **195**, 1150 (1962).
23. H. C. Urey, 'Ranger 7, Part 2, Experimenters' analyses and interpretations', *Jet Propulsion Lab. Tech. Rept. No.* 32-700 (1965).
24. H. C. Urey, *Rangers 8* and *9, Part 2, Experimenters' analyses and interpretations', Jet Propulsion Lab. Tech. Rept. No.* 32-800 (1966).
25. T. Gold, in *The Moon* (Eds. Z. Kopal and Z. Mikhailov), Academic Press, New York, 1962, p. 438.
26. B. W. Hapke, in *The Nature of the Lunar Surface* (Eds. W. N. Hess, D. H. Menzel, and J. A. O'Keefe), Johns Hopkins, Baltimore, Maryland, 1966.
27. H. C. Urey, *Rev. Geophys.*, **2**, 1 (1964).
28. C. E. Ken Knight, D. L. Rosenberg, and G. K. Wehner, to be published.
29. C. E. Ken Knight, D. L. Rosenberg, and G. K. Wehner, *Trans. Am. Geophys. Union* **47**, 486 (1966).

6

K. E. BULLEN
University of Sydney
Australia

The origin of the Moon IV

Introduction

This chapter is concerned with a possible mechanism for the origin of the Moon which the author proposed some years ago. The mechanism involves the ejection of the Moon from a primitive Earth–Moon body. From the time when Jeffreys[1] showed the untenability of the simple resonance theory of the origin of the Moon, the idea of a primitive Earth–Moon body has not been favoured. In the theory here discussed, resonance is involved, but only in an auxiliary role.

The theory involves an extension of a result of Ramsey[2] who, in investigating the interior of Venus, had noted certain unusual circumstances in which a planet of assigned mass and chemical composition could exist in more than one configuration. In one of the configurations, there would be a small core in the form of a phase transformation of the matter outside, the transformation being associated with a density jump taking place at a critical pressure—the pressure at the core boundary. In another configuration, the central pressure would not reach the critical value, and there would be no corresponding small core. The internal energies would be different in the different configurations, and in certain conditions a transition from one configuration to another could take place with an explosive release of energy. For the simple case he considered, Ramsey showed that the mass of the planet would have to be near that of Venus.

The author extended the theory to show that an explosive transition could also occur in a body of the Earth's mass if two suitable phase transformations were assumed to exist inside the body. The question was then examined as to whether a primitive Earth–Moon body, containing a small core no longer present, might have undergone a transition from a three-phase state to a two-phase state with a sufficient release of energy to form the Moon.

Details are given in papers by Bullen[3] and Datta[4], who carried out the formal computations under the present author's direction. In the following sections the calculations are summarized and discussed.

The Formal Calculations

A primitive Earth–Moon body was taken with mass M equal to the combined mass $(6.048 \times 10^{27}$ g) of the present Earth and Moon. The body was treated as spherically symmetrical, apart from rotation and tidal effects, and as chemically homogeneous.

Initially, in 'state I', the body was assumed to consist of three concentric zones containing the material in the form of separate phases X, Y, and Z. Let the radii of the outer boundaries of the zones be R, R_1, R_2, where R is the radius of the whole body. Let the densities of the phases X, Y, Z, be ρ_0, $\rho_0(1 + \lambda)$, $\rho_0(1 + \lambda + \mu)$, respectively. For ease of calculation the density was taken to be constant throughout any one zone. Hydrostatic pressure variation was also assumed. Let p_1 and p_2 be the critical pressures at which the changes from X to Y and from Y to Z take place.

The final state, 'state II', was taken to be a two-phase state in which the phase Z had disappeared. Let R' and R_1' be the radii of the outer boundaries of X and Y in state II. The central pressure in state II is required to be less than p_2.

$$M = (4/3)\pi\rho_0(R^3 + \lambda R_1^3 + \mu R_2^3) \tag{1}$$

$$p_1 = (2/3)\pi G\rho_0^2\{R^2 - R_1^2 + 2(\lambda R_1^3 + \mu R_2^3)(R_1^{-1} - R^{-1})\} \tag{2}$$

$$p_2 = p_1 + (2/3)\pi G\rho_0\{(1 + \lambda)^2(R_1^2 - R_2^2)$$
$$+ 2\mu(1 + \lambda)R_2^3(R_2^{-1} - R_1^{-1})\} \tag{3}$$

Let G be the constant of gravitation. For state I, the equations (1), (2), and (3) can then be derived by routine processes. For state II, the equations (1) and (2) apply when μ is put equal to zero and R, R_1 are replaced by R', R_1', respectively.

Numerical values of ρ_0 and λ were taken from data on the present Earth. These values, together with the assumed value of M, were sufficient to determine the configuration in state II uniquely and formally gave

$$R' = 6040 \text{ km}, \qquad R_1' = 3720 \text{ km}, \qquad p' = 3\cdot17 \times 10^{12} \text{ dyn/cm}^2$$

where p' is the central pressure in state II.

For state I, the assumed numerical data do not determine the configuration uniquely, and fifteen self-consistent solutions covering suitable ranges of values of R_2/R_1 and μ were worked out. Of these, nine had to be rejected because they gave $p_2 < p'$. The remaining six solutions were then examined in respect of the internal energies.

Let E be the energy connected with compressing the material in the phase X to form the phases Y and Z for the case of state I. Then we obtain equation (4).

$$E = (4/3)\pi\{\lambda p_1 R_1^3 + \mu(1 + \lambda)^{-1}(\lambda p_1 + p_2)R_2^3\} \tag{4}$$

Let F be the gravitational energy due to assembling the system in state I at zero pressure from dispersion at infinity. Then F is given by equation (5).

$$F = (8/15)\pi^2 G\rho_0^2[\mu\{2\mu - (1 + \lambda)\}R_2^5 + (2\lambda^2 - \lambda)R_1^5$$
$$+ 2R^5 + 5\lambda\mu R_2^3 R_1^2 + 5R^2(\lambda R_1^3 + \mu R_2^3)] \tag{5}$$

For state II, the corresponding energies, E' and F' say, are obtained on again putting $\mu = 0$, $R = R'$, and $R_1 = R_1'$.

The energy change ΔE in passing from state I to state II is $E + F - E' - F'$, and was computed for each of the six surviving models.

The results for the two models which gave the largest values of ΔE are given by (i) and (ii).

(i) $R = 5910$ km, $R_1 = 3790$ km, $R_2 = 1890$ km; $\mu = 1\cdot75$; $\Delta E = 2\cdot7 \times 10^{38}$ erg

(ii) $R = 5890$ km, $R_1 = 3800$ km, $R_2 = 1900$ km; $\mu = 2\cdot00$; $\Delta E = 3\cdot1 \times 10^{38}$ erg

Calculations of Lighthill[5] had implied that a mass of order $0.001M_E$ (M_E is the mass of the Earth) could be removed from a planet whose mass is of order M_E in a transition where ΔE is of the order of 10^{36} to 10^{37} erg. Since the mass of the Moon is of the order of $0.01M_E$, each of the above two models yields more than sufficient energy on transition to result in the ejection of mass equal to that of the Moon.

On interpolating between the results for these two and the other four models, it was found that, for a sufficient energy release, the minimum values of μ and R_2 formally required were 1·55 and 1500 km, respectively.

Discussion

The calculations are based on simple models which make no allowance for the variation of density inside particular zones or for complications connected with, for example, the existence of an inner core in the present Earth. Allowance for deviations of this character might be made in a variety of ways and would of course affect the numerical detail; but they are not likely to affect the order of magnitude of the energy release.

The essential result is that sufficient energy would be available to eject the Moon from the primitive body if a core of 1500 km radius were present in the primitive state, the core consisting of a phase transformation of the material outside, and if the accompanying density jump were in a ratio approaching 2.

For the mechanism to be feasible, the primitive state would be expected to be one of stable equilibrium, separated from the subsequent state by a potential barrier. The additional mechanism proposed for exciting the transition from state I to state II is resonance, which, instead of being the main influence as envisaged before 1930, would now serve in an auxiliary capacity by distorting the primitive body sufficiently to carry it over the potential barrier.

Objections have been raised against the theory on the ground that a Moon ejected in this way would have to return and coalesce with the original body. This objection is, however, based on a two-body argument, whereas all that the present theory requires is that the Moon should ultimately be left behind in orbit, without precluding the ejection of a quantity of additional matter, some of which might return to the Earth. A simple two-body argument therefore appears inadequate to refute the theory. Other objections have been raised as to how the Moon could acquire a suitable direction of motion to get into orbit. A sufficient answer is that a combination of resonant tidal action and explosive phase change would result in such distortions from simple symmetry that directions of motion of the ejected objects are not simply predictable. In any case, the course of an explosive event involving a dual mechanism does not readily lend itself to precise calculation.

The ejection would have to carry sufficient mass outside Roche's limit in order to form the Moon as an aggregated body and not a ring. Even if the initial ejection should not have carried enough material beyond Roche's limit, the difficulties again do not appear to be insuperable. A remark by Öpik[6] made while discussing another theory suggests that, if aggregation did not take place immediately, it could have done so later, after additional diminution of the Earth's mass. Further, in the event of a ring being first formed, subsequent contraction of the Earth could leave a significant part of the ring outside Roche's limit and able to aggregate.

The mechanism of ejection is more likely to be successful the nearer the primitive body would have been to a molten state at the time of ejection. In the event of a hot origin of the solar system, the optimum time would have been not too long after the formation of the Earth–Moon body itself. In the event of a cold origin, the optimum time would have been fairly near the stage when the body had heated to its maximum.

The theory, if unmodified, does meet a serious difficulty through the size of the density jump needed between the phases Y and Z. The needed ratio might be reduced a little by modifying the model conditions taken, but it is improbable that any likely reduction in this way would have much effect. If this difficulty should in fact prove to be insuperable, the formal calculation here presented can still be of value in enabling the energy ΔE to be calculated for the case of a smaller, more acceptable, density jump. The mechanism proposed would then be capable of providing a proportion, not the whole, of the energy required to eject the Moon, and could plausibly supplement the energy derivable from resonance alone.

There remains the intriguing fact that a number of lines of argument still point to the Moon having been once not far outside Roche's limit and also the fact that current theories of the Moon being captured by the Earth themselves remain open to criticism. Should there be a swing on new grounds to the view that the Moon has, after all, come out of the Earth, then the foregoing calculations, even if not providing the whole story, may still be of interest as showing a possible contributory source of energy.

References

1. H. Jeffreys, *Monthly Notices Roy. Astron. Soc.*, **91**, 169 (1930).
2. W. H. Ramsey, *Monthly Notices Roy. Astron. Soc.*, **110**, 325 (1950).
3. K. E. Bullen, *Nature*, **167**, 29 (1951).
4. A. N. Datta, *Monthly Notices Roy. Astron. Soc., Geophys. Suppl.*, **6**, 535 (1954).
5. M. J. Lighthill, *Monthly Notices Roy. Astron. Soc.*, **110**, 339 (1950).
6. E. J. Öpik, *Armagh Obs. Leaflet* (1955).

VII

Geochemical evidence on the nature of the Earth's mantle

1. Rare-earth fractionation and magmatic processes (J.-G. SCHILLING and J. W. WINCHESTER) 267

2. Geochemical studies in the ocean as evidence for the composition of the mantle (G. D. NICHOLLS) . . . 285

3. Segregation processes in the upper mantle (P. G. HARRIS) . 305

4. Isotopic composition of lead in oceanic volcanic rocks: evidence for chemical heterogeneity of the mantle (P. W. GAST) 319

5. Olivine nodules and the composition of the Earth's mantle (T. ERNST) 321

1

J.-G. SCHILLING*
and
J. W. WINCHESTER†

Department of Geology and Geophysics
Massachusetts Institute of Technology
Cambridge, Massachusetts, U.S.A.

Rare-earth fractionation and magmatic processes

Introduction

The rare-earth group of elements $_{57}$La to $_{71}$Lu, including $_{39}$Yt, has fascinated analytical chemists and geochemists for many years because of the close similarity in chemical properties within the group and the resulting challenge of chemical separation in the laboratory and great coherence of the group in nature. It has not been until quite recently, however, that analytical data on the natural occurrence of the rare earths have become precise enough to allow quantitative interpretation of geochemical abundance patterns. The high precision analyses for rare earths in silicate rocks and minerals now in the literature[1-11] have revealed that the group is fractionated smoothly and gradually as a function of atomic number Z. The absolute abundances of even Z elements are greater than those of adjacent odd Z owing to the greater number of stable isotopes of the former, but any natural sample may be compared element by element with a standard rock and the relative abundances computed. When this is done, the zig-zag variation of the absolute abundances with Z disappears and invariably a strikingly smooth curve pattern is found (see Coryell, Chase, and Winchester[12], figure 1). It is the purpose of this chapter to present some preliminary thinking on possible causes of the smooth rare-earth fractionation by chemical processes in basic silicate materials in the Earth, especially in the mantle.

Rare-earth Abundance Patterns

Stone meteorites were the first group of rocks to be analyzed with high precision for rare earths using neutron activation techniques[4,5] and a close similarity was noticed among the chondrite group. Because of this and because of the possible ultimate chondritic composition of the rare-earth mixture in the Earth as a whole, in our

* Present address: Graduate School of Oceanography, University of Rhode Island, Kingston, U.S.A.
† Present address: Department of Meteorology and Oceanography, University of Michigan, Ann Arbor, U.S.A.

laboratory we have compared each analysis of terrestrial rock with the chondrite average in the element-by-element way[12]. Figures 1 to 7 summarize some of the types of abundance patterns encountered in basic igneous rocks. The striking feature of all these patterns is the smoothness of the curves, in spite of the fact that the detailed history since primeval time most certainly was complex. Sometimes the relative abundance falls nearly exponentially with increasing Z, or, what amounts to the same thing, with increasing reciprocal ionic radius[13, 14] or Goldschmidt ionic potential. The majority of crustal rocks are enriched relative to chondrites in all the rare-earth elements, and the enrichment is most pronounced for the low-Z La end of the series. The gradual

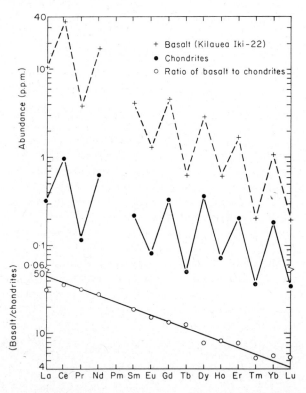

FIGURE 1   Abundance of the rare-earth elements in the basalt Kilauea Iki-22 (broken line) and mean of two chondrites (full line), plotted on a logarithmic scale as a function of atomic number. [Data from Schmitt and others[4].] The lower curve gives the ratios of the rare-earth abundances in basalt and chondrites. A best straight line has been drawn

lanthanide contraction of trivalent ionic radius with increasing Z underlies this systematic behavior. There are apparently only two singular elements in any samples of crustal materials and only under special conditions. Ce, which may be selectively oxidized to Ce^{4+}, is enriched in manganese nodules from the sea floor[15, 16]. Eu, which may be reduced to Eu^{2+}, is either enriched or depleted in minerals of granitic rocks and sometimes depleted in granites relative to chondrites[6, 17]. However, neither of these elements appears to have singular behavior in basic igneous rocks and we presume the trivalent oxidation state is the predominant state for Ce and Eu as well as for the rest of the rare-earth group.

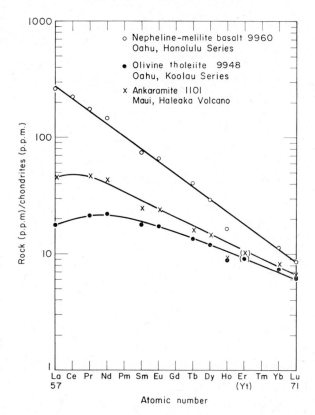

FIGURE 2   Abundances of the rare-earth elements relative to 20 chondrites[9] in the three basalts from the Hawaiian Islands, plotted on a logarithmic scale as a function of the atomic number. [Data from Schilling and Winchester[11]]

It is risky to categorize basic igneous rocks too sharply because intermediate types will certainly be found. Nevertheless, figures 1 to 7 illustrate some groups which are apparent from the data available at the present time. Figure 2 shows some basalts from Hawaii[11] where the olivine tholeiite and the nepheline–melilite basalts form end-member patterns between which the ankaramite and some other lava types lie. If lavas richer in rare earths than the olivine tholeiite were derived from the latter by a chemical fractionation, the rare-earth enrichment decreases with increasing Z, but the concentrations never drop below those in the olivine tholeiite.

The Mid-Atlantic Ridge tholeiite basalts of figure 3 are decidedly not the same in rare-earth pattern as the Hawaiian tholeiite, for they exhibit a broad maximum in the middle or heavy end of the series. Still strikingly different are the peridotites of figure 4 where there is a maximum in relative abundance near the heavy end, and the light rare earths are extremely low in concentration. Both figures are prepared from data published by Frey and Haskin[7] and Haskin and others[9].

Figure 5 shows some patterns where a marked leveling in the heavy element region occurs, generally characteristic of sedimentary and highly differentiated igneous rocks.

Finally, it should be pointed out that not all stone meteorites are the same in their rare-earth composition. According to data of Schmitt and Smith[4,5], the chondrites

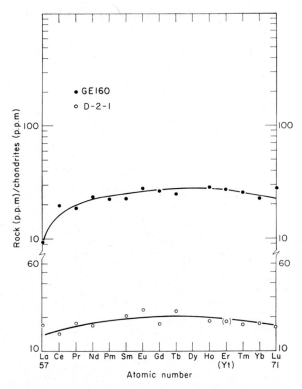

FIGURE 3   Abundances of the rare-earth elements relative to 20 chondrites[9] in two Mid-Atlantic Ridge tholeiites, plotted on a logarithmic scale as a function of the atomic number. [Data from Frey and Haskin[7] and Haskin and others[9]]

vary by about 30% in absolute rare-earth concentrations, but the relative composition of the rare-earth group is quite invariant. Carbonaceous chondrites are not different from ordinary chondrites in this respect. However, several Ca-rich achondrites (eucrites) are found to be about tenfold enriched relative to average chondrites, although the relative abundance pattern is still nearly the same, as shown in figure 6. In addition, unusual rare-earth patterns have been reported for some achondrites and pallasites, e.g. figure 7.

Theoretical Considerations

Earth scientists disagree on whether the Earth passed through a completely molten stage in the early evolution of the core, mantle, and crust or at most was only partly molten. Complete melting implies a process of fractional crystallization in the gradual solidification of the Earth, but a partially molten Earth might give rise to mass transfer and chemical differentiation by percolating melts. It seems to be a fact that, whatever the complexities of the actual history of the Earth, the crust of the Earth is enriched relative to chondritic meteorites (and presumably relative to the Earth's interior) in trace elements which do not fit easily into the structures of common rock-forming

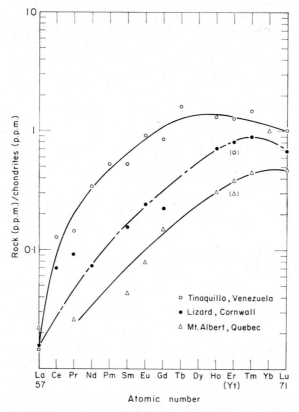

FIGURE 4   Abundances of the rare-earth elements relative to 20 chondrites[9] in three peridotites, plotted on a logarithmic scale as a function of the atomic number. [Data from Haskin and others[9]]

minerals. This effect is marked for the heavy elements U, Th, K, Rb, Sr, Ba, etc., and is probably determined by the large ionic sizes rather than the atomic weights. The rare earths, which are also enriched in crustal rocks, are generally enriched most strongly for the large-size La end of the series, as in figures 1 and 2. Since the rare earths have a very smoothly decreasing ionic radius with increasing Z, the relative abundances of these elements are sensitive to the details of the processes leading to their enrichment in the crust. It seems worth while, therefore, to try and predict what patterns may be produced by several feasible model processes.

We have considered the following chemical equilibrium processes which may lead to fractionation of the rare earths: (i) fractional crystallization according to the logarithmic (Doerner–Hoskins) distribution law[18], (ii) partial melting according to the homogeneous (Berthelot–Nernst) distribution law[19,20], (iii) fractional melting, i.e. successive stages of partial melting and liquid removal, (iv) zone melting, i.e. a molten spot moving through solid by fusion and crystallization, and (v) mixing of two or more rare-earth distribution patterns.

At the present time there are no direct measurements reported of partition ratios of the rare earths between melts and equilibrium solids directly applicable to the basic silicate systems of the lower and upper mantle and mantle-related material

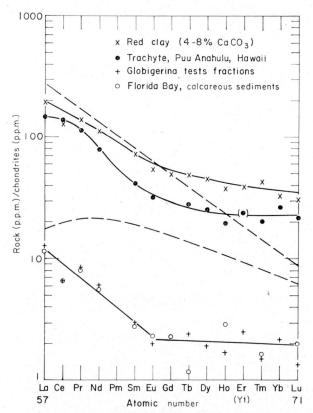

FIGURE 5   Abundances of the rare-earth elements relative to 20 chondrites[9] in three sedimentary materials and one trachyte from Hawaii, plotted on a logarithmic scale as a function of the atomic number. The two broken curves represent two basalts from the Hawaiian Islands shown in figure 2. [Data from the red clay and globigerina tests are from Volfovsky Spirn[16], for Florida Bay from Haskin and Gehl[10], and for the trachyte from Schilling and Winchester[11]]

found in the crust. Clearly any quantitative theory requires measurements of this type. However, some guesses can be made about the probable way the partition varies with Z, and a semiquantitative theory can be developed. Formation of the mantle presumably involves to a great extent dense magnesium iron silicates and spinels. If trivalent rare earths substitute in lattice sites smaller than Lu^{3+} (radius $r = 0.99$ Å), e.g. Mg^{2+} ($r = 0.78$ Å) or Fe^{2+} ($r = 0.83$ Å), we may expect progressive discrimination against the rare earths in the solid with increasing radius (decreasing Z) over the entire series from Lu^{3+} to La^{3+} ($r = 1.22$ Å). Masuda and Matsui[14] have made an assumption of a linear increase in the partition ratio of concentration, solid to liquid, with increasing Z, and this assumption is also used for calculations in the present chapter. It is further assumed that a joint effective partition ratio can be used for the polycrystalline aggregates and coexisting melts[21–26].

Fractional crystallization

Masuda and Matsui[14] first proposed that an exponential decrease in relative rare-earth abundance with Z (e.g. the Kilauea Iki basalt pattern of figure 1) could be

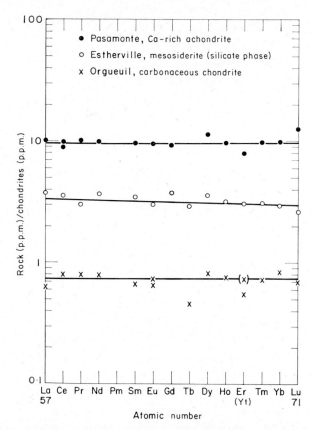

FIGURE 6 Abundances of the rare-earth elements relative to 17 chondrites in three meteorites, plotted on a logarithmic scale as a function of the atomic number. [Data from Schmitt and others[4,5]]

accounted for by the following model. An initially molten Earth of chondritic composition fractionally crystallized to form a mantle whose average rare-earth abundances were those of the Norton County Ca-poor achondrite and a crust as a residual liquid with average rare-earth abundances decreasing exponentially with Z as in Minami's shales (figure 7). The final Earth is assumed to have Bullen's value of crust to crust plus mantle mass ratio which equals 1/82. This model requires that the joint effective partition ratio of concentration, solid to liquid, of the system for the rare earths increases linearly with Z. Furthermore, numerical values of the partition ratio for each rare earth can be calculated from these data.

Fractional crystallization leads to expression (1) for concentration of a trace element in the residual liquid C_L, relative to the initial concentration C_0, where $0 \leqq x \leqq 1$

$$\frac{C_L(z)}{C_0(z)} = (1 - x)^{D(z) - 1} \tag{1}$$

is the fraction solidified and $D(z)$ is the joint effective partition ratio of each rare earth z between the polycrystalline solid and its melt. z is arbitrarily set equal to zero

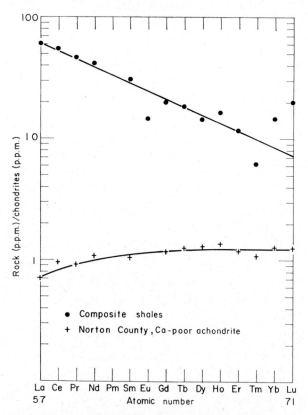

FIGURE 7   Abundances of the rare-earth elements relative to 20 chondrites[9] in one composite of shale and the Norton County Ca-poor achondrite plotted on logarithmic scale as a function of the atomic number. [Data for the composite shale are taken from Minami[43] and the meteorite from Schmitt and others[5]]

for La. If the phases crystallize simultaneously, $D(z) = C_S(z)/C_L(z) = \Sigma p_i D_i(z)$ $= 1/C_L \Sigma p_i C_{Si}$, where p_i is the modal abundance of each phase i. In spite of the limitations of the concept of a joint effective partition ratio, in the case of the Skaergaard intrusion it works surprisingly well[26,27], and we shall use it in the present work.

If we use the assumption for the rare-earth partition ratio, solid to liquid, made by Masuda and Matsui[14], which is given by equation (2), where D_0 pertains to La,

$$D(z) = D_0 + z\Delta D \qquad (2)$$

$D_0 + \Delta D$ to Ce, $D_0 + 2\Delta D$ to Pr, etc., fractional crystallization leads to concentrations in the residual liquid, relative to concentrations $U(z)$ in a standard rock, given by (3). If $\log \{C_0(z)/U(z)\}$ is independent of z or varies linearly with z, then the relative

$$\log \left\{ \frac{C_L(z)}{U(z)} \right\} = \log \left\{ \frac{C_0(z)}{U(z)} \right\} + (D_0 - 1) \log (1 - x) + z\Delta D \log (1 - x) \qquad (3)$$

residual liquid concentration $C_L(z)/U(z)$ is a straight line when plotted logarithmically against z (figure 8).

When rare-earth abundances in chondrites are used as the comparison standard,

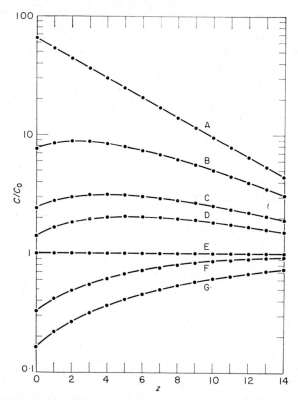

FIGURE 8   Fractional crystallization Earth model with relative abundances of the rare-earth elements. The straight line A, the C_L curve $(1 - x = 0.0087)$, represents the last residual liquid after fractional crystallization forming presumably protocrustal nuclei. C, D, F, G, which are various $\bar{C}_S$ curves, represent average relative rare-earth abundance for shells at various depths: C, 10–175 km; D, 10–400 km; F, 400–1000 km; G, 1000–2898 km. Curve B, the C_S curve where $1 - x = 0.0087$, represents the last solid to have crystallized which is in equilibrium with the residual liquid. These curves are calculated for $D_0 = 0.12$ and $\Delta D = 0.04$ and the Masuda and Matsui assumption $D = D_0 + z\Delta D$. The equations are given in the text

as in figures 1 and 2, some crustal rocks display a nearly linear trend on semilogarithmic plots. It is tempting to suggest that the model is essentially correct in these instances, that the values of $D(z)$ do indeed vary more or less linearly with z in these rocks, and that the original relative rare-earth distribution was that of chondrites. Of course, any multiple of chondritic concentrations, as in eucritic achondrites, for example, would also lead to the same slope of the residual liquid, and any linear variation of $\log \{C_0(z)/U(z)\}$ with z would lead to a linear residual liquid trend of different slope on the semilogarithmic plots.

The composition of the crystallizing solid can be calculated for any stage of the fractional crystallization, and this has been done in figure 8 for various depths according to the simple Earth model. It is significant that a maximum occurs in the light element region near Nd with a smooth decrease in relative abundance among the heavy elements. The same trend is observed in Hawaiian tholeiitic basalts as illustrated in figure 2, and an analysis of the Australian Delegate eclogite[5] shows a similar trend.

While keeping in mind all the hazards of speculating too far on such a contrived model, it may still be instructive to compute the amounts of the various rare earths in shells of the Earth at different depths of a fractionally crystallized Earth. Using values of $D_0 = 0.12$ and $\Delta D = 0.04$, and assuming that the primitive crust of residual liquid comprised 0.56% of the silicate mass of the Earth, we have compiled table 1 for the

TABLE 1   Distribution of rare earths with depth in a fractionally crystallized Earth

Depth (km)	F_M	F_{La}	F_{Lu}
0–10	0·0056	0·53	0·029
0–35	0·020	0·62	0·069
10–175	0·090	0·22	0·17
10–400	0·205	0·29	0·31
400–1000	0·267	0·086	0·26
1000–2898	0·522	0·084	0·39

two end-member rare earths La and Lu. F_M is the fraction of the mass of the mantle plus crust contained in the zone, and F_{La} and F_{Lu} are the fractions of the Earth's inventory of La and Lu in the same zone. Thus half the La but only 3% of the Lu are contained in the uppermost 10 km but about equal amounts of La and Lu are in the upper mantle to a depth of 400 km.

Partial melting

Melting of some portion of solid and equilibration between the interstitial melt and the entire residual solid may be important on a local scale in the formation of basalts from upper-mantle material. In general, the composition of the liquid $C_L(z)$ in terms of the primary material composition $C_P(z)$ and the fraction melted, $0 \leq y \leq 1$, is given by (4), where $D(z) = C_R(z)/C_L(z)$ is the partition between the entire residual

$$\frac{C_L(z)}{U(z)} = \frac{C_P(z)/U(z)}{y + D(z)(1 - y)} \qquad (4)$$

solid and the liquid, and the concentrations are compared with the standard distribution $U(z)$ as before.

A model for the formation of basalts by a two-step process is production of upper mantle material by fractional crystallization, as discussed above, followed by the partial melting of this upper mantle material to form lavas in the crust. Accordingly, figure 9 has been constructed assuming a primary material of composition similar to that shown in figure 8 in the C_S curve $(1 - x = 0.0087)$. The compositions of liquids and residual solids for 1%, 10%, and 50% partial melting are shown. It is noteworthy that small degrees of partial melting lead to liquid compositions not appreciably different from residual liquids after fractional crystallization. Therefore, the addition over geologic time of lavas formed by small degrees of partial melting to the primitive crust of a fractionally crystallized Earth will not change its rare-earth abundance pattern appreciably.

In the light of partial melting and fractional crystallization, the Hawaiian nepheline–melilite basalt (figure 2) may have been derived by fractional crystallization or it may represent a small degree of partial melting of the low-melting materials of the upper mantle, whereas the Hawaiian tholeiite would be a nearly complete melting product

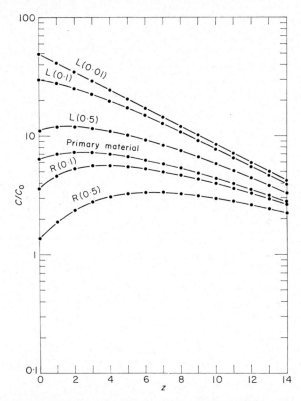

FIGURE 9   Partial melting model for formation of basalts. The primary material of composition shown in figure 8, curve C_S $(1 - x = 0.0087)$, is used for the upper mantle. The relative rare-earth composition for melts formed by 1%, 10%, and 50% melting of primary material are shown, L (0.01), L (0.1), and L (0.5), and the residual material, R (0.01), R (0.1), and R (0.5), respectively, are plotted on a logarithmic scale as a function of z. Thus a two-step model is implied: (i) formation of the upper mantle by fractional crystallization, primary curve, and (ii) partial melting of the upper mantle to produce basaltic melts, L

$$\frac{C_L(z)}{C_0(z)} = \frac{C_P(z)/C_0(z)}{y + D(z)(1 - y)}$$
$$C_R(z) = D(z)C_L(z)$$

of this material. The Australian Delegate eclogite may also represent the low-melting portion of the upper mantle but crystallized at depth.

Fractional melting

A process of possible physical significance is successive partial meltings and removal of the melt each time, where the homogeneous distribution law is assumed for each step. If we keep in mind a stepwise model, after n steps, the nth liquid has the composition (5) and the residual solid in equilibrium with this liquid has the composition (6).

$$\frac{C_{Ln}(z)}{U(z)} = \frac{C_P(z)}{U(z)} \frac{\prod_{i=1}^{n-1} D_i(z)}{\prod_{i=1}^{n} \{y_i + D_i(z)(1 - y_i)\}} \tag{5}$$

$$C_{Rn}(z) = C_{Ln}(z)D_n(z) \tag{6}$$

The first few liquids extracted for small values of the degree of melting y_i are very similar in rare-earth pattern to the liquids discussed above under fractional crystallization and partial melting, but after a very large number of small melting steps the solid becomes quite depleted in La relative to Lu. This process is clearly a sort of inverse of fractional crystallization. If such a process was important in the evolution of basalts from upper-mantle material, it seems necessary that the total fraction of melting and the number of steps involved were small if all the successive melts are to have major element compositions typical of basalts[28-31]. Therefore, in practice this process probably cannot be distinguished, by rare-earth measurements, from partial melting or fractional crystallization as they apply to basalts.

Zone melting

Following the development of zone-refining theory as applied to metallurgical problems[32], Harris[33] proposed that a zone-melting process may have been important in the development of igneous rocks of the Earth's crust and upper mantle, and Vinogradov[34-36] has reported experiments on the zone melting of meteorites. The physics of such a process as applied to the Earth was considered by Shimazu[37-40] and recently by Magnitskii[41]. It may be that rare-earth abundance patterns can provide a convenient test of the possible zone-melting history of basic igneous rocks because of the large number of elements having properties gradually varying with Z. Other trace elements do not enjoy this advantage.

Let us consider a vertical column of rock of length L and a process whereby a small zone $l \ll L$ is molten and moves up along the length of the column by progressive melting above and freezing below. Because most trace elements at equilibrium are enriched in the melt relative to the frozen material immediately below the moving zone, the zone gradually sweeps the trace elements up from the bottom of the column to the top. The bottom is depleted and the top is enriched in trace elements, and the middle remains unchanged. For a single pass of the zone, the concentration of trace element at any vertical location $0 \leqq x \leqq L - l$ along the column is given by (7),

$$\frac{C_x(z)}{C_0(z)} = 1 - \{1 - D(z)\} \exp \left\{ \frac{-D(z)x}{l} \right\} \tag{7}$$

where concentrations and the joint effective partition ratios are functions of the particular trace element or, in the case of the rare earths, the atomic number Z. Individual trace element concentrations in a rock sample do not easily reveal the possibility of such a zone-melting process in their history, but the relative concentrations of the rare earths are quite different from those predicted by the fractional crystallization and partial melting processes considered earlier. Figure 10 illustrates predicted rare-earth patterns for the solid at various heights along the column, by analogy with the Earth where zone melting might take place by a rising molten spot. A zone length of 10% of the column length has been assumed, and the calculations are based on a linear variation of partition ratio with atomic number.

Multiple passes of the rising zone will deplete an ever-increasing length at the bottom of the column and pile up trace elements in a wider region at the top, decreasing the length of steady-state concentration in the middle. In the limit of many passes, the trace element concentration reaches a steady-state condition of gradually increasing concentration with height. Figure 10 shows predicted rare-earth patterns for

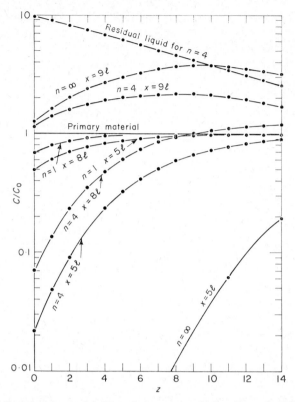

FIGURE 10   Zone-melting model. The relative rare-earth abundances at different depths measured in units of the zone length for a model Earth differentiated by multipass zone melting is plotted on a logarithmic scale as a function of z. The curves are computed for $n = 1, 4$, and ∞ and at height $x/l = 5$, 8, and 9 which would correspond approximately to depths of 1500 km, 600 km, and 300 km. The relative rare-earth concentrations in the last piling-up zone after four passes are also shown on the top. The equation is given in the text (equation 7), for $n = 1$. $L/l = 10$ for all curves

numbers of zone passes $n = 1$, $n = 4$, and $n = \infty$ for several depths and for one uppermost liquid, where the multipass cases were computed from Pfann's published curves[42].

It is noteworthy that for just a few passes there is in the middle to lower part of the column a rapid decrease of rare-earth concentration with decreasing atomic number so that La is very sharply depleted compared with the other elements. Higher up on the column the overall rare-earth concentrations are somewhat greater than initially before the zone-melting process began, and a maximum enrichment is found in the middle to heavy element region.

The peridotite analyses shown in figure 4 bear a striking resemblance to the predicted patterns at a depth in the Earth according to the zone-melting model, and the Mid-Atlantic Ridge basalts, with their maximum in the middle to heavy element region, are not unlike those at shallower depth. Not only are the peridotites of the same qualitative form as the prediction, but quantitatively the total rare-earth concentrations are very low as predicted if we assume a chondrite initial material. The Ridge basalts, on the other hand, have much higher overall concentrations and in fact agree closely with predictions if we assume an initial material of achondritic composition. It should be emphasized that, not only the shape of the patterns, but also the absolute rare-earth concentrations are worth examining critically.

The question whether zone melting is a physically possible process in early Earth history is complex, and it is certainly not likely that the actual steps were so simple as considered here. In fact, there are probably a number of physically different processes which could more or less conform to the same mathematical formalism. Perhaps these considerations will stimulate more careful thought in the future about the matter.

TABLE 2   Distribution of rare earths with depth in a zone-refined column of silicate rock[a]

Depth (km)	F_M	F_{La}	F_{Lu}
400–1000	0·2	$1·4 \times 10^{-3}$	0·25
1000–2898	0·655	$3·3 \times 10^{-9}$	0·04

[a] Steady-state values after infinite zone refining of a 2898 km column of uniform cross section assuming a zone height of 10% of the total height.

If a zone-melting process took place over a great range of depth in the Earth, we may ask how effectively the rare earths would be removed from the lower mantle. Table 2 is a calculation of the fractions, F_{La} and F_{Lu}, of La and Lu remaining in each of the depth ranges indicated after an infinite number of passes of the zone melting, on the assumption of $l/L = 0·1$. It is seen that La is especially well extracted from the deeper layers, but both La and Lu are lower in abundance than in a fractionally crystallized Earth. We may also suggest that the radioactive elements U, Th, and K should be more effectively removed from deep layers by multipass zone melting than by fractional crystallization, a point of interest in the problem of heat flow from the Earth.

Mixing

All of the foregoing discussion has been directed towards processes which could fractionate the rare earths by extraction processes involving solid–liquid equilibria. Mixing of different rare-earth abundance patterns, such as by complete assimilation of foreign material by a melt, must certainly take place. Perhaps the highly differentiated igneous rocks will never be satisfactorily explained unless such processes are considered. In the future it may be worth while to examine this problem more fully.

Conclusions

At the present time perhaps the most useful conclusions to reach are to decide what the interesting questions are which should be asked about the rare-earth elements in basic igneous rocks and their bearing on the upper mantle and the differentiation of the Earth.

(i) To what extent can the dynamics of physically different processes be revealed by rare-earth abundance measurements? The theoretical treatment worked out here depends quantitatively on assumed values of joint effective partition ratios of the rare-earth elements, and some ability to discriminate between processes was demonstrated.

It may be that different partition ratios would make further distinctions, although it may also be that new ambiguities arise. The rare earths are instructive for they show the relative inadequacy of single trace elements or trace element pairs to be sensitive indicators of the history of chemical differentiation. However, direct measurements of rare-earth partitions in interesting mineralogical systems are clearly needed.

(ii) Can it be that the very simple models of fractional crystallization, zone melting, etc., considered here are essentially good approximations to what has actually happened in the upper mantle and the crust? Or is there an accidental mathematical similarity between reality and the models? Given the many assumptions in the theoretical treatment here, any serious attempt to answer these questions would be dangerous. However, the great smoothness of rare-earth abundance curves relative to chondrites and the relative freedom from points of inflection suggests simplicity.

(iii) Do the rare earths reveal inhomogeneity in the upper mantle and different chemical differentiation processes of the crust from the upper mantle for different regions of the Earth? From a rare-earth standpoint, Hawaiian basalts suggest that partial melting of a solid derived ultimately from a fractionally crystallized chondritic Earth may have been operative. The peridotites indicate zone melting of chondritic matter, but the Mid-Atlantic Ridge basalts point more to Ca-rich achondrites as the primitive material.

(iv) More profoundly, do rare-earth abundances reflect processes which took place during the early differentiation of the Earth? Already evidence for a completely molten Earth and one which at most was only partially molten is indicated, and both an initially chondritic Earth and one of higher rare-earth concentrations approaching 10 times the chondritic one are implied. The alternatives may not be mutually exclusive, depending on inhomogeneities and the extent of equilibrium in the early differentiation of the Earth.

(v) In spite of the selectivity demonstrated for small rare-earth ions by some rock-forming minerals, how can we account for the simplicity of most rare-earth patterns for whole rocks compared with chondrites? The chemical histories since primeval times have most certainly been complex, and such things as formation of different minerals at different stages and crystal settling may be expected to produce irregularities in rare-earth patterns for individual rocks. It may be that processes within the mantle are simpler than this.

(vi) What additional chemical factors have influenced rare-earth abundance patterns? Oxidation–reduction conditions are critical for Ce and Eu, and the similarity of these elemental abundances to the other rare earths in whole rock suggests that both assume the $3+$ state in the equilibria of basic rocks. However, without separate mineral data one cannot say for sure. Furthermore, the role of water may be important in determining the partition of rare earths inasmuch as the smaller ions form stronger complexes in solution. Pegmatites have been observed to have a strong enrichment of the heavy rare earths, in contrast with granites which are frequently La enriched, and the difference may reflect the presence of volatiles in the late stages of differentiation.

(vii) In view of the generality of our understanding at the present time, can we still suggest specifically how the basic igneous rocks we have been discussing here originated? The tholeiites of Hawaii and of the Mid-Atlantic Ridge, for example, are very different in their rare-earth abundances. The Hawaiian tholeiites conform surprisingly well to the fractionally crystallized Earth model, and the *relative* rare-earth patterns in the Mid-Atlantic Ridge basalts are 'flat' as if they were 'nearly undisturbed chondritic rare-earth distribution patterns'[7]. Closer examination of these latter tholeiites, however, indicates the heavy rare-earth concentrations to be very high, some 30 times the chondritic and 3 times the Ca-rich achondritic concentrations and as high as Hawaiian trachyte (figure 5) and many granites[6,17]. Rather than being primitive and unaltered, it seems more likely that these tholeiites are quite differentiated but such that the relative rare-earth patterns are only slightly fractionated. In addition to zone melting, another possible process, in analogy to pegmatites, would involve water which may complex the heavy rare earths preferentially in solution. Partial melting of serpentinites and amphibolites at shallow depth with evolution of volatiles may have been important in the Mid-Atlantic Ridge, whereas in Hawaii, where earthquake foci are at greater depth, silicate melts may have been relatively dry.

In the long run, any satisfactory explanation of rare-earth abundance patterns will have to be according to models in agreement with geophysical observations, and it may be that satisfactory geophysical models for the differentiation of the Earth will have to agree with rare-earth geochemistry.

Acknowledgements

One of us (J.-G. S.) is grateful to NATO for a travel grant to the Conference on the Mantles of the Earth and Terrestrial Planets, Newcastle-upon-Tyne, to present this work of which the present chapter is a condensed summary. We are indebted to H. H. Hughes who contributed significantly to the initial stages of the theoretical work. Experimental portions of the work were supported in part by the U.S. Office of Naval Research, Contract Nonr 1841(74), and by a research assistantship to one of us (J.-G. S.) from the U.S. National Aeronautics and Space Administration, Grant NSG-496, through the Center for Space Research at Massachusetts Institute of Technology.

References

1. Yu. A. Balashov, A. B. Runov, A. A. Migdisov, and N. W. Turanskaya, *Geochemistry (USSR) (English Transl.)*, **1964**, No. 10, 951.
2. Yu. A. Balashov, *Geochemistry (USSR) (English Transl.)*, **1963**, No. 2, 107.
3. Yu. A. Balashov and N. V. Turanskaya, *Geochemistry (USSR) (English Transl.)*, **1962**, No. 4, 433.
4. R. A. Schmitt, R. H. Smith, J. E. Lash, A. W. Mosen, D. A. Olehy, and J. Vasilevskis, *Geochim. Cosmochim. Acta*, **27**, 577 (1963).
5. R. A. Schmitt, R. H. Smith, and D. A. Olehy, *Geochim. Cosmochim. Acta*, **28**, 67 (1964).
6. D. G. Towell, J. W. Winchester, and R. Volfovsky Spirn, *J. Geophys. Res.*, **70**, 3485 (1965).
7. F. A. Frey and L. Haskin, *J. Geophys. Res.*, **69**, 775 (1964).
8. T. R. Wildeman and L. A. Haskin, *J. Geophys. Res.*, **70**, 2905 (1965).
9. L. A. Haskin, F. A. Frey, R. A. Schmitt, and R. H. Smith, *Phys. Chem. Earth*, **7**, in press (1966).
10. L. Haskin and M. A. Gehl, *J. Geophys. Res.*, **67**, 2537 (1962).
11. J.-G. Schilling and J. W. Winchester, *Science*, **153**, 867 (1966).
12. C. D. Coryell, J. W. Chase, and J. W. Winchester, *J. Geophys. Res.*, **68**, 599 (1963).
13. D. H. Templeton and C. H. Dauben, *J. Chem. Soc.*, **76**, 5237 (1954).
14. A. Masuda and Y. Matsui, *Inst. Nucl. Study, Univ. Tokyo*, INSJ-53 (1963).

15. E. D. Goldberg, M. Koide, R. A. Schmitt, and R. H. Smith, *J. Geophys. Res.*, **68**, 4209 (1963).
16. R. Volfovsky Spirn, Ph.D. Thesis, Department of Geology and Geophysics, Massachusetts Institute of Technology, U.S.A. (1965).
17. J. W. Chase, J. W. Winchester, and C. D. Coryell, *J. Geophys. Res.*, **68**, 567 (1963).
18. H. A. Doerner and W. M. Hoskins, *J. Am. Chem. Soc.*, **47**, 662 (1925).
19. M. Berthelot, *Ann. Chim. Phys.*, **26**, 408 (1872).
20. W. Nernst, *Z. Physik. Chem. (Frankfurt)*, **8**, 110 (1891).
21. H. D. Holland and J. L. Kulp, *Am. Mineralogist*, **34**, 35 (1949).
22. H. Neumann, *Econ. Geol.*, **43**, 77 (1948).
23. H. Neumann, J. Mead, and C. J. Vitaliano, *Geochim. Cosmochim. Acta*, **6**, 90 (1954).
24. I. D. Ryabchikov, *Geochemistry (USSR) (English Transl.)*, **1960**, No. 4, 412.
25. I. D. Ryabchikov, *Geochem. Intern.*, **2**, 163 (1965).
26. W. L. McIntire, *Geochim. Cosmochim. Acta*, **27**, 1209 (1963).
27. L. R. Wager and R. L. Mitchell, *Geochim. Cosmochim. Acta*, **1**, 129 (1951).
28. I. Kushiro and H. Kuno, *J. Petrol.*, **4**, 75 (1962).
29. A. E. Ringwood, *J. Geophys. Res.*, **67**, 857 (1962).
30. A. E. Ringwood, in *Advances in Earth Sciences* (Ed. P. M. Hurley), M.I.T. Press, Cambridge, Massachusetts, 1966, p. 357.
31. A. Reay and P. G. Harris, *Bull. Volcanol.*, **27**, 3 (1964).
32. W. G. Pfann, *Trans. AIME*, **194**, 747 (1952).
33. P. G. Harris, *Geochim. Cosmochim. Acta*, **12**, 195 (1957).
34. A. P. Vinogradov, *Geochemistry (USSR) (English Transl.)*, **1961**, No. 1, 1.
35. A. P. Vinogradov, *Izv. Akad. Nauk SSSR, Ser. Geol.*, **1959**, No. 10, 3.
36. A. P. Vinogradov, *UN International Congress on the Peaceful Uses of Atomic Energy*, Geneva, 1958, pp. 255–69.
37. Y. Shimazu, *J. Earth Sci., Nagoya Univ.*, **7**, 1 (1959).
38. Y. Shimazu, *J. Earth Sci., Nagoya Univ.*, **7**, 91 (1959).
39. Y. Shimazu, *J. Earth Sci., Nagoya Univ.*, **8**, 72 (1960).
40. Y. Shimazu, *J. Earth Sci., Nagoya Univ.*, **9**, 185 (1961).
41. V. A. Magnitskii, *Izv. Akad. Nauk SSSR, Ser. Geol.*, **1964**, No. 11, 3.
42. W. G. Pfann, *Zone Melting*, 2nd ed., Wiley, New York, 1966.
43. E. Minami, *Nachr. Ges. Wiss. Goettingen, Math. Physik. Kl.*, **1**, 155 (1935).

2

G. D. NICHOLLS
University of Manchester
England

Geochemical studies in the ocean as evidence for the composition of the mantle

Introduction

There is general agreement that the magmas giving rise to basaltic volcanic lavas have been derived from the mantle and from this it follows that some, as yet unspecified, fraction of the upper mantle should correspond chemically to the composition of primitive basalt. The seismic velocities in the upper mantle beneath oceanic areas are too high for the upper mantle in these areas to be entirely basaltic in character, a view that is supported by various other lines of evidence. Basaltic magmas are, almost certainly, the consequence of partial, rather than complete, fusion of the mantle. In other words, the mantle undergoes a form of differentiation during the genesis of basaltic magma.

Basaltic lavas are not the only products of mantle differentiation reaching the surface. Almost all studies on the evolution of the atmosphere and hydrosphere have led to the conclusion that some low molecular weight compounds have been lost from the mantle by progressive degassing and liberated at the surface as components of volcanic gases. These low molecular weight compounds will be designated the 'volatile fraction', though this usage is not intended to imply that they are necessarily present in the mantle in a gaseous, or even a fluid, state.

The chemical composition of the upper mantle, from which these surface expressions of mantle-derived material come, can be considered to be a combination of these fractions, viz.

x parts volatile fraction composition
y parts basaltic lava fraction composition
z parts residual fraction composition

where $x + y + z = 1$.

The approach to be followed in this chapter is one of examining the possible compositions of each of the three fractions with an attempt to define limits in each case, and of evaluating x, y, and z as closely as possible, again with an attempt to define limits and thus to place limits on the chemical composition of the upper mantle under oceanic areas. Such an approach does not yield direct evidence of the mineralogical assemblages present in the upper mantle, nor does it bear on the question of the composition of the upper mantle under continental areas.

The Volatile Fraction

Progressive degassing of the interior of the Earth is the most likely source of the bulk of the atmosphere and hydrosphere as we know them today. In addition, some components so liberated have been locked up by chemical combination into material now existing in the solid state as rocks, e.g. carbon dioxide into calcium carbonate (limestones). Geochemists refer to the material now on, or in, the outer parts of the planet, which cannot be accounted for by translocation of igneous rock material, as 'excess volatiles'. Estimates of the quantities of these 'excess volatiles' have been provided by Rubey[1] and can be derived from data presented by Poldervaart[2] (see table 1). Estimates from these sources differ principally in the quantity of C expressed

TABLE 1   Estimates of the quantities of 'excess volatiles' in
units of 10^{20} g

	(1)	(2)
H_2O	16600	16300
Total C as CO_2	910	2490
S	22	24
N	42	44
Cl	300	335
A, F, H, B, etc.	13	13

Column (1), estimated quantities of 'excess volatiles' [from Rubey[1]]; column (2), estimated quantities of 'excess volatiles' [using the data of Poldervaart[2].]

as CO_2. Rubey's figure now appears to be probably low, while, on the other hand, accumulating data on the composition of deep sea sediments suggest that Poldervaart's figure may be rather high. Rubey's arguments that the composition of the 'excess volatiles' liberated at the Earth's surface during the last 500×10^6 years cannot have changed greatly appear quite valid still. The rate of loss may have varied—the data published by Ronov[3] suggest that it has.

'Excess volatiles' cannot be equated directly to the mantle volatile fraction since, in computing their amounts, no account is taken of any volatiles of mantle derivation still locked up in the present oceanic crust. However, they do afford a starting point in any attempt to deduce a composition of the volatile fraction of the mantle. From table 1 it is clear that water- and carbon-bearing gases are the more important constituents of the 'excess volatiles', and it must first be established whether this is still true if account is taken of other mantle-derived volatiles now present in the oceanic crust.

Over much of the deep ocean area there are three layers in the oceanic crust. The upper layer (layer 1) is almost certainly composed essentially of sediments and in computations of 'excess volatiles' the sediments of this layer are taken into account. The intermediate layer (layer 2) is now thought to be largely composed of basalt, though the possibility of some consolidated sediment occurring in this layer cannot be excluded. Analyses of fresh glassy representatives of these basalts (those less likely to have sorbed water from their surroundings during, and subsequent to, their consolidation) indicate water contents of less than 0·6 % (see Nicholls[4]) and even some of this water may have been acquired after the magma was erupted from the mantle.

Contents of other volatile constituents have not been reported and are certainly low, probably less than 0·01 %. Volatile contents in layer 2 are not taken into account in computing quantities of 'excess volatiles'. Until recently layer 3 was generally regarded as basalt, though it is improbable that layer 2 and layer 3 can be the same material. Hess[5] suggested that layer 3 may be serpentinite or partially serpentinized peridotite, and Nicholls[6] has noted various lines of evidence supporting this suggestion. Analyses of deep sea serpentinites published by Hess[7] gave contents of combined water in these rocks ranging from 10·99 % to 13·40 %. If any significant fraction of layer 3 is composed of serpentinite, appreciable quantities of combined water must be present in this layer. Protected as it is from contact with sea water over any extensive area by layer 2, layer 3 can be expected to have acquired its combined water from some source in the mantle. It may also contain other elements listed among 'excess volatiles', if such elements can be accommodated in the lattices of the serpentine group of minerals, e.g. chlorine. Any such volatiles now present in layer 3 are not included in summations of 'excess volatiles'.

It is tempting to proceed by assessing the amounts of volatile constituents in layers 2 and 3 and simply adding these to the quantities of 'excess volatiles', but such a procedure is probably invalid. The 'excess volatiles' figures given in table 1 represent the total amounts of these liberated throughout geological time. If current views on mantle convection currents are correct, or even approximate to the truth, layer 3 as it exists at present may have formed only during the later part of geological time. If the overall composition of 'excess volatiles' liberated during this later part of geological time was the same as the composition of the total 'excess volatiles', the above-mentioned procedure might be justifiable but, since it is not known that this is definitely so, it is unwise to proceed on the assumption that it is. Fortunately, the problem can be approached in a different way. This involves consideration of the possible channels of escape of mantle-derived volatiles. In considering possible channels of escape of the 'excess volatiles' Rubey[1] compared the percentage composition of these with the compositions of various emitted natural gases, etc., and concluded that the 'excess volatiles' may have reached the surface through hot springs and fumaroles. If some allowance is made for the possibility of recycled ground water being present in natural effluents, the correspondence in composition is quite good. However, compositions of emitted natural gases from continental areas are very variable and, as in all studies on volcanic gases, the sampling achieved up to the present time is dubiously representative. Furthermore, gases emitted in continental regions, even if mantle-derived originally, have penetrated some 35 km of continental crust, the upper part of which in many localities is composed of variable successions of sedimentary rocks. Interactions between the gases and such rocks, e.g. limestones, sulphide-bearing shales, evaporite sequences, etc., may have caused modification of the original gas composition, so that the emitted gases can no longer be regarded as representative of the original gas composition. The least contaminated mantle-derived volatiles reaching the Earth's surface from the interior would be expected to be volcanic gases emerging from oceanic volcanoes. The state of oxidation of Hawaiian volcanic gases is very close to that predicted for gases in equilibrium with a Mg–Fe silicate upper mantle[8], which suggests that they have suffered comparatively little contamination on their way to the surface. Consequently, some similarity might be expected between the composition of oceanic volcanic gases and that of the 'excess volatiles', if the latter are mantle derived. Ideally, comprehensive data on volcanic gas compositions from numerous oceanic volcanic islands should be used, but, in the absence of such, the composition of Hawaiian volcanic gases[9] will be taken as typical of oceanic volcanic gases. The lack of correspondence between 'excess volatiles' composition and Hawaiian volcanic gas composition is most marked (table 2). The latter is much richer in compounds of

TABLE 2   Comparison of 'excess volatiles' composition with the composition of Hawaiian volcanic gases

	(1)	(2)	(3)
H_2O	92·8	84·9	64·3
Total C as CO_2	5·1	13·0	23·9
S	0·13	0·1	10·0
N	0·24	0·2	1·6
Cl	1·7	1·7	0·1
A, F, H, B, etc.	0·07	trace	0·1

Column (1), composition of 'excess volatiles' [from the data of Rubey[1]]; column (2), composition of 'excess volatiles' [from the data of Poldervaart[2]]; column (3), composition of Hawaiian volcanic gases [from Eaton and Murata[9]].
The figures represent weight percentage composition.

C, S, and N and relatively impoverished in Cl and H_2O. The Hawaiian volcanic gases may be abnormally enriched in C, S, and N, though it may be significant that they are impoverished in those constituents, and only those constituents, which could enter the lattices of serpentine minerals. There is, therefore, justification for examining the possibility that oceanic volcanic gas compositions represent the escaping volatile fraction of the mantle less certain constituents which have been taken into the lattices of serpentine minerals during the formation of serpentinites in the oceanic crust. If the mantle convection current hypothesis was accepted, these 'volatile' elements incorporated into serpentinite would be released in the downturn of the convective system and would, in part or wholly, escape to the surface at localities distant from the oceanic volcanoes, possibly in the marginal regions of continents. This is, basically, the concept involved in the hypothesis of two-channel escape of emergent volatiles[6].

As a first approach to the problem let us assume that the composition of emitted 'excess volatiles' has indeed remained constant throughout geological time and let us use the results of such an assumption to guide consideration of the possible consequences of inconstancy of 'excess volatiles' composition. Theoretically it is possible, using this assumption, to calculate minimum quantities of volatiles escaping by other channels than oceanic volcanoes. If all the compounds of C, S, and N in the 'excess volatiles' have escaped through oceanic volcanoes, the amounts of other constituents escaping with them through the same channels can be computed from the oceanic volcanic gas composition and then subtracted from their amounts in the total mass of 'excess volatiles'. The resulting figures should be the minimum amounts escaping by other channels. Of the data on the three elements C, S, and N, that on N in the 'excess volatiles' composition is considered to be the most reliable and subsequent calculations are based on the geochemistry of this element.

If the average rate of escape during the last hundred million years has been equal to the average rate during the whole period of mantle degassing, the amounts escaping via other channels than oceanic volcanoes during this hundred million years are, using Rubey's data,

$$3314 \times 10^{19} \text{ g } H_2O, \qquad 63 \times 10^{19} \text{ g } CO_2, \qquad 66 \times 10^{19} \text{ g Cl}$$
$$2 \cdot 3 \times 10^{19} \text{ g others}$$

or, using Poldervaart's data,

$$3229 \times 10^{19} \text{ g } H_2O, \qquad 407 \times 10^{19} \text{ g } CO_2, \qquad 74 \times 10^{19} \text{ g Cl}$$
$$2 \cdot 3 \times 10^{19} \text{ g others}$$

Clearly, on this hypothesis, less than one-ninth of the 'excess volatiles' have escaped via oceanic volcanoes. The remainder must emerge through other channels such as continental and near-continental volcanoes, fumaroles, etc. If these volatiles reside temporarily in the serpentinite of layer 3, the amounts of such serpentinite formed during the last hundred million years may be calculated. From amounts of combined water in analyses published by Hess[7] the H_2O content of such serpentinites can be put at 12%. The amount of serpentinite which could hold these second channel 'volatiles' is 2770×10^{20} g using Rubey's data or 2690×10^{20} g using those of Poldervaart. These figures are substantially below the amounts of serpentinite formed during the last hundred million years according to the Hess hypothesis of mantle convection currents. If such currents flow at an average rate of $1 \cdot 25$ cm/year, $16\,800 \times 10^{20}$ g of serpentinite would have been formed during this period. This suggests that rather less than one-sixth of the volatiles held in the serpentinite escape to the surface after dehydration of the serpentinite in the convective downturns.

Hitherto, constancy of composition of emitted 'excess volatiles' throughout geological time has been assumed in this discussion. If variation in this composition has occurred, early differential loss of those components not taken into the serpentinite might be expected since, as shown above, recycling, of those components which are, must almost certainly occur. Possibly, therefore, the overall composition of 'excess volatiles' emitted during the last hundred million years may be richer in H_2O and Cl than the total overall composition of 'excess volatiles'. The validity of the arguments advanced by Rubey[1] for constancy of 'excess volatiles' composition imposes severe restrictions on possible variation, and consideration of the effect of any such change on the discussion advanced above shows that it merely modifies the proportion of serpentinite held volatiles that escape to the surface on dehydration. In other words, data available today do not permit any firm conclusion concerning the overall composition of 'excess volatiles' emitted during the last hundred million years. This would be of no great moment if the amount of nitrogen escaping into the Earth's atmosphere from the interior and the amount of serpentinite formed during this period were known, for, in that case, rigid assessment of the consequences of changing 'excess volatiles' composition would merely result in a redistribution of the mantle volatiles between that fraction escaping as 'excess volatiles' and that being recycled in the mantle. The amount of nitrogen escaping into the Earth's atmosphere during any given period depends not only on the composition of the emitted gases, etc., but also on the rate of escape, and it is pertinent to consider whether this rate has remained constant throughout the hundred-million-year period under discussion.

The rate of escape of 'excess volatiles' from the interior has not remained constant throughout the whole of geological time. Various workers have presented evidence for fluctuation in the rate (see Nicholls[6]), but over a period of a hundred million years it is unlikely to have departed from the mean rate by more than a factor of 5. There is some evidence that the rate during the last hundred million years has been less than the mean rate. If it had been equal to the mean rate, the Cl content of deep sea serpentinites, even assuming that the recycled fraction of the serpentinite 'volatiles' was pure water, would be about 0.04%. A search for Cl in samples of serpentinite dredged from the floor of the deep ocean revealed that the Cl content is less than 0.015%. If the rate of escape of volatiles was 5 times less than the mean rate, the Cl content in deep sea serpentinites would be about 0.008%. The probable average rate of escape of volatiles during the last hundred million years would therefore appear to be no more than two-fifths of the mean rate for the whole of geological time, and is likely to be nearer one-fifth. With this rate of escape for a hundred million years, 550×10^{20} g of serpentinite would suffice to hold the second channel 'excess volatiles' temporarily; for a rate two-fifths the mean 1100×10^{20} g would be required.

Another approach to this question of the rate of escape during the last hundred million years could be based on consideration of the implications of the proportions of volcanic gas and solid volcanic products liberated from oceanic volcanoes. Estimates of the amounts of gas emitted from volcanoes range from 0.4 to 1.1% by weight of total volcanic products[10]. In general, smaller amounts of gases are emitted (relative to solid products) from oceanic volcanoes than from continental ones, and so, for the present purpose, a figure towards the lower end of the range should be taken. The total amount of lava extruded from oceanic volcanoes during the last hundred million years is unknown, but if the whole of layer 2 of the oceanic crust is formed in this way 5600×10^{20} g of lava would have been extruded on the convective conditions assumed above. Possibly the whole of layer 2 is not basalt derived from oceanic volcanoes, but deep sea dredging results make it extremely unlikely that less than half of layer 2 is basalt. If we take as a minimum figure that 2800×10^{20} g of lava have been extruded from oceanic volcanoes during the hundred-million-year period being considered, the amount of gases escaping from oceanic volcanic sources would be about 11.5×10^{20} g (or, if all of layer 2 is basalt, 23×10^{20} g). If the average rate of escape of volatiles from oceanic volcanic sources during the last hundred million years had been equal to the mean rate for the whole of geological time, about 54×10^{20} g would have escaped through these channels. These data also suggest that during the period under consideration the average rate of escape of volatiles has been between one-fifth and two-fifths of the mean rate for all geological time. If we proceed on the basis of an average rate three-tenths of the mean (table 3 presents figures for calculations based on rates one-fifth and two-fifths of the mean as well as three-tenths), the amounts of mantle-derived volatiles that can be classified as 'excess volatiles' are 120×10^{20} g (using Rubey's data) or 128×10^{20} g (using Poldervaart's data). Some of these have already escaped into the atmosphere via oceanic volcanic sources, but some are still locked up in layer 3 serpentinite. The amount of such serpentinite is 825×10^{20} g (within the limits of accuracy of the data) leaving some 16000×10^{20} g of serpentinite carrying mantle-derived volatiles subject to recycling. If we attribute to such recycled volatiles the same composition as those lost to the atmosphere above the convective downturns, the amounts of such recycled volatiles can be calculated (table 3). By summation of the mantle-derived volatiles escaping as 'excess volatiles', the H_2O present in the basalts extruded to form layer 2, and the recycled mantle-derived

TABLE 3   Location of mantle-derived volatiles and computation of the composition of the mantle volatile fraction

Rate of escape of 'excess volatiles'	$\frac{1}{5}$ mean rate		$\frac{2}{5}$ mean rate		$\frac{3}{10}$ mean rate	
Excess volatiles	R	P	R	P	R	P
H_2O	74·3	72·1	148·4	144·4	114·4	108·6
CO_2	4	11·1	8·2	22·2	6	16·7
S	0·1	0·1	0·2	0·2	0·2	0·2
N	0·2	0·2	0·4	0·3	0·3	0·3
Cl	1·4	1·5	2·8	2·9	2·1	2·2
Total amount	80	85	160	170	120	128

Basalt (0·5% H_2O)						
Total amount of basalt	2800		5600		4200	
H_2O	14		28		21	

Serpentinite carrying recycled volatiles (12% H_2O and other volatiles in the proportions as liberated in the convective downturns)

H_2O	1950	1950	1885	1885	1920	1920
CO_2	38·5	247	37·5	238	38	244
Cl	38·5	45	37·5	44	38	44

Total in all locations						
H_2O	2038·3	2036·1	2061·4	2057·4	2052·4	2049·6
CO_2	42·5	258·1	45·7	260·2	44	260·7
S	0·1	0·1	0·2	0·2	0·2	0·2
N	0·2	0·2	0·4	0·3	0·3	0·3
Cl	39·9	46·5	40·3	46·9	40·1	46·2
Total	2121	2341	2148	2365	2137	2357

Percentage composition for mantle volatile fraction						
H_2O	96	87	96	87	96	87
CO_2	2	11	2	11	2	11
Cl	2	2	2	2	2	2
Others	trace	trace	trace	trace	trace	trace

All figures except those expressing percentage compositions are given in units of 10^{20} g for a period of a hundred million years.
Columns headed R are results of calculations using Rubey's data (see text); those headed P are the figures obtained using Poldervaart's data.

volatiles, the composition of the mantle volatile fraction can be estimated (table 3). It emerges that the percentage composition of the volatile fraction of the mantle is little affected by the choice of a rate of volatile escape, but is influenced by the composition chosen for the 'excess volatiles'. A preferred composition is 91% H_2O, 7% CO_2, 2% Cl with only a trace of other volatiles.

Values of x, y, and z

The data used in the previous section of this chapter permit an estimation of values of x, y, and z.

For an average rate of escape of 'excess volatiles' during the last hundred million years equal to one-fifth of the mean rate for the whole of the period of mantle degassing, the amount of volatile fraction in the volatile-rich parts of the mantle is calculated to be between 2120×10^{20} and 2341×10^{20} g, the amount of water-free basaltic fraction 2786×10^{20} g, and the amount of the residuum of the serpentinite from which the volatiles have been subtracted between 14660×10^{20} g and 14480×10^{20} g. On the reasonable assumption that the volatile-enriched parts of the mantle differentiate into these three fractions, the value of x under these conditions would be between 0·108 and 0·119, that of y 0·142, and that of z between 0·750 and 0·739.

For an average rate of escape that is two-fifths of the mean rate, the figures are the following: the amount of volatile fraction between 2148×10^{20} g and 2365×10^{20} g, the amount of water-free basaltic fraction 5572×10^{20} g, and the amount of serpentinite residuum between 14700×10^{20} and 14480×10^{20} g. Under these conditions x would be between 0·096 and 0·105, y between 0·248 and 0·249, and z between 0·656 and 0·646.

For the preferred average rate of escape (three-tenths of the mean rate) the figures are the following: the amount of volatile fraction between 2137×10^{20} and 2357×10^{20} g, the amount of water-free basaltic fraction 4179×10^{20} g, and the amount of serpentinite residuum between 14700×10^{20} and 14480×10^{20} g. These figures lead to a value for x between 0·102 and 0·112, a value for y 0·199, and a value for z between 0·699 and 0·689.

The preferred value for x is, therefore, 0·107 with extremes of 0·096 and 0·119. That for y is 0·199 with extremes of 0·142 and 0·249. A 'best' value for z is 0·694 with extremes of 0·646 and 0·750.

The Basaltic Lava Fraction

The compositions of volcanic lavas assigned to the basaltic group are very variable, taking the World as a whole. Petrological authorities differ in their opinions whether the variation in composition is continuous or whether definite types of basalt exist with rarer intermediates between them. The literature is bestrewn with a specialized terminology and, unfortunately, the same terms do not mean the same things to all petrologists. It is necessary to cut through this jungle of terminology and withdraw from the confused mass of data those which are significant in the present study. The principles to be followed are (i) and (ii).

(i) All basalts erupted through the continental crust will be omitted from consideration in the present context. The reasons for this extreme action are (*a*) the danger that such lavas have been contaminated during their ascent through the 35 km or so of crust, since the temperatures at which basaltic lavas are mobile considerably exceed those of incipient partial fusion of the majority of crustal rock types, and (*b*) the ever-present possibility of partial crystallization and fractionation of the molten basaltic material during this ascent. Contamination and/or fractionation effects would mean that the composition of the lavas extruded no longer equates to the composition of the fraction produced by partial fusion in the mantle.

(ii) In considering basalts from oceanic areas, greater importance will be assigned to the glassy and very fine-grained representatives than to those which carry phenocrysts, since such large crystals may have moved differentially within the liquid during ascent to the surface.

While the application of these principles considerably limits the range of basalt composition it still leaves a range of compositions from the so-called alkaline olivine basalt to the low-potassic high-alumina basalts of the deep ocean floor. Some of this range of composition must be due to postgenesis fractionation effects, but some may represent real variation in the composition of basaltic magmas generated in the mantle under different conditions.

In dealing with the chemical compositions of fine-grained or glassy basalts it is convenient to recalculate from the chemical analysis a mineralogical assemblage that could have been formed by complete crystallization of the lava under surface conditions. This assemblage is known as the 'norm' of the rock. The normative content of a mineral (the calculated content from the chemical analysis) is to be distinguished from the actual amount (if any) visible in the analysed sample. Certain normative mineral assemblages are not possible. For example, it is possible to write

$$\underset{\text{nepheline}}{NaAlSiO_4} + \underset{\text{orthopyroxene}}{4MgSiO_3} \equiv \underset{\text{olivine}}{2Mg_2SiO_4} + \underset{\text{albite}}{NaAlSi_3O_8}$$

and on the basis of experimental and observational evidence the right-hand side association is clearly the stable one for crystallization under surface or near-surface conditions. Thus, nepheline–olivine–albite and orthopyroxene–olivine–albite are possible assemblages under surface conditions; nepheline–orthopyroxene is not. Experimental studies on basalts and synthetic melts of similar composition have demonstrated the virtual impossibility, by any known process of surface or near-surface (within 5 km of the surface of the lithosphere) fractionation, of passing from a composition bearing normative nepheline to one with significant normative orthopyroxene, or vice versa. In other words, it is possible to recognize a *divide* in basaltic compositions between the *normative nepheline basalts* and basalts not containing normative nepheline but, instead, significant normative orthopyroxene (hypersthene). In this chapter this second type of basalt will be referred to as *tholeiitic* basalt and when this term is used henceforward it refers to basalt so defined. It has been used by other authors with a variety of meanings, sometimes more restrictive in their interpretation.

Both types of basalt occur in oceanic areas. Normative nepheline basalts are common on oceanic islands and are also found near the summits of sea mounts[11]. Very rarely have they been found on the deep ocean floor. The characteristic basalt of the deep ocean floor and the lower flanks of sea mounts is tholeiitic basalt. The variation in the character of the basalts between the lower and upper parts of sea mounts has been noted by Engel, Engel, and Havens[12] and attributed to fractionation effects, but this explanation runs entirely counter to the vast array of evidence on fractionation effects in basalts accumulated from experimental studies, detailed investigations of basaltic sills, etc. The normative nepheline basalts of the oceanic islands may represent the exposed representatives in a similar transition series, i.e.

oceanic islands may be regarded as the exposed parts of enormous sea mounts. Since
the normative nepheline basalts form the tops of these piles of volcanic lavas, they must
follow the tholeiitic basalts in sequence of eruption and, thus, it is probable that the
tholeiitic basalts approximate more closely to the most primitive basaltic magma type.

If we leave aside these normative nepheline basalts, therefore, for the moment
(they will have to be considered later), the tholeiitic basalts can be considered as
possibly representative of the basaltic fraction of the mantle. Despite certain well-
marked and highly distinctive chemical characteristics, e.g. very low potassium contents, suggesting a marked genetic relationship, these tholeiitic basalts display quite
a range of composition. This is especially noticeable in their alumina contents. Even
if attention is confined to the true glasses, encountered in the midoceanic ridge areas,
this variation persists. However, it can be readily explained in terms of near-surface
differentiation, e.g. by fractional crystallization. If we take, for example, the compositions of the two glasses given in table 4, columns (1) and (2), the liquid corresponding to the less aluminous one could be derived from that corresponding to the more

TABLE 4   Chemical compositions of basalts from the floor of the deep ocean

	(1)	(2)	(3)	(4)
SiO_2	48·13	50·47	49·34	47·41
TiO_2	0·72	1·04	1·49	2·87
Al_2O_3	17·07	15·93	17·04	18·02
Fe_2O_3	1·17	0·95	1·99	4·17
FeO	8·65	7·88	6·82	5·80
MnO	0·13	0·13	0·17	0·16
MgO	10·29	8·75	7·19	4·79
CaO	11·26	11·38	11·72	8·65
Na_2O	2·39	2·60	2·73	3·99
K_2O	0·09	0·10	0·16	1·66
H_2O^+	0·27	0·53	0·69	0·79
H_2O^-	0·02	0·06	0·58	0·61
P_2O_5	0·10	0·11	0·16	0·92
Total	100·29	99·93		

Column (1), high-aluminium tholeiitic basaltic glass, 28° 53′ N, 43° 20′ W, depth 3566 m [quoted in
Nicholls, Nalwak, and Hays[13]]; column (2), tholeiitic basaltic glass, 50° 44′ N, 29° 52′ W, depth
3890 m [quoted in Nicholls, Nalwak, and Hays[13]]; column (3), average composition of oceanic
tholeiitic basalts [given by Engel, Engel, and Havens[12], table 2]; column (4), average composition of
oceanic alkali basalt (nepheline normative) [given by Engel, Engel, and Havens[12], table 2].
The figures represent weight percentage composition.

aluminous one by the fractional crystallization and separation of plagioclase (25·6
parts per hundred of original liquid), olivine (12), pyroxene (6), and iron ore (1·4).
This mineralogical assemblage is not unlikely as an early precipitate, though the
amount of crystallization required appears rather excessive. This is but one of several
possibilities by which these two glass compositions could be related through processes
of near-surface fractional crystallization or fractional fusion (see also Nicholls[4]).
Various chemical characters of the more aluminous tholeiitic basalt suggest that it is
more primitive than the less aluminous variety, viz. the lower Fe to Mg ratio and the
more anorthitic nature of its normative plagioclase. It is tempting, therefore, to regard

this high-aluminium type of oceanic tholeiite as approximating closely in composition to the basaltic fraction of the mantle.

Various lines of evidence indicate that this is too facile an interpretation. A notable character of the tholeiites of the deep ocean floor, whether highly aluminous or not, is their poverty in potassium. Few samples so far obtained contain more than 0·3% K_2O; Engel, Engel, and Havens[12] have published an average composition for oceanic tholeiitic basalts (reproduced in table 4, column (3)) quoting a K_2O content of 0·16% with a mean deviation of 0·06%. In contrast, the K_2O content of the average alkali basalt (virtually equivalent to nepheline normative basalt of this chapter) listed by the same authors and given here in table 4, column (4), is 1·66% with a mean deviation of 0·24%. If the potassium content of the basaltic fraction of the upper mantle was as low as that of the high-aluminium tholeiitic basalt glass, it would be very difficult, if not impossible, to account for the potassium contents of the normative nepheline basalts. A further feature of the analysis of the high-aluminium tholeiitic basalt glass is its low content of titanium compared with the contents of this element in other analysed samples of oceanic basalts. In the published analyses of oceanic tholeiites contents of TiO_2 range up to 2·27% (in a sample from the Pacific—see Engel and Engel[14], table 1, analysis PV17). Engel, Engel and Havens[12] suggest an average content of 1·49% with a mean deviation of 0·39%. The nepheline normative basalts are still richer in titanium, values up to 3·64% TiO_2 (see Engel and Engel[14], sample PV71) having been reported, with 2·87% as the average value associated with a mean deviation of 0·24% (see Engel, Engel, and Havens[12]). Differentiation by fractional crystallization may account for part of this variation in titanium contents, but the range of values displayed by the analyses is too great for this to be an entirely satisfactory explanation.

A remarkable feature of the composition of the high-aluminium tholeiitic basalt glass is the close correspondence of the relative proportions of the different elements to those proportions which would exist in an amphibole. If we recast the analysis as an amphibole, the similarity is quite striking[4]. Yoder and Tilley[15] have demonstrated that under the pressure–temperature conditions to be expected at depths of 20 to 30 km beneath the midoceanic ridge system a normal mineralogical basaltic assemblage, viz. felspar–pyroxene–olivine, is stable under dry conditions but that, in the presence of abundant water, hornblende replaces these three minerals as the stable phase. Fusion of such an hornblendic fraction could explain the compositional characteristics of the high-aluminium tholeiite. The deficiency of the Yt group elements, coupled with the low Ti content (see Nicholls[4], table III, column (2)) may reflect the separation of a Ti-bearing spinellid mineral, e.g. Fe_2TiO_4-rich spinel from the liquid, either as a consequence of incongruent melting or by crystallization during the ascent of the liquid to the surface. Some estimate of the relative amount of spinellid so separated can be derived by adding sufficient Fe_2TiO_4-rich spinel to the high-aluminium tholeiitic glass to ensure that the composition of the resulting mix would correspond to amphibole proportions. It turns out to be small (about 7%). The composition of such a spinellid mineral is more difficult to estimate, but a reasonable composition would be FeO 34%, Fe_2O_3 37·7%, TiO_2 18·9%, MgO 9·4% (corresponding to 50% molecular Fe_2TiO_4, 50% molecular $MgFe_2O_4$). The results of such an addition are given in table 5, column (4). Failure of the spinellid mineral to separate out could account for the variation of titanium contents in the tholeiitic basalts,

TABLE 5   Composition of the 'basaltic fraction' of the mantle

	(1)	(2)	(3)	(4)
SiO_2	48·13	44·76		44·76
TiO_2	0·72	0·67	1·32	1·99
Al_2O_3	17·07	15·88		15·88
Fe_2O_3	1·17	1·09	2·64	3·73
FeO	8·65	8·05	2·38	10·43
MgO	10·29	9·57	0·66	10·23
MnO	0·13	0·12		0·12
CaO	11·26	10·47		10·47
Na_2O	2·39	2·22		2·22
K_2O	0·09	0·08		0·08
P_2O_5	0·10	0·09		0·09
Total	100·00	93·0	7·00	100·00

Column (1), analysis given in table 4, column (1), recalculated on a water-free basis; column (2), 93%
of the amounts given in column (1) of this table; column (3), 7% of a spinellid mineral of composition
50% molecular Fe_2TiO_4, 50% molecular $MgFe_2O_4$; column (4), sum of columns (2) and (3) of this
table to yield the composition of the 'basaltic fraction'.

though it would not explain the high contents of this element in the normative nepheline basalts. Failure to separate could be due to rapid eruption of the fused fraction,
though it is more likely to be due to another cause. If the water content of the upper
mantle was locally too low to result in complete conversion of the basaltic fraction to
hornblende, the fraction undergoing fusion would be, mineralogically, a mixture of
hornblende, plagioclase, pyroxene, and olivine. In such an assemblage the titanium
would be located preferentially in the pyroxene and would be liberated from this
lattice on fusion. In the less volatile-rich surroundings in which the magma is formed
under these conditions, spinellid minerals are less likely to form and, in consequence,
a greater proportion of the titanium should remain in the liquid phase. As will appear
subsequently, these conditions postulated for the formation of the more titanium-
rich tholeiites are intermediate between those suggested for the formation of the high-
aluminium tholeiites and the normative nepheline basalts.

Potassium presents a different problem. All the tholeiitic basalts from the deep ocean
floor are characteristically low in this element, whatever their titanium content. The
normative nepheline basalts from sea mounts, etc., are much richer in potassium, and
basalts are known from some of the oceanic islands, e.g. Tristan da Cunha, which
contain even more of this element. Such genetic relationships as may exist, between
typical deep ocean floor tholeiitic basalts and the normative nepheline basalts of the
sea mount summits, must involve an increase in potassium content as well as, and indeed contemporaneously with, the development of the normative nepheline character.
No process of fractionation within an essentially closed system under near-surface
conditions could achieve a passage from a low-potassium normative hypersthene
basalt to a high-potassium normative nepheline basalt. Among various alternative
suggestions are some which do not appeal. Volatile phase transfer of alkali metals
within the magma column should result in the appearance of high-potassium normative
nepheline basalts early in the eruptive sequence—they are late. Much more likely is the
assimilation by the magma of a phase that resisted fusion at an earlier stage. This
phase must be both potassium rich and silicon poor. The most likely one is phlogopite

(essentially $K_2Mg_6(Si_6Al_2)O_{20}(OH)_4$). With some fluorine replacing the hydroxyl group in the lattice this mineral would be stable to temperatures above those at which hornblende would break down. Persistence of the phlogopite to a late stage in any fusion process would be expected from the general properties of this mineral. The composition of phlogopite can be expressed as $2KAlSi_3O_8$ (orthoclase) $+ 6MgO + 2H_2O$, or, alternatively in terms of leucite, forsterite, MgO, and water. For a qualitative discussion of the chemical effects of phlogopite assimilation it is immaterial how the composition is expressed. The norm of the high-aluminium tholeiitic basalt glass contains 4·7 wt. % hypersthene. The addition of about 2% MgO to this composition would eliminate normative hypersthene; 2·8% MgO would convert the composition to one of a normative nepheline basalt. Phlogopite contains about 28% MgO, so the assimilation of 10% phlogopite would suffice to convert the high-aluminium tholeiite to a normative nepheline basalt. This basalt would then also contain about 1% K_2O. Once the basalt divide had been crossed by assimilation more potassium-rich basalts could be produced either by further assimilation or by fractional crystallization. The incorporation of the component elements of phlogopite into a liquid phase requires the destructive assimilation of this mineral, and the volatile content of that part of the mantle in which this occurs must be low enough to render the volatile-bearing lattice of phlogopite unstable at the fusion temperatures. Thus, such assimilation is only likely in parts of the mantle which have been depleted in their volatiles, either by long-continued vulcanicity at that particular locality or during a much earlier period of partial fusion of the mantle. The former suggestion helps to explain the late arrival of the normative nepheline basalts in the eruptive sequences of sea mounts and oceanic islands, the latter the eruption of normative nepheline basalts after long periods of quiescence in volcanic regions. On this hypothesis the genesis of high-potassium normative nepheline basalts requires even drier mantle conditions than those postulated earlier for the formation of high-titanium tholeiites. The well-known vesicular character of many normative nepheline basalts may, at first sight, appear to be at variance with this hypothesis, suggesting that the magmas from which such rocks were derived were richer in volatiles than the tholeiitic magmas. Vesicularity, however, is a function of the difference in the solubility of volatiles in the liquid phase at the place of magma genesis, on the one hand, and under surface conditions on the other. It is controlled more by the chemistry of the liquid and the change in physical conditions operating on the magma than by the volatile concentration at the site of magma genesis. It cannot be assumed that, because normative nepheline basalts are often vesicular, they must have formed in a volatile-enriched part of the mantle. In summary, the composition of the normative nepheline basalts in oceanic areas appears to require the presence of small amounts of phlogopite in the upper mantle.

The amount of phlogopite must, however, be very small. The amount of normative nepheline basalt can hardly be put at more than 0·5% of the total amount of oceanic basalt—it is probably much less than this. Even if it is assumed that a tholeiitic magma assimilates 33·3% of its own weight of phlogopite, the content of phlogopite in the basaltic fraction would only be 0·125% and, since this fraction makes up no more than one-fifth of the upper mantle, an upper limit on the average amount of phlogopite in the upper mantle can be put at 0·025%. Locally it may be much more abundant owing to differential melting out of tholeiitic basalt magma. Indeed, in order that normative nepheline basalt could form at all, such concentration by differential melting must occur. Consequently, the normative nepheline basalts should postdate the tholeiitic basalts associated with them and, as shown above, this is in accord with the evidence of their distribution. While posing a fascinating petrological problem, the existence of the high-potassium normative nepheline basalts in the oceanic area does not require a significant modification of the composition of the basaltic fraction already deduced, which may therefore be taken as that given in table 5, column (4), to a first approximation.

The Residual Fraction Composition

There are various possibilities of material representing the residual fraction of the mantle from which basalt has been removed by partial fusion of the mantle. Olivine-rich nodules are found in basalts in various parts of the World and are considered by some petrologists to be of mantle derivation. If so, they are likely to correspond to the residual fraction rather than the total mantle composition. A selection of analyses of these nodules taken from the literature is given in table 6. St. Paul's Rocks in mid-Atlantic are considered by some authorities to be part of the mantle thrust up through the crust, though it is more likely, as suggested by Tilley[16], that they represent mantle material from which basalt has been removed by differential fusion. Analyses of samples from these islets are also quoted in table 6. Furthermore, it may be suggested that the deep sea serpentinites likewise represent the residual fraction of the mantle subjected to hydration to serpentinite. Hess[7] has published four analyses of samples of deep sea serpentinites, two from the Mid-Atlantic Ridge and two from the Puerto Rico Trench. Recalculated to a water-free basis these analyses are also given in table 6. A general similarity between all the analyses in table 6 is immediately apparent, SiO_2 only varying from $43 \cdot 97\%$ to $48 \cdot 27\%$ and MgO from $39 \cdot 07\%$ to $44 \cdot 90\%$. However, the analyses of the serpentinites are consistently lower in aluminium and calcium and show much higher Fe^{3+} to Fe^{2+} ratios. The values of the ratio atomic $Fe^{3+} + Fe^{2+}$ to $Fe^{3+} + Fe^{2+} + Mg^{2+}$ for the serpentinites are, with one exception, very similar to those for the St. Paul's samples and the nodules. Thus, it is likely that the iron suffered oxidation during the serpentinization process. The four analyses of serpentinites have been recalculated with the iron redistributed between ferrous and ferric states in the same average proportions as in the St. Paul's samples, and these recalculated analyses are given in table 7. The effect of this recalculation is to extend the upper limit of the range of values for SiO_2 and MgO.

It is by no means obvious that the average of all ten analyses would give the 'best' estimate of the composition of the residual fraction of the mantle. The differences between the contents of calcium and aluminium in the peridotites and nodules, on the one hand, and the serpentinites, on the other, may be significant and reflect different conditions of formation of these samples. Partial fusion of the mantle under dry conditions would certainly leave more calcium and aluminium in the residue than similar fusion under wet conditions. The higher contents of these elements in the nodules and St. Paul's samples may indicate that the partial fusion of the mantle resulting in the formation of these materials took place under drier conditions than those obtained where the serpentinite residues formed. Since, in computing the composition of the basaltic fraction, an attempt was made to ascertain the total

TABLE 6 Chemical composition of samples possibly representative of the residual fraction of the upper mantle

	(1)	(2)	(3)	(4)	(5)	(6)	(7)	(8)	(9)	(10)
SiO_2	44·14	44·27	44·50	44·26	43·97	44·57	44·45	48·27	47·95	45·36
Al_2O_3	2·78	2·97	3·24	2·91	1·90	4·10	0·83	0·07	0·46	0·70
Cr_2O_3	0·25	0·41	—	0·50	0·42	0·46	0·29	0·38	0·28	0·46
Fe_2O_3	1·02	0·67	1·68	1·05	1·46	1·17	6·66	7·60	6·12	8·36
FeO	7·33	7·59	6·83	6·94	6·77	6·85	2·44	2·80	2·41	1·08
MgO	41·65	40·73	41·02	41·39	43·39	39·07	44·90	40·42	41·76	42·98
CaO	2·15	2·25	2·22	2·37	1·44	2·87	—	—	0·33	0·17
Na_2O	0·19	0·20	0·22	0·07	0·12	0·32	0·15	0·17	0·33	0·28
K_2O	0·01	0·01	0·05	nil	0·01	0·07	—	—	—	—
TiO_2	0·12	0·14	0·06	0·17	0·10	0·12	0·02	0·03	—	—
MnO	0·12	0·13	0·17	0·13	0·14	0·13	0·15	0·17	0·04	0·05
P_2O_5	—	0·02	0·1	n.d.	0·02	0·02	0·05	0·08	0·08	0·06
NiO	0·23	0·31	—	0·21	0·26	0·25	—	—	0·24	0·50
Atomic $\dfrac{Fe^{3+}}{Fe^{3+} + Fe^{2+} + Mg^{2+}}$	0·099	0·101	0·102	0·096	0·094	0·101	0·094	0·117	0·095	0·100

Column (1), olivine nodule from basalt, New South Wales [original analysis in Wilshire and Binns[17]]; column (2), olivine nodule in basalt, Ludlow, California [from Hess[18]]; column (3), olivine nodule, Ichinomegata, Japan [analysis supplied by H. Kuno to H. H. Hess and published in Hess[7]]; column (4), peridotite, St. Paul's Rocks, mid-Atlantic [original analysis in Tilley[19], table 1, analysis, 1]; column (5), peridotite, St. Paul's Rocks, mid-Atlantic [original analysis in Tilley[16].]; column (6), peridotite, St. Paul's Rocks, mid-Atlantic [Hess[7], table 1, analysis 11; column (8), deep sea serpentinite, Mid-Atlantic Ridge, Lamont Station 6 [original analysis given in Hess[7], table 1, analysis 4]; column (9), deep sea serpentinite, North Wall Puerto Rico Trench, Woods Hole dredge D10–6 [original analysis given in Hess[7], table 1, analysis 3]; column (10), deep sea serpentinite, North Wall Puerto Rico Trench, Woods Hole dredge D2–2 [original analysis given in Hess[7], table 1, analysis 2].
All analyses are calculated on a water-free basis.
n.d., not determined.

TABLE 7   Compositions of deep sea serpentinites recalculated on a water-free basis and with a ferric–ferrous atomic ratio of 0·16

	(1)	(2)	(3)	(4)
SiO_2	44·69	48·57	48·20	45·67
TiO_2	0·02	0·03	—	—
Al_2O_3	0·84	0·07	0·47	0·71
Cr_2O_3	0·29	0·38	0·28	0·46
Fe_2O_3	1·50	1·72	1·41	1·54
FeO	7·12	8·15	6·68	7·28
MnO	0·18	0·17	0·04	0·05
MgO	45·15	40·66	41·98	43·27
CaO	—	—	0·33	0·17
Na_2O	0·15	0·17	0·29	0·28
K_2O	—	—	—	—
P_2O_5	0·06	0·08	0·08	0·06
NiO	—	—	0·24	0·51

Column (1), deep sea serpentinite, Mid-Atlantic Ridge, Lamont Station 6 [original analysis given in Hess[7], table 1, analysis 1]; column (2), deep sea serpentinite, Mid-Atlantic Ridge, Lamont Station 20 [original analysis given in Hess[7], table 1, analysis 4]; column (3), deep sea serpentinite, North Wall Puerto Rico Trench, Woods Hole dredge D10–6 [original analysis given in Hess[7], table 1, analysis 3]; column (4), deep sea serpentinite, North Wall Puerto Rico Trench, Woods Hole dredge D2–2 [original analysis given in Hess[7], table 1, analysis 2].

composition of this fraction such as would be liberated by partial fusion under wet conditions, greater weight should be placed on the analyses of the serpentinite residues in the present context. But care must be exercised in using these analyses. When samples are collected from subaerial exposures, geologists select those for analysis which are judged to be representative of the rock type being studied. With dredged samples from the floor of the deep ocean there is no assurance that a particular sample is truly representative of a large body of rock. Furthermore, the size of dredged samples is largely a matter of fortune and is not subject to human decision as to the optimum size of a sample that can be regarded as representative of a particular rock mass. These points have to be considered in interpreting the analyses of any dredged material, but particularly so during examination of the analyses of these serpentinites. The analyses of the nodules and St. Paul's peridotite can be used to control speculation about the significance of individual serpentinite analyses.

Two of the serpentinite analyses contain more sodium than has been found in the nodules and in the two analyses of St. Paul's peridotite in which care was taken to exclude sea salt contamination from the final figures[15]. It is not clear from the literature whether these high-sodium figures were corrected for possible sea salt contamination, but they appear rather high and some suspicion of contamination may justifiably be held. Both these samples were obtained from the Puerto Rico Trench and it is possible that the serpentinite from this locality is richer in sodium than that occurring elsewhere. However, the determined sodium contents of the nodules and peridotites suggest that the sodium contents in the Mid-Atlantic Ridge serpentinites are closer to the true contents of this element in the mantle residual fraction. The Mid-Atlantic Ridge serpentinite from Lamont Station 20 has a very low content of aluminium and is also distinguished by its unusually high ratio for atomic $Fe^{3+} + Fe^{2+}$ to

$Fe^{3+} + Fe^{2+} + Mg^{2+}$. This latter feature would be distinctly odd if the low aluminium content is to be attributed to a more extensive 'melting-out' of the basaltic fraction. Magnesium is rather low and silicon rather high in this sample. Clearly, in the present context, it must be interpreted with caution. Averaging the four recalculated serpentinite analyses in table 7 is unlikely to give the best estimate of the composition of the residual fraction of the mantle and some weighting of the figures is almost certainly required. From the figures in table 7 the following composition is suggested as the current 'best estimate' of the composition of the residual fraction of the mantle.

SiO_2	45·18%	by weight (mean of columns (1) and (4) in table 7)
TiO_2	0·02%	(table 7, column (1))
Al_2O_3	0·78%	(mean of columns (1) and (4) in table 7)
Cr_2O_3	0·38%	(mean of columns (1) and (4) in table 7)
Fe_2O_3	1·52%	(mean of columns (1) and (4) in table 7)
FeO	7·20%	(mean of columns (1) and (4) in table 7)
MnO	0·18%	(table 7, column (1))
MgO	44·21%	(mean of columns (1) and (4) in table 7)
CaO	—	(greater weight placed on figures for Mid-Atlantic Ridge serpentinites)
Na_2O	0·15%	(table 7, column (1))
K_2O	—	
P_2O_5	0·06%	(mean of columns (1) and (4) in table 7)
NiO	0·32%	(to bring total to 100)

The Composition of Volatile-rich Parts of the Mantle

Having now derived best estimates of the compositions of the three fractions defined earlier in this chapter and values of x, y, and z, we can now proceed to recombine the fractions in an attempt to deduce a composition for the volatile-rich parts of the mantle. The result of such an operation is given in table 8, column (1). Examples of the figures obtained using other possible, though less probable, values of x, y, and z are given in table 8, columns (2), (3), (4), and (5). In column (6) of this table the ranges of possible contents for the various constituents are also given. It must be emphasized that the composition given in table 8, column (1), only refers to volatile-rich parts of the mantle such as may occur beneath the midocean ridge system.

Variation of the Composition of the Upper Mantle

It is immediately obvious that the whole of the upper mantle cannot have the composition given in table 8, column (1). Such a composition would be essentially a serpentinite at temperatures below 500 °c. Under the abyssal plains this temperature is unlikely to be encountered at depths less than 25 km below the sea floor, and, if the upper mantle in these areas was of this water-rich composition the crust–mantle seismic discontinuity would be expected at such depths. It is much nearer the surface.

TABLE 8   Chemical composition of the volatile-rich parts of the mantle

		(1)	(2)	(3)	(4)	(5)	(6)
Values of	x	0·107	0·108	0·119	0·096	0·105	
x, y, and z	y	0·199	0·142	0·142	0·249	0·249	
used	z	0·694	0·750	0·739	0·655	0·646	
SiO_2		40·27	40·25	39·75	40·73	40·34	39·75–40·34
TiO_2		0·41	0·30	0·29	0·51	0·51	0·29– 0·51
Al_2O_3		3·70	2·84	2·83	4·46	4·45	2·83– 4·46
Cr_2O_3		0·26	0·29	0·28	0·25	0·25	0·25– 0·29
Fe_2O_3		1·79	1·67	1·65	1·93	1·91	1·65– 1·93
FeO		7·08	6·87	6·80	7·32	7·20	6·80– 7·32
MnO		0·14	0·16	0·15	0·15	0·15	0·14– 0·16
NiO		0·22	0·24	0·24	0·21	0·21	0·21– 0·24
MgO		32·73	34·60	34·13	31·50	31·12	31·12–34·60
CaO		2·08	1·49	1·49	2·61	2·61	1·49– 2·61
Na_2O		0·54	0·43	0·43	0·65	0·65	0·43– 0·65
K_2O		0·02	0·01	0·01	0·02	0·02	0·01– 0·02
P_2O_5		0·06	0·06	0·05	0·06	0·06	0·05– 0·06
H_2O		9·74	9·82	10·83	8·74	9·57	8·74–10·83
CO_2		0·75	0·76	0·83	0·67	0·74	0·67– 0·83
Cl		0·21	0·21	0·24	0·19	0·21	0·19– 0·24
Total		100·00	100·00	100·00	100·00	100·00	

Columns (1), (2), (3), (4), and (5), various possibilities for the composition of the volatile parts of the upper mantle, using different values of x, y, and z; column (6), range of possible compositions for the volatile-rich parts of the upper mantle.
Figures for chemical constituents are given as weight percentages.

Consequently the upper mantle under the abyssal plains cannot be as rich in H_2O as the composition given in table 8, column (1). Among the possibilities to be considered is one that it is virtually dry but contains the non-volatile constituents in the same proportions as occur in the volatile-rich parts of the mantle. Another is that it represents residual material from which not only the volatiles but also basalt have been removed by partial fusion. Or, again, it may be something intermediate between these two. The two limiting compositions are given in table 9, columns (1) and (2). Column (3) of this table reproduces the preferred composition for the volatile-rich parts of the mantle given in table 8. Thus table 9 affords some idea of the possible range of composition in the upper mantle based on data available at present. If the views advanced in this chapter are correct, or even approximate to the truth, there may well be localized pockets of mantle material of composition lying outside these limits. An example would be a region of the mantle enriched in phlogopite by the melting out of most of the basaltic fraction as suggested above. However, such pockets are likely to be of very small dimensions compared with those of the upper mantle as a whole. The only thing that appears reasonably certain is that it is extremely likely that variations in chemical composition occur within the upper mantle within the range of compositions given in table 9.

An interesting possibility, which at this time can be no more than imaginative speculation, is that the volatile-rich parts of the mantle under the midoceanic ridge system represent virgin undifferentiated mantle material rising from the deep interior for the first time in the history of this planet, while the intervening parts of the upper

TABLE 9   Possible variations in the composition of the upper
mantle

	(1)	(2)	(3)
SiO_2	45·1	45·2	40·3
TiO_2	0·5	0·0(2)	0·4
Al_2O_3	4·1	0·8	3·7
Cr_2O_3	0·3	0·4	0·3
Fe_2O_3	2·0	1·5	1·8
FeO	7·9	7·2	7·1
MnO	0·2	0·2	0·1
NiO	0·2	0·3	0·2
MgO	36·7	44·2	32·7
CaO	2·3	—	2·1
Na_2O	0·6	0·1(5)	0·5
K_2O	0·0(2)	—	0·0(2)
P_2O_5	0·1	0·0(5)	0·1
H_2O	—	—	9·7
CO_2	—	—	0·8
Cl	—	—	0·2
Total	100·0	100·0	100·0

Column (1), composition of material from which volatiles have been lost, but from which the basaltic fraction has not been removed by partial fusion; column (2), composition of material from which both volatiles and the basaltic fraction have been removed by partial fusion; column (3), composition of volatile-rich parts of the upper mantle, such as may occur beneath the midoceanic ridge system. Figures for the chemical constituents are given as weight percentages.

mantle represent residual material from which the volatile constituents and the basaltic fraction have been removed, wholly or in part, by differential fusion.

Finally, it should be emphasized again that this chapter is only concerned with the chemistry of the upper mantle. In studies on the possible mineralogical nature of this material, whether approached from an experimental standpoint or by deduction from physical properties, there may be some value in knowing limits to the overall chemical composition of the assemblage present. Hypotheses on the nature of the upper mantle which fail to conform to the geochemical data are no more reliable than those which fail to satisfy the results of geophysical investigations. With the ever-increasing investigation of the nature of the floor of the deep oceans and growing interest in the chemistry of the volatile products of volcanic action it is likely that the limitations imposed by geochemical data on possible compositions for the upper mantle will become more and more stringent.

References

1. W. W. Rubey, *Bull. Geol. Soc. Am.*, **62**, 1111 (1951).
2. A. Poldervaart, *Geol. Soc. Am., Spec. Papers*, **62**, 119 (1955).
3. A. B. Ronov, *Geokhimiya*, **5**, 493 (1959).
4. G. D. Nicholls, *Mineral. Mag.*, **34**, 373 (1965).
5. H. H. Hess, 'History of ocean basins', *Petrologic Studies: A Volume to Honor A. F. Buddington*, Geological Society of America, New York, 1962, p. 599.
6. G. D. Nicholls, *Phil. Trans. Roy. Soc. London, Ser. A*, **258**, 168 (1965).

7. H. H. Hess, 'The oceanic crust, the upper mantle and the Mayaguez serpentinized peridotite', *A Study of Serpentinite, Publ.* 1188, National Academy of Sciences–National Research Council, Washington, 1964.
8. H. D. Holland, 'Model for the evolution of the Earth's atmosphere', *Petrologic Studies: A Volume to Honor A. F. Buddington,* Geological Society of America, New York, 1962, p. 447.
9. J. P. Eaton and K. J. Murata, *Science,* **132,** 925 (1960).
10. A. Holmes, *Principles of Physical Geology,* Nelson, London, 1965.
11. A. E. J. Engel and C. E. Engel, *Science,* **144,** 1330 (1964).
12. A. E. J. Engel, C. E. Engel, and R. G. Havens, *Bull. Geol. Soc. Am.,* **76,** 719 (1965).
13. G. D. Nicholls, A. J. Nalwalk, and E. E. Hays, *J. Marine Geol.,* **1,** 333 (1964).
14. C. E. Engel and A. E. J. Engel, *Science,* **140,** 1321 (1963).
15. H. S. Yoder Jr. and C. E. Tilley, *J. Petrol.,* **3,** 342 (1962).
16. C. E. Tilley, *Geol. Mag.,* **103,** 120 (1966).
17. H. G. Wilshire and R. A. Binns, *J. Petrol.,* **2,** 185 (1961).
18. H. H. Hess, *J. Marine Res. (Sears Found. Marine Res.),* **14,** 423 (1955).
19. C. E. Tilley, *Am. J. Sci.,* **246,** 483 (1947).

3

P. G. HARRIS

Department of Earth Sciences
University of Leeds
England

Segregation processes in the upper mantle

In this chapter are discussed the chemical and mineral composition of the upper mantle and the processes of magmatic segregation that can operate in the development of the mantle and the crust.

Chemical Composition of the Upper Mantle

As Urey (see section VI, chapter V of this book) has pointed out earlier in this book, there are difficulties in assuming that the solar system is so uniform in composition that the analyses of chondritic meteorites can be used to calculate the chemical composition of the Earth. Although chondrites may be the best source of information on isotopic ratios, or on the relative abundance of elements of similar behaviour, they are not quantitatively applicable to the absolute abundance of the major elements. Also, even if one could derive the composition of the Earth's mantle from analyses of chondrites, one cannot be sure that the mantle is chemically homogeneous and that its upper and lower regions are of the same composition.

The best evidence for the composition of the upper mantle comes from terrestrial rocks themselves. Two sources of information are available—ultrabasic rocks, and ultrabasic xenoliths or inclusions in volcanic rocks. (Ultrabasic is used in the geological sense of an igneous rock with a relatively low SiO_2 content of less than 45% and a high MgO content.) These two sources of data will be discussed in detail elsewhere[1,2] but are summarized briefly here.

Some ultrabasic rocks have been formed by the accumulation of olivine crystals settling from a basaltic liquid. However, others, especially those in orogenic areas and those dredged from the sea floor, appear to have been derived directly from the mantle. The difficulty in using the compositions of ultrabasic rocks lies not only in the uncertainty of deciding which rocks are of mantle origin, but also in the variability of composition among the rocks. There is a range of composition from a rock consisting almost entirely of olivine ('dunite') through to one entirely of pyroxene, this variation sometimes occurring even within a single body. It is difficult to decide if these types represent different samples of an inhomogeneous mantle, or are due to changes superimposed on the material after it has left the mantle. Even the average composition and the range of variation within an individual ultrabasic body usually are not known.

In the absence of any better information, White[3] has collected the analyses of ultrabasic rocks and from the graphical distribution of the constituent oxides selected the dominant composition. This probably represents average upper-mantle material undepleted in the fusible constituents (table 1, column (1)).

The other source of information, ultrabasic xenoliths or 'olivine nodules', is reviewed in detail by Ernst (see section VII, chapter 5 of this book). In summary, volcanic vents and eruptive rocks often contain foreign blocks or xenoliths of rock that have remained solid during eruption. These xenoliths are particularly frequent in pyroclastic or ash eruptions, in which the lava has had a high gas content and has been erupted explosively or at high speeds. The xenoliths probably were torn from the solid walls of the conduit by the ascending lava. Xenoliths are of a wide range of types, including local country rocks, plutonic equivalents of the volcanic liquid itself ('cognate xenoliths'), and ultrabasic material consisting chiefly of olivine and pyroxene. The latter, often called 'olivine nodules' have been described from over 200 localities in the World, almost always associated with alkali basalt[4].

The mineralogy is similar to that of ultrabasic rocks[5] and does not change in different types of host rock. Although some ultrabasic nodules, the pyroxene-rich ones, may be cognate or related to the liquid medium, the majority appear to be completely accidental, the composition of the spinel phase present being some criterion of this[6]. Within olivine nodules the composition of each mineral phase, olivine, orthopyroxene, clinopyroxene, and spinel, is fairly uniform at all localities. However, there is a wide range in the relative proportions of each mineral even in a single occurrence[7]. This indicates some degree of heterogeneity or mineral segregation in the parent material. It is thought that olivine nodules are direct samples of the upper mantle, although petrologists are by no means unanimous on this (see review by Wilshire and Binns[8]).

Whereas the mineralogy of olivine nodules in basalts indicates original pressures of the order of 10–20 kb, a different group of igneous rocks contains xenoliths with a mineral assemblage stable at much higher pressures. Kimberlites, the source rocks of diamonds, occur in pipes or vents within the stable continental-shield areas. Kimberlites normally contain a wide range of xenolithic material including blocks of garnet peridotite. The garnet peridotite has a similar bulk chemistry to the olivine nodules but differs in mineralogy, containing olivine, orthopyroxene and clinopyroxene, and the garnet, pyrope[9]. The presence of pyrope and the low aluminium content of the pyroxene indicate high-pressure conditions of formation, equivalent perhaps to depths of about 150 km[10].

Both the olivine nodules and the garnet peridotite nodules probably represent upper-mantle material, but were sampled from regions of different pressure and temperature, and of different mineral assemblages. The variability in the proportions of the mineral components of olivine nodules and the probability that basalt is derived from the upper mantle by partial melting indicate that the upper mantle is likely to be heterogeneous. Its composition will range from an olivine rock, the infusible residue left after the basaltic liquid has been extracted, through to the original olivine–pyroxene rocks. This range is reflected in the olivine nodules. A comparison of the chemical composition of those nodules undepleted in the basaltic components (i.e. with high contents of CaO and Al_2O_3) show them to be very similar to garnet peridotite nodules, and very similar to the dominant composition in ultrabasic rocks[1], supporting the suggestion that all three groups represent mantle material (see table 1). It should be emphasized that this is not the average composition of the upper mantle, but rather represents a probable composition of unfused or undepleted upper mantle.

TABLE 1   Composition of rocks of upper-mantle origin

	(1)	(2)	(3)
SiO_2	44·2	45·7	44·18
TiO_2		0·13	0·09
Al_2O_3	2·5	2·7	2·81
Fe_2O_3	} 8·2	1·6	1·16
FeO		5·7	7·34
MnO	0·17	0·12	0·14
MgO	41·7	41·5	40·95
CaO	2·23	2·0	2·49
Na_2O	0·25	0·22	0·22
K_2O	0·015	0·03	0·04
Cr_2O_3		0·35	0·30
NiO			0·27

Column (1), dominant ultrabasic rock composition, from analyses with between 1% and 5% of Al_2O_3 and CaO [from White[3]]; column (2), average of three published analyses of garnet peridotite nodules [from Reay[11]]; column (3), average of five analyses of olivine nodules with CaO and Al_2O_3 contents of between 2% and 3% [from Harris, Reay, and White[1]].

Those elements such as Na, K, U, and Th that would readily enter the liquid phase during partial melting vary by a factor of 50–100 from their lowest to their highest abundance values in ultrabasic rocks and xenoliths. Obviously it is difficult to give any real concentration for these constituents in mantle material.

Mineralogy of the Upper Mantle

In most ultrabasic rocks, the compositions of the minerals indicate that they have formed or recrystallized at low pressures. On the other hand, the minerals of ultrabasic nodules seem to preserve the high-pressure conditions of their formation, and give some idea of the possible mineralogy at depth. Presumably, the ultrabasic nodules were transported to the surface too quickly for any major recrystallization or readjustment of phase composition to occur in response to the new pressure environment.

Other information on the possible minerals existing at depth in the Earth is provided by experimental studies on the stability of minerals at high pressures (see especially the *Carnegie Institution of Washington Yearbook*, in which are contained the *Annual Reports of the Geophysical Laboratory*). Some of this work is reviewed by Clark and Ringwood[12].

At low pressures, olivine Mg_2SiO_4, orthopyroxene $MgSiO_3$, and clinopyroxene

$CaMg(SiO_3)_2$ have relatively ideal compositions. Most of the small amount of aluminium present in the rock is contained in plagioclase and spinel, and perhaps amphibole. With increase in pressure, first the plagioclase and then the spinel disappear, the aluminium entering instead the pyroxene minerals. The degree of substitution of aluminium in the pyroxenes increases with pressure, in orthopyroxene reaching an experimental limit[13] of about 19% Al_2O_3 at 18–20 kb. In practice, the orthopyroxenes from olivine nodules rarely contain[5] much more than 5% Al_2O_3 since the nodules themselves have only low alumina contents. At pressures higher than 20–30 kb the aluminium-bearing garnet, pyrope, becomes stable. With further increase in pressure the amount of pyrope increases, accompanied by a diminution in the aluminium content of the pyroxene.

In garnet peridotite nodules from kimberlite, the coexistence of pyrope and of a pyroxene containing[9,14] only 1–2% of Al_2O_3 is thought to indicate original pressures of the order of 40–50 kb. This change in the distribution of aluminium is accompanied by a change in its coordination number from four to six.

At pressures greater than 100 kb, a variety of possible polymorphic rearrangements and high-pressure reactions are possible. Olivine could recrystallize to a denser spinel-type polymorph, pyroxene to a denser corundum-structure polymorph, and silicates could disproportionate to the denser phases of stishovite (SiO_2) and periclase (MgO) (for bibliography see Clark and Ringwood[12]). The deeper polymorphic transformations are accompanied by a change in coordination of silicon from four to six.

Since these mineral changes are temperature as well as pressure dependent, the depth of each transformation will depend on the local thermal gradient. Any transformation zone will be deepest in the regions of high heat flow and thermal gradient—the orogenic areas, the Mid-Atlantic Ridge, etc.—and will be relatively shallow in areas of low thermal gradient such as the Pre-Cambrian shields and cratons.

Melting in the Upper Mantle

Not a great deal is known of the ultimate heat sources within the Earth—how much of the heat is radiogenic, or original heat, or is due to gravitational energy released in the segregation of the Earth's core. Nor are there any factual data on ways in which this heat can be localized, for example by conversion to mechanical energy by convection currents within the mantle, with subsequent heat release where the currents push against the continental margins. It is impossible at present to derive any theoretical model for the location, depth, and speed of melting.

However, some generalizations can be made. It would be expected that melting within the upper mantle would be partial rather than complete. The usual value for the heat of fusion of silicates is of the order of 100 cal/g. The temperature interval between incipient and complete melting in peridotite material of very low water content is probably of the order of 500 degc, and the heat required to raise peridotite through this temperature interval would be about 150 cal/g (C_p is about 0·3 cal/g degc). So the conversion of solid upper-mantle material from an initial temperature of incipient melting to a completely molten state would require about 250 cal/g of rock. A small degree of partial melting would require 100 cal/g of liquid formed, and only a few calories for each gramme of the original material.

Of the various possible sources of heat, the one most commonly invoked is radiogenic. However, the radioactive content of mantle material is extremely low, equivalent perhaps to a heat production of the order of 10^{-7} cal/g year. Even under optimum conditions, complete fusion by radiogenic heat would require a time interval of more than 10^9 years. It is unlikely that complete melting could occur under these conditions. Once any appreciable proportion of liquid had formed, it would tend to segregate from the denser residual solid, and move upwards. The liquid would selectively contain the radioactive elements. The residual solid, impoverished in these, would have only a very slow rate of radiogenic heating.

Complete fusion is likely only under special conditions of rapid heating, such as the release of energy by Earth movements. Presumably, melting from these causes would be of very local and restricted extent.

One mechanism that has been frequently invoked as the cause of rapid melting is that of pressure release[15,16]. Within the pressure range of upper-mantle melting, i.e. up to 50 kb, the melting point of olivine increases by about 5 degC for each kilobar increase in pressure. For other silicates, the increase is about 8 degC/kb. The temperature of the beginning of melting of upper-mantle material probably is about equally affected by pressure. By way of example, at 60 km depth and 20 kb pressure, material would still be solid at 120 degC or more above its melting point at atmospheric pressure. If the material was at this elevated temperature, and the load pressure was completely relieved suddenly, the material would undergo some degree of melting. The excess heat above the lowered melting point, about 36 cal/g (120 degC times 0·3 cal/g degC), would be sufficient to permit 36% of the material to melt (heat of fusion 100 cal/g). However, calculations of this sort are valid only for anhydrous monomineralllic materials with no temperature interval between incipient and complete melting.

In anhydrous mantle material, the temperature interval between incipient and complete melting is probably[17] between 300 and 400 degC, and in figure 1 is represented by the gap between lines A and C_0. The presence of water would increase this temperature interval. The effect of water in silicates is to lower the melting point, while the solubility of water in molten silicates increases with pressure. For silicate liquids saturated in water, the liquidus and solidus temperatures diminish with increasing water pressure, at least within the limits of present experimental studies[18] of 10kb. In slightly hydrous mantle material (e.g. 0·1% H_2O), it is probable that the water will be held in hydrated minerals at low temperatures, but that these will decompose before the melting point, or on first formation of a liquid. If so, at temperatures near those of melting, the mantle would contain solid mineral phases and a very small amount of water fluid. Under these conditions the first-formed liquid would be completely saturated in water and would have a melting temperature considerably lower than for anhydrous material. At pressures up to 30–40 kb, the first-formed liquid is assumed to be basalt of one sort or another. For this reason, in figure 1 the solidus or beginning of melting curve, D, is that for the liquidus or completion of melting curve for basalts in the presence of water found by Yoder and Tilley[18]. From the data of Hamilton, Burnham, and Osborn[19], the water content of the water-saturated initial liquid would be about 10% at 7 kb and perhaps about 20% at 20 kb. The initial liquid would be saturated with water, only for a fraction of a per cent of melting. At greater degrees of melting, there would be insufficient water present to saturate the liquid phase. The

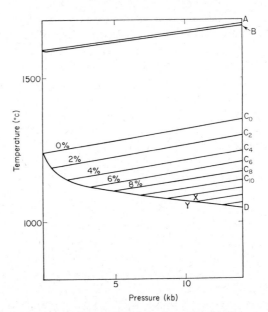

FIGURE 1   The melting behaviour of peridotite.

A, the liquidus or temperature of complete melting of anhydrous mantle material (peridotite); B, the liquidus for slightly hydrous mantle material; C_0, the solidus or temperature of incipient melting of anhydrous mantle material; D, the solidus for hydrous mantle material (this is assumed to be the liquidus curve found for basalt at high water pressures by Yoder and Tilley[18]); C_2, C_4, C_8, etc., each line shows the effect of pressure on melting for basalt of constant water content and chemical composition. It should be noted that only part of this diagram is based on experimental data

liquid would have a successively lower water content and require a correspondingly higher temperature with each increase in the degree of melting. At complete fusion of mantle material, the water content of the liquid would be so low that the liquidus temperature would be almost the same as for anhydrous material (line B of figure 1). For liquids of constant composition and water content, the effect of pressure on the crystallization temperature will be more or less parallel to that for anhydrous materials. Each of the lines C_0, C_2, C_4, C_6 of figure 1 shows the crystallization temperature for basalt of constant composition and water content. It should be emphasized that these lines do not represent progressive stages of melting.

If hydrous mantle material was held at a temperature high enough to cause a very small degree of melting, i.e. at X just above curve D in figure 1, and the liquid was saturated in water, release of pressure would cause a reduction in the solubility of water in the liquid, and the liquid would solidify. In the same way, reduction of pressure from a point Y below the solidus would increase the temperature required for melting, and would remove the material further from the field of liquid stability. If, on the other hand, a sufficient degree of melting had already occurred so that there was not enough water present to saturate the liquid phase, then a reduction in pressure would not cause the water to exsolve from the liquid phase. So long as the liquid remained undersaturated in water, so that a reduction in pressure did not cause a reduction in its water concentration, pressure release would lower the crystallization temperature of the liquid. However, the solution effects would not be as great as expected, because the solid dissolved would be more refractory than the liquid, and because each additional amount of silicate dissolved would dilute the water concentration.

In the example quoted above for anhydrous monominerallic material, a pressure reduction of 20 kb would permit 36% of melting. In actual mantle material already partly molten, and in which the liquid phase was undersaturated in water, the same pressure reduction might permit only about a 15% increase in melting. The reduction of load pressure through tectonic movement is likely to be very much less than 20 kb under nearly all circumstances, so the increase in degree of partial melting permitted by this mechanism will be much smaller than 15%.

The Composition of the Liquid Phase

The possible degree of fusion that occurs within the mantle is important, because it affects the composition of the liquid phase. At small degrees of fusion, the liquid has a eutectic or minimum-melting composition, controlled by the melting relationships of the mineral phases existing in that particular pressure–temperature environment. With a different mineral assemblage stable in a different pressure environment, one would expect a different composition of the first-formed liquid. With increasing degrees of fusion, the liquid composition changes progressively toward that of the original solid.

Phase relationships in the system Mg_2SiO_4, $CaMg(SiO_3)_2$, SiO_2 (olivine, clinopyroxene, silica) indicate that, at low or atmospheric pressures, melting of an olivine-rich mineral assemblage gives an initial liquid deficient in olivine. This was confirmed by the experimental melting of peridotite at atmospheric pressure[17]. At low degrees of fusion the liquid was olivine free if its composition was calculated as theoretical mineral phases (the 'normative' mineral composition or 'norm'). This liquid corresponded to a basalt, similar to the tholeiitic basalts of Hawaii. With an increasing degree of fusion, the liquid became magnesium rich, corresponding to the volcanic rock 'picrite basalt' or 'oceanite', with a high olivine content.

Experimental studies at high pressures indicate that, with increasing pressure, the first-formed liquid in the mantle becomes increasingly deficient in silica ('undersaturated') and high in magnesium[20,21]. The origin of the various basalt types has been attributed to the effect of pressure in controlling the liquid composition. Each of the major basalt types may have formed in a different pressure–temperature environment[18,22].

In the dominant basalt type, tholeiitic basalt, the World-wide similarity in eruptive temperatures and chemical composition especially for the major components, Si, Mg, Fe, Al, Ca, Na, indicates that the basalt liquids have approached equilibrium with the solid phases of the mantle before eruption. This is confirmed by the experimental crystallization of basaltic liquids in which the three main phases, olivine, clinopyroxene, and plagioclase, begin to crystallize over a very small temperature interval[18]. The erupted basalt liquid appears to be saturated in the main components of the stable mineral phases of the mantle. Subsequent cooling and crystallization of the basalt can change the concentration of these components especially through the effects of fractional crystallization. The changes can be in the relative concentrations of cations that substitute for one another in a mineral series, e.g. Fe for Mg, or Na for Ca. The other effect of crystallization is to change the residual liquid towards a eutectic composition of feldspar and quartz or feldspar and feldspathoid. These changes can be predicted from experimental phase studies and observed in actual geological occurrences[23].

In summary, under equilibrium conditions, volcanic liquids are saturated in the major components of the mantle. Therefore, the concentrations of these components in a volcanic liquid indicate the last pressure–temperature conditions under which the liquid approached equilibrium with the crystalline mantle.

The minor elements can be considered in three groups. Some are sufficiently close in ionic character (size, charge, bond type, etc.) to substitute for the major elements in crystal lattices. For example Ni, Co, Mn, and Sc substitute for Mg and Fe, Ge for Si, etc. Their distribution in the mantle and in any liquid phase is governed by their behaviour relative to the corresponding major element. A few minor elements, such as Cr and Ti, are sufficiently abundant in the mantle or in basaltic liquids for their own mineral phases to be formed.

The third group of trace elements are unable for reasons of ionic size, valency, etc., to substitute for any of the major elements in the crystal lattices of mantle minerals, and are too low in concentration for their own minerals to crystallize from the liquid phase. That is, any basalt liquid is undersaturated in these elements. Such elements include K, Rb, Ba, U, Th, Nb, Cl, C (as CO_2 or elemental carbon), and under some conditions H as water. During partial melting these elements should be concentrated almost entirely in the liquid phase. Any concentration process, such as fractional crystallization operating in the liquid phase, should leave them in the residual liquid since their concentrations are below saturation. This group of trace elements are what one might call the 'residual' trace elements. Their behaviour has been described in terms of their distribution coefficients or distribution 'factors' by Neumann, Mead, and Vitaliano[24], where

$$K = \frac{\text{concentration in the crystal phases}}{\text{concentration in the liquid phase}}$$

Although the residual trace elements have values of K considerably less than unity, it is unlikely that they ever reach zero. The accidental retention of the trace element in lattice defects, in liquid inclusions in the crystal, or in the interstitial liquid between crystals probably is sufficient to prevent K falling to very low values. Under these conditions, the effect of concentration processes will not be the maximum theoretically possible.

Concentration Processes in the Upper Mantle

There are three sorts of concentration or segregation processes likely to operate between the liquid and solid phases of the mantle.

The first is the melting process itself. In the liquid phase, the concentration of the major components varies only slightly during the first 10% or more of melting. On the other hand, the residual trace elements should vary inversely in concentration with the degree of fusion. For example if the concentration of an element in the original solid was X parts per million, 1 % of liquid should contain $100X$ parts per million, and 10 % of liquid should contain $10X$ parts per million, for values $K = 0$. For the more probable value of $K = 0.1$, 1 % fusion should contain about $9X$ parts per million, and 10 % fusion about $5X$ parts per million.

The second concentration process, fractional crystallization and crystal settling, occurs after the liquid has formed and moved upwards into a cooler environment. The effects of crystallization fractionation have been studied in a number of bodies of igneous rock such as the Skaergaard intrusion in Greenland. Normally in igneous bodies at shallow depth the liquid cools rapidly and protects itself from extensive reaction with the surrounding rocks by a shell of its own crystallization products.

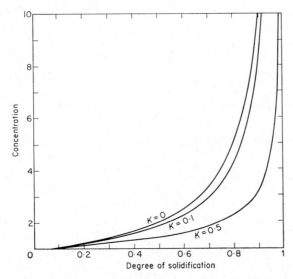

FIGURE 2   The effect of fractional crystallization on the concentration of trace elements in the residual liquid

This permits the body to behave as a closed system, and the residual liquid changes towards a eutectic composition, though in special circumstances this is overshadowed by changes due to preferential ionic substitution in the crystal phases, e.g. changes in the Mg to Fe ratio. In fractional crystallization, the trace element behaviour can be calculated from the distribution coefficient[24]. For elements of low coefficient ($K < 1$), the concentration will increase exponentially as the proportion of residual liquid becomes smaller (figure 2) and may reach very high values in the final last fraction of liquid.

Normally, in shallow bodies within the crust, the previous crystallization history can be deduced from the major components as well as the residual trace elements. However, a body of liquid within the upper mantle, e.g. at 30–40 km, should cool extremely slowly. This should permit ample opportunity for reaction with the surrounding solid material and for the major components in the liquid to attain equilibrium with the crystalline environment by solution and crystallization. For the major components, this liquid would be indistinguishable from one formed directly in the same pressure–temperature environment. On the other hand, the residual trace elements with which the liquid was undersaturated would not attain equilibrium with the environment. The effect of concentration processes would be that predicted and would not be substantially altered by reactions with the crystalline environment. In other words, provided that conditions are suitable for the liquid to tend towards equilibrium with its crystalline environment, fractional crystallization can change the concentration of the residual trace elements without markedly affecting the major components.

A similar effect should be produced by a third concentration process akin to zone refining[25]. A body of liquid formed at depth will be lighter than its surroundings and dynamically unstable. Provided that the environment is hot enough, the liquid can move upwards by solution of its roof and crystallization at its floor. The major elements with which the liquid is saturated crystallize to form relatively pure mantle minerals, the trace elements with which the liquid is undersaturated remaining in the liquid. In the upward path, the liquid acts as a scavenger, picking up the trace impurities from the digested mantle material in the same way that a liquid zone removes impurities from crystalline material during zone refining. The major chemistry of the liquid should alter in response to changes in phase mineralogy at successively higher levels and lower pressures, the final liquid having a major element composition similar to that of an original liquid formed directly at that final environment. Only the trace element composition would show the previous concentration history of the liquid phase. Since the minor constituents concentrated in this way include H_2O, CO_2, K, etc., which reduce the liquidus temperature, any extensive concentration of these could effectively lower the temperature at which the liquid could exist, and lengthen its potential upward path into the colder regions of the upper mantle. The concentration effects of such a zone-refining process will depend on the distribution coefficient K and the number of zone lengths traversed[26].

In liquids derived from the mantle and erupted at the surface, i.e. in basalts, one should be able to separate two sorts of information. The major element composition is determined by the last pressure–temperature environment in which the liquid approached equilibrium with the crystalline mantle. For liquids erupted soon after formation this is the environment of melting, but for other liquids it might be merely the final resting place prior to eruption. The content of residual trace elements reflects the previous concentration history of the liquid—how many times its own volume of mantle material has been processed in its formation and ascent.

Although adequate data for the quantitative consideration of these factors are not available, one example can be considered.

Engel, Engel, and Havens[27] have compared the tholeiitic basalts dredged from the ocean floor with alkali basalts from oceanic islands and sea mounts. The major elements do not differ markedly between the two groups, but the residual trace elements indicate that a very great deal of concentration has gone on in the production of the alkali basalts, at least thirtyfold, compared with the tholeiitic basalts (table 2).

Crustal Segregation

The composition of the Earth's crust differs markedly from that of the mantle. In a simplified pattern, if the lower crust corresponds to basalt and the upper part to granite

TABLE 2   Contents of some elements in oceanic basalts

	(1)	(2)	Relative increase
	%	%	
SiO_2	49·3	47·4	
Al_2O_3	17·0	18·0	
MgO	7·2	4·8	
$FeO + Fe_2O_3$	8·8	10·0	
CaO	11·7	8·7	
Na_2O	2·7	4·0	
K_2O	0·16	1·7	10
P_2O_5	0·16	0·92	6
	p.p.m.	p.p.m.	
Rb	1 ?	33	30
Sr	130	815	6
Ba	14	498	35
Zr	95	333	$3\frac{1}{2}$
Nb	<30	72	?
U	0·1	$0·44–1·4^a$	4–14
Th	0·2	$2·0–8·8^a$	10–40

Column (1), average composition of oceanic tholeiitic basalts [from Engel, Engel, and Havens[22]]; column (2), average composition of alkali basalts from oceanic islands and sea mounts [from Engel, Engel, and Havens[27]].
[a] Values for alkali olivine basalts are taken from Heier and Carter[28].

or granodiorite, this can be explained in a simple two-stage process of partial melting and liquid segregation:

$$peridotite \rightarrow basalt \rightarrow granite$$

   The final liquid fraction in the crystallization of basalts has been observed to be siliceous and similar to a granite or granodiorite in composition[29]. This granitic liquid can be attained either by the first product of melting or the final liquid fraction after crystallization of basalt. The only difficulty is that the volume relationships of the upper and lower crust do not accord with this. One would expect to derive only 20–30% of a granitic residuum from a basalt, instead of the about equal proportions of upper and lower crust.
   It has been suggested alternatively that andesite volcanicity is the main progenitor of continental crust—that under special conditions andesites, higher in SiO_2 and lower in MgO than basalts, may form from the mantle. These andesites, in turn, on melting would give a granitic liquid and leave a solid residue, the basic lower crust:

$$mantle \rightarrow andesite \Big< \begin{array}{l} granitic\ liquid\ (upper\ crust) \\ basic\ residue\ (lower\ crust) \end{array}$$

There is some geochemical support for this[30], but the matter is by no means resolved.

Segregation in Other Planets

The products of the partial melting of the mantle depend on the composition of the initial solid and on the pressure–temperature conditions of melting. Under low pressure conditions, melting of an olivine–pyroxene–plagioclase assemblage would give a liquid corresponding to a tholeiitic or olivine-poor basalt. This liquid would be the same for a wide range of olivine contents or ultrabasic compositions of the original solid, and certainly from chondritic silicate to terrestrial peridotite. In the smaller planetary and lunar bodies such as Moon and Mars, where pressures are relatively low, a tholeiitic basalt is the most likely eruptive material.

In bodies smaller or colder than the Earth, melting processes are likely to be relatively simple and the volcanic liquids fairly uniform. In larger or hotter bodies, the liquids could have a much more complex history of crystallization, remelting, etc., and perhaps be derived from greater depth. Under these circumstances, the liquids should be more variable than terrestrial ones, with greater concentration or segregation effects.

The possibility of a granitic crust probably is related to this. In a small or relatively cold body, a basalt liquid once solidified near the surface would be unlikely to be remelted, and the formation of highly siliceous rocks by remelting processes seems unlikely. Some small amounts of siliceous volcanic rocks might form from the fractional crystallization of basalt, but these would be insignificant quantitatively. The relative abundance of the volcanic rock types would resemble that of Iceland, rather than that of any continent. In Iceland, the rocks are dominantly primitive tholeiitic basalts, with only minor siliceous volcanic rocks.

References

1. P. G. Harris, A. Reay, and I. G. White, to be published (1966).
2. P. G. Harris, *Trans. Am. Geophys. Union*, **47**, 176 (1966).
3. I. G. White, to be published (1966).
4. R. B. Forbes and H. Kuno, *The Upper Mantle Symp.*, New Delhi, 1964, I.U.G.S., Copenhagen, 1965, pp. 161–79.
5. C. S. Ross, M. D. Foster, and A. T. Myers, *Amer. Mineralogist*, **39**, 693–737 (1954).
6. J. Babkine, F. Conqueré, J.-C. Vilminot, and K. D. Phan, *Bull. Soc. Franc. Mineral Crist.*, **88**, 447–55 (1965).
7. J.-C. Vilminot, *Bull. Soc. Franc. Mineral. Crist.*, **88**, 109–20 (1965).
8. W. G. Wilshire and R. A. Binns, *J. Petrol.*, **2**, 185–208 (1961).
9. P. H. Nixon, O. von Knorring, and J. M. Rooke, *Am. Mineralogist*, **48**, 1090–132 (1963).
10. F. R. Boyd and J. C. England, *Carnegie Inst. Wash. Yearbook*, **63**, 157–61 (1964).
11. A. Reay, *Mantle Composition and Partial Fusion of Possible Mantle Material.* Ph.D. Thesis, University of Leeds (1965).
12. S. P. Clark and A. E. Ringwood, *Rev. Geophys.*, **2**, 35–88 (1964).
13. F. R. Boyd and J. C. England, *Carnegie Inst. Wash. Yearbook*, **59**, 47–52 (1960).
14. M. J. O'Hara and E. L. P. Mercy, *Trans. Roy. Soc. Edinburgh*, **65**, 251–314 (1963).
15. N. L. Bowen, *The Evolution of the Igneous Rocks*, Dover Publications, New York, 1956.
16. H. S. Yoder, *J. Geol.*, **60**, 364–74 (1952).
17. A. Reay and P. G. Harris, *Bull. Volcanol.*, **27**, 115–27 (1964).
18. H. S. Yoder and C. E. Tilley, *J. Petrol.*, **3**, 342–532 (1962).
19. D. C. Hamilton, C. W. Burnham, and E. F. Osborn, *J. Petrol.*, **5**, 21–39 (1964).
20. I. Kushiro, *Carnegie Inst. Wash. Yearbook*, **64**, 103–12 (1965).

21. B. T. C. Davis and J. F. Schairer, *Carnegie Inst. Wash. Yearbook*, **64**, 123–6 (1965).
22. I. Kushiro and H. Kuno, *J. Petrol.*, **4**, 75–89 (1963).
23. F. J. Turner and J. Verhoogen, *Igneous and Metamorphic Petrology*, McGraw-Hill, New York, 1960.
24. H. Neumann, J. Mead, and C. J. Vitaliano, *Geochim. Cosmochim. Acta*, **6**, 90–9 (1954).
25. P. G. Harris, *Geochim. Cosmochim. Acta*, **12**, 195–208 (1957).
26. W. G. Pfann, *Zone Refining*, Wiley, New York, 1966.
27. A. E. J. Engel, C. G. Engel, and R. G. Havens, *Geol. Soc. Am. Bull.*, **76**, 719–34 (1965).
28. K. S. Heier and J. C. Carter, in *The Natural Radiation Environment* (Eds. J. A. S. Adams and W. M. Lowther), University of Chicago Press, Chicago, 1964.
29. E. A. Vincent, *Mineral. Mag.*, **29**, 46–62 (1950).
30. S. R. Taylor and A. J. R. White, *Nature*, **208**, 271–3 (1965).

4

P. W. GAST

Lamont Geological Observatory
Palisades, New York, U.S.A.

Isotopic composition of lead in oceanic volcanic rocks: evidence for chemical heterogeneity of the mantle

---

Abstract

The isotopic composition of lead in young mantle-derived volcanic rocks varies with change in the relative abundance of uranium and lead in the mantle source regions that have resulted from much earlier volcanic epochs. Alkaline volcanic materials from Gough, Tristan da Cunha, Ascension, St. Helena, Tenerife, the Azores, the Society Islands, Samoa, the Marquesas, and Raratonga have been investigated. The lead isotope compositions from a single island are nearly constant. Variations between islands in a group, e.g. the Society Islands or the Azores, are real but small. Comparisons over long distances, e.g. the Society Islands to Raratonga or Tristan da Cunha to St. Helena, indicate the existence of major differences in the mantle U to Pb ratios. These variations date back to times of the order of one billion years and suggest that the suboceanic mantle has been the site of volcanism for a substantial part of geologic time.

Both Pleistocene and Tertiary volcanic rocks from Iceland have been analyzed. Unlike the $^{87}Sr/^{86}Sr$ ratios reported by Moorbath and Walker in 1965 the Pb isotope ratios are found to be variable.

5

T. ERNST

Mineralogisches Institut
Universität Erlangen-Nürnberg
West Germany

Olivine nodules and the composition of the Earth's mantle

What are the relations between the olivine nodules—which are found as inclusions in basalts—and the material of the Earth's mantle? And what are the arguments for the assumption that the nodules have their origin in the upper mantle?

This is a very old problem which is still unsolved today. There are various hypotheses concerning the origin of the peridotitic and other ultramafic inclusions in basalts. Therefore, every report—and also the present one—has a subjective character. But the author believes that in this problem of the outer mantle of the Earth the mineralogist and petrologist are able to make important contributions, especially towards the composition, the fabric, and the possible reactions of material from the deeper crust or the upper mantle.

First, there is the assumption that the primary formation of basaltic magma takes place in the mantle at depths of approximately 50 to 100 km. To the mineralogist this is a rather great depth, because the geological processes which bring material to the surface are mostly limited to the crust. The arguments for the localization of the basaltic magma came from geophysical data, especially from the interpretation of earthquake wave velocities connected with volcanic activity.

Second, we can investigate the peridotitic nodules. Are they 'letters from the depth' and therefore fragments of rocks brought to the surface by the basaltic melts, or are they crystallization products of these basaltic melts either at great depths or in shallower regions?

By chemical–analytical investigations it is possible to distinguish between different groups of basaltic rocks within individual provinces of eruption. Olivine nodules are predominantly bound to alkaline basalts all over the World. We have made the same observations throughout the Hessian basalt region of West Germany, especially in the Vogelsberg, a Tertiary volcano which covers at least 2500 km². The Vogelsberg is particularly suited for the study of the relations between olivine nodules and basalts because it consists of flows of different composition in close connection with each other.

The mineralogical and chemical compositions of the nodules differ little in spite of the variation of the enclosing basalts. These inclusions are predominantly lherzolites. It is remarkable that they consist only of four minerals: olivine $(Mg, Fe)_2SiO_4$, bronzite $(Mg, Fe)SiO_3$ (that is orthorhombic pyroxene), chromium-bearing diopside $(Ca, Mg)Si_2O_6$ (monoclinic pyroxene), and picotite (a chromium spinel). The chemical composition shows a characteristic high magnesium content of about 41% and a low silica content close to 44%. The iron content is relatively low and equal for the principal phases, olivine and bronzite, which contain about 10 mole % iron.

The lherzolitic inclusions are found predominantly in strongly alkaline basalts, where the silica content is insufficient to form feldspars as the only salic minerals, and therefore nephelite is the characteristic mineral. Besides, there are other basalts with lower relative undersaturation or none at all. In such rocks other ultramafic inclusions are found which will be discussed later.

Of the minerals of the lherzolitic inclusions, especially the bronzites differ strikingly from the pyroxenes which crystallized from the basaltic melt at surface conditions. For the alkaline basalts with low silica content, the monoclinic Ti-augite is characteristic. At higher silica contents of the melts, pigeonite is found: this is a monoclinic pyroxene with low calcium content.

Only at relatively high silica contents are orthorhombic pyroxenes found. But these rocks are then andesitic in composition and in the proper sense not basalts any more. These relations found in the Vogelsberg district are also known from other volcanic provinces, for example from the region of San Juan, Colorado[1], and also from other districts.

Irving, Gonyer, and Larsen[2] claim that orthopyroxene is uncommon in rocks with less than 54% SiO_2. This applied especially to olivine-bearing lavas. The large enstatite phenocrysts found very rarely in alkaline basalts were apparently unstable and therefore attacked by the basaltic magma during cooling. The reaction rims around the enstatites consist mainly of olivine, and in part also marginally of augite. It is very likely that these phenocrysts are coarse-grained remains of ultrabasic rocks.

Furthermore, accumulations of fine-crystalline olivine are found which are surrounded by augite and very rarely show a core of bronzite. We are interpreting these 'Olivin-Augen' (olivine eyes) as products of a transformation of bronzite to olivine. The orthorhombic pyroxenes crystallized from andesitic melts have an iron content of approximately 30 mole % which is much higher than the iron content of about 10 mole % of the bronzites of the nodules.

So we can say that from the olivine alkali basaltic melts, no enstatite crystallized under surface conditions; on the other hand, the enstatite-bearing 'dolerites' are not basalts in the proper sense, but andesitic rocks which contain no olivine nodules.

The question of the stability of orthopyroxenes in alkaline basalts has been treated comprehensively by Yoder and Tilley[2]. From the results of their experiments they concluded that at high pressure orthoenstatite and jadeite $(NaAlSi_2O_6)$ become stable in composition, which at low pressures yield normative nepheline and alkali feldspar.

So, at high pressures (10 kb) the formation of bronzite in equilibrium with nepheline is possible from a chemical point of view, as Yoder and Tilley[2] wrote: 'in short the hypersthene-bearing nodules in alkaline basalt are inherited from depths where they constitute a compatible assemblage with Ne-normative liquids. The preservation of such nodules at the surface requires special conditions to be discussed next'. Apart from the chemical point of view, there are other characteristic features of the nodules that we have to discuss. They are of a geochemical and petrographical nature.

If we assume that the nodules are the material of the mantle of peridotitic layers in the deeper zones of the Earth, then a process of assimilation by the basaltic magma must have taken place. This should be indicated by a scatter in the chemical analyses or in the normative values, or even better in the Niggli values. Niggli values are the relations of molecule numbers of certain element groups in the chemical analyses, such as al for $(Al + Fe^{3+})$, fm for $(Mg + Fe^{2+})$, c for Ca, and alk for $(Na + K)$. In a representation of these Niggli values for si (for Si), it appears that the more acid rock types show only small variations of al, fm, c, and alk, although the si value can vary within rather wide limits. On the other hand, a larger variation of al, fm, c, and alk occurs at low si. The larger variation in lavas of lower silica content is clearly seen in the Niggli representation. The much smaller range of variation in the more acidic rock types would indicate that these rocks which are named 'trapp' in the Vogelsberg district would represent the primary basaltic magma there.

The formation of lavas lower in silica may have been caused by differentiation or by contamination caused by assimilation. If ultrabasic material (olivine nodules) has been assimilated, then some trace elements, particularly nickel in relation to magnesium or iron, should be important criteria. It was found that the highest parts per million values of nickel occur in rocks of lowest si. Here, the ratio of nickel to the fm values is higher by a factor of 2·5 to 3 than in the andesitic rocks (gabbro dioritic magma type). In our study the highest ratio has been found in the 'trapp' basalt of Gonterskirchen which contains a remarkably high amount of olivine nodules (470 parts per million Ni) (see Schütz[3]). The Ni to fm ratios are not proportional to the fm values but show a definite enrichment. Wedepohl[4] discussed the problem of the origin of the olivine nodules in detail. He compared the theoretical composition of olivine segregated from a magma with the measured composition of the mineral in olivine nodules. In the case of a crystallization from the basaltic magma the olivine should contain less than 2000 parts per million Ni. According to Wedepohl the olivine of the nodules cannot be interpreted as early segregations from the basaltic melts because of their high nickel content (more than 5000 parts per million Ni in cases of less than 0.2% S, i.e. where pentlandite $(Fe, Ni)_9S_8$ is nearly absent).

The fabric of the olivine nodules is another significant point in the discussion of their origin. The fabric has already led the author in 1935[5] to interpret the nodules as metamorphic rocks, although other opinions have also been given. The author's arguments will be illustrated by a series of figures and the results of more recent investigations will be added.

(i) The nodules, mostly of lherzolitic character, often have an angular shape. Bleibtreu[6], Schadler[7], Ernst[8], and Cross[9] described similar phenomena from Hawaii. The author interpreted these nodules with an angular shape as fragments of metamorphic rocks formed by fracturing processes. MacDonald spoke of a partition by lavas[10].

(ii) The olivine nodules show signs of mechanical stress: (*a*) a preferred crystal orientation of the olivine grains which is especially striking in the strongly interlocked crystals (the results are represented in fabric diagrams which give the spacial distribution of special optical directions on the equal-area Schmidt net) (see figures 1–3), (*b*) the so-called 'translation lamellae' in olivine in uniform arrangement (see figure 4), (*c*) joints and cracks which do not appear in the surrounding basalt (see figure 5), (*d*) undulating extinction (see figure 6), (*e*) rows of pores ('Fahrtenporen') which have to be interpreted as recrystallized cracks.

FIGURE 1   Olivine flattened in the schistosity plane. Olivine nodule from Westberg near Hofgeismar, Hessia, West Germany. Crossed polarizer

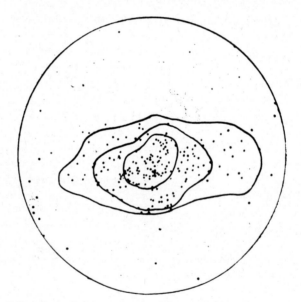

FIGURE 2   *X* directions of olivine, perpendicular to schistosity, represented in Schmidt net. Olivine nodule, Westberg

A more recent study of the fabric of olivine nodules has been made by the author's coworker Schütz[3]. The results are similar to those obtained by Collée[11] from Leiden. Schütz has examined samples of basalts from the Zinster Berg (Oberpfalz, Bavaria), Gonterskirchen (Vogelsberg), and Hirzstein (Habichtswald near Kassel, Hesse), all in West Germany.

Two nodules each from the Zinster Berg and from Gonterskirchen showed the

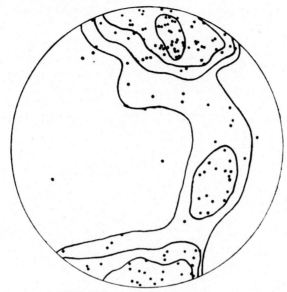

FIGURE 3   *X* directions of olivine form a girdle with two maxima, represented in Schmidt net. Olivine nodule, Westberg

FIGURE 4   'Translation lamellae' in olivine in uniform arrangement. Westberg. Crossed polarizer

normal case with flattening ('Plättung') with the optical direction α of the olivine perpendicular to the schistosity. However, in samples from the Hirzstein, tectonites with two intersecting girdles were found which resembled those described by Collée from the Auvergne. The figures indicate that two defined cycles must have been present. The data were plotted on the equal-area Schmidt net after the method of Kalsbeck[12]. It is interesting that they are practically the same for olivine and orthopyroxene. Collée attributed them to two different phases of deformation: (i) a primary

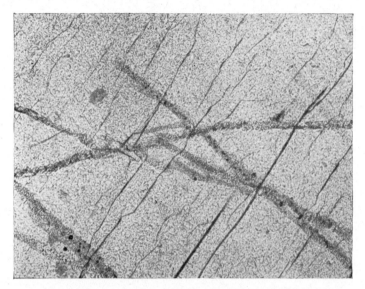

FIGURE 5   Joints and cracks in olivine. Olivine nodule, Westberg. Plane polarized light

foliation, and (ii) a subsequent secondary shearing. In our samples from Hirzstein it cannot be decided with certainty whether this fabric is due to one single deformation or to two, but in any case the material of the nodules must have been under stress.

FIGURE 6   Undulating extinction in olivine. Olivine nodule, Westberg. Crossed polarizer

In the basaltic rocks also other inclusions are found apart from the lherzolitic and dunitic inclusions. These inclusions are ultrabasic in character, too, but they also contain hornblende, feldspar, and garnet in different combinations with the minerals of the lherzolites. Here we probably have a dependence of the composition of these inclusions from the special character of the basaltic rocks in which they are found. The author believes, as does de Roever[13], that these ultrabasic rocks, gabbroid or hornblenditic, are products of a transformation of lherzolite or dunite by the basaltic magma.

The place of origin of the olivine nodules is, of course, a matter of dispute. Because of their uniform composition observed in different volcanic regions, it seems reasonable to attribute them to a common zone of the Earth, possibly to the upper mantle. This would, however, imply that these olivine nodules represent only remains of assimilated rocks which have in part reacted with the already present alkali-rich magma (see figure 7).

An assimilation of these peridotitic rocks can only mean a limited addition which

FIGURE 7   Olivine nodule attacked by the basaltic magma. Disintegration of enstatite.
Westberg. Crossed polarizer

would lead to some variation in composition. Consequently, the basaltic lavas with their amounts of alkalis, earth-alkaline metals, and alumina cannot have formed through a simple melting of peridotitic rocks with a composition similar to that of the nodules.

From the experimental studies of Yoder and Tilley[2], and Kushiro[14] we must conclude that at very high pressure the feldspar albite $Na(AlSi_3O_8)$ disappears, and olivine (forsterite), too, so that a pyroxenite becomes stable with an assemblage of pyroxenes, spinel, and anorthite $Ca(Al_2Si_2O_8)$. The pyroxenes would be both clino-pyroxenes and orthopyroxene. The relative amounts of pyroxenes to anorthite and spinel would change with pressure. With rising temperature, garnet (e.g. $Mg_3Al_2Si_4O_{12}$ or $Fe_3Al_2Si_4O_{12}$ or solid solutions) would appear in the system; then, eclogite would be a stable assemblage. Eclogite is a rock with the same chemical composition as basalt but with other minerals, namely pyroxene and garnet.

So, after the hypothesis given on the basis of experimental investigations, the origin of the basaltic magmas can be explained by the melting and transformation of eclogitic material. The different types of eclogite could lead to different types of basalt. The eclogite itself could be assumed to have originated from a partial melting of garnet peridotite which would then be the primary starting material.

It is a problem whether the peridotitic inclusions in basalts can be the remains of a transformation of the garnet peridotite to eclogitic and later basaltic melts or whether they were incorporated from peridotitic metamorphic rocks. Here the geochemical data, especially the distribution of the elements Ca, Al, and others in the different phases of basalts and inclusions, should lead us to a solution of the problem of the origin, and the significance of the olivine nodules and the origin of the primary basaltic melts. Here the recent investigations of Vilminot[15] and White[16] are of special interest.

References

1. J. Irving, F. A. Gonyer, and E. S. Larsen, *Am. Mineralogist*, **21**, 679 (1936).
2. H. S. Yoder and C. E. Tilley, *J. Petrol.*, **3**, 342 (1962).
3. D. Schütz, *Neues Jahrb. Mineral., Abhandl.*, **105** (1966–67).
4. K. H. Wedepohl, *Neues Jahrb. Mineral., Montash.*, **9–10**, 237 (1963).
5. T. Ernst, *Nachr. Ges. Wiss. Goettingen, Math. Physik. Kl. IV, Geol. Mineral.*, **1**, 147 (1935).
6. K. Bleibtreu, *Z. Deut. Geol. Ges.*, **35**, 489 (1883).
7. D. Schadler, *Mineral. Petrog. Mitt.*, **32**, 508 (1914).
8. T. Ernst, *Chem. Erde*, **10**, 631 (1936).
9. W. Cross, *U.S. Geol. Surv. Profess. Papers*, **88**, 97 (1915).
10. G. A. MacDonald, *Bull. Geol. Soc. Am.*, **60**, 1541 (1949).
11. A. L. G. Collée, *Leidse Geol. Mededel.*, **28**, 1 (1963).
12. F. Kalsbeck, *Neues Jahrb. Mineral., Monatsh.*, **7**, 173 (1963).
13. W. P. de Roever, *Neues Jahrb. Mineral., Monatsh.*, **9–10**, 243 (1963).
14. I. Kushiro, *Carnegie Inst. Wash. Yearbook*, **64**, 109 (1964).
15. J.-C. Vilminot, *Bull. Soc. Franc. Mineral. Crist.*, **88**, 109 (1965).
16. A. J. R. White, Dissertation, University of California, Berkeley (1965).

VIII

Surface evidence relating to planetary evolution

A. The Earth

1. Review of palaeomagnetic evidence for the displacement of continents, with particular reference to North America and Europe–northern Asia (J. HOSPERS) 331

2. A synthesis of World-wide palaeomagnetic data (K. M. CREER) 351

3. The World-wide distribution of deep and shallow earthquakes (L. R. SYKES) 383

B. Mars

4. The *Mariner IV* mission to Mars (E. A. GAUGLER) . 385

5. Surface conditions of Mars as suggested by *Mariner* photographs (L. B. RONCA) 413

6. Statistical theories of lunar and Martian craters (A. H. MARCUS) 417

7. The problem of the figure of Mars (S. K. RUNCORN) 425

C. The Moon

8. The nature of the lunar surface as determined by systematic geologic mapping (J. F. MCCAULEY) . 431

9. Evidence for volcanism and faulting on the Moon (G. FIELDER) 461

10. Minor lunar tectonics (L. B. RONCA) . . . 473

1

J. HOSPERS
University of Amsterdam
The Netherlands

Review of palaeomagnetic evidence for the displacement of continents, with particular reference to North America and Europe–northern Asia

Introduction

Origin of the natural remanent magnetization of rocks

There are a number of ways in which rocks may acquire a natural remanent magnetization which, in one way or another, is related to the Earth's magnetic field (for a general reference concerning this and following topics see Irving[1]).

For *igneous rocks* the natural remanent magnetization is usually a thermoremanent magnetization acquired on cooling or on reheating and cooling. Furthermore, isothermal remanent magnetization may, and almost invariably is, acquired in the direction of the present-day (or at least recent) geomagnetic field. It is appropriate to remark here that isothermal remanent magnetization, in palaeomagnetism, should perhaps more properly be called viscous remanent magnetization, which can be subdivided into normal-temperature viscous remanent magnetization and moderate-temperature viscous remanent magnetization.

For *sedimentary rocks* a number of additional mechanisms have been distinguished. The most obvious one is that the natural remanent magnetization of a sediment is acquired during sedimentation. As the sediment being deposited contains permanently magnetized particles, derived from the parent rock, the magnetic particles will be aligned to some extent by the Earth's magnetic field and hence give the sediment a depositional remanent magnetization. Other obvious carriers of natural remanent magnetization in sediments are certain types of coatings or cements that are deposited between the grains. This is denoted as chemical remanent magnetization. Thirdly, a sediment may also acquire normal- or moderate-temperature viscous remanent magnetization. Lastly, it has been demonstrated that under the influence of an increase in pressure a remanent magnetization may be acquired, denoted as piezoremanent magnetization. Piezoremanent magnetization is also referred to as pressure-promoted remanent magnetization. Of course, if a significant increase in temperature occurs during burial of a sediment, subsequent cooling will also produce thermoremanent magnetization in the sediment.

Stability tests

Field tests. These facts need to be considered when the stability and significance of the natural remanent magnetization of rocks are discussed.

First of all, it should be emphasized that positive results of field tests of magnetic stability, such as the *bedding tilt test* and the *conglomerate test*, do not prove complete stability, but only demonstrate the absence of complete instability and the presence of a certain degree of stability, depending on the amount of scatter in the data.

The same applies to the inference that reversely magnetized rocks are completely stable. This is not always correct; only exact *reversals* of 180° show that the rocks investigated are completely stable. Usually, however, reversals are not exact and none of these methods or inferences can therefore prove complete stability; most often, all that can be demonstrated is the presence of some degree of stability.

Demagnetization in the laboratory. It has been demonstrated that there is a need for rigorous demagnetization of samples. The principal methods used are *thermal demagnetization* and *alternating magnetic field (a.c.) demagnetization.* Here again, certain assumptions underlie the interpretation of the results obtained by these types of magnetic cleaning. The assumption is that the original magnetization acquired by the rock when, or soon after, it originated will be the most stable fraction of the natural remanent magnetization and hence be the last to disappear. For both igneous and sedimentary rocks this means that the natural remanent magnetization which only disappears in the highest temperature ranges or in the strongest a.c. fields is considered as the original magnetization.

This may well be correct for igneous rocks. For sedimentary rocks, however, there must be doubts, as it is known that sedimentary rocks may acquire a chemical remanent magnetization at a time much later than their time of deposition, and that this is, magnetically speaking, not 'soft' but equally 'hard' as the depositional remanent magnetization acquired on deposition, which is caused by particles carrying thermo-remanent or chemical remanent magnetization derived from the parent rock. A possible example here is the stable new magnetization acquired in Permian times which dominates the original magnetization of Devonian sandstones in Britain[2].

Demagnetization by steady fields has also been used as a stability test, especially by Russian workers. Results of this test provide only a general guide to magnetic stability, and do not permit the direction of the original magnetization to be determined.

Basic assumption of palaeomagnetic interpretation

At a certain point in the course of a palaeomagnetic study the basic assumption of palaeomagnetic interpretation must be introduced. This assumption is simply that the mean direction of the permanent magnetization of the rocks represents the mean direction of the ancient geomagnetic field at the place of observation.

This assumption must necessarily be one which cannot always be justified. We shall now consider why this assumption may be in error for much of the palaeomagnetic data available at present.

(i) Stability tests by means of field tests have not always been carried out.

(ii) When carried out, they can only rarely demonstrate complete stability.

(iii) Absence of laboratory demagnetization tests yields a specimen which may be seriously contaminated with non-relevant magnetizations of various origins and ages.

(iv) When laboratory demagnetization tests are carried out there may be justifiable doubt as to the significance of the fraction of natural remanent magnetization which remains and which is interpreted as the original magnetization.

(v) Tectonic corrections which take into account both small-scale movements and movements of large geotectonic units cannot always be applied correctly, as the required data on the nature of tectonic movements of an area are not always available.

(vi) Mean directions of magnetization are subject to statistical uncertainties.

Determination of virtual geomagnetic poles

It is customary to calculate *virtual geomagnetic pole positions* from mean directions of magnetization obtained from rocks. This calculation is based on three assumptions: (i) that the mean direction of magnetization represents the mean direction of the ancient geomagnetic field at the sampling site, (ii) that the mean geomagnetic field over the entire Earth's surface was that of a geocentric magnetic dipole, and (iii) that the virtual geomagnetic pole position thus determined pertains to the point in time when the rocks were formed.

Of these three assumptions, the first one is most seriously in doubt. This has just been discussed and no more need be said about it now. As to the second assumption, that of a geocentric dipolar field, as will be seen below, it is practically certain that this assumption is correct. Concerning the third assumption, it is obvious that the virtual geomagnetic pole position does not correspond to the physical age of the rock, but to that of its magnetization which may be of a later date.

These difficulties, which are inherent in all palaeomagnetic work, are generally recognized by students of the subject.

In this chapter we shall consider one particular aspect of these uncertainties, namely the question of the extent to which a mean direction of magnetization obtained from sediments represents the ancient mean geomagnetic field at the sampling site. To this end the possibility that the original magnetization and/or the natural remanent magnetization of *sediments* may contain *systematic errors* in their *inclinations* will be considered. This investigation is applied to palaeomagnetic data as they are at present available[1] with some later additions.

Possible Systematic Errors in the Palaeomagnetic Inclination of Sediments

Sources of systematic errors

The following sources of systematic errors in the palaeomagnetic inclination of sediments may be considered.

(i) It is now well established by experiments on the deposition of sediments on horizontal bottoms that depositional remanent magnetization may show inclinations which are too small (too flat). This may be due either to 'particle rolling' or to the effect of shape anisotropy of the magnetic grains. The resulting discrepancies between the inclinations of the ambient field and the depositional remanent magnetization are referred to as *inclination errors*. Inclination errors up to 25° in the most unfavourable cases may thus originate.

(ii) When the surface of deposition is *tilted*, another deviation occurs which may also be explained by 'particle rolling'. If the slope is downward in the direction of magnetic north, and situated on the present northern magnetic hemisphere, magnetic particles will settle on a rough northward sloping surface and hence more frequently roll forwards than backwards. This increases the inclination. If, however, the initial slope is oriented differently, so that, for example, it dips towards the magnetic south, one may expect particle rolling on the slope to decrease the inclination and hence to reinforce the inclination error. In that case the inclination in the sediment will still more strongly be decreased.

(iii) Experiments on *compaction* of sediments show that inclinations of the depositional remanent magnetization may be decreased by as much as 10° because of compaction. This, of course, can only occur in sediments which are able to suffer compaction, such as clays[3,4].

(iv) It is also evident that a sediment is *anisotropic* because of the bedding which it acquires during its deposition[5]. This anisotropy even exists when, to the naked eye, there is no visible evidence of bedding. Accordingly the pore space in a sediment must be anisotropic, and accordingly the magnetic cement will be anisotropically magnetized. Experiment has shown that sediments can indeed anisotropically acquire their chemical remanent magnetization[6]. Because of the anisotropy of the pore space one may expect the cement to form a number of plate-shaped bodies in combination with a number of more or less equidimensional bodies. These plates are most likely to be horizontal and one is therefore most likely to find palaeomagnetic inclinations which are too flat.

(v) Experiments[7,8] have further shown that artificial sediments under *uniaxial pressure*, with or without increased temperature, acquire a piezoremanent magnetization directed along that component of the ambient magnetic field which is at right angles to the direction of uniaxial pressure. This process is very likely to play a role in natural sediments which have been buried at some depth in the Earth.

Furthermore, piezoremanent magnetization is in essence a chemical remanent magnetization and hence likely to be magnetically hard, and extremely resistant to a.c. or thermal cleaning. If the uniaxial pressure is vertical, as it would be when only simple burial takes place, this would produce inclinations which are too flat.

(vi) It must be expected that in sediments which have *not* been magnetically cleaned moderate-temperature viscous and thermo- or chemical remanent magnetizations may be present, acquired later in geological history, as well as a normal-temperature viscous remanent magnetization acquired in recent times. This may have changed their original inclinations to either larger or smaller values, as well as having influenced their declinations.

In conclusion, one must accept that there are many possible sources of systematic errors in palaeomagnetic inclinations, particularly in those derived from sediments, and that these errors are most likely to *decrease* the inclination.

Search for systematic errors in palaeomagnetic inclinations

These considerations can be tested initially by two approaches.

(i) Palaeomagnetic inclinations obtained from sediments and igneous rocks of the same geological age and of the same geographic locality have been compared. The author has been able to locate only four instances where such a comparison can be made. In three of them (the Late Pre-Cambrian Copper Harbor Formation in the

U.S.A., the Carboniferous sediments and lavas of Derbyshire, England, and the Jurassic–Cretaceous volcanic rocks and red siltstones of Mozambique, Africa) there is some evidence of the palaeomagnetic inclinations in the sediments being too low. In the fourth instance (Triassic sediments and igneous rocks from the U.S.A.) there is no such difference. The material for such a comparison is hence incomplete, and inconclusive.

(ii) Comparisons of results within one continent have also been made. Here the choice is restricted because one can only use late Tertiary or Quaternary results, as earlier ones may be affected by tectonic movements, continental drift, or polar wandering. It appears that the Quaternary varved clays of New England, U.S.A., and the Plio-Pleistocene sediments of the Chelekan Peninsula, U.S.S.R., do in fact show inclinations which are too small compared with the average for their respective continents and ages. This becomes apparent from the excessive palaeomagnetic co-latitudes of the virtual palaeomagnetic poles. In other words, the calculated pole positions lie too far away from the sampling site.

Though, in principle, systematic errors in the palaeomagnetic inclination of sediments may be expected to occur, there is apparently very little reliable evidence to demonstrate irrefutably either their presence or absence by means of these approaches on the basis of material available at present.

Effect of systematic errors in palaeomagnetic inclinations

Nevertheless, on the basis of data available at present, it is possible to detect systematic errors in the palaeomagnetic inclination of sediments by using an entirely different approach which the author refers to as 'palaeomagnetic triangulation'. Before discussing this method, it is necessary to consider the effect on virtual palaeomagnetic pole positions of systematic errors in the palaeomagnetic inclination.

A *palaeomagnetic inclination*, which is too *small*, will yield a set of diametrically opposite palaeomagnetic poles on the Earth's surface, of which the *nearer* one, which is the one at less than 90° of arc from the sampling site measured along a great circle (the palaeomeridian), will lie too far away, and the *further* one, at more than 90° of arc from the sampling site, will lie too near to the sampling site. This may also be stated by saying that in this case the palaeomagnetic equator has a tendency to be pulled towards the sampling site. To put it yet another way, one may say that there is, in this case, a tendency for the nearer palaeomagnetic pole to be situated at up to 90° from the sampling site.

Palaeomagnetic triangulation

The foregoing considerations lead to the expectation that there may exist a *discrepancy* between palaeomagnetic *declinations* and *inclinations*. Accordingly, palaeomagnetic data have been subjected to the procedure referred to above, called 'palaeomagnetic triangulation'. The procedure is as follows. Let us assume one knows for two widely separated sampling sites A and B on the same continent, for a given geological period *P*, both the palaeomagnetic declinations and inclinations. It is then a simple matter to draw for both sites A and B the palaeomeridians and plot, on the Earth's surface, the virtual geomagnetic pole positions calculated by means of the usual dipole formula. If everything is as it should be, these palaeomeridians should intersect at the coinciding virtual geomagnetic pole positions.

This method has been used before by others for various purposes. Runcorn has used it earlier as a means of testing the hypothesis that, in the geological past, the Earth's magnetic field might have been a quadrupole instead of a dipole field, and van Hilten[9] has used it in an effort to demonstrate the expansion of the Earth in the course of geological history. More in line with the author's approach, Fuller[5] has used it to determine a Permian palaeomagnetic pole position from data for North America and Greenland, and Helsley[10] has used it for Permian data for North America, Greenland, and Europe, without reaching definite conclusions.

The method of palaeomagnetic triangulation has yielded interesting results for North America (see table 1). The following comments apply to this table.

(i) Intersections of palaeomeridians can be reliably obtained for the Carboniferous, Permian, Triassic, and Cretaceous Periods.

(ii) The geographic positions of the intersections of the palaeomeridians are shown in table 1. The coordinates refer to the position in the general Pacific area (column 6).

(iii) These intersections of great circles (palaeomeridians) are considered to represent the true mean geomagnetic pole positions for the relevant geological period. This is based on the hypothesis that palaeomagnetic inclinations, which are not used in this construction, may be subject to systematic errors, whereas palaeomagnetic declinations are only thought to be subject to random errors.

(iv) As the great circle distance from the average sampling site to the intersection of palaeomeridians is less than 90°, the intersections listed in table 1 represents the nearer pole, as shown in column (7) (the statement itself is based on the great circle distances listed in column (9)).

(v) Comparison of the great circle distance of the geomagnetic pole from the sampling site (column 8) with the great circle distance of the intersection of the palaeomeridians from the site (column 9) shows that the nearer pole is shifted away from its true position for the Carboniferous and Permian data.

(vi) Taking into account the statistical uncertainty in the palaeomagnetic colatitude (dp in column (8)) it appears that this shifting away is statistically significant for the Carboniferous and Permian data.

(vii) Systematic errors in inclination are thought to be responsible for this shift. If we assume that only a systematic decrease of palaeomagnetic inclination is operative, it follows that the great circle distance of the geomagnetic pole from the sampling site (column 8) cannot exceed 90°. If we take dp into account again, it appears that, for the Carboniferous and Permian data, the great circle distance of 90° is only significantly exceeded in three out of six cases. The average excess is 1·0°. This cannot be considered as truly significant because of uncertainties in the position of the mean sampling site and in the position of the mean virtual geomagnetic pole, each of which amount to at least 1°. The Carboniferous and Permian data are therefore considered as positive evidence of the presence of systematic errors in the palaeomagnetic inclination of these sediments.

(viii) The Triassic data show no statistically significant shift and therefore no systematic errors in the palaeomagnetic inclination. This may be ascribed to the presence of igneous rocks (column 3) among these data.

(ix) The Cretaceous data, which are wholly based on igneous rocks, show no statistically significant shift and hence no systematic errors in inclination either.

TABLE 1 Results of palaeomagnetic triangulation for North America

(1)	(2)	(3)	(4)	(5)	(6)	(7)	(8)	(9)
Carboniferous data								
6.63	Barnett Formation	S	31 N, 99 W	41 N, 135 E		N	93° ± 8°	82°
6.66	Naco Formation	S	35 N, 112.5 W	35 N, 122 E	49 N, 145 E	N	93° ± 8°	72°
6.67, 6.68 and Black[11] combined	Canadian sediments	S	48 N, 64 W	31 N, 133 E		N	99.5° ± 7°	80°
Permian data								
7.46 and 7.49–7.52 (incl.) Black[11]	various formations red beds, Prince Edward Island	S	36 N, 107.5 W	38 N, 105 E		N	100° ± 10°	73°
		S	46 N, 64 W	40 N, 125.5 E	59.5 N, 131 E	N	93.5° ± 2°	74°
Helsley[10]	Dunkard Series	S	39.5 N, 81 W	44 N, 122 E		N	94° ± 2°	78°
Triassic data								
8.41–8.44 (incl.) 8.30, 8.31, 8.32, 8.40	various formations	S and I	41 N, 74 W	63.5 N, 106.5 E	56 N, 106.5 E	N	76.5° ± 15°	83°
	various formations	S	39 N, 110 W	54 N, 105 E		N	82° ± 6°	80°
Cretaceous data								
10.11, 10.12	intrusive rocks	I	45.5 N, 72 W	67 N, 171 W		N	52° ± 7°	54°
10.17	Isachsen diabase	I	79 N, 104 W	69 N, 180 E/W	67 N, 178 W	N	20° ± 15°	22°
10.18	granite plutons	I	38 N, 120 W	70 N, 171 E		N	48° ± 5°	44°

Column (1), reference number in Irving[1] or other reference; column (2), rock unit; column (3), rock type (I is igneous, S is sediment); column (4), geographical coordinates of mean of sampling sites (degrees); column (5), geographical coordinates of virtual geomagnetic pole in general Pacific area (degrees); column (6), geographical coordinates of mean intersection of palaeomeridians in Pacific area (degrees); column (7), N is nearer pole, F is further pole; column (8), great circle distance of Pacific pole from site ± dp (dp is the statistical uncertainty in palaeomagnetic colatitude for $P = 95\%$); column (9), great circle distance of mean intersection of palaeomeridians from mean sampling site. The data were collected by S. I. van Andel.

(x) In terms of systematic errors in the palaeomagnetic inclination of the Carboniferous and Permian data in table 1, it is clear that, as stated above, a systematic decrease occurs. When the data given in table 1 are used to compare calculated with observed palaeomagnetic inclinations at the sampling sites, it appears that inclinations which should range from about 10° to 30° are flattened to an inclination which is statistically not significantly different from zero.

Two examples from North America of this palaeomagnetic triangulation are shown. The first example (figure 1) concerns exclusively sedimentary rocks of Carboniferous

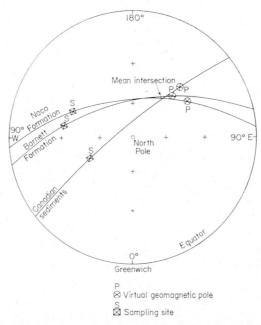

FIGURE 1   Stereographic polar projection of the Earth's northern hemisphere showing sampling sites, palaeomeridians, and virtual geomagnetic poles for the Carboniferous data for North America listed in table 1. All data are based on sediments

age in North America. The difference between the mean pole position and the mean intersection is clearly visible. The data used are the same as those in table 1. This difference is therefore statistically significant. The second example (figure 2) concerns exclusively igneous rocks of Cretaceous age in North America. Here, the mean intersection and the mean pole position coincide. The data are again the same as those used in table 1 and the coincidence is statistically significant.

The method of palaeomagnetic triangulation has also been applied to Europe and northern Asia (table 2). Here the following comments apply.

(i) Permian data are available for western Europe and Russia (Permian I). Spain and Italy have been omitted because they are situated in a mobile zone. Permian data are also available for Siberia (Permian II). Permian I and Permian II data do not yield very much different intersections of palaeomeridians (column 6).

(ii) Results shown in columns (8) and (9) show that there is no evidence here of a significant difference between the position of the intersection of palaeomeridians and the virtual geomagnetic poles for Permian I data. This may well be ascribed to the presence of igneous rocks among these data.

TABLE 2 Results of palaeomagnetic triangulation for Europe and northern Asia

(1)	(2)	(3)	(4)	(5)	(6)	(7)	(8)	(9)
Permian I (Europe) data								
7.04, 7.05, 7.07, 7.09, 7.12–7.18, 7.54,	European Permian without Spain and Italy	mainly I	53 N, 3 E	43 N, 166 E	47 N, 165 E	N	84° ± 4°	80°
7.31, 7.34, 7.37, 7.38	Russian sediments	S	58 N, 50 E	42 N, 169 E		N	68° ± 6°	62°
Permian II (Siberia) data								
7.57	Beloyarsk Suite	S	54 N, 91 E	43 N, 157 E	48 N, 145 E	N	43° ± ?	34°
7.39	ultrabasic rocks of Maymecha–Kotuy	I	72 N, 102 E	40 N, 150 E		N	39° ± 7°	31°
Triassic I (Europe) data								
8.3, 8.4, 8.6–8.8	European Triassic without Spain	S	51 N, 1 E	48 N, 139 E	65 N, 119 E	N	75° ± 15°	55°
8.14	Russian Triassic	S	51 N, 48 E	51 N, 159 E		N	63° ± 18°	38°
Triassic II (Russia and Siberia) data								
8.14	Russian Triassic	S	51 N, 48 E	51 N, 159 E	64 N, 125 E	N	63° ± 18°	41°
8.20, 8.21, 8.25	various Siberian rocks	I and S	71 N, 102 E	45 N, 146 E		N	34° ± 23°	12°

Position of combined intersections in column (6): Permian I and II data, 48 N, 155 E; Triassic I and II data, 64 N, 122 E.
Column (1), reference number in Irving[1]; column (2), rock unit; column (3), rock type (I is igneous, S is sediment); column (4), geographical coordinates of mean of sampling sites (degrees); column (5), geographical coordinates of virtual geomagnetic pole in general Pacific area (degrees); column (6), geographical coordinates of mean intersection of palaeomeridians in Pacific area (degrees): column (7), N is nearer pole, F is further pole; column (8), great circle distance of Pacific pole from site ± dp; column (9), great circle distance of mean intersection of palaeomeridians from mean sampling site. The data were collected by S. I. van Andel.

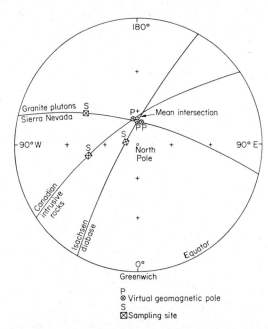

FIGURE 2   Stereographic polar projection of the Earth's northern hemisphere showing
sampling sites, palaeomeridians, and virtual geomagnetic poles for the Cretaceous data
for North America listed in table 1. All data are based on igneous rocks

(iii) Permian II data are not very useful in considering errors in the palaeomagnetic
inclination because statistical parameters for the Beloyarsk Suite are lacking. The
small discrepancy of 1° for the Siberian ultrabasic rocks is too small to be taken
seriously.

(iv) A mean position of the intersections of Permian I and Permian II data is shown
at the bottom of table 2.

(v) Triassic data are also available. As the data from western Europe and Siberia
yield practically coinciding palaeomeridians, proper palaeomagnetic triangulation can
only be carried out by combining the Russian Triassic data with either the western
European data (Triassic I) or the Siberian data (Triassic II). The intersections thus
found are very close together (column 6). A mean Triassic position is shown at the
bottom of table 2.

(vi) All Triassic data show a statistically significant shift of the nearer pole away
from the intersection, as is evident from a comparison of columns (8) and (9), if we
take into account the value of dp. The only instance where the significance may be
doubted is the last entry in the table which contains data from igneous rocks.

Some provisional conclusions

From the material presented in tables 1 and 2 it may be permissible to draw the
following conclusions.

(i) Igneous rocks appear to yield smaller discrepancies between intersection points
of palaeomeridians and virtual geomagnetic pole positions than sedimentary rocks.

(ii) Large errors in inclination are found among the Palaeozoic sedimentary rocks
of North America, all indicating a flattening of palaeomagnetic inclinations.

(iii) Though no such flattening of the inclination is found in the Permian results for Europe and northern Asia which are of better quality than the North American Palaeozoic results, a significant flattening of the inclination does occur in the Triassic results for Europe.

These results are indicative of substantial errors, causing flattening of the palaeomagnetic inclination. However, van Hilten[9] has used intersecting palaeomeridians (as stated above) in an effort to demonstrate the expansion of the Earth with geological age. The author agrees with van Hilten that the phenomenon of non-coinciding intersections of palaeomeridians and mean palaeomagnetic poles exists, and also agrees that phenomenologically this non-coincidence, assuming certain conditions about the

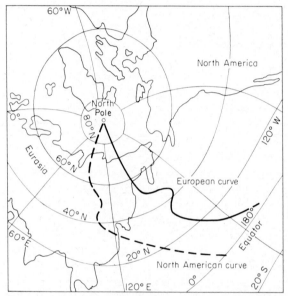

FIGURE 3   Polar wandering curves for Europe (full line) and North America (broken line) for Palaeozoic and later times. [Modified after Collinson and Runcorn[14]]

mode of expansion of the Earth to be fulfilled, can be equally well explained by expansion as by inclination errors. However, energy considerations[12] and considerations based on a decrease of G with time[13] are unable to account for a 20% increase in the Earth's radius since Permian times. Accordingly, van Hilten's hypothesis must be rejected and the intersections of palaeomeridians must be interpreted as the true position of the geomagnetic poles on the surface of an Earth, the radius of which has not changed appreciably.

Polar Wandering Curves of Eurasia and North America

Polar wandering curves for Europe and North America

A convenient starting point for our discussion is the polar wandering curves suggested by Collinson and Runcorn[14], which constitute a milestone in palaeomagnetic research. The following comments apply to these curves (figure 3).

(i) The European and North American curves do not coincide, and have hence been used as a strong argument for continental drift having affected Europe and North America.

(ii) However, the North American curve lies west of the European curve. This means that, seen from North America, the North American curve lies beyond the European one.

(iii) The European curve, based on igneous and sedimentary rocks, is the more reliable of the two curves, because it is based on more data, because a considerable proportion of the rocks used are igneous rocks, and because most of the material has been tested for magnetic stability either in the field or in the laboratory. The North American curve is less reliable because of fewer data, a preponderance of sedimentary rocks, and a fairly widespread lack of stability tests, particularly laboratory demagnetization. In particular, the Palaeozoic part of the North American curve is based on reconnaissance material, obtained from sedimentary rocks which have not been demagnetized.

(iv) It can be shown by a simple construction that the Palaeozoic part of the North American curve lies at approximately 90° from the sampling sites in the western U.S.A. This fact already became apparent for the Carboniferous and Permian data when we discussed table 1 above. The same fact is apparent from sketches by Irving[1] (figures 9.27–9.32) of the position of the palaeoequator in the U.S.A., based on palaeomagnetic data, which demonstrate that from Cambrian to Triassic times the palaeoequator had become 'stuck' in the U.S.A., and during the entire Palaeozoic Era was never more than 8° away from Salt Lake City.

(v) The European and North American polar wandering curves as drawn by Collinson and Runcorn show, going from older to younger times, that the curves first diverge before Permian times, and then converge from Permian to Triassic times. This is difficult to explain if one assumes a simple drifting apart of Europe and North America, as continents which drift apart must produce (from old to young) converging polar wandering curves but cannot produce diverging curves, unless an oscillatory movement is assumed.

The presence of systematic flattening of the palaeomagnetic inclinations, the occurrence of which was demonstrated in the sections above, and the foregoing comments on the polar wandering curves proposed by Collinson and Runcorn suggest that large inaccuracies are present in the data upon which these curves are based (particularly in the Palaeozoic part of the North American curve) and that the curves are not so different as they are presented.

Polar wandering curves for Europe–northern Asia and North America

It is now of interest to inspect the later polar wandering curves for Europe–northern Asia and North America (figure 4) proposed by Irving[1]. Here it is to be noted that, for the Cambrian, Ordovician, and Silurian Periods, the Eurasian curve no longer lies to the east of the North American curve but to the west of it, that around Silurian times the two curves cross each other, and that between Triassic and Cretaceous times the two polar wandering paths cross each other again.

At this stage, the results of our palaeomagnetic triangulation, listed in tables 1 and 2, will be introduced. As stated above, the (mean) intersections of the palaeomeridians are considered as the true mean geomagnetic pole positions pertaining to the relevant

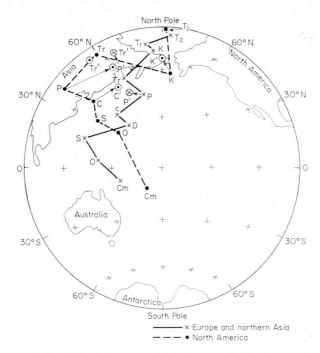

FIGURE 4 Equatorial equal-area net of the general area of the Pacific Ocean. The Cambrian and younger pole positions for Europe–northern Asia and North America, according to Irving[1], are shown. In addition are shown (by means of symbols with a prime, e.g. Tr′) the poles found by palaeomagnetic triangulation, as listed in tables 1 and 2. Geological age symbols are denoted by the following: T_2, Upper Tertiary; T_1, Lower Tertiary; K, Cretaceous; J, Jurassic; Tr, Triassic; P, Permian; C, Carboniferous; D, Devonian; S, Silurian; O, Ordovician; Cm, Cambrian

continent and to the relevant geological period. These intersections are hence plotted on Irving's picture of polar wandering paths for North America and Europe–northern Asia (figure 4), denoted as poles found by palaeomagnetic triangulation and distiguished from the other poles by an appropriate symbol.

Figure 4 shows that the Permian eastward bend in the curve for Europe and northern Asia is smoothed out because the new (triangulated) Permian pole moves towards the west. In addition, the Triassic pole for Europe and northern Asia is shifted towards the Triassic pole for North America. The same figure shows that the North American pole positions for the Carboniferous, Permian, and Cretaceous Periods, found by triangulation, are displaced towards the European curve by considerable amounts. Only the Triassic pole for North America is not very much changed. Accordingly, where new pole positions can be found by palaeomagnetic triangulation, these new pole positions bring the separate polar wandering curves closer together.

Proposed common polar wandering curve for North America and Europe–northern Asia

Derivation of common curve. The new data allow a polar wandering curve to be proposed, which may represent the *common polar wandering curve* for North America and Europe–northern Asia. This curve is arrived at as follows (figure 5).

(i) The reliable mean pole positions for Europe–northern Asia, supplied by Irving[1]

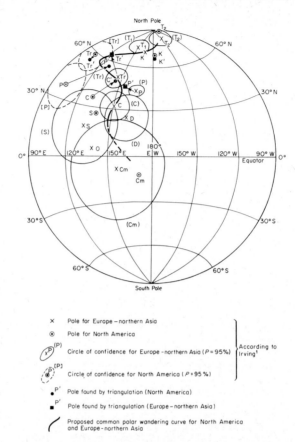

×   Pole for Europe – northern Asia

⊙   Pole for North America

⊗(P)   Circle of confidence for Europe – northern Asia (P = 95%)

⊙(P)   Circle of confidence for North America (P = 95%)

•P′   Pole found by triangulation (North America)

■P′   Pole found by triangulation (Europe – northern Asia)

Proposed common polar wandering curve for North America
and Europe – northern Asia

According to
Irving[1]

FIGURE 5   Equatorial equal-area net of the general area of the Pacific Ocean, showing
all old and new (triangulated) data for Europe–northern Asia and North America, as
well as the proposed polar wandering curve common to Europe–northern Asia and
North America. Geological age symbols as in figure 4

(table 6.2), have been used but the Permian and Triassic positions have been replaced
by those found by palaeomagnetic triangulation (table 2).

(ii) These positions have been plotted together with their circle of confidence to the
extent that this quantity is known. It is to be noted that the radius of the circle of
confidence for $P = 95\%$ for European–northern Asian poles amounts to 6–7° for
Cenozoic and Mesozoic results, to 10–20° for Upper Palaeozoic results, and to still
higher values for the Lower Palaeozoic results (33° for the Cambrian).

(iii) A curve, as shown, can then be drawn which is nowhere outside the circles of
confidence (known or inferred on the basis of geological age), and is close (within a
few degrees) of the triangulated Permian and Triassic poles. This curve may hence be
considered as a valid polar wandering curve for Europe–northern Asia.

(iv) On the same plot are also shown the reliable mean pole positions for North
America, supplied by Irving[1] (table 6.2), but the Carboniferous, Permian, Triassic,
and Cretaceous poles have been replaced by those found by palaeomagnetic triangulation (table 1).

(v) All North American mean poles of Carboniferous or younger age are from 2°

to 5° away from the curve. North American poles older than Carboniferous are subject to the same large uncertainties as the European poles of the same age. However, as it is, they appear to fit the common curve quite well.

Discussion of common curve. The present author is of the opinion that the curve given may represent the polar wandering curve common to North America and Europe–northern Asia, as it is in agreement with all data. The following points should be noted (figure 5).

(i) The Lower Palaeozoic part of the common curve is uncertain.

(ii) The bend around Permian–Triassic times is not related to relative movements of Europe and North America, but to the movement of the palaeomagnetic pole.

(iii) Comparison of great circle distances between Eurasian and North American poles is meaningless for Cambrian–Silurian poles (the American Cambrian pole is inside the 95 % circle for the Eurasian pole, the American Ordovician pole is unreliable, and the American Silurian pole is inside the 95 % circle for the European pole).

(iv) The North American Carboniferous and Permian poles lie in higher geographic latitudes than the European ones (16° and 11°, respectively). This may well be due to viscous remanent magnetization pick-up in the recent field in the American (non-demagnetized) samples, or to earlier remagnetizations.

(v) The Triassic, Cretaceous, and Upper Tertiary poles for North America and Eurasia are not significantly different for $P = 95\%$, if we assume a radius of the circle of confidence of about 7° (which is normal for poles of this age) when one is not actually given by Irving[1] (table 6.2).

(vi) On the common polar wandering curve (figure 6), pole positions for the Upper Tertiary (T_2), Cretaceous (K), and Triassic (Tr) times may be fixed with considerable confidence. Pole positions for Permian (P) and Carboniferous (C) times may also be found, though with less accuracy. The pole positions for Silurian (S) and Cambrian (Cm) times are uncertain.

Comparisons with other data. We shall now compare both palaeomagnetic and palaeo-climatic data with the new data presented here.

(*a*) First let us make some palaeomagnetic comparisons. It is of interest to compare the common polar wandering curve with palaeomagnetic poles for South America, data for which are given by Creer[15]. This comparison is made in figure 6. It is obvious that there is, at first sight, a certain disagreement between the common curve and the South American pole positions. However, there is close agreement for the Carboniferous Period, possibly suggesting that North America, South America, and Europe–northern Asia may not substantially have changed their relative positions since Carboniferous times. It is to be noted that for the other poles the disagreement is nearly exclusively (the Triassic excepted) one in present geographical latitude, but not in present longitude. This may be interpreted as a pulling apart of the poles of equal age towards the present north and south mean geomagnetic poles. In other words, this may indicate the presence of undetected thermo- or viscous remanent magnetization acquired in a Cenozoic normal or reversed geomagnetic field.

The South American evidence could be seen as a suggestion that South America may conceivably have a common polar wandering curve with North America and Europe–northern Asia.

Results from other continents must be very much extended before they can be

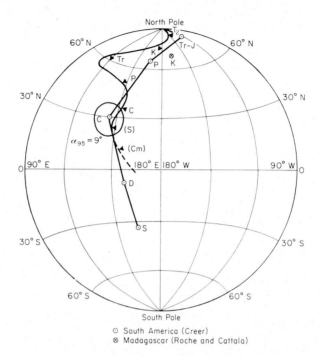

FIGURE 6   Comparison of the proposed common polar wandering curve for Europe–
northern Asia and North America with palaeomagnetic pole positions for South America and Madagascar. Geological age symbols as in figure 4

compared on equal footing with those for Eurasia and North America. However, it
may be noted that the Cretaceous pole for Madagascar obtained by Roche and Cattala[16] falls close to the Cretaceous pole on the common curve (this is shown in figure 6).

(*b*) Next let us make some palaeoclimatic comparisons. In figure 7 a comparison
is made between the palaeomagnetic common polar wandering curve for North
America and Europe–northern Asia, on the one hand, with a polar wandering curve
suggested by Lotze[17], based on the distribution of salt and related evaporites, on the
other hand. Lotze drew the northern hemisphere band, going back in geological
history, from Quaternary to Cambrian times. The author believes that there is only
one small mistake in his series of reconstructions, as in the Cambrian Period he combined parts of the northern and parts of the southern hemisphere belts into one. This
can easily be corrected, and yields an additional Cambrian pole on his plot of calculated geographical pole positions at about 170° E, 20° N. Lotze's polar wandering
curve lies approximately along the meridian of 170° E.

The general agreement between Lotze's polar wandering curve based on palaeoclimatological data from Eurasia, Africa, and North America with a polar wandering
curve based on palaeomagnetic data from Eurasia and North America suggests that
at least since Cambrian times (that is, for the last 600 million years) the Earth's magnetic field has been that of a dipole.

In figure 7 a comparison is also made with palaeoclimatological poles derived by
Bain[18], based on data from all continents. The plotted ancient palaeoclimatological
poles show what, to the author's mind, is an anomalous position of the Permian pole,

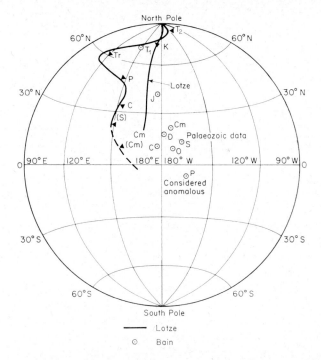

FIGURE 7 Comparison of the proposed common polar wandering curve for Europe–northern Asia and North America with pole positions based on palaeoclimatic data. Geological age symbols as in figure 4

and a somewhat too southern position of the Jurassic pole. Otherwise, there is good agreement with Lotze's data, and, as there are large uncertainties in all palaeoclimatic pole positions, fair agreement with the palaeomagnetic data which themselves are far from certain. Shifting the uncertain Palaeozoic part of the common palaeomagnetic curve towards the east would bring about a quite suggestive agreement.

Reality of continental drift. It is the author's opinion that continental drift having affected Eurasia and North America in Cambrian and later times is no longer an established fact and is now open to very serious doubts. It may also now be doubted whether continental drift has affected the other continents.

This has serious implications because it should be remembered that the hypothesis of continental drift experienced a revival in the first place because of the apparent discrepancy between the polar wandering curves of Europe and North America. Only later was this hypothesis apparently supported by the find of large-scale wrench faulting in the bottom of the Pacific Ocean and by hypotheses founded on investigations of the midoceanic ridges.

The present author is therefore inclined to doubt the reality of continental drift in times later than the Cambrian. However, he wishes to state that (i) large wrench faults as found in the Pacific Ocean and on the continents no doubt exist and may well, in the course of geological history, produce displacements which might be called *moderate continental drift*, and (ii) movements of more limited extent in mountain chains, midoceanic ridges, rifts, and other large- or small-scale tectonic movements will also produce deviations from a completely static picture of the distribution of continents and oceans throughout geological history.

The processes just mentioned accordingly must produce polar wandering curves for individual continents which cannot be expected to match each other exactly.

Polar Wandering and its Rate

The data presented here tend to contradict continental drift and point towards simple polar wandering, at least since the Cambrian Period. The evidence points to a shift of the geographic North Pole, with its associated mean geomagnetic pole, from near the present equator in the Pacific Ocean where it was situated in Cambrian times, towards (in what is now a northern direction) its present position. The time rate of displacement is hence approximately 90° in 600 million years, or about 0·1° to 0·2° per million years, or about 1 to 2 cm/year. Its path lies somewhere along the meridians of 150° E to 180° E, perhaps more towards the west in Mesozoic times.

The discovery of a low-velocity layer in the Earth's upper mantle has important bearings on the proposed process of polar wandering. This low-velocity layer may very well constitute a layer which, because of its reduced strength, can act as a slip layer along which the entire crust together with the uppermost mantle can slide over the remainder of the Earth. Changes in the moment of inertia in the crust and uppermost mantle might hence cause polar wandering. This polar wandering, however, will force the crust and upper mantle to adapt itself to the non-spherical figure of the Earth, and may cause the faulting and folding which is observed at the surface. It is to be expected that in this case wrench faulting will play a prominent role.

Finally, a few words about mantle convection would be in order. There is an increasing body of evidence suggesting that thermal convection may occur in the Earth's mantle. If this is indeed so, the author suggests that convection in an upward direction does not penetrate above the low-velocity layer. The author therefore is reluctant to accept continental drift, or its causation by changing patterns of convection cells which reach the actual crust.

This is not to say that continental drift may not have occurred in earlier than Cambrian times. The form-fitting work on continents done by Bullard, Everett, and Smith[19] and in particular the superb fit between South America and Africa should not be lightly dismissed. The present author hence would like to suggest that continental drift may have taken place in the past, probably even caused by convection currents, but in a very early stage of the Pre-Cambrian, when the crust was first formed.

Acknowledgements

The author wishes to thank his assistant, Mr. S. I. van Andel, for collecting and processing the data compiled in tables 1 and 2, and for preparing the diagrams on which figures 1 and 2 are based.

References

1. E. Irving, *Paleomagnetism and its Application to Geological and Geophysical Problems*, Wiley, New York, 1964.
2. F. H. Chamalaun and K. M. Creer, *J. Geophys. Res.*, **69**, 1607–16 (1964).

3. A. Ya. Vlassov, G. V. Kovalenko, and Yu. D. Tropin, *Bull. Acad. Sci. USSR, Geophys. Ser. (English Transl.)*, **1961**, 775–7.
4. A. Ya. Vlassov and G. V. Kovalenko, *Bull. Acad. Sci. USSR, Geophys. Ser. (English Transl.)*, **1962**, 415–7.
5. M. D. Fuller, *J. Geophys. Res.*, **68**, 293–309 (1963).
6. D. Greenewalt, *J. Geophys. Res.*, **67**, 3562 (1962).
7. N. Kawai, H. Ito, K. Yaskawa, and S. Kume, *Mem. Coll. Sci., Univ., Kyoto, Ser. B*, **26**, 235–9 (1959).
8. H. Domen, *J. Geomagnetism Geoelectricity*, **13**, 66–72 (1962).
9. D. van Hilten, *Tectonophysics*, **1**, 3–71 (1964).
10. C. E. Helsley, *J. Geophys. Res.*, **70**, 413–24 (1965).
11. R. F. Black, *Nature*, **202**, 945–8 (1964).
12. A. E. Beck, *J. Geophys. Res.*, **66**, 1485–90 (1961).
13. R. H. Dicke, *Science*, **138**, 653–64 (1962).
14. D. W. Collinson and S. K. Runcorn, *Bull. Geol. Soc. Am.*, **71**, 915–58 (1960).
15. K. M. Creer, *Nature*, **203**, 1115–20 (1964).
16. A. Roche and L. Cattala, *Nature*, **183**, 1049–50 (1959).
17. F. Lotze, 'The distribution of evaporites in space and time', in *Problems in Palaeoclimatology* (Ed. A. E. M. Nairn), Interscience, London, New York, Sydney, 1964, pp. 491–507.
18. G. W. Bain, 'Climatic zones throughout the ages', *Polar Wandering and Continental Drift, Soc. Econ. Paleontologists Mineralogists, Spec. Publ. No.* 10, 100–30 (1963).
19. E. C. Bullard, J. E. Everett, and A. G. Smith, 'The fit of the continents around the Atlantic', *Symp. on Continental Drift, Phil. Trans. Roy. Soc. London, Ser. A*, **258**, 41–51 (1965).

2

K. M. CREER

Department of Geophysics and Planetary Physics
School of Physics
University of Newcastle upon Tyne
England

A synthesis of World-wide palaeomagnetic data

The Palaeomagnetic Method

The use of rock magnetic data in investigations of the hypotheses of continental drift and polar wandering requires that we postulate a model geomagnetic field because we do not know how the actual geomagnetic field behaved over extended intervals of geological time. The validity of the conclusions drawn from palaeomagnetic investigations thus depends on the accuracy of the model field. The model used by all workers in palaeomagnetism is that, everywhere on the geosurface, the elements of the geomagnetic field averaged over times of the order of 10^5 years or so, are identical with those produced by a geocentric magnetic dipole aligned along the ancient axis of rotation. Such a model field is reasonable from both theoretical and experimental viewpoints. It can be shown theoretically that Coriolis forces dominate fluid motions in the core: palaeomagnetic poles calculated from sequences of Quaternary rocks from many places are coincident with the present pole of rotation. The latter evidence is valid because geological evidence indicates that neither continental displacements nor polar wandering occurred during the Quaternary Age.

There are two basic methods of deducing the ancient positions of land masses relative to one another and to the poles.

(i) For an axial dipole field, the palaeolatitude L is related to the angle of inclination I of the average cleaned remanent magnetization vector for a suitably thick sequence of lavas or sediments by the formula $2 \tan L = \tan I$. The azimuth of the horizontal component of this vector (after having corrected for the geological structure), the declination D, is the direction of the ancient meridian.

Since our model of the ancient field is an axially symmetric one, all palaeolongitudes are equivalent and, provided we restrict ourselves to a consideration of data for one geological period or for one continent, we cannot deduce longitude differences between continents in the geological past.

(ii) The positions referred to on the present latitude–longitude grid of the poles of the palaeomagnetic dipole may be computed by spherical trigonometry from D and I (see Creer, Irving, and Runcorn[1]). Since we use the axial dipole field model, we deduce that these poles were coincident with the ancient geographical poles. The line connecting poles for successive geological periods for a particular continent is called the

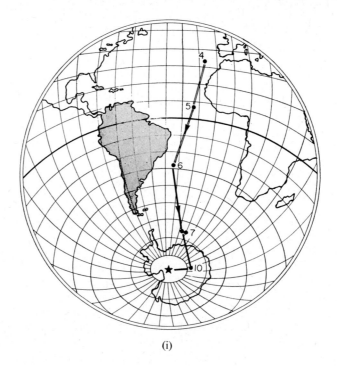

(i)

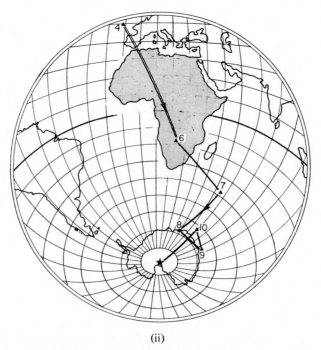

(ii)

FIGURE 1   Polar wandering curves for palaeomagnetic South Poles for (i) South America
(ii) Africa. (See table 10 for key to symbols)

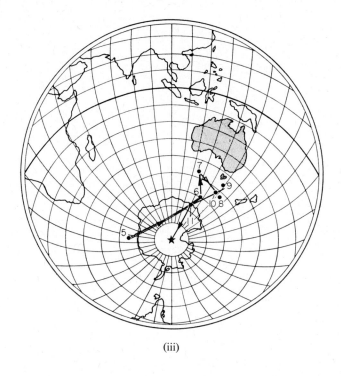

(iii)

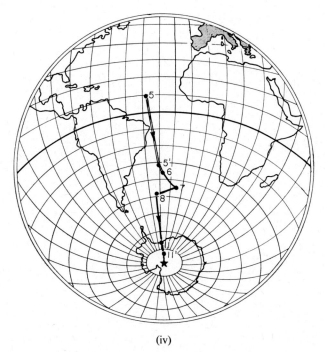

(iv)

FIGURE 1 (contd.)   Polar wandering curves for palaeomagnetic South Poles for
(iii) Australia, (iv) Europe and Russia. (See table 10 for key to symbols)

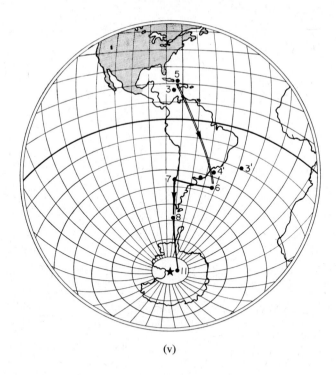

(v)

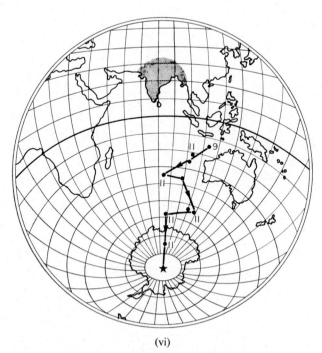

(vi)

FIGURE 1 (contd.)   Polar wandering curves for palaeomagnetic South Poles for
(v) North America, (vi) India. (See table 10 for key to symbols)

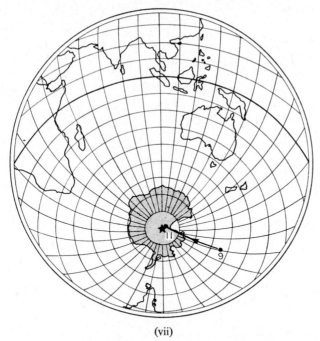

(vii)

FIGURE 1 (contd.)   Polar wandering curve for palaeomagnetic South Poles for (vii)
Antarctica. (See table 10 for key to symbols)

polar wandering curve for that continent, and such curves are shown for all the continents in figure 1 (i) to (vii).

The ambiguity in palaeolongitude can be resolved under certain circumstances, as
we shall see in the next section, if data for different continents for a succession of
geological periods are considered together. It turns out that these circumstances, viz.
that there was a substantial time interval when the pole moved relative to a fixed
distribution of continents, apply to the Earth during the Upper Palaeozoic time. This
chapter describes how a geographic reconstruction can be made of the continents for
that interval of geological time from palaeomagnetic data by mating polar wandering
curves for those continents.

A list of symbols used in this chapter is given in table 10.

The Fit of South America and Africa

Polar wandering curves, constructed from the available data listed in tables 1 and 2,
for South America and Africa are not coincident (figure 1 (i) and (ii)). From this it
follows that these continents have not always occupied their present positions relative
to one another. For the interval between the Silurian and the Upper Permian Ages the
curves are similar in shape and of similar length. Creer[2] has shown that these curves
can be superimposed on one another and that, when this is done, the two continents are
brought into adjacent positions. The best method of demonstrating this is with a set of
spherical shells on each of which is drawn a particular continent and its polar wandering curve (figure 2). In the future, when we have more precise data, the best procedure
will be to compute the palaeogeography.

TABLE 1 Summary of palaeomagnetic poles for South America

Reference No. (Irving[14])	Physical age (10⁶ years)	Formation	Place Latitude	Place Longitude	South Pole Latitude	South Pole Longitude	α	Reference No. (this chapter)
4.15	450–400	Urucum	19° S	58° W	34° N	16° W	9°	4(i)
5.48	400–350	red beds	23° S	66° W	9° N	22° W	10°	5(i)
a	320–270	Taiguati	17° S	65° W	28° S	34° W	9°	6(i)
a	320–270	Piaui	5° S	43° W	65° S	13° W	10°	—
a	270–230	red beds	30° S	68° W	65° S	13° W	6°	7(i)
9.53	140–120′	Serra Geral	22–32° S	46–56° W	78° S	54° E	4°	10(i)
9.52		red beds	38° S	71° W	86° S	172° E	25°	
12.48	<2	basalts	39° S	71° W	83° S	126° E	7°	11(i)

See also Creer[2, 9, 17, 23].
a Published since Irving[14].
′ Potassium–argon ages.

TABLE 2 Summary of palaeomagnetic poles for Africa

Reference No. (Irving[14] or footnote)	Physical age (10⁶ years)	Formation	Place Latitude	Place Longitude	South Pole Latitude	South Pole Longitude	α	Mean Pole Latitude	Mean Pole Longitude	Reference No. (this chapter)
4.09	415–385	red beds	33° S	18° E	50° N	11° W	4°	50° N	11° W	4(ii)
6.56	315–280	Dwyka varved clays (−)	18° S	29° E	36° S	29° E	10° }	17° S	23° E	6(ii)
6.57	315–280	Dwyka varved clays (+)	18° S	29° E	−7° N	17° E	12° }			
(i)ᵃ	250–225	Ecca red beds	10° S	29° E	38° S	65° E	16°	38° S	65° E	7(ii)
(iii)ᵃ	209′	Shawa ijolite	19° S	31·5° E	64° S	85° E	14° }	66° S	67° E	8(ii)
(ii)ᵃ	225–180	red beds	16° S	28° E	68° S	50° E	6° }			
9.25–9.27 (iv)ᵃ	190′–154′	Karroo and Stormberg lavas	26–32° S	26–30° E	67° S	98° E	4°	67° S	98° E	9(ii)
(iii)′	109′	Lupata volcanics	16° S	34° E	62° S	79° E	4°	62° S	79° E	10(ii)
(vi)ᵃ	25–11	volcanics	1° S	37° E	82° S	43° W	5–10° }	79° S	41° W	11(ii)
(vi)ᵃ	<11	volcanics	1–9° S	34–37° E	76° S	40° W	8° }			

(i) Opdyke[24], (ii) Opdyke[25], (iii) Gough and Brock[26], (iv) van Zijl, Graham, and Hales[27], (v) Gough and Opdyke[28], (vi) Nairn[29].
a These data without a reference number were published too recently to have been included in the lists in Irving[14], and supersede many of the African data included in those lists. The latter are omitted here because they were not 'cleaned'.
′ Potassium–argon ages.

TABLE 3 Summary of Australian palaeomagnetic data

Reference No. (Irving[14])	Physical age (10⁶ years)	Formation	Place Latitude	Place Longitude	South Pole Latitude	South Pole Longitude	95%	oval	Mean South Pole for period Latitude	Longitude	Reference No. (this chapter)
5.32	415–385	Canberra igneous rocks	35° S	149° E	71° S	8° E	14°	24°			
5.33	395–360	Murrumbidgee	35° S	149° E	58° S	28° E	5°	11°	64° S	5° E	5(iii)
5.36	370–345	Yawal Stage basalts	37° S	150° E	60° S	20° W	8°	15°			
6.58	315–280	Upper Kuttung sediments	33° S	151° E	48° S	134° E	11°	11°	60° S	139° E	6(iii)
6.59	315–280	Patterson toscanite	33° S	152° E	73° S	146° E	4°	5°			
7.43	280–255	lower marine basalts	35° S	151° E	46° S	122° E	9°	9°	45° S	127° E	7(iii)
7.42	248	upper marine latites	33° S	152° E	44° S	132° E	12°	12°			
8.28	230–210	chocolate shales	34° S	151° E	49° S	160° E	14°	14°	54° S	151° E	8(iii)
8.29	215–195	Brisbane tuff	29° S	153° E	57° S	143° E	10°	11°			
9.28	178	Gibraltar syenite	35° S	150° E	46° S	146° E	24°	24°			
9.29	168	Prospect dolerite	34° S	151° E	51° S	161° E	13°	13°			
9.30	167	Tasmanian dolerites	42° S	147° E	51° S	160° E	6°	6°	46° S	149° E	9(iii)
9.32	140	Noosa intrusives	26° S	153° E	36° S	132° E	24°	25°			
9.33	—	Gingenbullen dolerite	35° S	150° E	53° S	144° E	15°	15°			
10.09	109–99	Cygnet alkalines	43° S	147° E	50° S	158° E	10°	10°	53° S	148° E	10(iii)
10.10	93	Mt. Dromedary igneous rocks	36° S	150° E	56° S	138° E	9°	9°			
11.093	60–23	older volcanics	38° S	145° E	67° S	123° E	11°	12°	65° S	130° E	11(iii)
11.094	60–23	New South Wales basalts			63° S	137° E	20°	20°			

TABLE 4　Survey of European and Russian palaeomagnetic poles

Reference No. (Irving[14])	Physical age (10^6 years)	Formation	Place		South Pole				Mean Pole		Reference No. (this chapter)
			Latitude	Longitude	Latitude	Longitude			Latitude	Longitude	
5.04	405–370	Midland Valley lavas	57° N	3° W	10° N	38° W	9°		10° N	38° W	5(iv)
—	405–370	high-temperature component, Old Red Sandstone, Wales	52° N	3° W	(2·5° N)	(62° W)	(15°)		—	—	—
	405–370	Roragen sediments (cleaned)	62° N	12° E	19° S	20° W	15°				
5.11 to 5.15 (96 to 100)[b]	405–345	Dniester sediments	49° N	25° E	44° S	62° W	6°	6°	31·6° S	30·0° W $(N = 6,\ \alpha = 13{\cdot}1°,\ \delta_m = 6{\cdot}4°)$	5'(iv)
	370–345	Frasnian sediments	59° N	32° E	29° S	21° W	6°	6°			
5.08 5.09	405–370	Old Red Sandstone, Wales	52° N	3° W	38° S	24° W	4°	4°			
5.02	370–345	Old Red Sandstone, Portishead	51·5° N	3° W	28° S	35° W	5°	5°			
5.18 to 5.30 (81 to 95)[b]	405–345	red beds, Siberia	35° N	95° E	27° S	25° W	5°				
6.38	345–28	British Carboniferous (1)	54° N	3° W	16° S	21° W	8°	8°	35·2° S	28·2° W $(N = 5,\ \alpha = 15{\cdot}9°,\ \delta_m = 7{\cdot}4°)$	6(iv)
6.39	345–28	British Carboniferous (2)	54° N	3° W	43° S	34° W	6°	6°			
6.55 = 6.48 to 6.54	345–305	Siberian Carboniferous	54° N	91° E	40° S	49° W	18°	18°	[a]34·6° S	33·7° W $(N = 25,\ \alpha = 8{\cdot}8°,\ \delta_m = 4{\cdot}7°)$	
6.42	315–280	Donbas combined	48° N	38° E	39° S	7° W	—	—			
6.46	345–305	Tikvin combined	59° N	34° E	34° S	32° W	—	—			
7.01	280–230	Esteral pyromeride	43·5° N	7° E	46° S	38° W	18°	9°	43·6° S	14·7° W $(N = 24,\ \alpha = 3{\cdot}6°,\ \delta_m = 2{\cdot}0°)$	7(iv)
7.02	280–230	Esteral rhyolite	43·5° N	70° E	45° S	49° W	5°	3°			
7.03	280–230	Esteral dolerite	43·5° N	70° E	53° S	15° W	5°	3°			
7.05	280–230	Esteral sediments	43·5° N	70° E	47° S	25° W	4°	2°			
7.06	265–240	Montcenis sandstone	46·5° N	4·5° E	38° S	18° W	5°	3°			
7.07	265–230	Nideck porphyry	48° N	6° E	43° S	12° W	5°	3°			
7.08	280–255	St. Wendel sandstone	49·5° N	7° E	45° S	5° E	4°	2°			
7.09	280–255	Rotliegende (sediments + lavas)	48° N	7° E	40° S	10° E	14°	14°			
7.11	280–230	Nahe igneous rocks	50° N	8° E	46° S	13° W	13°	7°			
7.13	270'	igneous complex	60° N	10° E	47° S	23° W	2°	1°			
7.14	279'	Exeter traps	51° N	4° W	43° S	16° W	20°	10°			
7.15	281'	Whin Sill	55° N	2° W	37° S	11° W	3°	3°			
7.16	280–230	Mauchline lavas	55° N	4·5° W	36° S	5° W	8°	4°			
7.17	280–230	Mauchline sediments	55° N	4·5° W	37° S	13° W	12°	6°			
7.18	280–230	Ayrshire kylites	55° N	4·5° W	34° S	17° W	12°	6°			
7.22	245–230	Upper Tartarian sediments (1)	61° N	46° E	48° S	15° W	14°	9°			
7.23	245–230	Upper Tartarian sediments (2)	59° N	51° E	49° S	11° W	7°	5°			
7.24	245–230	Upper Tartarian sediments (3)	53° N	52° E	48° S	18° W	11°	8°			
7.26	245–230	Lower Tartarian sediments (1)	54° N	52° E	45° S	9° W	10°	7°			
7.27	245–230	Lower Tartarian sediments (2)	61° N	45° E	41° S	8° W	11°	6°			
7.28	245–230	Lower Tartarian sediments (3)	57° N	54° E	45° S	13° W	11°	7°			
7.33	255–235	Kazanian red beds (2)	57° N	55° E	44° S	13° W	11°	7°			
7.36	260–245	Ufimian red beds (2)	56° N	55° E	43° S	12° W	9°	6°			
7.38	280–255	Donbas red beds	48° N	38° E	33° S	19° W	9°	5°			

No.	Age	Name	Lat.	Long.	Pole lat.	Pole long.	dp	dm	Mean pole
8.01	230–210	Vosges sandstone (1)	49° N	7° E	62° S	13° W	17°	28°	
8.02	230–210	Vosges sandstone (2)	49° N	7° E	28° S	37° W	6°	12°	
8.04	230–210	Vosges sandstone	47° N	8° E	55° S	21° W	10°	10°	
8.06	200–180	Keuper marls	53° N	2° W	43° S	46° W	6°	12°	
8.10	230–210	Serebryansk suite	48° N	38° E	60° S	45° W	4°	6°	
8.11	230–210	Bashunchak suite	48° N	47° E	57° S	38° W	4°	6°	
8.12	230–210	Tananyk suite	47° N	52° E	49° S	22° W	5°	9°	
8.13	230–210	Buzuluk suite	53° N	52° E	54° S	16° W	15°	19°	50·5° S 33·3° W
8.15	230–195	Siberian traps (1)	66° N	88° E	61° S	63° W	6°	6°	$(N = 17, \alpha = 6\cdot8°,$
8.16	230–195	Siberian traps (2)	67° N	89° E	48° S	32° W	8°	10°	$\delta_m = 3\cdot7°)$
8.17	230–195	Siberian traps (3)	67° N	92° E	65° S	24° W	15°	16°	8(iv)
8.18	230–195	Siberian traps (4)	63° N	114° E	60° S	47° W	23°	23°	
8.19	230–195	Siberian traps (5)	75° N	108° E	59° S	66° W	25°	25°	
8.21	230–180	Taimyr Red sandstone	71° N	101° E	40° S	33° W	8°	10°	
8.22			71° N	101° E	32° S	17° W	6°	8°	
8.23			71° N	101° E	35° S	30° W	5°	6°	
8.24			71° N	101° E	34° S	34° W	6°	8°	
11.001	38–23	Gergovie intrusive rocks	46° N	3° E	72° S	65° W	12°	16°	
11.012	60–23	Skye lavas and intrusive rocks	57·5° N	6° W	74° S	23° W	4°	5°	
11.013	60–23	Ardnamurchan	57·5° N	6° W	69° S	15° W	15°	22°	
11.014	60–23	Rhum gabbro	57° N	6·5° W	69° S	9° W	10°	14°	
11.015	60–23	Mull lavas	56·5° N	6° W	82° S	111° E	28°	31°	78·4° S 31·5° W
11.016	60–23	Mull intrusive rocks	56·5° N	6° W	72° S	47° W	11°	14°	$(N = 13, \alpha = 5\cdot5°,$
11.017	60–23	Arran dykes	55·5° N	7° W	78° S	31° W	12°	15°	$\delta_m = 3\cdot0°)$
11.018	60–23	Antrim lower basalts (1)	55° N	6·5° W	73° S	45° W	6°	8°	11(iv)
11.019	60–23	Antrim lower basalts (2)	55° N	6·5° W	80° S	22° E	12°	15°	
11.020	60–23	Antrim upper basalts	55° N	6·5° W	69° S	71° W	19°	25°	
11.022	60–23	Antrim intrusive rocks	55° N	6·5° W	79° S	22° W	11°	13°	
11.023	60–23	Antrim sediments	55° N	6·5° W	78° S	35° W	5°	6°	
11.025	60–23	Northwest dykes	55·5° N	3° W	85° S	133° E	25°	28°	

[a] This Carboniferous pole has been computed using all the reliable entries ($N = 25$) in Irving[14] which are grouped together as 6.38, 6.39, 6.55, 6.42, and 6.46 above.

[b] Kalashnikov's numbers.

[c] Potassium–argon ages.

TABLE 5   Summary of North American palaeomagnetic data

Reference No. (Irving[14])	Physical age (10⁶ years)	Formation	Place Latitude	Place Longitude	South Pole Latitude	South Pole Longitude	95% oval		Mean South Pole for period Latitude	Longitude	Reference No. (this chapter)
3.07	470–435	Trenton conglomerate	42·5° N	75° W	9° N	74° W	8°	10°	18° N	74·5° W	3(v)
3.08	470–435	Trenton Group	43·5° N	75° W	27° N	75° W	10°	10°			3(v)
3.06	445–425	Juniata	40° N	79° W	20° S	27° W	5°	9°	20° S	27° W	3'(v)
4.11	425–405	Rosehill	39·5° N	79° W	20° S	44° W	10°	15°	27° S	42° W	4'(v)
4.12	425–405	Clinton iron ore	34° N	87° W	34° S	41° W	7°	12°			
5.38	405–360	Onondaga limestone	42·5° N	74° W	21° N	73° W	7°	7°	21° N	73° W	5(v)
6.61	345–305	Barnett Formation (−)	31° N	99° W	41° S	36° W	2°	4°			
6.62	345–305	Barnett Formation (+)	31° N	99° W	39° S	57° W	3°	6°			
6.67	345–305	Codroy Group	48° N	59° W	37° S	21° W	4°	8°	37·1° S ($N = 6$, $\alpha = 13·8°$,	42·1° W $\delta_m = 6·7°$)	6(v)
6.68	345–280	east Canadian sediments	48° N	66° W	30° S	27° W	3°	5°			
6.64	315–280	Naco, Carizzo Creek	36° N	113° W	46° S	67° W	2°	4°			
6.65	315–280	Naco, Fossil Creek	34° N	112° W	23° S	50° W	4°	7°			
7.47	280–260	Abo (1)	34° N	106° W	42° S	63° W	9°	18°			
7.48	280–260	Abo (2)	35° N	108° W	17° S	92° W	12°	17°			
7.50	280–250	Yeso	35·5° N	105° W	41° S	53° W	2°	3°	35·0° S ($N = 6$, $\alpha = 17·3°$,	74·3° W $\delta_m = 8·3°$)	7(v)
7.51	290–250	Supai	35° N	110° W	40° S	70° W	9°	9°			
7.52	290–250	Sangre de Cristo	35° N	105° W	38° S	99° W	7°	9°			
—	290–250	Dunkard Series	40° N	81° W	44° S	57° W	3°	5°			
8.30	260–200	Chugwater	43° N	107° W	48° S	68° W	5°	5°			
8.31	230–195	Moenkopi	38° N	110° W	57° S	73° W	10°	10°	59·8° S ($N = 6$, $\alpha = 13·6°$,	72·1° W $\delta_m = 6·6°$)	8(v)
8.41	205–180	New Oxford	40° N	77° W	66° S	6° W	8°	8°			
8.42	190	Newark Group	40·5° N	75° W	63° S	72° W	3°	4°			
8.43	205–180	Connecticut Valley	42° N	73° W	54° S	94° W	8°	15°			
8.44	205–180	Massachusetts lavas	42° N	72·5° W	55° S	92° W	6°	11°			
11.100	60–34	Green River	39·5° N	108° W	78° S	12° E	6°	7°			
11.104	20–10	Ellensburg	46° N	120° W	85° S	65° E	13°	15°	85·9° S ($N = 4$, $\alpha = 8·1°$,	28·7° E $\delta_m = 3·5°$)	11(v)
11.106	27–11	Colombia River basalts	46·5° N	120·5° W	85° S	137° E	9°	14°			
11.107	27–1	basalts	61° N	134° W	85° S	30° W	5°	6°			

TABLE 6   Summary of palaeomagnetic poles for India

Reference No. (Irving[14])	Physical age (10⁶ years)	Formation	Place		South Pole		95% oval		Reference No. (this chapter)
			Latitude	Longitude	Latitude	Longitude			
9.23	180–100	Rajmahal traps	25° N	88° E	15° S	112° E		12	9(vi)
9.44	180–100	Sylet traps	25° N	91° E	16° S	120° E	8	11	9(vi)
11.080	95–34	Linga	22° N	79° E	37° S	97° E	2	3	11(vi)
11.081	95–34	Khandala	18·5° N	73·5° E	25° S	101° E	4	5	11(vi)
11.085	95–34	Nipani (L)	16·5° N	74° E	35° S	85° E	5	6	11(vi)
11.087	95–34	Amba (L)	17° N	73·5° E	22° S	103° E	3	5	11(vi)
11.084	95–34	Nipani (U)	16·5° N	74° E	52° S	110° E	5	6	11(vi)
11.086	95–34	Amba (U)	17° N	73·5° E	52° S	116° E	3	5	11(vi)
11.088	95–34	Pavagadh (L)	22·5° N	71·5° E	58° S	89° E	4	8	11(vi)
11.092	63	Pavagadh (U)	22·5° N	71·5° E	75° S	91° E	4	8	11(vi)

(Formations Linga through Pavagadh (U) are bracketed as ← Deccan traps →)

See Radhakrishnamurty[30], Athavale, Radhakrishnamurty, and Sahastrabudhe[31], Deutch, Radhakrishnamurty, and Sahastrabudhe[32].

TABLE 7 Summary of palaeomagnetic poles for Antarctica

Reference No. (Irving[14])	Physical age (10⁶ years)	Formation	Place		South Pole			Reference No. (this chapter)
			Latitude	Longitude	Latitude	Longitude	α	
9.37	163–127'	Ferrar dolerite	78° S	161° E	58° S	142° W	5	9(vii)
a	163–127'	Wright Valley intrusions	78° S	162° E	51° S	132° W	11	
a	163–127'	Theron Mts.	80° S	30° W	54° S	136° W	18	
11.126	95–43	Andean intrusions	65° S	64° W	86° S	2° W	6	11(vii)
12.55	70	Cape Hallett volcanic rocks	72° S	171° E	81° S	94° E	8	
12.66	1	South Shetland lavas	63° S	61° W	82° S	129° W	6	12(vii)

See Blundell[33].
a Not contained in Irving[14].
' Potassium–argon ages.

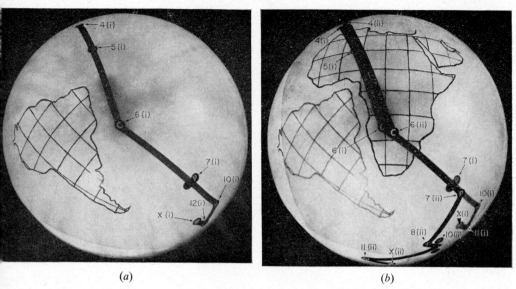

FIGURE 2 Photographs of polar wandering curves (South Poles) drawn on spherical shells (*a*) that for South America (i) alone and (*b*) that for Africa (ii) superimposed on that for South America (i)

This palaeogeographic reconstruction of South America and Africa is very similar to that deduced by earlier workers on the drift hypothesis, e.g. Wegener[3] and du Toit[4], but the line of reasoning used is quite independent of theirs. One of their most convincing arguments was to point out the goodness of fit of the Atlantic coastlines and shelf edges of the Old and New Worlds, and this has recently been studied again in great detail by Bullard, Everitt, and Smith[5]. The reconstruction based on palaeomagnetic data, although not of such great precision as that obtained by fitting continental edges, is based on firmer physical reasoning. The palaeomagnetic method can be taken to validate the criterion of matching shelf edges for deducing ancient continental positions, and the latter approach can now sensibly be used to obtain the precise relative positions of these two continents. Palaeomagnetism has the additional advantage of informing us of (i) the palaeolatitude of the reconstructed continents, and (ii) the time when they began to separate, information which we cannot obtain by studying their shapes alone. The agreement between the palaeomagnetic and other reconstructions (e.g. Wegener's and du Toit's) of the Palaeozoic positions of South America and Africa encourages us to attempt to use the palaeomagnetic data for other continents in the same way.

European and North American Palaeomagnetic Data

European data

Far more palaeomagnetic work has been done on rocks from Europe and the U.S.S.R. (table 4) than from any other land mass; this is evident from an inspection of available World-wide paleomagnetic data presented in tables 1–7. Poles for the same geological period computed from different formations exhibit dispersions with standard deviations of 15–25° (see table 8). Although these are of the order expected owing to palaeosecular variation[6], it would be surprising if this were really the cause since most of the

TABLE 8 Comparison of mean palaeomagnetic South Poles for west Europe and Russia

Period	West Europe					Russia					West Europe + Russia				
	N	Longitude	Latitude	δ	δ_m	N	Longitude	Latitude	δ	δ_m	N	Longitude	Latitude	δ	δ_m
Triassic	4	31·8° W	47·7° S	17·7°	8·8°	13	34·1° W	51·2° S	14·3°	4·1°	17	33·3° W	50·5° S	15·2°	3·7°
Permian	15	15·6° W	43·3° S	11·8°	3·1°	9	13·2° W	44·1° S	5·6°	1·9°	24	14·7° W	43·6° S	9·8°	2·0°
Carboniferous	13	27·3° W	30·4° S	23·3°	6·5°	12	17·0° W	38·9° S	23·6°	6·8°	25	31·7° W	34·6° S	23·7°	4·7°
Devonian (D I)	3	26·3° W	28·5° S	11·8°	6·8°	3	34·0° W	34·6° S	20·2°	11·7°	6	30·0° W	31·6° S	14·8°	6·4°

formations examined appear thick enough to give the axial dipole. In this chapter, however, no attempt will be made to explain fluctuations of the pole within geological periods but rather to study the progression of the mean pole from one geological period to the next.

Mean poles calculated for each geological period are listed in table 4 and are labelled. Poles from U.S.S.R. (mainly from west of latitude 100° E) have been averaged with those for west Europe, and are not very different from those listed for Britain by Creer, Irving, and Runcorn[1], although many more data are now available. An up-to-date version of their original polar wandering curve (but on the South Poles rather than the North Poles) is shown in figure 3. It appears impossible, at first sight,

FIGURE 3   Polar wandering curve (South Pole) for Europe from Cambrian onwards. Standard error circles are plotted. [Data computed from Irving[14]]

to reconcile this curve with the polar wandering curves for the southern hemisphere continents of South America and Africa (see the preceding section), whether Wegenerian drift is allowed for or not.

One solution to this problem was suggested by thermal demagnetization experiments on Old Red Sandstone rocks from south Wales on which the first Devonian palaeomagnetic measurements had been made[7]. From these measurements a palaeomagnetic axis was computed with South Pole at 39° S 25° W (see table 9) and this pole was taken to be that of the Devonian geomagnetic field[8]. Other Devonian formations, particularly from the U.S.S.R., subsequently gave similar results (see tables 4 and 9). These directions will be referred to as D I, as they were in a previous discussion[9]. However, a previously undetected weak component in the natural

TABLE 9   Principal directions of remanent magnetism and palaeomagnetic poles of Devonian rocks from Britain

Formation		Directions of remanent magnetism			Palaeomagnetic South Pole	
		D	I	α	Latitude	Longitude
Anglo–Welsh Cuvette; Old Red Sandstone sediments, natural remanent magnetization (D I)	35 sites	196°	−4°	5°	39° S	25° W
Anglo–Welsh Cuvette; Old Red Sandstone sediments, high-temperature direction (D II)	5 sites	66°	−37°	16°	2° N	63° W
Midland Valley; Old Red Sandstone lavas, normal flows (D II)	8 sites	51°	−44°	13°	3° N	47° W
Midland Valley; Old Red Sandstone lavas, reversed flows (D II)	8 sites	216°	+58°	8°	9° N	31° W
Cwmbran, south Wales; Old Red Sandstone sediments, D I direction	49 samples	183°	−4°	8°	40° S	7° W
Cwmbran, south Wales; Old Red Sandstone sediments, D II direction	5 samples	245°	+35°	9°	1° N	62° W

remanent magnetism of these Old Red Sandstone rocks was revealed after thermal demagnetization by cooling in zero magnetic field from temperatures higher than the Curie point of magnetite, 575 °C. Within experimental error this direction (N 66° E, −37°, α = 16°) for 34 specimens from 5 sites (35 sites were sampled in the original survey) is parallel (see table 9) to the direction of natural remanent magnetism (N 51° E, −44°, α = 13°) computed for lavas of Old Red Sandstone age from 9 sites in the Midland Valley of Scotland[10] (pole 5·04 in table 4). This direction has been referred to as D II by Creer[9]. Chamalaun and Creer[11] and Chamalaun[12] have argued that in the Old Red Sandstone sediments the component D II is due to haematite. In some samples it was entirely impressed by the Devonian geomagnetic field. In other samples, this high-temperature component is a mixture of D I and D II directions. It is argued that the dominant component of the natural remanent magnetism (direction D I) was acquired later, in the Carboniferous or Permian Ages.

It is necessary, at this stage, to point out that Stubbs' work on the Old Red Sandstone lavas of Scotland was thorough and reliable, and that sufficient attention has not been taken of it until now possibly because the only record of it is in his Ph.D. dissertation[13,14]. Stubbs' criterion of stability was that the dispersion of directions of samples from any flow should cause a circle of confidence of less than 30°, and on this basis he rejected 14 of the 44 flows he sampled. 16 of the remaining 30 were from the Lower Devonian Age and 8 of these were normally magnetized and 8 reversely magnetized along axis D II. The remaining 14 flows were from the Middle Devonian Age and the between-flow scatter of mean natural remanent magnetism directions of these was large: their meaning still cannot be interpreted, although it is noted that two of these are close to the direction D I. Lower Old Red Sandstone lavas were later sampled by Nairn[15] (1960) at Ethie in the Midland Valley, and their mean direction $D = $ N 35° E, $I = +5°$, $\alpha = 11°$ has been supposed mistakenly to be the dominant Devonian direction D I. In fact a more critical inspection reveals that the distribution of sample directions shows pronounced streaking between Stubbs' D II direction and that of the present dipole field. Some workers in palaeomagnetism have been reluctant to accept Stubbs' Devonian result because he did not carry out alternating field 'cleaning' on his samples. This technique was not properly developed when he made his measurements. Nevertheless, that those flows selected by Stubbs' criterion of stability are in fact the most resistant to demagnetization by alternating fields has recently been shown by Embleton[16] who is making a new study of these lavas.

FIGURE 4   European Devonian D I (closed circles) and Carboniferous (closed squares) North Poles. Data from table 4

If the remagnetization hypothesis[11,12] is accepted, it becomes necessary to extend it and to postulate a regional remagnetization of Devonian rocks in the late Palaeozoic Age, because many palaeomagnetic data obtained from Devonian rocks from Europe and the U.S.S.R. (see tables 4 and 9) apparently confirm the Old Red Sandstone direction (D I) originally accepted (and still accepted by many workers) as representative of the Devonian palaeomagnetic field. Is it reasonable to postulate such a widespread remagnetization of Devonian rocks? Two reasons may be given in support. First, as illustrated in figure 4, Devonian poles corresponding to direction D I form a single group when plotted with poles for Carboniferous rocks from Europe and U.S.S.R. (These poles are those listed in table 4.) Second, the Permian and late Carboniferous Ages were times of intensive production of red beds in northern hemisphere continents. Therefore it is highly plausible that red cement was deposited in older rocks too in the Permo-Carboniferous time. All palaeogeographic reconstructions show the present northern hemisphere continents in near-equatorial latitudes in the Upper Palaeozoic Age while the Gondwanic continents were situated at high latitudes. This explains how Lower Palaeozoic rocks from the Laurasian continents could have been remagnetized in the Upper Palaeozoic Age while those from Gondwanic continents were not remagnetized.

The remagnetization hypothesis can, of course, be subjected to experimental test by

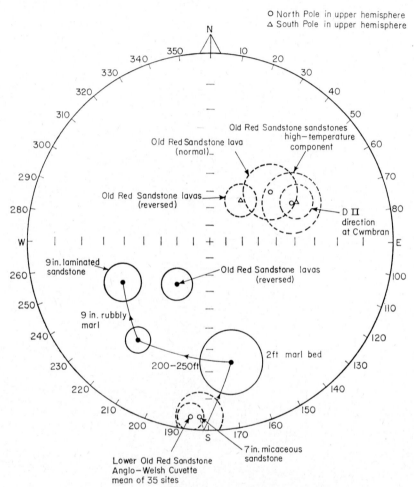

FIGURE 5 Independent determinations of Devonian field directions D I and D II obtained from Old Red Sandstone sediments and lavas from Britain

carrying out thermal demagnetization experiments on Lower Palaeozoic, especially Devonian, rocks. It is worth noting in this respect that most such rocks whose palaeomagnetism has been studied till now are red beds. It is necessary to perform these experiments very carefully for it must be remembered that in the Old Red Sandstone the weak component D II is not always revealed even above 600 °C, the dominant direction D I being carried partly by haematite as well as magnetite in some samples. It is realized that various laboratory tests of the stability of the remanent magnetization have been carried out on Devonian red beds of the U.S.S.R., but these are held not to be relevant because the point at issue is not one of stability; the secondary (D I) component of the Old Red Sandstone of south Wales has very high stability, a.c. cleaning in magnetic fields of peak intensity 2000 Oe reducing its intensity by less than 5% with no significant change in direction.

Other hypotheses to explain the two apparently valid natural remanent magnetism directions D I and D II found in Devonian rocks have been considered by Creer[9]. One is that they were caused by a shift of the Lower Devonian poles from an axis producing direction D II to one producing D I. However, at Cwmbran in south Wales in a large brickpit there is evidence of a shift in direction in lower Old Red Sandstone rocks from D I to D II (see table 9 and figure 5). It is therefore necessary to invoke successive flips between two stable rotation axes. Another possible explanation is that the geomagnetic axis may have oscillated along the line joining the poles of D I and D II instead of fluctuating randomly about a mean position centred on the Devonian rotation axis as is usually assumed in models of the long term behaviour of the geomagnetic field[6]. A consequence of such shifts of either the geographic or geomagnetic axis would be that directions D I and D II would be observed in Gondwanic rocks. There is no evidence of this in data at present available.

However, the main purpose of this section is to stress the rather strong evidence that two significantly different palaeomagnetic poles can be derived from studies of Devonian rocks and not to discuss possible explanations more than necessary. If the pole corresponding to direction D II is accepted as representing the true Devonian geomagnetic field, we may define a new polar wandering curve for Europe[2,17,18]. On the remagnetization hypothesis Devonian direction D I represents the Carboniferous or Permo-Carboniferous field. The new polar wandering curve for Eurasia is shown in figure 1 (iv) and is seen to be very similar in shape to the South American and African curves.

Mesozoic and Tertiary poles are also listed in table 4.

North American data

These are listed in table 5. The Palaeozoic poles fall into two groups; those computed from data from Silurian rocks lie close to the Carboniferous poles, while those computed from data from Ordovician and Devonian rocks lie some distance away. That the relative position of these two groups of poles is similar to that of the two European poles D I and D II may be seen by comparing figure 1 (iv) and (v).

Now the Ordovician Trenton and Juniata rocks, the Silurian Rose Hill Formation and the Devonian Onondaga limestone all have one feature in common, viz. they experienced penecontemporaneous folding. Application of the fold test, and in the case of the Trenton conglomerate, of the conglomerate test, indicates that their natural remanent magnetisms are not depositional, but postdate the folding. It is unlikely that the natural remanent magnetisms are younger than the Devonian Age, partly because the folding was penecontemporaneous and partly because their well-grouped directions are oblique to both the present field and to the Tertiary and Mesozoic fields. Poles 3 and 5 on the North American curve correspond to pole 5 on the European curve, while poles 4' and 6 on the former correspond to poles 5' and 6 on the latter: pole 3, for the Juniata Formation, lies off the new polar wandering curve for North America illustrated in figure 1 (v), but by no more than about twice the radius of the circle of confidence, which is conventionally taken to represent the limit of significance. Whatever might be the reason for this Palaeozoic polar shift common to both European and North American curves, it is a curious fact that it can be used to derive a plausible continental reconstruction as shown in the following subsection.

Mesozoic and Tertiary poles for North American rocks are also listed in table 5.

Combination of European and North American data

All available palaeomagnetic data have been taken account of in constructing the new European and North American polar wandering curves. Both exhibit a large polar movement in the Upper Palaeozoic time and this feature, it will be remembered, is also characteristic of the South American and African curves (see p. 363). It is

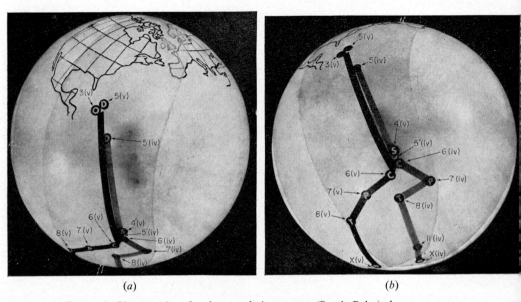

(a)   (b)

FIGURE 6 Photographs of polar wandering curves (South Poles) drawn on superimposed spherical shells. European (iv) shell superimposed on North American (v). (a) and (b) are taken from slightly different angles

therefore pertinent to ask whether by superimposing the Upper Palaeozoic portions of the European and North American curves we can sensibly deduce the relative positions of these land masses during those times, as we did for South America and Africa (figure 2).

North America and Europe are thus found to take up positions with their Atlantic coasts in close proximity (see figure 6) confirming Wegener's hypothesis that the northern hemisphere continents were grouped together in the Palaeozoic Age forming the supercontinent of Laurasia.

The precision of the reconstruction may be estimated as follows. There are two principal sources of error. We have noted a considerable scatter in poles determined for different formations of European and Russian Carboniferous rocks, and similarly for Devonian formations giving directions D I (figure 4). The angular standard deviations for Devonian D I, Carboniferous, Permian, and Triassic formations (see table 8) are respectively 14·8°, 23·7°, 9·8°, and 15·2°. Angular standard deviations for separate populations of west European and of Russian rock formations are also given in table 8. These dispersions may be due to random polar shifts of relatively minor magnitude superimposed on the secular trend described by the polar wandering curves so that we may conclude that there is a probability of 63 % (assuming a Fisherian distribution) that a palaeomagnetic pole determined by exhaustive studies of *a single formation* of a particular age lies within an angular distance equal to the circular standard deviation δ of the mean palaeomagnetic pole for that geological period.

Nevertheless, palaeomagnetic pole positions computed from *several* reliable formations are considerably more precise (see table 8). Given a population of N estimates of the palaeomagnetic pole for a given period, the accuracy of *the mean pole* is given by the circular standard error $\delta_m = \delta/N^{1/2}$ or circle of confidence α. There is a 63 %

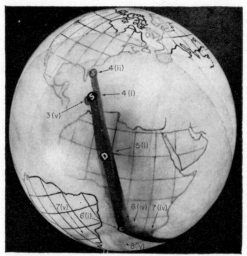

FIGURE 7 Photograph of polar wandering curves (South Poles) drawn on spherical shells. European (iv), North American (v), African (ii), and South American (i) shells are superimposed

probability that the *true mean pole* lay within δ_m and a 95 % probability within α of the computed mean pole (again assuming a Fisherian distribution).

Another important source of error arises because the palaeomagnetic pole computed from remanent magnetic data of a sedimentary rock formation may not correspond to the geomagnetic field appropriate to the time of deposition but to some time subsequent to this. We have already discussed this with regard to North American and European Palaeozoic rock formations on p. 367.

The Relative Positions of Laurasia and Gondwanaland

In view of the success of the method of superimposing the Upper Palaeozoic positions of the two pairs of polar wandering curves (pp. 363, 370) we now extend the method to the four polar wandering curves in order to reconstruct the Upper Palaeozoic geography of Laurasia and Gondwanaland. If we use the globe and the four spherical shells, the reconstruction shown in figure 7 is deduced. This reconstruction differs from Wegener's and du Toit's and is at variance with the recently demonstrated accurate fit of opposing Atlantic continental shelves[5] mainly in that there is a gap between

Laurasia and Gondwanaland of about 1500 km at its narrowest between northwest Africa and eastern U.S.A. The Tethys Sea thus completely separated these two continents in the Upper Palaeozoic Age according to the palaeomagnetic method of continental reconstruction. Recently Melville[19] has argued from studies of angiosperms that Laurasia and Gondwanaland belonged to different floral provinces in the Upper Palaeozoic Era. His glossopteris line which marks the northern boundary of the region, in which this typical Gondwanic genus flourished, runs through South America along the line of the Amazon Basin and through Africa along a line following the upper reaches of the river Niger in a northeast direction to the Mediterranean coast of Egypt. Thus the northern part of South America and northwest Africa are believed

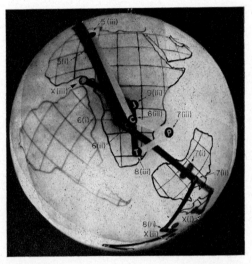

FIGURE 8   Photograph of polar wandering curves (South Poles) drawn on spherical shells. South American (i), African (ii), and Australian (iii) curves superimposed

to have been parts of Laurasia. It is pertinent to note that none of the African palaeomagnetic data come from the northwest of that continent and none of the South American data quoted come from north of the Amazon.

Consideration of Australian Data

Palaeomagnetic data for Australia (table 3) are about as numerous as those for North America. The Mesozoic and Tertiary data are much more abundant and reliable than those of the Palaeozoic. Nevertheless we notice that the Australian polar wandering curve also exhibits a substantial movement of about 50° between Carboniferous and Devonian poles (6 and 5). Using the globe and spherical shells again, we superimpose this portion of the Australian curve on the master Upper Palaeozoic curve and hence find the ancient position of Australia relative to the other continents (figure 8). This differs not only from the well-known reconstruction of Wegener, but also from those of du Toit and King[20] all of whom place Antarctica between the southern coast of Australia and the southeast coast of Africa. However, a reconstruction in which the south coast of Australia lay roughly parallel to the southeast coast of Africa, as inferred from the palaeomagnetic data, has been previously deduced from geological studies by Ahmad[21].

Against the background of the reconstruction shown in figure 8, obtained by superposition of all three Carboniferous poles (South America, Africa, and Australia) and rotation about this common pole to bring the Upper Palaeozoic curves into coincidence, the Devonian poles for South America and Australia coincide within experimental error. However, the Australian Permian pole is not coincident with the common South American and African Permian pole so that, according to the palaeomagnetic data, Australia must have begun to separate from the main land mass of Gondwanaland (i.e. South America plus Africa) before the Permian but later than the Carboniferous Age.

This reconstruction is probably in better agreement with the evidence for the Permo-Carboniferous glaciation than du Toit's: the size of ice cap necessary to account for this being considerably smaller than required by du Toit.

Consideration of data from India and Antarctica

These data are summarized in tables 6 and 7. There are no data for the Palaeozoic Era, so that the method used above to deduce ancient continental configurations cannot be applied in the cases of India and Antarctica. By studying the Mesozoic and Cainozoic portions of the polar wandering curves, however, we can draw some conclusions about the palaeogeography of these continents.

In all continental assemblages based on geological information, India is placed off the east coast of Africa near Ethiopia and Tanzania. When the spherical shell inscribed with India and its polar wandering curve is so placed on the globe marked with the Palaeozoic geography deduced in previous sections of this chapter (figure 10(*a*) and (*b*)), the polar wandering curve is seen (figure 10(*c*)) to converge towards the African curve, going back in time. The proximity of the African and Indian Cretaceous poles, 10(ii) and 10(vi) respectively, should also be noted.

Antarctica's position in the Palaeozoic supercontinent is more difficult to elucidate. We may again proceed by moving the spherical shell for Antarctica with its polar wandering curve over the Palaeozoic globe. A reconstruction which seems to be most reasonable on this basis is shown in figure 10(*c*) in which the Antarctican Jurassic pole 9(vii) lies close to the Australian Jurassic pole 9(iii). However, to avoid overlap of Antarctica on to South America and South Africa, it has been necessary to follow a suggestion put forward by several eminent specialists on the geology of Antarctica[34,35], viz. that east and west Antarctica had separate identities in the past. The sites where palaeomagnetic samples were collected are near the boundary line whose exact position is not entirely clear. However, it is most probable that they are located in what was east Antarctica, which comprises the larger part and which possesses a Pre-Cambrian basement whereas west Antarctica does not. East Antarctica thus fits against the coasts of Chile and eastern Australia as shown in figure 10(*c*). It is interesting to note that the gap left between Argentina, South Africa, and southeast Australia is just the right size to hold west Antarctica which is shown in this position—this is where du Toit placed it in his reconstruction. There is, however, no palaeomagnetic evidence to support this step.

M.E.—13

Du Toit's Reconstruction of Gondwanaland and Palaeomagnetism

One difficulty which limits interpretation of the palaeomagnetic data arises because it is not possible to establish equality of geological age of rock formations in such presently widely separated continents as, for example, Africa and Australia, especially when we are concerned with the type of rock often used in palaeomagnetic studies, viz. unfossiliferous red beds. Secondly, as discussed on p. 367, the magnetic age of many sediments is younger than the fossiliferous age. Thirdly, even from Eurasia, we do not have enough data to deduce exactly when the large (Devonian–Pennsylvanian?) movement of the pole across the Palaeozoic supercontinents occurred. We have seen that the reconstruction based on palaeomagnetic data differs from traditional reconstructions in two ways: (i) there is a gap between Laurasia and Gondwanaland, and

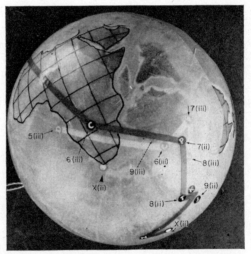

FIGURE 9   Photograph of polar wandering curves (South Poles) for Africa (ii) and Australia (iii). Spherical shells adjusted on a globe illustrating du Toit's reconstruction of Gondwanaland

(ii) the position of Australia relative to Africa. At this stage of the work it is impossible to establish firmly these conclusions.

Another approach, previously adopted by Creer[17], is to enquire whether the palaeomagnetic data are consistent with one of the traditional reconstructions. It is instructive, in particular, to investigate one of the reconstructions of Gondwanaland in this way and, for this purpose, du Toit's has been chosen, though any one of the others could equally well have been used. When the Australian, South American, and African curves are plotted against the background of du Toit's reconstruction, the Upper Palaeozoic parts more or less overlap. However, the mean Australian Devonian pole does not coincide with the South American Devonian pole but rather lies between the Devonian and Carboniferous parts of the master curve (figure 9). The three (South American, African, and Australian) curves, however, diverge in the Mesozoic (Pre-Cretaceous) Age implying that Gondwanaland did not break up until then, a conclusion which may be more compatible with geological evidence than that derived on

p. 372, where it was deduced that Australia separated from Africa in the Permo-Carboniferous Age.

Going back in time, the polar wandering curves for India and Antarctica were seen[17] to converge towards the point where the South American, African, and Australian Mesozoic curves meet to form the common Palaeozoic curve. These palaeomagnetic data are thus more or less, but not quite, consistent with the drift hypothesis as propounded by du Toit. It is noted, for example, that the polar wandering curve for Antarctica, which extends back only to the Jurassic time (figure 1 (vii)), has to be doubled back on itself[17] to make it join the Upper Permian pole common to South America, Africa, and Australia. Does this indicate that the position of Antarctica deduced by du Toit needs modifying? Such a suspicion was aroused on p. 372 where a close inspection of the Australian data led us to conclude that Australia was adjacent to Africa, in which case Antarctica could not have been where du Toit placed it on his maps.

Time of Onset of Drift

We have seen how the 50° polar shift recorded in the palaeomagnetic records of South America, Africa, Europe, North America, and Australia has allowed the reconstruction of the relative position of these continents during the Upper Palaeozoic Era. By studying the manner in which the Mesozoic curves for the individual continents diverge from the Palaeozoic master curve (figure 10) we can deduce, in principle, when the supercontinents broke up.

The Carboniferous poles for all the above-mentioned continents are coincident. The Permian pole for North America lies off the joint curve: the Permian poles for Europe and Australia lie on the joint curve, but closer to the Carboniferous point than the South American plus African Permian pole.

Thus between the Carboniferous and Permian Ages the initial movements, which culminated in the break up of the Palaeozoic supercontinent into the continental distribution we know today, occurred: North America, Europe, and Australia were displaced from South America and Africa. The continental displacements necessary to explain the non-coincidence of the Permian poles plotted with respect to the Upper Palaeozoic palaeogeography need not have been great; we can use the model globe and spherical shells to illustrate a possible Permian palaeogeography postulating a minimum amount of Permo-Carboniferous drift: Australia appears to have drifted away from Africa, while Europe approached Africa and North America drifted southwards relative to Europe. It is not necessary to postulate appreciable widening of the North Atlantic Basin. South America and Africa remained rigidly connected in the Permian Age (these poles coincide) but by the Cretaceous time (for which the palaeomagnetic poles are not coincident) relative movement had occurred between these two continents so as to start the South Atlantic Basin. There are no reliable palaeomagnetic data for South American rocks for the interval between the Permian and Cretaceous Ages so the exact time of separation of South America and Africa cannot yet be deduced by this method. Palaeomagnetic data at present available indicate that these are the youngest of the present continents, as defined in terms of individual identity, and this is perhaps reflected by the fact that the fit of the

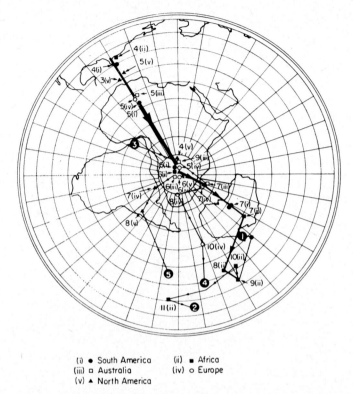

(i) ● South America   (ii) ■ Africa
(iii) □ Australia   (iv) ○ Europe
(v) ▲ North America

FIGURE 10(*a*)   Polar wandering curves for South America, Africa, Australia, Europe, and North America drawn on the reconstruction obtained by superimposing their Upper Palaeozoic parts. The pole of the projection is the Carboniferous South Pole common to all these continents.

The other symbols in these figures are described in the tables at the beginning of this chapter. Present South Poles are indicated by white numbers on the large black dots. The other numbers indicate the geological period, while the Roman numerals indicate the continent to which particular palaeomagnetic poles belong

continental shelf edges of this pair of continents is better than for any other pair of present-day continents which have drifted from juxtaposition in past geological time.

On the Reality of Drift

The principal palaeomagnetic argument taken to support the hypothesis of drift is that the polar wandering curves for the different continents, when drawn on the present World globe, diverge from the present geographic poles (figure 1 (i) to (vii)). If there had been polar wandering but no continental drift, a single polar wandering curve would be obtained, common to all continents. We now ask whether there is a tenable alternative explanation of why palaeomagnetic data from different continents are such that different polar wandering curves are computed from them. Hospers (see section VIII, chapter 1 of this book) has developed a triangulation method of deducing palaeomagnetic poles for a given continent, because it has sometimes been argued that the determination of the azimuth of the ancient meridian is more secure than that of palaeolatitude. By using data of the same age from two (preferably three) widely separated sites (on one land mass) the palaeomagnetic pole can be located by finding where the two (three) great circles defining the palaeomeridian directions intersect. Hence the calculation of palaeolatitude from the inclination of the remanent magnetism is avoided. When this technique is applied to certain North American and European data, Hospers maintains that the corrected poles for given geological periods coincide and hence that it is not necessary to invoke the hypothesis of continental drift to explain the data. The correction to the observed paleomagnetic poles is explained by invoking the presence of an inclination error. Is this feasible?

There are two reasons why one should suppose not. Firstly, while it has been

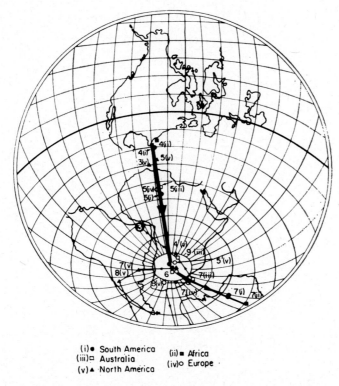

(i)● South America   (ii)■ Africa
(iii)□ Australia   (iv)○ Europe
(v)▲ North America

FIGURE 10(*b*)   See caption to figure 10(*a*) (including note about symbols)

demonstrated experimentally[22] that the inclination recorded by the remanent magnetism of sedimentary rocks which were magnetized by the depositional process is less than that of the ambient magnetic field, the remanent magnetization of most of the rock formations in question is not depositional. Some of the formations are igneous: some are red beds whose magnetization was probably acquired after deposition during crystallization of some of the contained iron oxide minerals. Secondly, the triangulation technique can only be applied to formations which are of the same magnetic age (probably to within a million years or so) and it cannot be shown that the assumption is true. Hence Hospers's conclusions are not based on sound physical reasoning and are probably due to an accidental set of circumstances. The effect of applying a correction for the inclination error is to bring a palaeomagnetic pole closer to the continent of origin of data. The spherical geometry of the positions of North America, Europe, and their respective polar wandering curves is such that corrections for inclination error are of the right sign to explain the non-coincidence of their polar wandering curves. But the argument only makes sense physically if it can be shown that the

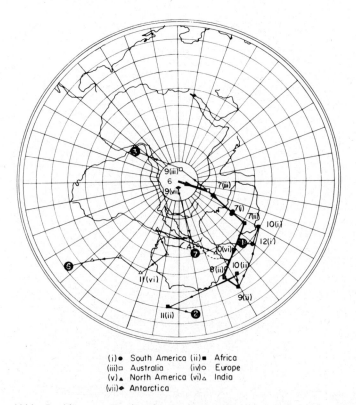

(i)● South America (ii)■ Africa
(iii)□ Australia   (iv)○ Europe
(v)▲ North America (vi)△ India
(vii)◆ Antarctica

FIGURE 10(c)   In this reconstruction the continents of India and Antarctica have been placed so that their polar wandering curves (which range in time back to the Mesozoic only) converge towards the curves for the other continents. The Indian Cretaceous pole for Antarctica lies close to that for Australia. Note that it is necessary to separate east from west Antarctica to make a sensible reconstruction. (See also note about symbols in caption to figure 10(a))

inclinations of the remanent magnetism of the rock formations studied are likely to be systematically low: this is not so.

In fact, the palaeomagnetic data which lend most substantial support to the drift hypothesis are those from Australia and India whose polar wandering curves strongly diverge from the European. As far as the European and North American continents are concerned, relative continental movement appears to have been substantially smaller than their common movement relative to the pole. The true test of the triangulation method would be to apply it to the Australian and European polar wandering curves or to the Indian and European curves. Only if it accounted for the divergence of these pairs of curves should it be taken seriously as a hypothesis to rival continental drift.

Lower Palaeozoic and Pre-Cambrian Data

A preliminary study of Cambrian palaeomagnetic data for South and North America, Europe, and Australia, reveals that they are not in agreement with the positions of the continents deduced from Upper Palaeozoic data. However, it is premature to discuss the reasons for this.

Insufficient dated Pre-Cambrian data exist to make a global interpretation of these yet, but when adequate data have been assembled for successive subdivisions of Pre-Cambrian time the palaeomagnetic method should yield important clues concerning the evolution of the Earth. One obvious application is to the expansion hypothesis[36], for palaeomagnetic measurements covering a few billion of years should detect even a slow increase in radius of 0·5 mm/year.

Conclusions

A critical examination of *all* palaeomagnetic data at present available has enabled us to derive a palaeogeographic reconstruction of the continents of South America, Africa, Australia, North America, and Europe for the Upper Palaeozoic Age. This reconstruction, illustrated in figure 10(*a*) and (*b*), stands on its own merits, having been deduced without reference to either geological or other geophysical evidence of which it is therefore completely independent.

That such completely different disciplines as geomagnetism and solid-state magnetism on the one hand and geology, palaeontology, and palaeobotany on the other should lead to similar deductions is strong support indeed for the hypothesis of continental drift. Although Wegener's theory to explain continental drift was soon shown to be untenable and although no-one has since put forward a satisfactory theory of continental drift consistent with the physics and chemistry of the Earth, the circumstantial evidence for drift now appears overwhelming. However, it is obvious that much remains to be done before the exact arrangement of the continents during the Upper Palaeozoic Age is deduced. This chapter has revealed that the palaeomagnetic data suggest that Australia was adjacent to Africa, whereas Wegener and du Toit place Antarctica between them. We have, as yet, insufficient knowledge of the geology of Antarctica to deduce with confidence its relationship with respect to the other Gondwanic continents and there are no palaeomagnetic data for the Palaeozoic time. Another problem which has not been considered here concerns the relative positions of Angaraland: was Siberia part of the European–west Russian block in the Upper Palaeozoic? Furthermore, were northwest Africa and South America north of the Amazon parts of Gondwanaland or did they belong to Laurasia as has been concluded by Melville[19] from his studies of the distribution of glossopterids? Without undue optimism the palaeomagnetist can reasonably expect to make a positive contribution to these problems during the next decade by sampling in the appropriate regions. By improving the palaeomagnetic record for the Lower Palaeozoic Era we can also expect to deduce whether the palaeogeography of that era was similar to that deduced here for the Upper Palaeozoic Era, so establishing whether more than one major episode of continental drift occurred in Phanerozoic time.

TABLE 10   List of symbols used

Symbol		Geological age
1		Pre-Cambrian
2		Cambrian
3	(O)	Ordovician
3′		Ordovician, presumed Carboniferous magnetic age
4	(S)	Silurian
4′		Silurian, presumed Carboniferous magnetic age
5	(D, D II)	Devonian
5′	(D I)	Devonian, presumed Carboniferous magnetic age
6	(C)	Carboniferous
7	(P)	Permian
8	(T)	Triassic
9	(J)	Jurassic
10	(K)	Cretaceous
11	(E)	Tertiary
11′	(N)	Upper Tertiary
12	(Q)	Quaternary
X	X	Present

Symbol	Quantity
D	declination
I	inclination
δ	circular standard deviation
δ_m	circular standard error
α	radius of circle of confidence (95%)

Symbol	Table	Continent
(i)	1	South America
(ii)	2	Africa
(iii)	3	Australia
(iv)	4	Europe and Russia
(v)	5	North America
(vi)	6	India
(vii)	7	Antarctica

References

1. K. M. Creer, E. Irving, and S. K. Runcorn, 'Geophysical interpretation of palaeomagnetic directions from Great Britain', *Phil. Trans. Roy. Soc. London, Ser. A*, **250**, 144–56 (1957).
2. K. M. Creer, 'A reconstruction of the continents for the Upper Palaeozoic from palaeomagnetic data', *Nature*, **203**, 1115–20 (1964).
3. A. Wegener, *Die Entstehung der Kontinente und Ozeane*, Vieweg, Brunswick, 1941.
4. A. du Toit, *Our Wandering Continents*, Oliver and Boyd, Edinburgh, 1937.
5. E. C. Bullard, J. E. Everitt, and A. G. Smith, 'The fit of the continents around the Atlantic', *Phil. Trans. Roy. Soc. London, Ser. A*, **258**, 41–51 (1965).
6. K. M. Creer, 'The dispersion of the geomagnetic field due to secular variation and its determination for remote times from palaeomagnetic data, *J. Geophys. Res.*, **67**, 3461–76 (1962).
7. K. M. Creer, E. Irving, and S. K. Runcorn, 'The direction of the geomagnetic field in remote epochs in Great Britain', *J. Geomagnetism Geoelectricity*, **6**, 163–8 (1954).
8. K. M. Creer, 'The natural remanent magnetization of certain stable rocks from Great Britain', *Phil. Trans. Roy. Soc. London, Ser. A*, **250**, 111–29 (1957).
9. K. M. Creer, 'Palaeolatitudes of the continents in the Devonian as revealed by the natural remanent magnetization of rocks', in *Problems in Palaeoclimatology* (Ed. A. E. M. Nairn), Interscience, London, 1965, pp. 269–85.
10. P. M. Stubbs, *A Palaeomagnetic Study of the British and European Trias and of the British Old Red Sandstone*, Ph.D. Thesis, London University (1966).
11. F. H. Chamalaun and K. M. Creer, 'Thermal demagnetization studies of the Old Red Sandstone of the Anglo–Welsh Cuvette', *J. Geophys. Res.*, **69**, 1607–16 (1964).
12. F. H. Chamalaun, 'Origin of the secondary magnetization of the Old Red Sandstone of the Anglo–Welsh Cuvette', *J. Geophys. Res.*, **69**, 4327–37 (1964).
13. P. M. Stubbs, Ph.D. Thesis, quoted in reference 14.
14. E. Irving, *Palaeomagnetism*, Wiley, New York, 1964.
15. A. E. M. Nairn, 'Palaeomagnetic results from Europe', *J. Geol.*, **68**, 285–306 (1960).
16. B. Embleton, M.Sc. Dissertation, University of Newcastle (1966).
17. K. M. Creer, 'Palaeomagnetism and du Toit's reconstruction of Gondwanaland', *Nature*, **204**, 369–70 (1964).
18. K. M. Creer, 'Palaeomagnetism and the results of its application to South American rocks', *Bol. Paranaense Geografia*, **1964**, May, 93–138.
19. R. Melville, 'Continental drift, Mesozoic continents and the migrations of the angiosperms', *Nature*, **211**, 116–20 (1966).
20. L. C. King, 'Basic palaeogeography of Gondwanaland during the late Palaeozoic and Mesozoic Eras', *Quart. J. Geol. Soc. London*, **1958**, 114.
21. F. Ahmad, 'An estimate of the rate of continental drift in the Permian Period', *Nature*, **210**, 81–3 (1966).
22. R. F. King, 'The remanent magnetism of artificially deposited sediments', *Monthly Notices Roy. Astron. Soc., Geophys. Suppl.*, **7**, 115–34 (1955).
23. K. M. Creer, 'Palaeomagnetic data from the Gondwanic continents', *Phil. Trans. Roy. Soc. London, Ser. A*, **258**, 27–40 (1965).
24. N. O. Opdyke, 'The palaeomagnetism of the Permian red beds of southwest Tanganyika', *J. Geophys. Res.*, **69**, 2477–87 (1964).
25. N. O. Opdyke, 'The palaeomagnetism of some Triassic red beds from north Rhodesia', *J. Geophys. Res.*, **69**, 2495–7 (1964).
26. D. I. Gough and A. Brock, 'The paleomagnetism of the Shawa ijolite', *J. Geophys. Res.*, **69**, 2489–93 (1964).
27. J. S. V. van Zijl, K. W. T. Graham, and A. L. Hales, 'The palaeomagnetism of the Stormberg lavas II', *Geophys. J.*, **7**, 169–82 (1962).
28. D. I. Gough and N. O. Opdyke, 'The palaeomagnetism of the Lupata alkaline volcanics', *Geophys. J.*, **7**, 4 (1963).

29. A. E. M. Nairn, 'Palaeomagnetic measurements on Karroo and Post Karroo rocks, a second progress report', *Overseas Geol. Mineral Resources (G.B.)*, **9**, 302–20 (1964).
30. C. Radhakrishnamurty, *Remanent Magnetism of the Igneous Rocks in the Gondwana Formation of India*, D.Sc. Thesis, Andra University, India (1963).
31. R. N. Athavale, C. Radhakrishnamurty, and P. W. Sahastrabudhe, 'Palaeomagnetism of some Indian rocks', *Geophys. J.*, **7**, 304–13 (1963).
32. E. R. Deutch, C. Radhakrishnamurty, and P. W. Sahastrabudhe, 'The remanent magnetism of some lavas in the Deccan traps', *Phil. Mag.*, **3**, 170–4 (1958).
33. D. J. Blundell, 'Palaeomagnetic investigations in the Falkland Is. dependencies', *Brit. Antarctica Surv. Sci. Rept. No.* 39 (1962).
34. E. Thiel, 'Antarctica, one continent or two?', *Polar Record*, **10**, 335–48 (1961).
35. G. P. Woollard, 'The land of the Antarctic', *Sci. Am.*, **207**, 151–66 (1962).
36. K. M. Creer, 'An expanding Earth?', *Nature*, **205**, 539–44 (1965).

3

L. R. SYKES

Lamont Geological Observatory of Columbia University
Palisades, New York, U.S.A.

The World-wide distribution of deep and shallow earthquakes

Abstract

Earthquakes are one of the principal sources of information about the physical processes that occur in the upper mantle and in the crust of the Earth. Nearly all deep earthquakes and a large percentage of the World's shallow earthquakes are associated either with island arcs or with other similar arcuate structures. The occurrence of deep-focus earthquakes indicates that materials as deep as 700 km (more than 1/10 the radius of the Earth) are involved in the development of island arcs. Although a great amount of new seismological data has become available during the last decade, the spatial distribution of earthquakes has not been studied extensively since the classical investigations of Gutenberg, Richter, and Benioff.

New earthquake data for several island arcs, the midoceanic ridges, and several major fault zones were presented. The distribution of earthquakes was compared with the distribution of volcanoes, deep-sea trenches, fracture zones, gravity anomalies, and heat-flow anomalies. Recent data indicate that seismic activity in many island arcs is confined to very narrow zones that dip under the arcs to depths as great as 700 km. Within the accuracy of the computations the dip of this zone is independent of depth.

The distributions of all tectonic elements—deep earthquakes, shallow earthquakes, volcanoes, and trench—display a pronounced curvature at the northern end of the Tonga arc. Hence, the tectonic processes responsible for the origin of these features are intimately related for depths from about 0 to 700 km. Seismic activity along the midoceanic ridges is of shallow focus and is confined to narrow, linear zones along the ridge crest. The greater areal scatter of earthquake epicenters along the continental extensions of the oceanic ridges suggests that either the stress distribution or the response of continental materials differ from that found in oceanic areas.

References

1. H. Benioff, 'Orogenesis and deep crustal structure—additional evidence from seismology', *Bull. Geol. Soc. Am.*, **65**, 385–400 (1954).
2. B. Gutenberg and C. F. Richter, *Seismicity of the Earth*, 2nd ed., Princeton University Press, Princeton, 1954.

3. L. R. Sykes, 'Seismicity of the south Pacific Ocean', *J. Geophys. Res.*, **68**, 5999–6006 (1963).
4. L. R. Sykes, 'The seismicity of the Arctic', *Bull. Seismol. Soc. Am.*, **55**, 501–18 (1965).
5. L. R. Sykes, 'The seismicity and deep structure of island arcs', *J. Geophys. Res.*, **71**, 2981–3006 (1966).
6. L. R. Sykes and M. Ewing, 'The seismicity of the Caribbean region', *J. Geophys. Res.*, **70**, 5065–74 (1965).
7. L. R. Sykes and M. Landisman, 'The seismicity of east Africa, the Gulf of Aden and the Arabian and Red Seas', *Bull. Seismol. Soc. Am.*, **54**, 1927–40 (1964).
8. D. G. Tobin and L. R. Sykes, 'Relationship of hypocenters of earthquakes to the geology of Alaska', *J. Geophys. Res.*, **71**, 1659–67 (1966).

4

E. A. GAUGLER

National Aeronautics and Space Administration (NASA)
U.S.A.

The *Mariner IV* mission to Mars

The *Mariner IV* program was initiated by the National Aeronautics and Space Administration in November 1962. Its objective was to conduct the first *in situ* (fly-by) scientific investigation of the planet Mars using the *Atlas–Agena* launch vehicle during the 1965 Mars opportunity. The Jet Propulsion Laboratory was delegated the project responsibility for this mission. They relied heavily on technology previously developed for the *Mariner II* and *Ranger* spacecraft[1].

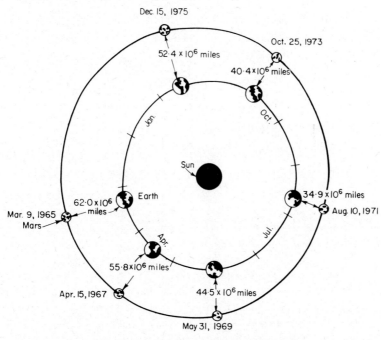

FIGURE 1   Earth–Mars oppositions 1965–1975

Earth–Mars oppositions occur only every 25 months. Because of the relative eccentricity of Mars' orbit as compared with the Earth's, the kinetic energy required to overcome the Sun's gravitational potential energy varies considerably from opportunity to opportunity. These differences in energies can be related to the distances at opposition as illustrated in figure 1. In this respect the 1965 opportunity was an unfavorable one.

If the orbit of Mars lay in the ecliptic plane, then the minimum energy trajectory would be an ellipse with the Earth at launch and Mars at encounter being 180° apart on the major axis.

The actual ballistic energy curve is shown in figure 2. The discontinuity where one would expect a minimum represents the fact that the orbit of Mars is inclined 1° 51' to the ecliptic plane. On a type I trajectory the spacecraft travels less than 180° and on a type II it travels more than 180°. This figure also suggests how critical it is to

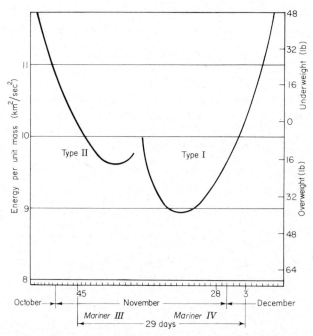

FIGURE 2   Variability of the ballistic energy–payload weight during the *Mariner* 1964 launch window

maintain development schedules since the entire launch window is less than one month in a two year program. *Mariner IV* was launched on a type I trajectory as shown in figure 3.

A front (Sun-facing) view of the *Mariner IV* spacecraft is shown in figure 4. It is an attitude-controlled spacecraft with the four solar panels always facing normal (within ± 9 mrad) to the spacecraft–Sun line by means of a control system employing solar sensors and cold gas jets[2]. In order to stabilize the spacecraft around its roll axis, it employs a star tracker which is fixed on the star Canopus. The star tracker utilizes an optical system and an image dissector which is electronically gimbaled. Canopus is the second brightest star in the sky and is located within 15° of the South Ecliptic Pole. Since the spacecraft always faces the Sun, and Canopus is not at the South Ecliptic Pole, it is necessary to periodically change the cone angle of the star tracker. This was controlled electrostatically. It was programmed into the on-board computer and could be commanded from the ground[3].

For communications purposes, the spacecraft uses a 10 w transmitter operating at 2300 megacycles. The transmitted frequency is controlled either by an on-board

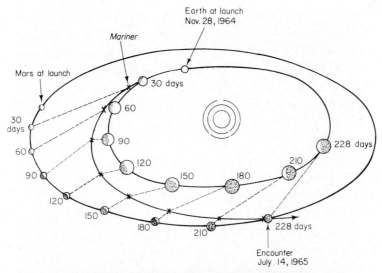

FIGURE 3   *Mariner IV* trajectory to Mars

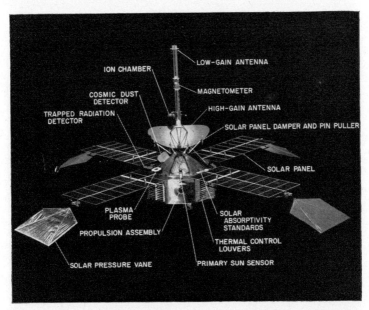

FIGURE 4   Front (Sun-facing) view of the *Mariner IV* spacecraft

crystal-controlled oscillator or at a fixed ratio of the ground transmitted frequency by a spacecraft transponder. Two antennae are employed, an omnidirectional antenna and a fixed-position parabolic high-gain antenna. The geometry is such that the high-gain antenna was pointing at Earth throughout most of its flight as shown in figure 5.

The spacecraft receives its electrical energy from four solar panels containing 28 224 type p on n boron-diffused silicon cells. This provides 700 w at the Earth's distance of 1 astronomical unit (A.U.) from the Sun and falls to 325 w at the vicinity of Mars.

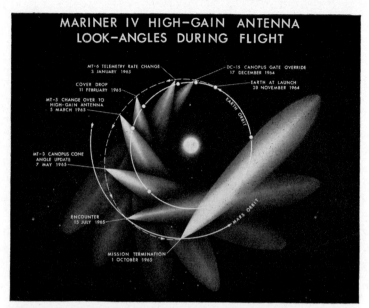

FIGURE 5   *Mariner IV* high-gain antenna look-angles during flight

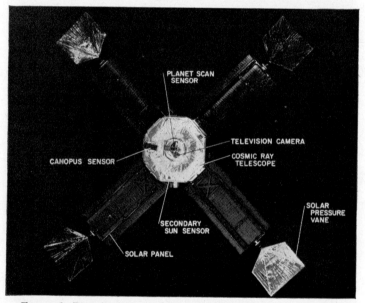

FIGURE 6   Rear (antisolar-facing) view of the *Mariner IV* spacecraft

The rear (antisolar-facing) view of the spacecraft is shown in figure 6. The temperature of the spacecraft is controlled both actively and passively. The active control is by means of louvers which are controlled by thermostatically operating bimetallic springs. Passive control is achieved by reflecting and painted surfaces in radiative equilibrium with space environment.

The effect of solar light pressure is such that the spacecraft is deflected a total distance of about 19000 km when it reaches the orbit of Mars. In order to minimize the consumption of gas in the attitude control system, the spacecraft is trimmed by means of four solar sails, one located at the end of each solar panel. They operated as an adaptive control system. These vanes are canted away from the Sun and serve to displace the center of pressure behind the center of mass. This is a dynamically stable configuration.

Each sail was 7 ft^2 in area, and the total assembled weight was less than 1·5 lb. Whenever the attitude of the spacecraft reached a predetermined end of a limit cycle and the corresponding attitude control jet fired, the corresponding solar vane was moved in a direction to reduce the assumed pressure imbalance[4]. Although this system was successful in reducing the attitude-controlled gas consumption, for reasons yet unexplained, a random torque unbalance of ±5 dyn cm was observed over periods as short as 1–2 hours and never longer than 9 hours.

For reliability many of the spacecraft systems are redundant. With the exception of the midcourse maneuver, the spacecraft is completely automated by means of an on-board computer. Provision is made to back up the on-board computer by commands sent from the ground. Because of the 24 min round trip velocity of light transit time to Mars at encounter, it was necessary to send the back-up ground commands before it was known that the on-board computer had functioned properly.

The spacecraft weight was 575 lb including 59·4 lb for scientific experiments. Table 1 shows a list of scientific experiments together with the names of the principal investigators[5].

The spacecraft was tracked and telemetry received by a network of 85 ft radio telescopes known as the Deep Space Institute Facility (DSIF). A typical 85 ft dish antenna is shown in figure 7. The incoming signal is amplified by means of a synthetic crystal ruby maser operating in liquid helium at 4·2 °K and located at the focus of the Cassegrainian telescope. A significant fact is that, by using a rubidium standard, the system frequency is stable to 1 part in 10^{12} over a one hour period. This permits a radial spacecraft velocity of approximately 1 mm/sec to be detected.

Mariner IV was launched on November 28, 1964, from Cape Kennedy. Although some difficulty was encountered in initially locking the star tracker on the star Canopus, the spacecraft remained locked on Canopus for the balance of the mission. It was necessary to adjust the star tracker system by switching off star brightness gates by ground command to prevent the star tracker from being disturbed by what is believed to have been solar-illuminated dust particles that passed within the field of view of the star tracking system.

On December 5, 1965, upon command from the ground, the spacecraft was reoriented 39° in pitch and 156° in roll. The midcourse motor, with the spacecraft in an autopilot configuration and having a nominal 50 lb of thrust, was fired for 20 sec. This had the effect of increasing the spacecraft velocity 17 m/sec and deflected the trajectory by $\frac{1}{4}$°. The effect of this maneuver was to change the distance of closest approach to Mars from 249452 km to 9846·6 km. The spacecraft trajectory was deliberately biased by that initial value to reduce the prelaunch probability of the accompanying *Agena* vehicle of impacting Mars to less than 1 part in 10^4. This was to prevent biological contamination of Mars for future biological exploration. After midcourse maneuver the spacecraft also met these same biological contamination constraints. The aiming point × in figure 8 was selected in a region considered

TABLE 1   Scientific experiments and principal investigators

Experiment	Weight (lb)	Power (w)	Purpose	Principal investigator
magnetometer	7·50	7·30	measure magnitude and other characteristics of the planetary and interplanetary magnetic fields	E. J. Smith Jet Propulsion Laboratory
ionization chamber	2·71	0·46	measure charged-particle intensity and distribution in interplanetary space and in the vicinity of the planet	H. V. Neher California Institute of Technology
cosmic-dust detector	2·10	0·20	measure momentum distribution, density, and direction of cosmic dust	W. M. Alexander Goddard Space Flight Center
solar-plasma probe	6·41	2·65	measure the very-low-energy charged-particle flux from the Sun	H. S. Bridge Massachusetts Institute of Technology
trapped-radiation detector	2·20	0·35	measure intensity and direction of low-energy particles	J. A. Van Allen State University of Iowa
cosmic-ray telescope	2·58	0·60	measure direction and energy spectrum of protons and alpha particles	J. A. Simpson University of Chicago
occulation	—	—	obtain data relating to scale height and pressure in the atmosphere of Mars	A. Kliore Jet Propulsion Laboratory
television	11·28	8·00	obtain pictures of Mars two orders of magnitude better than those obtained from Earth	R. B. Leighton California Institute of Technology

85 ft

210 ft

FIGURE 7   Radio telescope antennae of NASA's deep space network

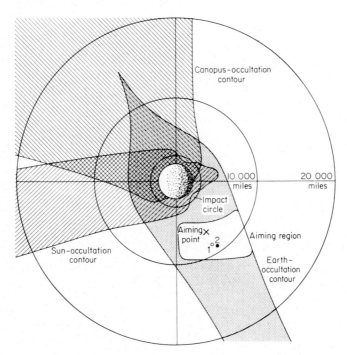

FIGURE 8   *Mariner IV* aiming plot with constraints

optimum for scientific exploration. It also met the spacecraft operating constraints of being outside the regions where the Sun and Canopus are occulted by the planet. At encounter the spacecraft appeared to pass some 500 miles farther away from the planet Mars (2 in figure 8) than the interplanetary tracking data had predicted (1 in figure 8). Although this is still unexplained, current beliefs are that it is associated with a corrected value for the astronomical unit together with the effect of forces due to the attitude control system on the spacecraft's trajectory.

On its near-Earth trajectory, *Mariner IV* passed through the magnetosphere at 112° to the Sun–Earth line on the morning side. Because of the movement of the shock

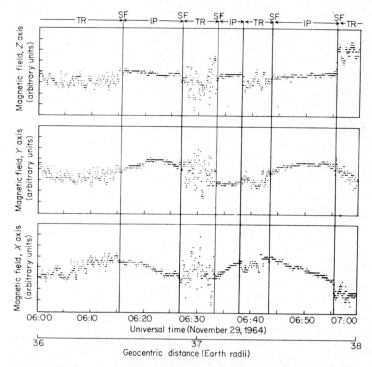

FIGURE 9   Magnetic measurements indicate that *Mariner IV* penetrated the solar wind–magnetosphere shock front seven times

front, associated with the interaction of the 'supersonic' solar wind with the Earth's magnetic field, the probe appeared to penetrate the shock front on seven different occasions (figure 9)[6–8].

On January 28, 1965, the *Mariner IV* spacecraft passed through the Earth's anti-solar point at $3300R_E$ (Earth radii) and at a geocentric angle less than 1° N of the ecliptic plane. The *Explorer XVII* (*Imp III*) satellite had previously detected the Earth's wake in the solar wind at $43R_E$ (figure 10).

This phenomena had been likened to a comet's tail which may extend a significant fraction of an astronomical unit. Others had speculated that the blue clearing phenomena on Mars might be related to the Earth's wake since it appears at opposition. A diligent search was made but no evidence was found in either the particles' or fields' data for the Earth's wake at this relative position in space. Although a significant

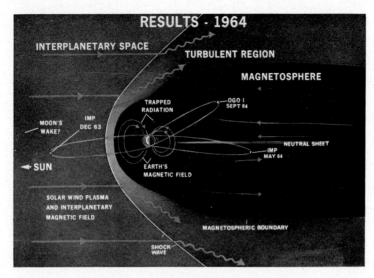

FIGURE 10   The Earth's magnetospheric wake

region in ecliptic longitude was explored, a slight deviation in celestial latitude might have been sufficient to explain the negative results. It is hoped that this will be further investigated on forthcoming *Pioneer* missions[9,10].

On its interplanetary journey, *Mariner IV* experienced six class I and six class II solar flares. In some cases, similar scientific experiments were being flown on Earth satellites. This provided an excellent opportunity to observe solar events simultaneously at two different points in space. In the case of these twelve solar events, some were seen at both places in space while others could be seen on *Mariner* and not on Earth and vice versa. Figure 11 shows an example of the onset phase of a back-scattered solar cosmic-ray event as seen by the University of Chicago cosmic-ray telescope which was pointing in the antisolar direction. The same event was also observed by the University of Chicago experiment on *Imp II*. By analyzing events such as these on widely separated positions around the Sun it should be possible to understand the mechanism of propagation of solar cosmic rays[11-14].

A new type of energetic particle event was reported, namely the impulsive emission of ≥ 40 kev electrons from the Sun (figure 12). These electrons were actually observed on three occasions. They had a steeply falling energy spectrum, isotopic angular distribution and (as seen from Earth) seemed to be associated with radio bursts and X-rays from the Sun. Because of the low relative mass of the electrons compared with protons, this may become a new tool for investigating the interplanetary medium since the electron gyroradius is only $\sim 10^{-6}$ A.U. (see Van Allen and Krimigis[15]).

The cosmic dust detector experienced 235 hits during the *Mariner IV* to Mars mission compared with 2 to 3 hits on the *Mariner II* to Venus mission (figure 13). The sensitivity of the *Mariner IV* instrument was 6×10^{-5} dyn sec. This represents an increase in sensitivity sufficient to place the flux of cosmic dust particles out to 1·2 A.U. at the same level as the *Mariner II* experiment in to 0·72 A.U. Between Earth and Mars at 1·36–1·43 A.U. the flux increased by a factor of 5 to $3·3 \times 10^{-4}$

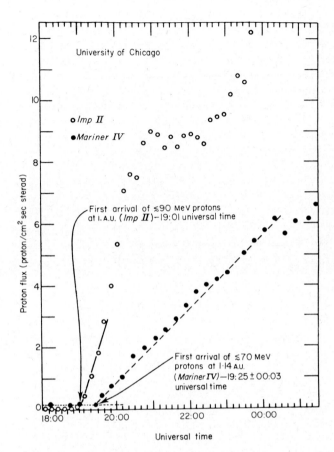

FIGURE 11   Onset phase of February 5, 1965, solar proton event as seen on *Mariner IV*
and *Imp II*

particles/m^2 sec (π sterad). The flux then decreased with increasing radial distance
from the Sun with no enhancement in flux observed in the vicinity of Mars. It has
been suggested that the peak flux represents the true interplanetary rate and that
the lower values represent the effect of the gravitational field of the planets sweeping
out the dust particles[16].

The encounter geometry is indicated in figure 14. The spacecraft experienced a
16·5° deflection in its trajectory owing to the gravitational effect of Mars. The
encounter geometry was selected to provide occultation of the *S*-band telemetry signal
by Mars. This occurred $1\frac{1}{4}$ hours after the time of closest approach. The total phase
change of the radio signal due to entrance into occultation is shown in figure 15. In the
last two minutes before signal extinction, the 2300 megacycle (~ 13 cm) carrier was
first speeded up by the ionosphere and then slowed down by the neutral atmosphere.
The refractive effect of the ionosphere was an 11 cycle (wavelengths) decrease which
made the probe appear to be 75 cm closer to the Earth. The atmosphere refractive
effect amounted to 30 cycles and shifted the apparent position of the probe 2 m away
from the Earth. The extinction of the signal occurred at 50·5° S latitude and 177° E

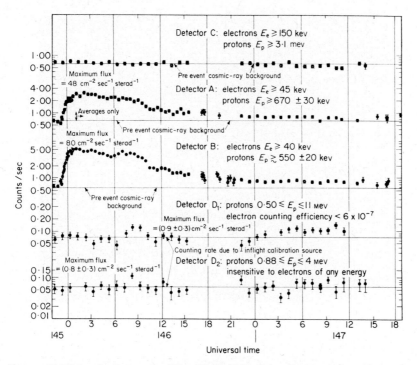

FIGURE 12 Solar electron event of May 25–28, 1965, observed with *Mariner IV* at helio-centric distance of 1·486 A.U., Earth–Sun–probe angle = 40·20°. [From Van Allen and Krimigis[15]]

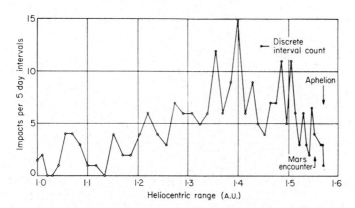

FIGURE 13 *Mariner IV* cosmic dust impacts. [Courtesy of W. M. Alexander]

longitude during late winter at an area known as Electris–Mare Chronium and at 13:00 local time. The surface refractivity was determined to be $3·6 \pm 0·2$ N units. Scale height near the surface was 9 ± 1 km. By means of model atmosphere studies, it is suggested that the Martian atmosphere is mostly CO_2 and has a surface pressure of 4·1–6·0 mb and a near surface temperature of some 180 °K. As figure 16 shows, the day-time ionosphere seems to consist of two layers with a topside plasma scale height of 22 ± 3 km.

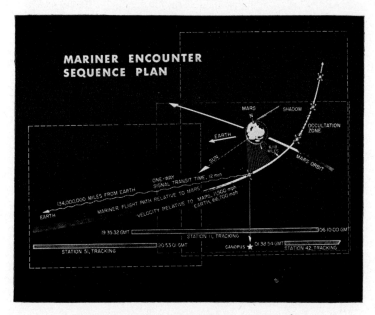

FIGURE 14   *Mariner IV* encounter sequence plan

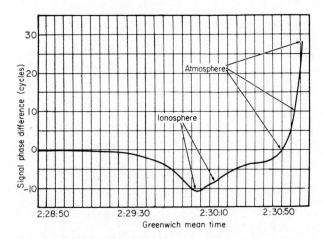

FIGURE 15   Signal phase difference during occultation. [Courtesy of A. Kliore]

The signal came out of occultation at 60° N latitude and 34° W longitude during late summer at a local time of 00:30 at a region known as Mare Acidalium. Unfortunately, owing to a computation error, the spacecraft transponder became locked up with the ground transmitter during the time when the signal was being refracted by the atmosphere (9 sec after occultation). Therefore, the exit-occultation data are less reliable than the entrance data. The surface refractivity was reported to be $4·2 \pm 0·3$ N units. The scale height near the surface was 12 ± 1 km. The indications are that the surface pressure is some 3 mb higher over the exit region (7·5–9·7 mb), with a near-surface temperature of some 240 °K. However, no night-time ionosphere

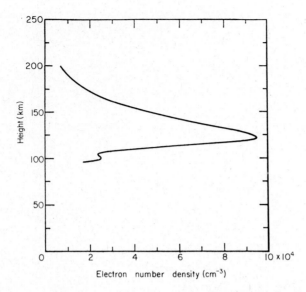

FIGURE 16 Electron number density profile of the Martian ionosphere

was detected and an upper limit[17-20] on the electron density for the night-time ionosphere is $<4 \times 10^3$ electrons/cm³.

The radius of Mars at entrance occultation (50·5° S latitude) was determined to be 3384 ± 3 km. At exit occultation (60° N latitude) it was 3379 ± 4 km.

By study of the *Mariner IV* trajectory a new value for the ratio of the mass of the Sun to the mass of Mars was determined. It is 3 098 600 ± 600. (This is based upon $GM_{Sun} = 0.132 711 41 \times 10^{12}$ km³/sec² (see Null[21]).)

The particles' and fields' experiments did not detect the presence of Martian radiation belts at 3·9 Mars radii or any effect of the interplanetary data which has definitely been attributed to the planet. An anomaly in the magnetic field, which occurred just after the time of closest approach to Mars, has not been explained. This places an upper limit on the magnetic moment of Mars at 0·1 % of that of the Earth and probably <0·03 %. This implies some rather interesting possibilities, namely that the solar wind impinges directly on the Martian atmosphere and that the production of secondary particles by high-energy cosmic rays occurs below the surface of the planet[22-24].

One of the objectives of the television experiment was to obtain photographs of Mars at a resolution two orders of magnitude better than the best photographic resolution obtained on Earth. This has been likened to the improvement Galileo obtained when he looked at the Moon with his telescope compared with the naked eye.

Figure 17 is a remarkable photograph showing Mars and the Moon side by side. It is apparent that the whole disk of Mars appears to be about the size of a small lunar crater. Mars is actually twice the diameter of the Moon but it is so much farther away (31 × 10⁶ km).

Figure 18 is one of the best photographs of Mars ever taken (at the 1939 opposition). Figure 19 is one of the best pictures taken of the same side of Mars, but at the 1965 opposition.

FIGURE 17   Occultation of Mars by the Moon

M39 0727 R2159

FIGURE 18   One of the best photographs ever taken of Mars (1939) M39 0727 R2159. Explanation of identification: sample M39 0727 R2519: M, planet; 39, year; 07, month; 27, day (universal time); R, spectral region; 2159, universal time hour. [Courtesy of the Lowell Observatory]

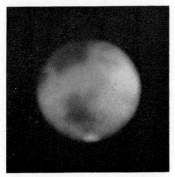

FIGURE 19   One of the best photographs taken of the same side of Mars during the 1965 opposition M65 0309 Y0652. [Courtesy of Lowell Observatory]

M65 0309 Y0652

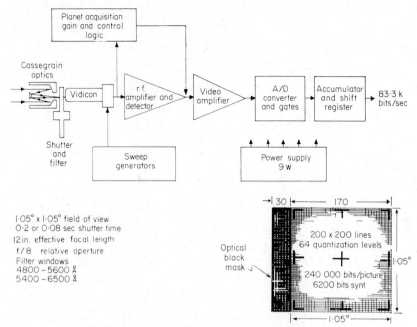

1·05° x 1·05° field of view
0·2 or 0·08 sec shutter time
12 in. effective focal length
f/8 relative aperture
Filter windows
4800 – 5600 Å
5400 – 6500 Å

FIGURE 20   *Mariner IV* television simplified schematic diagram.
24 sec read out, 24 sec erasure and prepare

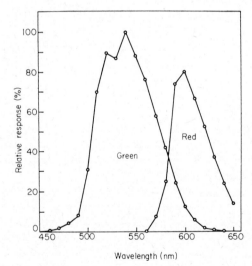

FIGURE 21   Relative vidicon spectral response with either of the two filters in place

An outline of the *Mariner IV* television system is shown in figure 20. A slow-scan vidicon tube of the electrostatic deflection type (in order to save weight) is at the 12 in. focal length of a Cassegrainian f/8 reflecting telescope system. The field of view is 1·05° × 1·05°. A filter wheel containing alternating pairs of two different color (red, green) filters is inserted in the optical system. The overall spectral response with each filter is shown in figure 21. A picture is taken every 48 sec using a different filter.

However, only two out of three pictures are stored on the spacecraft tape recorder for subsequent transmission back to Earth. Thus the picture filtering sequence is red–green–green–red, etc. The image on the surface of the vidicon (0·22 in. × 0·22 in.) is scanned and subsequently reproduced as 200 lines, each line containing 200 discrete elements of picture information. The light intensity of each element is digitized as 64 different shades of gray requiring 6 bits. The number 63 corresponds to black and 0 denotes white. Thus there are more than 240 000 bits picture (figure 22). The final surface resolution varies from picture to picture but is about 3 km.

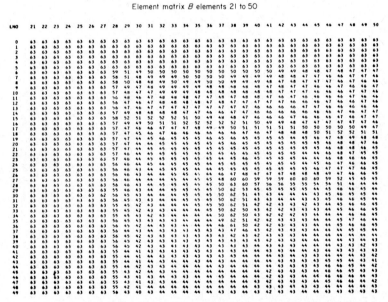

Figure 22   Data matrix of upper left-hand corner of picture 11

Twenty-one pictures plus 22 lines of an additional picture were recorded and transmitted back to Earth. The plan of pictures on the surface of Mars is shown in figure 23. It would have been desirable to photograph an area in Mars where canal-like markings have been consistently reported as well as the feature Syrtis Major. However, from an operational point of view, it was deemed necessary that the encounter occur when Mars was over the Goldstone tracking station in California because NASA's most powerful transmitter was located there, together with the fact that project support at the Jet Propulsion Laboratory was more accessible. Since Mars and the Earth have almost the same period of rotation, it was not possible under our mission constraints to photograph the more interesting side of the planet. An attempt was made to photograph Triverium Charontus which has shown some interesting radar anomalies as seen from Earth, but this did not materialize.

It should be noted that the subsolar point is just to the right of picture number 3. Because of the high Sun angle, it is not to be expected that surface features should show up in any great detail. Because only a limited range in data numbers representing different shades of gray appeared in any one picture, the pictures were subsequently enhanced by expanding the limited range in data numbers to cover the entire dynamic

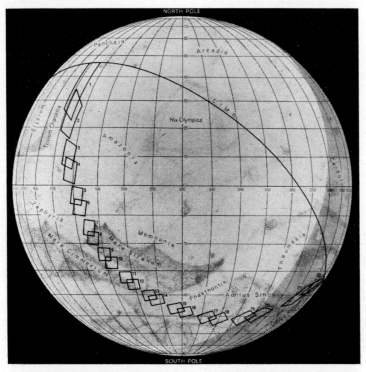

FIGURE 23   Plan of the *Mariner IV* pictures on the Martian surface

range of the picture. This was done on a digital computer and had the effect of making the relatively dark areas appear as shadows and relatively light areas appear as frost. Therefore, extreme care must be used in interpreting these pictures, and referral back to the numeric data print-out is suggested.

Three versions of picture number 1, taken with a red filter, are shown in figure 24. It was fortunate that the limb of the planet was captured in this picture. Surprisingly enough, the 'black sky' appeared to be more than half as bright as the surface of the planet. This and the cloud-like structure appearing where one would expect to see black space have produced several theories, but are still unexplained. If the 'clouds' are real features, they must be at an altitude of 100 km.

Picture number 2, shown in figure 25, was taken with a green filter. A considerable area of overlap with picture number 1 can be discerned.

Picture number 7, shown in figure 26, is the first picture to show crater-like features. They are estimated to be 10–40 km in diameter.

Picture number 9, shown in figure 27, contains two craters, 30 km in diameter, one having a central peak. Many smaller craters are also visible.

The most significant picture is number 11, shown in figure 28. It was taken with a green filter. The largest crater is 150 km in diameter. A linear feature can be detected extending across the picture from the lower left and through the center to the right edge. Other craters shown range in size from 5–70 km in diameter.

Picture number 13, shown in figure 29, shows a change in elevation of 4000 m, which may be a very large crater.

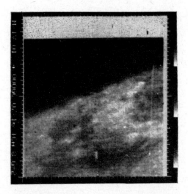

 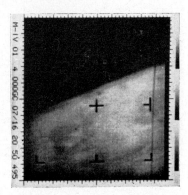

FIGURE 24   Picture 1. Viewed with data block at left, north is at top. Sun is 25° from the zenith, from the southeast in the photo. Time taken, 5:18:33 p.m. PDT, July 14, 1965; slant range, 10 500 miles; area covered, along the limb about 410 miles, from limb to edge of the photo about 800 miles; location (picture center), 35° N latitude, 172° E longitude; map description, bright region between Trivium Charontis and Propontus II Phlegra, a bright region, is on the limb; filter, orange; overlap, lower right corner overlaps picture number 2. Remarks: top frame, most recent intermediate step of data processing, including contrast enhancement factor of two and fiducial marks removed; lower left frame, raw picture; lower right frame, with preliminary processing as released Thursday, July 15, 1965

Picture 14, figure 30, shows what is really believed to be frost on the rims of craters.

A selection of the remainder of pictures is shown in figures 31–34. Here the Sun angle ranged from 66° to >90° from the zenith, and shadows should have appeared. Again, for reasons which are unknown at this time, some anomalous light was scattered into the camera, and little detail can be discerned.

The twenty-one pictures covered less than 1 % of the surface of Mars, and on these pictures some 70 craters can be detected. If one assumes the rest of the Martian surface has an equivalent density of crater population, then 10 000 craters may be assumed to exist on its surface. No sharp features are observed. Slopes up to 10° can be detected. The rims of the craters rise to about 100 m above the surrounding surface and have depths many hundreds of meters below the rims. The largest change in elevation is 4000 m. No evidence of mountain chains or other evidence of internal stress and deformation is observed. This, together with the lack of an appreciable magnetic

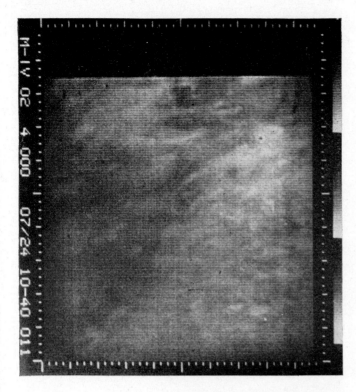

FIGURE 25 Picture 2. Viewed with data block at left, north is at the top. Sun is 20° from the zenith, from the southeast in the photo. Time taken, 5:19:21 p.m. PDT, July 14, 1965; slant range, 10100 miles; area covered, east–west 290 miles, north–south 530 miles; location, 27° N latitude, 174° E longitude; map description, bright region northeast of Trivium Charontis; filter, green; overlap, upper left corner overlaps picture number 1. Remarks: the picture shown has a contrast enhancement factor of two

FIGURE 26 Picture 7. Viewed with data block at left, north is at top. Sun is 29° from the zenith, from the north in the photo. Time taken, 5:25:45 p.m. PDT, July 14, 1965; slant range, 8400 miles; area covered, east–west 180 miles, north–south 180 miles; location, 13° S latitude, 186° E longitude; map description, bright region in southeastern Zephyria, near Mare Sirenum; filter green; contrast enhancement factor, two

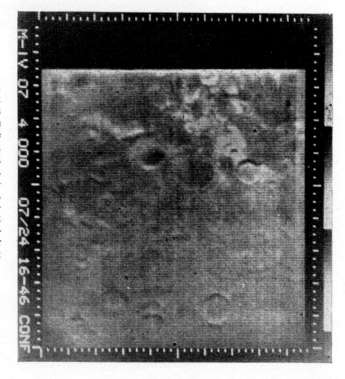

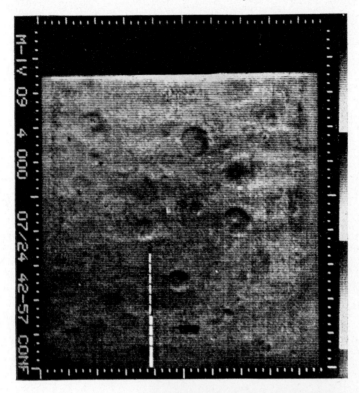

FIGURE 27 Picture 9. Viewed with data block at left, north is at top. Sun is 38° from the zenith, from the north in the photo. Time taken, 5:28: 09 p.m. PDT, July 14, 1965; slant range, 8100 miles; area covered, east–west 170 miles, north–south 160 miles; location, 23° S latitude, 191° E longitude; map description, Mare Sirenum, bordering on Atlantis in the southwest corner of the frame; filter, orange; contrast enhancement factor, four

FIGURE 28 Picture 11. Viewed with data block at left, north is at top. Sun is 47° from the zenith, from the north in the photo. Time taken, 5:30:33 p.m. PDT, July 14, 1965; slant range, 7800 miles; area covered, east–west 170 miles, north–south 150 miles; location, 31° S latitude, 197° E longitude; map description, Atlantis, between Mare Sirenum and Mare Cimmerium; filter, green; contrast enhancement factor, four

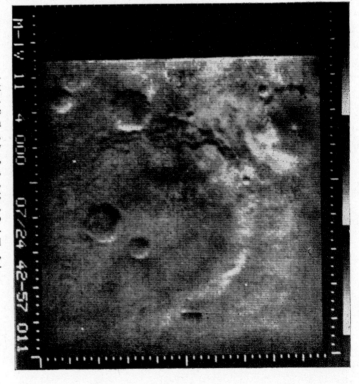

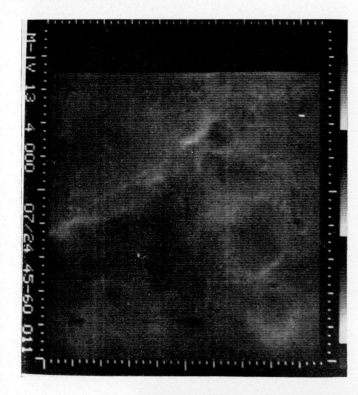

FIGURE 29 Picture 13. Viewed with data block at left, north is at top. Sun is 57° from the zenith, from the north in the photo. Time taken, 5:32:57 p.m. PDT, July 14, 1965; slant range, 7600 miles; area covered, east–west 170 miles, north–south 140 miles; location, 39° S latitude, 205° E longitude; map description, border between Mare Cimmerium to the north and the bright region Phaethontis; filter, orange; overlap, lower right corner overlaps picture number 14; contrast enhancement factor, four

FIGURE 30 Picture 14. Viewed with data block at left, north is at top. Sun is 60° from the zenith, from the north in the photo. Time taken, 5:33:45 p.m. PDT, July 14, 1965; slant range, 7600 miles; area covered, east–west 170 miles, north–south 140 miles; location, 41° S latitude, 208° E longitude; map description, bright region, north-western Phaethontis; filter, green; overlap, upper left corner overlaps picture number 13

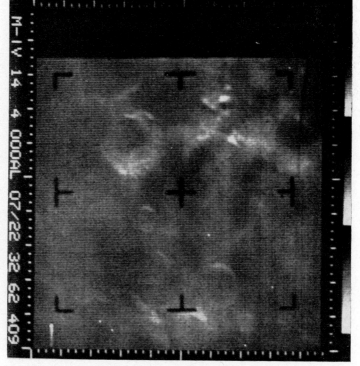

M.E.—14

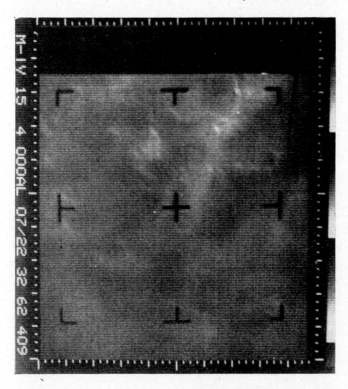

FIGURE 31 Picture 15. Viewed with data block at left, north is at top. Sun is 66° from the zenith, from the north in the photo. Time taken, 5:35:21 p.m. PDT, July 14, 1965; slant range, 7500 miles; area covered, east–west 180 miles, north–south 140 miles; location, 45° S latitude, 216° E longitude, map description, bright region is Phaethontis; filter, green; overlap, lower right corner overlaps picture number 16; contrast enhancement factor, two

FIGURE 32 Picture 16. Viewed with data block at left, north is at top. Sun is 69° from the zenith, from the north in the photo. Time taken, 5:36:09 p.m. PDT, July 14, 1965; slant range, 7500 miles; area covered, east–west 190 miles, north–south 140 miles; location, 47° S latitude, 221° E longitude; map description, bright region in Phaethontis, near Aonius Sinus; filter, orange; overlap, upper left corner overlaps picture number 15; contrast enhancement factor, two

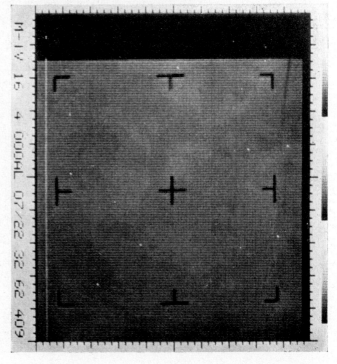

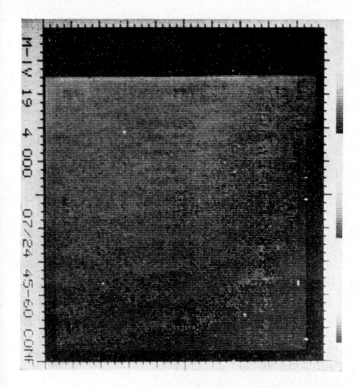

FIGURE 33 Picture 19. Viewed with data block at left, north is at the upper right. Sun is 88° from the zenith, from the northwest in the photo. Time taken, 5:40:09 p.m. PDT, July 14, 1965; slant range, 7500 miles; area covered, northeast–southwest 240 miles, northwest–southeast 150 miles; location, 51° S latitude, 253° E longitude; map description, dark region in Aonius Sinus, terminator in eastern corner of frame; filter, green; overlap, lower right corner overlaps picture number 20 in the terminator region; contrast enhancement factor, four

FIGURE 34 Picture 20. This frame is almost entirely beyond the terminator. Its upper left corner overlaps picture number 19 in the terminator region

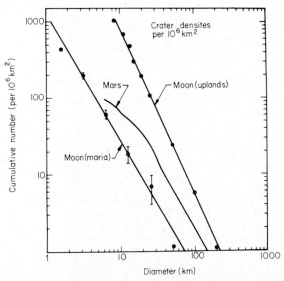

FIGURE 35   Mars crater densities against diameters. [Courtesy of R. Leighton]

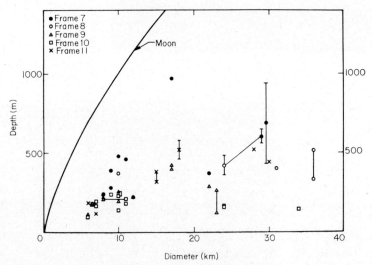

FIGURE 36   Mars crater depths against diameters. [Courtesy of R. Leighton]

moment and low atmospheric pressure, suggest that the Martian surface is a very ancient one. Estimates depending on the assumed meteoritic infall rate suggest that the surface is hundreds of millions to several billions of years old[25].

A crater distribution curve is shown in figure 35. The distribution is very similar to that of the Moon with the exception that the number of small craters is less prevalent presumably owing to the fact that Mars has an atmosphere. A distribution curve of crater depths is shown in figure 36[26].

On October 1, 1965, the post-encounter phase of the *Mariner IV* mission was terminated. As is apparent from figure 5, the beam of the high-gain antenna was about to pass outside of the range of the antennae located on Earth. Upon command from the

Earth, the spacecraft transmitter was switched over to the omnidirectional antenna to facilitate reacquisition in 1967. During 1967, it is possible that six months of continuous interplanetary data may be received since the spacecraft will approach within 47×10^6 km of the Earth.

After October 1965, the signal of *Mariner IV* was monitored once each month. By integration it was possible to learn that the spacecraft carrier was still being transmitted and telemetry sidebands were observed (figure 37). On April 1, 1966, the spacecraft reached superior conjunction and passed about $\frac{1}{2}°$ above the solar disk. Using the new 210′ DSIF radio telescope (figure 7) at Goldstone, California, the effects

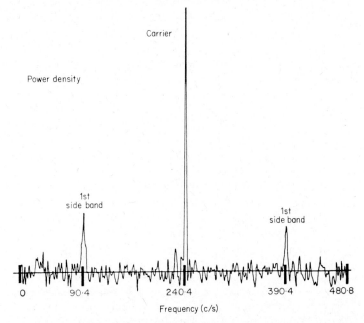

FIGURE 37   *Mariner IV* signal detected on December 1, 1965, when the spacecraft was beyond the communication range with Earth. Total power, -177.7 dʙm in 480·8 c/s band; carrier power, 179·9 dʙm; integration, 83 min; RX system noise temperature, 36·8 °ᴋ; TX frequency, 2 297 588 078 cycles/atomic sec

of solar coronal occultation were observed. The results of this experiment will be reported in the scientific literature[27]. It has also been possible to update periodically the Canopus cone angles by command from Earth in order to prepare for the 1967 reacquisition. Starting on May 3, 1966, telemetry was again received, but it had a high bit error rate (10%) owing to the lack of sufficient communication signal level margin. However, it is still possible to extract useful scientific data. It is also possible to monitor the operating conditions of the spacecraft.

On October 1, 1965, the *Mariner IV* spacecraft had already exceeded its design lifetime. How much longer it will continue to function cannot be determined. By the latter part of 1968 it is expected that the attitude control gas will have been exhausted, and the spacecraft will probably lose its attitude control stabilization.

For review articles on *Mariner IV* the reader is referred elsewhere[28,29]. For a complete description of *Mariner IV*, it is suggested that elements of the *Mariner Mars 1964 Project Report* be consulted[30–37].

References

1. D. Schneiderman, J. N. James, and G. A. Reiff, 'Recent *Mariner* spacecraft design and flight', *Astronaut. Acta*, **2**, 83–96 (1965).
2. J. R. Scull, 'Guidance and control of the *Mariner* planetary spacecraft', *IFAC Symp. on Automatic Control in the Peaceful Uses of Space, Norway, 1965*.
3. G. S. Davis and G. W. Meisenholder, 'The *Mariner IV* Canopus sensor', *Intern. Astronaut. Congr., 16th, Athens, 1965*.
4. T. J. Donlin and J. C. Randall, 'A solar vane actuation system for spacecraft and attitude control', *ASME Conf., LaFayette, Indiana, 1964*.
5. F. L. Schutz, 'The *Mariner IV* science subsystem', *Intern. Elec. Electron. Engrs. Conf., Miami, 1965*.
6. P. J. Coleman Jr., E. J. Smith, L. Davis Jr., and D. E. Jones, 'Measurements of magnetic fields in the vicinity of the magnetosphere and in interplanetary space', *Space Research VI, Proc. Intern. Space Sci. Symp., Mar del Plata, Argentina, 1965*, North-Holland, Amsterdam, to be published.
7. G. L. Siscoe, L. Davis Jr., E. J. Smith, P. J. Coleman Jr., and D. E. Jones, 'Hydromagnetic waves in the transition region: *Mariner IV*', to be published.
8. J. A. Van Allen, S. M. Krimigis, and L. A. Frank, 'Observations with University of Iowa equipment on *Mariner IV*, November 1964–February 1965', *Univ. Iowa Rept. No. 65-5* (1965).
9. J. A. Van Allen, 'Absence of 40 kev electrons in the Earth's magnetospheric tail at 3300 Earth radii', *J. Geophys. Res.*, **70**, 4731–9 (1965).
10. J. A. Van Allen, 'Further remarks on the absence of a very extended magnetospheric tail', *J. Geophys. Res.*, **71**, 2406–7 (1966).
11. J. J. O'Gallagher and J. A. Simpson, 'The interplanetary propagation of solar flare particles simultaneously observed by Earth satellites and the *Mariner IV* space probe', *Bull. Am. Phys. Soc.*, **11**, 411 (1966).
12. C. Y. Fan, G. Gloeckler, and J. A. Simpson, 'Protons and helium nuclei within interplanetary magnetic regions which co-rotate with the Sun', *Proc. Intern. Conf. on Cosmic Rays, 9th*, Institute of Physics and Physical Society, London, 1966, pp. 109–11.
13. J. A. Simpson and J. J. O'Gallagher, 'Proton and alpha particle studies on *Mariner IV*', *Trans. Am. Geophys. Union*, **46**, 15 (1965).
14. J. J. O'Gallagher and J. A. Simpson, 'The heliocentric intensity gradients of cosmic ray protons and helium during minimum solar modulation', *Enrico Fermi Institute for Nuclear Studies Preprint No. 66-112*.
15. J. A. Van Allen and S. M. Krimigis, 'Impulsive emissions of ∼40 kev electrons from the Sun', *J. Geophys. Res.*, **70**, 5737 (1965).
16. W. M. Alexander and C. W. McCracken, 'Zodiacal dust: measurements by *Mariner IV*', *Science*, **149**, 1240–1 (1965).
17. A. Kliore, D. L. Cain, G. S. Levy, V. R. Eshleman, G. Fjeldbo, and F. D. Drake, 'Occultation experiment: results of the first direct measurement of Mars's atmosphere and ionosphere, *Science*, **149**, 1243–8 (1965).
18. D. L. Cain, A. J. Kliore, and G. S. Levy, 'The *Mariner IV* occultation experiment: summary of data and reduction methods', *AIAA Aerospace Sci. Meeting, 3rd, New York, 1966*.
19. A. Kliore, D. L. Cain, and G. S. Levy, 'Radio occultation measurement of the Martian atmosphere over dark and illuminated regions with the *Mariner IV* space probe', *Joint Intern. Astron. Union and COSPAR Symp. on Moon and Planets, Vienna, 1966*.
20. G. Fjeldbo, W. C. Fjeldbo, and V. R. Eshleman, 'Models for the atmosphere of Mars based on the *Mariner IV* occultation experiment', *J. Geophys. Res.*, **71**, 2307–16 (1966).
21. G. Null, '*Mariner IV* astrodynamical constants', *Jet Propulsion Lab. Tech. Rept. No. 32-881*.
22. P. J. Coleman Jr., L. Davis Jr., E. J. Smith, and D. E. Jones, 'Magnetic measurements near Mars', *Science*, **149**, 1241–2 (1965).

23. J. A. Van Allen, L. A. Frank, S. M. Krimigis, and H. K. Hills, 'Absence of Martian radiation belts and implications thereof', *Science*, **149**, 1228–33 (1965).
24. J. J. O'Gallagher and J. A. Simpson, 'Search for trapped electrons and a magnetic moment at Mars by *Mariner IV*', *Science*, **169**, 1233–9 (1965).
25. R. B. Leighton, B. C. Murray, R. P. Sharp, J. D. Allen, and R. K. Sloan, '*Mariner IV* photography of Mars—initial results', *Science*, **149**, 627–30 (1965).
26. R. B. Leighton, 'The photographs from *Mariner IV*', *Sci. Am.*, **214**, 54–68 (1966).
27. R. M. Goldstein and others, 'The superior conjunction of *Mariner IV*', *Jet Propulsion Lab. Tech. Rept. No.* 32-1092.
28. 'Report from Mars: *Mariner IV* 1964–65', United States Government Printing Office, Washington, D.C.
29. O. W. Nicks, 'A review of the *Mariner* results', *Space Research VII, Proc. Intern. Space Sci. Symp., Vienna, 1966*, to be published.
30. 'From project inception through midcourse maneuver', *Mariner Mars 1964 Project Report, Mission and Spacecraft Development, Jet Propulsion Lab. Tech. Rept. No.* 32-740, Vol. I.
31. *Mariner Mars 1964 Project Report, Mission and Spacecraft Development, Jet Propulsion Lab. Tech. Rept. No.* 32-740, Vol. II, Appendixes.
32. *Mariner Mars 1964 Project Report, Mission Operations, Jet Propulsion Lab. Tech. Rept. No.* 32-881.
33. *Mariner Mars 1964 Project Report, Spacecraft Performance and Analysis, Jet Propulsion Lab. Tech. Rept. No.* 32-882.
34. *Mariner Mars 1964 Project Report, Scientific Experiments, Jet Propulsion Lab. Tech. Rept. No.* 32-883.
35. *Mariner Mars 1964 Project Report, Television Experiment, Investigators' Report, Jet Propulsion Lab. Tech. Rept. No.* 32-884, Part I.
36. *Mariner Mars 1964 Project Report, Television Experiment, Picture Element Matrices, Jet Propulsion Lab. Tech Rept. No.* 32-884, Part II.
37. *Tracking and Data Acquisition Support for Mariner Mars 1964, Cruise to Post Encounter Phase, Jet Propulsion Lab. Tech. Manual No.* 33-239, Vol. II.

5

L. B. RONCA

Lunar-Planetary Research Branch
Space Physics Laboratory
Air Force Cambridge Research Laboratories
L. G. Hanscom Field
Bedford, Massachusetts, U.S.A.

Surface conditions of Mars as suggested by *Mariner* photographs

Because of the absence of characteristic silicate emission spectra in the middle infra-red, it has been suggested[1] that less than 20% of the surface materials of Mars are silicates. Polarization measurements[2] indicate that the surface material is mainly limonitic ($FeO(OH).n\,H_2O + Fe_2O_3.n\,H_2O$). Also, limonite matches in brightness and color index the surface of Mars[3]. More recently other researchers[4,5] found correspondence between limonitic material or weathered rocks and the optical properties of the Martian surface. Also it was recognized[6] that the yellow haze has the same photometric and polarimetric properties as very fine dust composed of the same hydrated iron oxide.

The evidence in favor of a limonite-like cover on Mars is convincing, although it is difficult to understand the nature and origin of such a cover. The discussion can be presented by dividing it into two parts: (i) the origin of the iron, and (ii) its hydration and oxidation.

The iron could be original to the planet, being part of the silicate minerals present on the surface. It is possible that the material near the surface of Mars is richer in iron than surface material on the Earth. Observations and theoretical calculations indicate that Mars has a small nucleus or no nucleus at all, indicated by the absence of a detectable magnetic field, as shown by *Mariner IV*. In this book there are several chapters discussing this point. Anderson and Phinney's thermal calculations (see section III, chapter 3 of this book) show that Mars is probably undifferentiated, and Bullen's calculations (see section III, chapter 4 of this book) based on the moment of inertia criterion show that the core is small or absent and that the surface density could be very high, as much as $3 \cdot 8$ g/cm^3. As originally proposed by Urey[7] it is generally accepted that a planet's core has grown through geological time by slow migration of the iron through the body of the planet toward its center. If this differentiation has not occurred in the case of Mars, it is not surprising that iron could be present on the surface in higher amounts than on the surface of the Earth.

Another possible source of iron is meteoritic impact, which could be important for Mars, owing to its nearness to the asteroidal belt[8]. It will be shown below, however, that it is not necessary to have material of high iron content in order to have a limonitic covering. Rocks having an iron content similar to that of Earth's ferric igneous rocks would suffice.

The problem of oxidation and hydration of iron appears to be more difficult to account for. On the Earth, limonite is not an endogenous mineraloid, but a product of the interaction between endogenous minerals and the hydroatmosphere, that is, it is a result of weathering. The situation could be different on Mars, but this appears unlikely, as the thermodynamic properties of limonite are uncompatible with any magmatic environment. On the Earth, red soils consisting of limonite and limonite-stained mineral particles are generally found in hot and humid areas of tropical, or almost tropical, climate. If limonitic deposits are extensive on Mars, this could indicate a past climatic environment which was drastically different. However, this is not necessarily so, and *Mariner* photographs bring some doubts to this possibility.

Mariner IV photographs furnished pictures of Mars with a ground resolution of a few kilometers. A recent study of Tiros and Nimbus photographs of the Earth at the same resolution[9] shows that hydroerosional patterns are discernible at this resolution. None are found on *Mariner*'s photographs. Although *Mariner IV* photographs present only approximately 1 % of the total Martian surface, they cut across the parallels and are very likely to be typical of the whole surface.

The postulated water-rich atmosphere of Mars, if it existed, must have been present before the formation of the craters. However, if the formation of a red soil occurred *before* the craters, the reworking of the surface during cratering would have almost completely obliterated the weathered layer on the surface[10]. On geological grounds[11] the difficulty of preserving a limonitic deposit in an aeolian environment was pointed out. The hypothesis is presented that, rather than extensive deposits of limonite, the Martian surface is covered by a thin weathered coating. Such coating of limonitic material is consistent with both spectroscopic and polarimetric evidence. Aeolian erosion could strip some of the limonite and transport it as very fine dust. While in suspension in the atmosphere this dust could occupy great volumes, but it seems unlikely that it could be significant as a sedimentary deposit.

Could the present Martian atmosphere produce a weathered coating in the time elapsed since cratering? The Martian atmosphere is very tenuous, perhaps as low as five millibars, and the water content is quite low. However, the presence of liquid water on Mars, for a few hours a day in the interstices of rock fragments and powders, is not to be excluded. The atmospheric environment on the surface seems to be near or above the triple point of water, thus indicating that temporary microenvironments may exist where liquid films of water can exist. It has been speculated[12] that the low amount of water measured spectroscopically in the atmosphere does not necessarily imply a total absence of liquid water. It could be the result of the low night temperatures. During the night, excess water above the vapor pressure will crystallize, while in the day there will be only a limited time to reestablish equilibrium between water and vapor. The ground, heated directly from the Sun, could have liquid water in the interstices or a water-saturated pore structure, but it must be remembered that the presence of liquid water does not seem to be essential for a chemical alteration of the surface.

Most of the research done on the subject of weathering has been for environments in which liquid water is readily available. Only recently was it recognized that weathering does occur in below-freezing environments. Until more data are available from Mars, the best place to look for clues to deduce Martian weathering is the frigid areas on the surface of our planet. Great care must be exercised in the comparison, however, as the conditions of terrestrial frigid areas are by no means identical with those of the Martian environment. Laboratory experiments would give little information, as the factor time, perhaps billions of years, is practically impossible to scale down satisfactorily.

The fundamental property of minerals which ultimately produces weathering is adsorption. It is in the adsorbed water layer on the exposed surface that the chemical processes take place. Briefly, the process can be simplified as follows. At the surface of a crystal unsatisfied valences will react with water molecules. Hydration and hydrolysis occur, whereby strong bases, such as potassium, calcium, and magnesium, are removed and hydroxyl ions replace oxygen anions. When first formed the new compounds may be amorphous, but soon orientation occurs and phyllosilicate clay minerals are formed. At the same time, or shortly after, the iron present is completely or partially converted to iron hydroxide, which will age into the complex mineraloid called limonite.

In an environment where liquid water is extremely scarce or nonexistent, chemical weathering is strongly reduced but not completely absent, as shown by Antarctica. Several areas of Antarctica are permanently devoid of liquid water and are subjected to an atmosphere very low in water vapor. Weathering effects, in the form of thin superficial coatings, have been discovered five degrees from the South Pole, at 3000 m elevation. The possibility is small that this weathered coating was formed in preglacial times, as erosion is unlikely to have permitted the exposure of the same surface for about one million years, the approximate minimum age of the glaciations in Antarctica[13]. The fundamental difference between the 'temperate' weathering and this 'cold' weathering appears to exist in the slowness of the leaching in the latter case. A complete suite of new minerals, properly called cryogenic minerals, may be formed, as hydrated chlorides of sodium and magnesium, hydrated carbonates, and hydrated sulfates, mixed with ferruginous material. Fragmentation increases the surface energy and considerably helps the process. In a below-freezing environment, where only water vapor is present, the adsorption layer will develop more slowly, but it will develop eventually. The chemical processes which take place will follow the general law, according to which a drop in temperature reduces the velocity of the chemical reactions. On the other hand, there are other aspects of the chemistry of weathering which seem to be encouraged by a drop in temperature. Tyutyunov[14] shows that the entropy and enthalpy of the system increase and that the thickness of the water film adsorbed from water vapor increases with decreasing temperature. Also he calculates that the net intensity of the process of cation exchange does not depend on temperature, and that oxidation–reduction reactions become stronger with a drop in temperature. Many weathering processes need energy to proceed, the source of which is generally the Sun. Tyutyunov[14] calculates theoretically that the solar energy is actually utilized most effectively at a temperature below zero degrees Celsius. When the area of the surface of a crystal increases sharply during fragmentation, the physiochemical properties of the system become more active. Thus the cratering process on Mars, which probably produced intensive fragmentation, would increase the chemical weathering.

The above considerations were obtained by observations made on weathering in the frigid areas of the Earth. There is no reason why they should not be also valid for the surface of Mars. Owing to the alien character of the Martian environment, other processes may be helping chemical weathering. Urey[7] discussed photodissociation of water molecules which could produce oxygen. Such a process would enhance weathering of all exposed rocks. There may be other processes still unsuspected.

In conclusion, *Mariner IV* photographs show the absence of large hydroerosional patterns on the surface of Mars, thus casting doubts on the hypothesis of past wet conditions on that planet. Observations on frigid areas of the Earth and theoretical considerations indicate that, even in an environment where liquid water is rare or absent and water vapor is the predominant phase, weathering can take place. A collection of weathered Antarctic rocks has been gathered and work is in progress to determine their spectral and polarimetric characteristics, and to determine if the postulated model corresponds to the data available from Mars.

References

1. W. M. Sinton and J. Strong, *Astrophys. J.*, **131**, 459 (1960).
2. A. Dollfus, 'Polarization studies of planets', in *Planets and Satellites* (Eds. G. P. Kuiper and B. M. Middlehurst), University of Chicago Press, Chicago, 1961, p. 379.
3. V. V. Sharanov, *Astron. Zh.*, **38**, 459 (1961).
4. C. Sagan, J. P. Phaneuf, and I. Michael, *Icarus*, **4**, 43 (1965).
5. A. B. Binder and D. P. Cruikshank, *Commun. Lunar Planetary Lab., Univ. Ariz.*, **2**, 193 (1964).
6. A. Dollfus, *Ann. Astrophys.*, **28**, 722 (1965).
7. H. C. Urey, *The Planets*, Yale University Press, New Haven, Connecticut, 1952.
8. C. Sagan, *Icarus*, **5**, 102 (1966).
9. S. D. Kilston, R. D. Drummond, and C. Sagan, *Icarus*, **5**, 79 (1966).
10. J. W. Salisbury, *Icarus*, **5**, 291 (1966).
11. R. A. Van Tassel and J. W. Salisbury, *Icarus*, **3**, 264 (1964).
12. C. R. Weston, *Am. Scientist*, **53**, 495 (1965).
13. L. B. Ronca and E. J. Zeller, *Am. J. Sci.*, **263**, 416 (1965).
14. I. A. Tyutyunov, *An Introduction to the Theory of the Formation of Frozen Rocks*, translated from Russian, Macmillan, New York, 1964.

6

A. H. MARCUS
University of Cambridge
England
and
Case Institute of Technology
Cleveland, Ohio, U.S.A.

Statistical theories of lunar and Martian craters

Introduction

The problem of the origin of lunar craters can be investigated in two ways: the right way, and statistically. The right way, in this case, is to examine the craters with the full battery of physical, chemical, and geological techniques by which terrestrial craters can be studied. In the first place this cannot be done at present—photographic and visual observations at great distances furnish virtually all the information we have about lunar craters. In the second place, such evidence might not be conclusive even if it were available, since most lunar craters appear to have been greatly modified after their birth by lava flooding, isostatic compensation, micrometeor erosion, or other internal and external mechanisms. These sometimes drastic modifications could easily conceal clues to the origin of lunar craters, as wind and water erosion, and volcanic-tectonic mechanisms have concealed the origin of many terrestrial craters and ring structures. Perhaps, in view of these difficulties, the statistical approach *is* the right approach.

Many scientists believe that the great majority of lunar craters are of exogenic (meteoroidal impact) origin, and that as far as craters are concerned the Moon is merely an 'impact counter'. Others maintain that most lunar craters are of endogenic (so-called volcanic) origin, which implies that craters are the 'surface boundary conditions' for whatever processes are going on in the lunar interior. The available statistical evidence, which will be described in the next section, definitely favors a modified impact hypothesis which allows for important internal processes (to be described briefly and simply as 'crater-filling activity'). The endogenic hypothesis is not precluded, however, but only because there is no generally acceptable quantitative description of this hypothesis.

Empirical Crater Statistics

Some of the most notable early work in crater statistics was done in Great Britain by MacDonald[1-3] and Young[4, 5]. MacDonald's studies of lunar altitudes and the crater depth–diameter relationship have been greatly improved upon only in the last few years[6]. Young discovered that the number of craters of diameter x is approximately inversely proportional to a certain power of x, say x^{s+1}; in other words, the number $N(>x)/A$ of craters per unit area whose diameters are larger than x is an inverse power law given by (1), with index s. The empirical estimation and theoretical prediction of

$$N(>x)/A = Cx^{-s} \tag{1}$$

C and s have become key problems in crater statistics. MacDonald and Young antici-pated many of the important techniques of modern statistical studies of lunar craters: the separation of continental and mare regions, allowance for the effects of oblitera-tion of small craters by larger ones which form nearby, and allowance for the flooding or filling of craters.

The first valid statistical test of the meteoroidal impact hypothesis was carried out by Arthur[7]. He argued that impact craters must be distributed essentially at random over the lunar surface. The difference between continental and mare regions is prob-ably due to internal causes, however, so these regions were considered separately. He found no reason to reject the hypothesis of randomness of centers of large craters on either continental or mare regions, but he was keenly aware of a limitation on the validity of his procedure, especially on the continents; the obliteration of small craters by large ones which form nearby will change an initially random distribution of crater centers into an apparently clustered distribution. This point has quite properly received a great deal of attention recently, for example by Fielder[8,9] and Marcus[10-12]. Even so, many craters smaller than 10 km in diameter appear to be really clustered, proving that they are of secondary impact or internal origin.

In 1960 four scientists, working independently, used results on terrestrial explosion craters and on the frequency distribution of asteroidal and meteoritic masses to predict the frequency distribution of crater diameters on the lunar maria[13-16]. Their work has been revised and extended by McGillem and Miller[17], Dodd, Salisbury, and Smalley[18], Baldwin[19], and Hartmann[20]. Although their theoretical efforts have not been highly successful, the empirical estimates appear to be quite consistent and of high reliability. For equation (1) they obtain a value of s between 1·95 and 2·12 on continental regions, with C about equal to 0·10 per square kilometer for x in kilo-meters. The mare values of s and C depend on the particular mare chosen, but s varies between 1·54 and 1·78 and C between 10^{-3} and 2×10^{-3} per square kilometer. Their theoretical values of s vary between 2·4 and 2·7, in any case significantly larger than the observed values. These authors correctly attribute the discrepancy in s to the obliteration of small craters by large ones and to the differential loss of small craters as a result of flooding by lava or dust. We deal with these points in a quantita-tive manner in the last two sections.

Up till now we have been discussing craters whose diameters are a kilometer or larger. The *Ranger 7, 8,* and *9* spacecraft, and the Russian *Luna 9* lunar lander, have photographed craters of less than a meter in diameter. So far we have seen statistics only for the *Ranger 7* (see Hartmann[21], Shoemaker[22]). A detailed ana-lysis[23] of the diameter distribution of small craters in Mare Cognitum shows that there are far more of these craters than predicted by analogy with secondary craters from terrestrial explosions. It seems likely that many small lunar craters are of internal origin.

The *Mariner IV* spacecraft showed a heavily cratered, surprisingly Moon-like surface on Mars. More than 70 craters were counted on frames 5 to 14 (see Leighton and others[24]). The craters counted were, however, only those of relatively sharp and pristine appearance; if 'ghost' or 'dimple' type craters had also been counted, the total number might be several times as large. The diameter distribution is roughly two segments of the form of equation (1). For $x > 20$ km Baldwin[25] gives $s = 2.0$, which appears to fit the data better than the value 1·71 proposed by Öpik[26]; the density coefficient C is only about $\frac{1}{7}$ as large as that for continental lunar craters. For $x < 20$ km the curve is much flatter, with $s = 1.0$ and $C = 2.5 \times 10^{-4}$ per square kilometer; this may be in part due to observational loss. The low density and weathered appearance of Martian craters suggests that erosion or crater-filling activity has been active on the Martian surface. If so, we can say nothing about the age of the craters on Mars. The similarity of the diameter distribution to that on the Moon suggests a similar history, that is a high density of presumably impact craters of which many have been lost by obliteration, crater filling, and erosion.

In this brief chapter we have been able to mention only a few of the more important of the 80 or so books and papers presenting empirical statistical studies of craters. We must now turn our attention to theoretical analyses of these data.

A Statistical Theory

The author has developed a statistical theory of the formation and survival of lunar craters[10-12,23,27-30]. The model takes into account the following factors: the randomness in space and time of the birth of primary and secondary craters, the damage or obliteration of older craters by newer ones which form nearby, and the disappearance of craters as a result of filling by dust or lava. The model is specified by the following functions: $p(x)$, the underlying probability density function of the diameter x of newborn craters, $f(t)$, the mean number of primary craters born per unit area per unit time at time t (the rate of crater formation), $a(t)$, the mean volume of crater-filling material per unit area of surface added per unit time at time t (the crater-filling rate), and $H(x)$, the initial floor-to-rim height of a crater of diameter x. It is also assumed that the maximum crater diameter is x_M and the diameter of the smallest observable crater is x_0, and that all craters are initially paraboloidal in shape.

The theory can be very extensively generalized, if desired. The functions $p(x)$ and $H(x)$ can be made time dependent, and the crater-filling rate $a(t)$ can be allowed to depend on the diameter x of the crater. It is also possible to deal with craters of any initial shape, including the possibility of a shape dependent on the size and time of origin of the crater. In this chapter we shall forgo generality in favor of simplicity of presentation.

From the basic model functions we derive two important auxiliary functions. The first is the birthday $t_0(x, t)$ of the oldest x-sized crater not quite completely filled up by time t, which is defined as the solution to equation (2), provided a positive solution

$$H(x) = 2 \int_{t_0(x,t)}^{t} a(u)\, du \qquad (2)$$

t_0 exists; otherwise, $t_0 = 0$, by which convention we mean that at time $t = 0$ the region of interest was entirely free of craters. The factor 2 takes account of the fact that only half as much material is needed to fill up a paraboloidal crater as is needed to fill up a circumscribed rectangular cylinder.

The second function is the average area within which a newborn crater of diameter larger than x must fall in order to completely obliterate a given crater of diameter x. This damage rate is simply given by equation (3). If, as usual, $\Lambda_1(x)$ converges for all

$$\Lambda_1(x) = \int_x^{x_M} \tfrac{1}{4}\pi(y - x)^2 p(y)\, \mathrm{d}y \qquad (3)$$

x_M, we shall choose $x_M = \infty$.

The basic result, for our purposes, is that the expected number of craters per unit area per unit diameter interval at time t, whose diameters are equal to x, is given by the simple formula (4). The function $\xi(x; t)$ is known as the expected number density.

$$\xi(x; t) = \frac{p(x)}{\Lambda_1(x)}\left[1 - \exp\left\{-\Lambda_1(x)\int_{t_0(x,t)}^t f(u)\,\mathrm{d}u\right\}\right] \qquad (4)$$

The expected cumulative number is then simply (5).

$$\langle N(>x)/A\rangle_{\mathrm{av}} = \int_x^\infty \xi(y; t)\, \mathrm{d}y \qquad (5)$$

Information about fluctuations in crater counts can also be extracted from the model, but only with considerable effort. The basic statistical problem is that the formation of a large crater can cause the immediate loss of a random number of smaller previously existing craters. The underlying stochastic model is that of a 'multivariate immigration with multiple death process'. We shall forgo the somewhat lengthy mathematical description of this process (for details see Marcus[12]).

The Meteoroidal Impact Hypothesis

As an application of our statistical theory we shall compute the frequency distribution of crater diameter predicted by the meteoroidal impact hypothesis. Let C with various affixes denote different positive constants. The number of asteroids or meteorites whose mass exceeds m is given by (6), where $0.67 \leqq \gamma_1 \leqq 0.80$ (see Brown[31], Piotrowski[32]).

$$N(>m) = C'm^{-\gamma_1} \qquad (6)$$

The kinetic energy T of a particle of mass m moving with speed v relative to the lunar surface is given by $T = \tfrac{1}{2}mv^2$. An empirical observation from terrestrial explosion crater experiments[33] relating the diameter x of a crater to the weight (energy) W of explosive is (7), where $3.0 < \gamma_2 \leqq 3.4$. If W is proportional to T, and if the distribution

$$x = C''W^{1/\gamma_2} \qquad (7)$$

of v is not too spread out (a sufficient condition[34] is that the integral

$$\int_0^\infty v^{2\gamma_1 - 1} P_v(v)\, \mathrm{d}v$$

is finite, where $P_v(v)$ is the probability density of v), then the initial number of craters of diameter greater than x is given approximately by (8), where (9) holds true and

$$\text{(initial) } N(>x) = C'''x^{-\gamma} \tag{8}$$

$$\gamma = \gamma_1\gamma_2 \tag{9}$$

$2 \cdot 0 < \gamma \le 2 \cdot 7$. The author prefers $\gamma_1 = 0 \cdot 67$, $\gamma_2 = 3 \cdot 4$, and thus $\gamma = 2 \cdot 25$. From equation (8) we obtain (10) and (11). We have chosen the size of the smallest observable crater as $x_0 = 1$ for convenience. This involves no awkward rescaling, since

$$p(x) = \gamma x^{-\gamma - 1} \quad \text{for } 1 \le x < \infty \tag{10}$$

$$= 0 \quad \text{for } x < 1$$

$$\Lambda_1(x) = \pi/\ 2(\gamma - 1)(\gamma - 2)x^{\gamma - 2}\} \tag{11}$$

terrestrial observations of lunar craters have very nearly $x_0 = 1$ km. This derivation of equation (8) has been standard since 1960.

We consider the case where no crater-filling activity has occurred, and thus $t_0(x, t) = 0$. If the cumulative crater-forming activity

$$\int_0^t f(u)\,du$$

is very great, as would apply to the lunar continents, then except for very large values of x we have approximately

$$\xi(x; t) = 2\gamma(\gamma - 1)(\gamma - 2)/\pi x^3$$

and thus approximately equation (12). This remarkable formula explains the index

$$\langle N(>x)/A \rangle_{av} = \gamma(\gamma - 1)(\gamma - 2)/\pi x^2 \tag{12}$$

$s = 2 \cdot 0$ observed for continental craters! For $c = 0 \cdot 10$ we require $\gamma = 2 \cdot 13$, but a small amount of crater-filling activity will permit a considerably larger value of γ. Let us consider in detail the effects of crater filling.

Crater Filling and the Nature of the Maria

When crater filling is assumed to change the crater distribution significantly, it becomes necessary to take the relative time scale of crater formation and crater filling into account. We consider a useful special case which permits the simple calculation of many possible lunar histories. Let us assume that craters are formed by meteoroidal impacts. It seems plausible that the number of crater-forming bodies has been diminished by collisions with the Moon and planets at a rate roughly proportional to the total number of bodies present. Thus equation (13) applies. If the crater-filling

$$(t) = b_0 e^{-\beta t} \tag{13}$$

mechanism is micrometeoritic debris, it again seems plausible to assume that this has been collected by the Moon and planets at an exponentially decreasing rate (14). If the

$$a(t) = a_0 e^{-\alpha t} \tag{14}$$

ratio of micrometeors to large crater-forming planetesimals has remained approximately constant, we might expect $\alpha = \beta$ as well. This same argument applies to crater-filling debris ejected from newly formed impact craters.

It is also necessary to specify the initial crater depth $H(x)$. There is no really reliable theoretical or empirical work for craters many kilometers in diameter. We shall use a reasonably flexible interpolation formula (15). The work of MacDonald[2] and Bald-

$$H(x) = C_0 x^\delta \tag{15}$$

win[6] suggests that $\delta = 0.5$ or so for large craters, but $\delta = 1.0$ for craters smaller than 1 km.

Upon combining these results we obtain approximately, for $a_0 \gg b_0$, equation (18)

$$\zeta^*(x; t) = C_6 x^{-s-1} \tag{18}$$

and thus approximately (19) on the maria where s and C_6 are given by (20) and (21),

$$\langle N(>x)/A \rangle_{av} = C x^{-s} \tag{19}$$

$$s = \gamma - \left(\frac{\beta}{\alpha}\right)\delta \tag{20}$$

$$C_6 = sC = \left(\frac{\gamma b_0}{\beta}\right)\left(\frac{\alpha C_0}{2a_0}\right)^{\beta/\alpha} \tag{21}$$

respectively.

Using the *a priori* guess that $\alpha = \beta$, $\gamma = 2.25$, $\delta = 0.5$, we have (22). For x in kilo-

$$s = 1.75$$
$$C = 9b_0 C_0/14 a_0 \tag{22}$$

meters $C_0 = 1.0$ approximately; therefore on the maria a_0/b_0 equals 300 to 600. The result $s = 1.75$ is in excellent accord with the observations.

The crucial quantities δ and β/α can be estimated from the distribution of depths of craters of a given diameter. The author hopes to publish shortly a detailed report[30] about this fascinating problem, with applications to extensive unpublished data of Fielder. Some preliminary calculations most emphatically show $\beta \neq \alpha$, and suggest that the values (23) are more nearly correct for large craters. Using $\gamma = 2.25$ we

$$\beta/\alpha = \tfrac{3}{2}$$
$$\delta = \tfrac{1}{3} \tag{23}$$
$$C_0 = 1.3$$

obtain again $s = 1.75$, but $a_0^{3/2}/\alpha^{1/2} b_0$ equals 225 to 450 which seems to be all the information we can derive about a_0, b_0, and α.

The reader will notice that neither of the limiting distributions equation (12) or equation (19) is time dependent. Equation (12), which may apply to the continents, may be called the 'saturation cratering' distribution. Equation (19), which may apply to the maria, may be called the 'equilibrium distribution between crater forming and crater filling'.

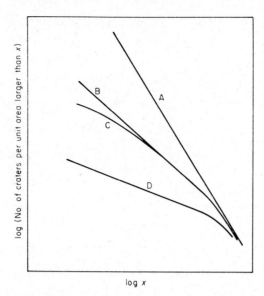

FIGURE 1   Distribution theory. Curve A, initial distribution, slope $-\gamma < -2$; curve B, 'saturation cratering' distribution, slope -2; curve C, 'saturation cratering' distribution with some crater filling; curve D, 'equilibrium distribution' between crater forming and crater filling, slope $-s > -2$. x is the diameter of the crater

The distribution theory is summarized in figure 1.

If the preceding calculations are taken literally, we must revise some of our ideas about the maria. The maria cannot simply be very young objects. If they were, the index s of the mare diameter distribution would be exactly equal to γ. In fact s is much less than γ, less even than the 'saturation cratering' index of $2\cdot0$. The impact hypothesis is thus untenable without invoking very extensive crater-filling activity in the maria. If s differs from one mare to the next, the cause is strictly internal, perhaps because α varies between maria.

We have not considered the possibility that craters are of internal origin, since the model functions cannot be specified at all. The entire body of theory could just as well describe craters of internal origin if their underlying size distribution is also like that of equation (10).

References

1. T. L. MacDonald, 'The altitudes of lunar craters', *J. Brit. Astron. Assoc.*, **39**, 314–24 (1929).
2. T. L. MacDonald, 'The distribution of lunar altitudes', *J. Brit. Astron. Assoc.*, **41**, 172–83, 228–39 (1931).
3. T. L. MacDonald, 'Considerations on lunar slopes', *J. Brit. Astron. Assoc.*, **42**, 291–4 (1932).
4. J. Young, 'Preliminary report of a statistical investigation of the diameters of lunar craters', *J. Brit. Astron. Assoc.*, **43**, 201–9 (1933).
5. J. Young, 'A statistical investigation of the diameters and distribution of lunar craters', *J. Brit. Astron. Assoc.*, **50**, 309–26 (1940).
6. R. B. Baldwin, *The Measure of the Moon*, University of Chicago Press, Chicago, 1962.

7. D. W. G. Arthur, 'The distribution of lunar craters', *J. Brit. Astron. Assoc.*, **64**, 127–32, 154 (1954).
8. G. Fielder, 'Distribution of craters on the lunar surface', *Monthly Notices Roy. Astron. Soc.*, **129**, 351–61 (1965).
9. G. Fielder, 'Tests for randomness on the distribution of lunar craters', *Monthly Notices Roy. Astron. Soc.*, **132**, 413–22 (1966).
10. A. H. Marcus, 'A stochastic model of the formation and survival of lunar craters: IV. On the nonrandomness of crater centers', *Icarus*, **5**, 190–200 (1966).
11. A. H. Marcus, 'Comments on "Distribution of craters on the lunar surface" ', *Monthly Notices Roy. Astron. Soc.*, **134**, 269–74 (1966).
12. A. H. Marcus, 'A multivariate immigration with multiple death process, and applications to lunar craters', *Biometrika*, **54**, 315–24 (1967).
13. C. R. O. Jaschek, 'Earth satellites and lunar formations', *Observatory*, **80**, 119–20 (1960).
14. T. J. Kreiter, 'Dating lunar surface features by using crater frequencies', *Publ. Astron. Soc. Pacific*, **72**, 393–8 (1960).
15. E. J. Öpik, 'The lunar surface as an impact counter', *Monthly Notices Roy. Astron. Soc.*, **120**, 404–11 (1960).
16. E. M. Shoemaker, R. Hackman, and R. E. Eggleton, 'Interplanetary Correlation of Geologic Time', *Advan. Astronaut. Sci.*, **8**, 70–89 (1960).
17. C. D. McGillem and B. P. Miller, 'Lunar surface roughness and crater statistics', *J. Geophys. Res.*, **67**, 4787–94 (1962).
18. R. T. Dodd, J. W. Salisbury, and V. G. Smalley, 'Crater frequency and interpretation of lunar history', *Icarus*, **2**, 466–80 (1963).
19. R. B. Baldwin, 'Lunar crater counts', *Astron. J.*, **69**, 377–92 (1964).
20. W. K. Hartmann, 'On the distribution of lunar crater diameters', *Commun. Lunar Planetary Lab., Univ. Ariz.*, **2**, 197–203 (1964).
21. W. K. Hartmann, 'Secular changes in meteoritic flux through the history of the solar system', *Icarus*, **4**, 207–13 (1965).
22. E. M. Shoemaker, 'Preliminary analysis of the fine structure of the lunar surface in Mare Cognitum', *Jet Propulsion Lab. Tech. Rept. No.* 32-700, 75–134 (1965).
23. A. H. Marcus, 'A stochastic model of the formation and survival of lunar craters: V. Approximate diameter distribution of primary and secondary craters', *Icarus*, **5**, 595–605 (1966).
24. R. B. Leighton, B. C. Murray, R. P. Sharp, J. D. Allen, and R. K. Sloan, '*Mariner IV* photography of Mars: initial results', *Science*, **149**, 627–30 (1965).
25. R. B. Baldwin, 'Mars: an estimate of the age of its surface', *Science*, **149**, 1498–99 (1965).
26. E. J. Öpik, 'Comments: *Mariner IV* and the craters on Mars', *Irish Astron. J.*, **7**, 92–104 (1965).
27. A. H. Marcus, 'A stochastic model of the formation and survival of lunar craters: I. Distribution of diameter of clean craters', *Icarus*, **3**, 460–72 (1964).
28. A. H. Marcus, 'A stochastic model of the formation and survival of lunar craters: II. Approximate diameter distribution of all observable craters', *Icarus*, **5**, 165–77 (1966).
29. A. H. Marcus, 'A stochastic model of the formation and survival of lunar craters: III. Filling and disappearance of craters', *Icarus*, **5**, 178–9 (1966).
30. A. H. Marcus, 'A stochastic model of the formation and survival of lunar craters: VI. Initial depth, distribution of depths and lunar history', *Icarus*, **6**, 56–74 (1967).
31. H. Brown, 'The density and mass distribution of meteoritic bodies in the neighborhood of the Earth's orbit', *J. Geophys. Res.*, **65**, 1679–83 (1960).
32. S. Piotrowski, 'The collisions of asteroids', *Acta Astron., Ser. A*, **5**, 115–36 (1953).
33. R. B. Vaile Jr., 'Pacific craters and scaling laws', *J. Geophys. Res.*, **66**, 3413–38 (1961).
34. A. H. Marcus, 'Comments on "Distribution of energy of meteoritic bodies" ', unpublished (1966).

7

S. K. RUNCORN

Department of Geophysics and Planetary Physics
School of Physics
University of Newcastle upon Tyne
England

The problem of the figure of Mars

The problem of the figure of Mars is the large discrepancy between the optical determination of the ellipticity of its surface and the ellipticity determined dynamically.

All the optical observations of the difference between the polar and equatorial radii give an ellipticity of 1 part in 100 while the dynamical determination gives 1 part in 192. The dynamical determination is indirect and is an ellipticity based on some simple theory of the interior calculated from measurements of its external gravitational field. One such ellipticity is that which, if Mars were of uniform density, would give the observed differences in the moments of inertia about the polar and the equatorial axes $\phi = 0°$, $\phi = 90°$ (C, A, and B respectively).

MacCullogh's relation, equation (1), gives the potential U outside a body of any shape and density distribution, at a field point (r, θ, ϕ), the origin of the coordinate system being at the centre of mass.

$$U = \frac{GM}{r} + \frac{G(A + B + C - 3I)}{2r^3} \tag{1}$$

In equation (1) I is the moment of inertia about the line joining the centre of the mass to the field point, M is the mass, and G the gravitational constant.

$$I = C \cos^2 \theta + A \sin^2 \theta \cos^2 \phi + B \sin^2 \theta \sin^2 \phi \tag{2}$$

If we suppose Mars is axisymmetrical so that $A = B$, we therefore find equation (3).

$$U = \frac{GM}{r} + \frac{G(C - A)(1 - 3 \cos^2 \theta)}{2r^3} \tag{3}$$

The second harmonic of the gravitational potential, which depends on the difference between the two principal moments of inertia, can be determined from the precession of the poles of the orbits of the satellites Deimos and Phobos. Now an ellipticity ε, the fractional difference between the equatorial and polar axes, can be defined dynamically as well as optically. If Mars were covered by an ocean, the surface would set along an equipotential of the Martian gravitational field. In its atmosphere, the surfaces of constant density will coincide with the equipotential surfaces, neglecting any circulation. Let the angular velocity of Mars be ω and let us consider a point on the surface (x, y, z). The vector sum of the gravitational force (∇U) and the centrifugal force $(\omega^2 x, \omega^2 y, 0)$ must be perpendicular to the equipotential surface. Thus on the level surface

$$U + \tfrac{1}{2}\omega^2 r^2 \sin^2 \theta = c$$

where c is constant. As the centrifugal force is small compared with the gravitational force, the ellipticity is small compared with one. Thus terms containing ε, ω^2, and $C - A$ will be of the first order of smallness and products of them can be neglected.

The equipotential surface is approximated by an ellipsoid of revolution about the polar axis of ellipticity ε. Thus its equation will be

$$\frac{x^2}{a^2} + \frac{y^2}{a^2} + \frac{z^2}{a^2(1 - \varepsilon)^2} = 1$$

or, to the first order, equation (4), where a is the equatorial radius.

$$r = a(1 - \varepsilon \cos^2 \theta) \tag{4}$$

If we substitute (4) in (3) to the first order of small quantities, equations (5a) and (5b) hold, where Φ is the ratio of the centrifugal force to the gravitational force at the equator and ε is known as the dynamical ellipticity.

$$\frac{3(C - A)}{2Ma^2} = \varepsilon - \tfrac{1}{2}\Phi \tag{5a}$$

$$U = \frac{GM}{r} + \frac{GMa^2}{r^3}(\varepsilon - \tfrac{1}{2}\Phi)(\tfrac{1}{3} - \cos^2 \theta) \tag{5b}$$

If it is assumed that the solid planet is in hydrostatic equilibrium, then this ellipticity is also that of the solid surface, but the same dynamical quantities will yield other values of the solid surface if other hypotheses about its physical constitution and behaviour are made. For instance, if the planet is assumed to be rigid and of uniform density, the ellipticity ε' is given by

$$\varepsilon' = \frac{5(C - A)}{2Ma^2}$$

and is independent of ω.

By Gauss' device of supposing that the satellite is replaced by a ring of equal mass (m/unit length) occupying the circular orbit of radius R, the torque on a ring element dl is

$$2mR \, dl \left.\frac{dU}{d\theta}\right|_{r=R} = \frac{GMma^2(\varepsilon - \tfrac{1}{2}\Phi)}{R^2} 2dl \sin 2\theta$$

This is equal to the rate of change of angular momentum of satellite ring which equals $2\pi m R^3 (2\pi/T)\{(2\pi \sin \theta')/t\}$, where T and t are the orbital and precessional periods of the satellites respectively, and θ' is the angle between the pole of the orbital plane and the axis of Mars.

Thus, if θ' is small,

$$t = \frac{R^2}{a^2} \cdot \frac{T}{\varepsilon - \tfrac{1}{2}\Phi}$$

Woolard[1] found that the ratios of precession of Phobos and Deimos are 158·484°, and 6·279 50° per tropical year, when allowance is made for the Sun's contribution, and, if $a = 0·520$ times the Earth's radius, then the data give $\varepsilon = 0·0052$ and $0·0051$ respectively. Thus the dynamical ellipticity is very accurately determined. ε/Φ is found to be 1·22.

Now the quantity Φ varies a little according to the values of mass and radius of Mars taken, which have in the past been under some dispute. If, however, we use the *Mariner IV* value of the mass and Dollfus' value of the radius, which appears to agree with the *Mariner IV* value, we obtain $0·461 \times 10^{-2}$. Further, Wilkins'[2] redetermination (see section II, chapter 1 of this book) of the precession of the nodes of the orbits of Deimos and Phobos gives slightly different values of $C - A$. The best value of the ellipticity of the equipotential surface, which would be the real ellipticity of Mars if it were a fluid and which is the ellipticity of its fluid envelope, i.e. its atmosphere, is about 1/192.

An important feature of Wilkins' measurements is that he was able to obtain the period of the precession of the node of the orbital plane of Phobos and Deimos and he was also able to obtain the period of rotation of the pericentre of Phobos but not of Deimos. His results are interesting because his values for the daily motion of the node of the orbital plane for Phobos is 0·438° and for Deimos 0·018° per day. He finds that for Phobos the motion of the pericentre is 0·436. Now the dynamical theory shows that to first order the motion of the node and the motion of the pericentre should be the same so there is an internal consistency in his results which is very important, so that questioning the value of this dynamical ellipticity seems fruitless. Further values of $\varepsilon - \frac{1}{2}\Phi$ obtained from the two satellites are in good agreement: for Phobos $2·718 \times 10^{-3}$ and for Deimos $2·888 \times 10^{-3}$. From these values one can obtain ε equal to about 1/192.

If Mars were known to be in hydrostatic equilibrium, we could determine C as follows. Each equipotential surface within Mars (of varying ellipticity) is an equal density and pressure surface in this case. But the information obtained from the precession of the nodes of the orbits of Deimos and Phobos is the value of the ellipticity of the equipotential gravitational surface outside Mars. This theory does not in itself say anything about the internal structure. For this we have recourse to the famous theory of Darwin and Radau. They calculated the ellipticity which a fluid would have if it was rotating with angular velocity ω, on the assumption that it was in hydrostatic equilibrium. They found that the ellipticity of different surfaces vary and an equation relating the ellipticity to radius can be found. An approximation suggested by Radau, which is true if there is not a very great difference between the central density and the surface density, enables a simple result to be obtained. This approximation must be very accurately true for Mars. The approximate treatment by Radau and Darwin gives equation (6).

$$\frac{C}{Ma^2} = \frac{2}{3}\left\{1 - \frac{2}{5}\left(\frac{5}{2}\frac{\Phi}{\varepsilon} - 1\right)^{1/2}\right\} \tag{6}$$

Thus

$$C = (0·984)(\tfrac{2}{3}Ma^2)$$

and therefore Mars is close to being a body of uniform density.

The formula (6) shows that the variation of density with radius, in its effect on the ellipticity, can be specified by the moment of inertia factor. This formula is interesting because if $\varepsilon = 1.25\Phi$ then C/Ma^2 is equal to 0·4, the value for a uniform sphere and $\varepsilon = \varepsilon'$.

Urey[3] had already pointed out that this was nearly true for Mars and concluded that the planet has no core or only a small one. With the new values, C/Ma^2 turns out to be 0·372 which is rather close to 0·4 and confirms the view that Mars cannot have a very large iron core and must be a reasonably uniform body, presumably not differentiated as its uncompressed density is considerably greater than that of olivine.

It is, however, doubtful if this procedure is valid. The surface ellipticity has many times been determined by optical methods in yellow light. de Vaucouleurs[4] reviews the best measurements and gives 9·315″ ± 0·010″ and 9·415″ ± 0·02″ as the polar and equatorial diameters at unit distance respectively. The ellipticity is then 0·0105 ± 0·0005. In red light and from the motion of surface markings, the smaller values 9·19″ ± 0·03″ and 9·28″ ± 0·03″ are obtained and may refer to the solid surface. In either case the ellipticity determined is about twice that found by dynamical methods. Because it is likely to have a larger error than the dynamical ellipticity, it has been wrongly ignored. The persistent disregard of this observation is of course convenient because by substituting it in (6) we obtain an imaginary number.

There have been two attempts to resolve this problem of the discrepancy between the optical and the dynamical ellipticity. Both explanations are most difficult to accept since the *Mariner IV* observations (see Gaugler, section VIII, chapter 4 of this book). Urey[3] suggested that it might be that there was some kind of equatorial mountain range which tended to cause optical measurements of the equatorial diameter to be overestimated. The height of the mountains needed is something like 16 km and the fact that the *Mariner IV* photographs were taken through the equatorial region and failed to show any feature of this kind is strong evidence against this hypothesis. If the white areas on these photographs are frost, then of course this equatorial mountain belt would have been easily picked out.

The other attempt to resolve the discrepancy between the optical and dynamical ellipticity which has been suggested at various times is that a thick atmosphere might give rise to systematic errors in the optical determinations. As the *Mariner IV* observations indicate quite a thin atmosphere, this explanation is now rather unlikely.

If therefore the optical ellipticity is correctly determined, Mars is not in hydrostatic equilibrium. We may then conclude that the equipotential surface in the atmosphere of Mars tangential at the equatorial surface of Mars is elevated 16 km above the surface at the poles. The measurement of the thickness of the atmosphere was made by *Mariner IV* by the occultation of radio signals from the space vehicle at 55° N and at 60° S (see Kliore, Cain, and Levy[5]). Measurements at two quite different latitudes would have enabled the question to be settled. The astronomical methods give an average over the disk of 83 mb (Dollfus) (cf. 7 mb from *Mariner IV*). The discrepancy is one which it is important to test critically; the astronomical method should be applied to the equatorial and polar regions.

The bulge represents a strain of 1/200 and its maintenance requires a stress difference of 1000 b or 10^9 dyn/cm². Classical elasticity and the hypothesis of a finite stress, below which flow did not occur even over long times, long sufficed in the discussion of geophysical problems. The evidence for continental drift on the Earth has caused a more sophisticated view to be taken, which accords well with the modern theory of solids. Flow may be assumed to occur even under very small stresses over times of the order of the geological scale at depths in the Earth a few tens of kilometres where the temperatures are elevated. It is useful, though not strictly correct, to use a viscosity. It will be then seen that, in order that Mars is rigid enough to maintain the bulge since its formation 4×10^9 years ago (about 10^{17} sec), its internal viscosity must be greater than 10^{28} P. If Mars is of uniform density, its ellipticity calculated dynamically is still only a half of the optical one.

Gordon[6] has argued that diffusion of atoms through grains is the important creep mechanism in the polycrystalline Earth's mantle at low stresses. The atomic migration is driven by the applied stresses, its vacancy sources and sinks being the grain boundaries. Thermal activation causes the diffusion and thus, in the Earth's mantle, the viscosity so calculated rises by more than six orders of magnitude in the first one or two hundred kilometres from the surface owing to the high geothermal gradient at the surface. Gordon finds that pressure causes an increase of viscosity below about 500 km depth but, as the pressure then exceeds that of the centre of Mars, we can conclude that viscosities lower than 10^{28} P are to be expected in Mars, except near the surface, unless the temperatures in its interior were everywhere less than 1000 °C, say.

It is interesting to compare Mars with the Moon. If the bulge on the Moon is 1 or 2 km, then the stress difference that has to be supported by the material in the deep interior of the Moon is about 50 dyn/cm^2. Now the bulge on Mars is ten times as large and the gravitational force on Mars' surface is about three times that on the Moon's surface; thus in Mars the stress difference is getting very close to the breaking stress of rocks even at ordinary temperatures and pressures. If creep can occur underneath these very high stresses, rates as small as 10^{-20} sec^{-1} would have caused the bulge to have disappeared in the course of a thousand million years. This creep rate has to be compared with those which are very commonly found in the laboratory in metals (10^{-8} sec^{-1}) at moderately high temperatures.

The possibility that convection within Mars is a cause of the distortion of the surface has not hitherto been considered. It is easy to see that this must be a second harmonic symmetrical about the axis of rotation with hotter, less dense material rising around the equator and colder material falling at the poles. If no motion were taking place, the systematic difference in temperature necessary to cause the observed bulge would be 500 degC, if we take 3×10^{-5} degC^{-1} as the volume coefficient of expansion of olivine. The process of convection would increase the required temperature difference, and this seems remarkably large. However, even if such convection exists, theory and experiment alike suggest that a second harmonic convection would only occur if the core of Mars was no greater than one-third the radius of the outer boundary of the convecting shell, which is perhaps 50–200 km below the external surface.

If it were proved that the optical ellipticity is an observational effect, then equation (6) applies and again the radius of the core can be no greater than a few hundred kilometres.

In contrast with Jupiter and Saturn, Mars emits no non-thermal radiation and thus neither a radiation belt nor the associated planetary magnetic field is assumed to exist. This need not be held to support the hypothesis of no core in Mars, but merely that all the conditions for the spontaneous generation of a field by dynamo action are not present. These are motions in a fluid core to provide the energy—derived presumably from energy released by radioactivity. The core of Mars even if it exists may not be fluid. Further, a core must be of a certain size, other physical constants being equal, if the generation of new lines of magnetic force is to predominate over the natural decay of a magnetic field in a conductor of finite conductivity. A liquid core of such small radii which we have been considering is not likely to be a dynamo.

A further piece of evidence points to the core of Mars being small or non-existent or solid. The liquid cores of the Earth and Jupiter[7] do not rotate at exactly the same speed as the mantles; there is no reason why they should—the viscous forces in spheres of such size are negligible. Only the weak electrical conductivity in their mantles— the result of semiconduction processes—enables coupling to occur between the mantle and core. If the planetary magnetic field were constant and rotating with the core, any relative rotation of core and mantle dies away because of eddy current losses, providing, as in the case now with the Earth and Jupiter, the magnetic and rotational axes are not the same. However, in the Earth owing to turbulence in the core (and we may predict that the same will occur in any other planet with a liquid core) the magnetic field varies (the geomagnetic secular variation). These variable torques operate on the mantle, and fluctuations occur in the length of the Earth's day. A similar rather irregular change in the rotation of Jupiter occurs, with periods of about 50 years, if one follows Hide's theory of the red spot, that it is an atmospheric column anchored to a major surface feature of the Jovian mantle (perhaps a large meteor crater?). On the other hand, Ashbrook[8] has shown that the period of rotation of Mars has remained remarkably constant to a thousandth of a second since the eighteenth century. This is an order of magnitude more constant than the rate of rotation of the Earth and again argues in favour of a core, the moment of inertia of which is proportionately much less than the Earth's and to insignificant electromagnetic coupling between the mantle and core if this exists.

References

1. E. W. Woolard, *Astron. J.*, **51**, 33 (1944).
2. G. A. Wilkins, *The Theory of Orbits in the Solar System and in Stellar Systems*, *Intern. Astron. Union Symp.*, *25th, 1964*.
3. H. C. Urey, *The Planets*, Yale University Press, New Haven, 1952.
4. G. de Vaucouleurs, *Icarus*, **3**, 187 (1964).
5. A. Kliore, D. L. Cain and G. S. Levy, *Space Research VII*, *Proc. Intern. Space Sci. Symp.*, *Vienna, 1966*, to be published.
6. R. B. Gordon, *J. Geophys. Res.*, **70**, 2413 (1965).
7. S. K. Runcorn, *Cosmic Magnetism*, Oliver and Boyd, Edinburgh, 1967.
8. J. Ashbrook, *Astron. J.*, **58**, 145 (1953).

8

J. F. McCAULEY

U.S. Geological Survey, Flagstaff
Arizona, U.S.A.

The nature of the lunar surface as determined by systematic geologic mapping*

Introduction

Since 1961, the U.S. Geological Survey has been conducting, under the auspices of the National Aeronautics and Space Administration (NASA), a program of systematic geological mapping and analysis of the lunar surface. The primary data sources are (i) published and unpublished telescopic photographs, and (ii) visual telescopic observations with the Lick Observatory 36 in. refractor and the U.S. Geological Survey 30 in. reflector. Supplemental sources of data include infrared, photometric, polarimetric, and colorimetric measurements from the existing literature and from a variety of unpublished sources. The results of these investigations are compiled on lunar topographic charts prepared by the U.S. Air Force, Aeronautical Chart and Information Center (ACIC), St. Louis, Missouri, at a scale of 1:1 000 000.

To date the work has been concentrated in the equatorial region between latitudes 32° N and S and longitudes 70° E and W. This area has been divided into 28 individual regions or quadrangles (figure 1). Geologic maps of these quadrangles are now available either in preliminary form as U.S. Geological Survey open-file reports or as published *U.S. Geological Survey Miscellaneous Geologic Investigations*. The maps already published have been called regions; future maps will be called quadrangles with no change in format.

The primary purpose of the research has been to discover regional stratigraphic and structural relations from which an improved understanding of the history of the lunar crust can be developed. The work has identified many major problem areas for later large-scale investigations and also has provided a large body of observational data on the lunar surface against which to test theories of the nature of the lunar interior as well as the origin of the Moon itself. The program has shown convincingly that the lunar surface is geologically heterogeneous with a physical history of complexity comparable with that of the Earth. Oversimplified models invoking a single major process to explain the present configuration of the lunar surface are, therefore, as inadequate as they are for the Earth.

The purpose of this chapter is to touch upon some of the major advances in the general field of stratigraphy and structure made since the initial descriptions of lunar

* Publication authorized by the Director, U.S. Geological Survey.

geological mapping by Shoemaker[1] and Shoemaker and Hackman[2] and from these to develop a regional picture of the nature of the lunar surface. Detailed descriptions of the methodology and review of all the arguments used to support the conclusions presented are beyond the length limitations of the chapter.

The major source of information for this review is the *Annual Reports of the Branch*

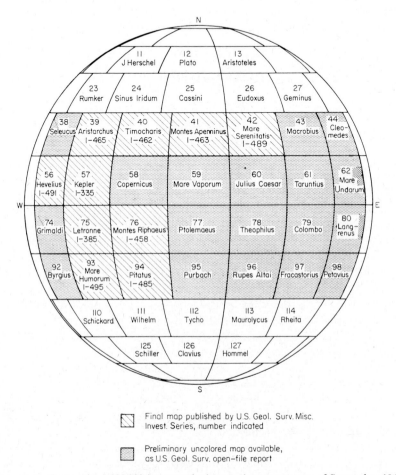

FIGURE 1   Status of 1:1 000 000 lunar geologic mapping program as of September 1966

of Astrogeology, U.S. Geological Survey open-file reports prepared annually since 1962 for the National Aeronautics and Space Administration. This series includes a large amount of detailed stratigraphic description and interpretation not otherwise available, and the work contained therein has been liberally cited throughout the chapter. The review presented is not comprehensive, however, but is restricted to general discussions of the geological relations around three of the major mare basins in the central and western parts of the visible hemisphere, along with descriptions of a limited number of noteworthy volcanic features.

Original Stratigraphic Nomenclature

Time-stratigraphic units

Although geological investigations of the lunar surface began with Gilbert[3], application of the basic concepts of stratigraphy—mainly the principles of superposition and intersection—to systematic geological mapping of limited areas was first undertaken by Shoemaker and Hackman[2]. This work was concentrated around the large ray crater Copernicus in the west-central part of the visible hemisphere. It led to the establishment of a lunar time scale consisting of four major time-stratigraphic units called systems, by extension of terrestrial practice. They were, from oldest to youngest, the Imbrian, Procellarian, Eratosthenian, and Copernican Systems and represented mappable stratigraphic units formed during corresponding periods of lunar history. Three of these time-stratigraphic units, the Imbrian, Eratosthenian, and Copernican, are still in general use by the U.S. Geological Survey on the 1:1 000 000 scale maps, although their strict time implications have been modified by later workers as a result of detailed investigations at a distance from the Copernicus region.

Imbrian System. Basic to the early mapping effort of Shoemaker and Hackman[2] was the recognition of an extensive but discontinuous blanket of material around Mare Imbrium that has distinctive topographic characteristics. Near Montes Apenninus at the southern edge of Mare Imbrium, where it is roughest, the surface consists of closely spaced hills and valleys, averaging about one to four kilometers across. This type of topography, generally described as hummocky, is present around Mare Imbrium and other large basins and craters (figure 2). It is overlain by younger units at many places around the basin but, on the southeast and southwest, material with the same morphology can be traced more or less continuously for a radial distance of about 500 km. As the distance from the basin increases, the surface becomes progressively smoother, until it is topographically indistinguishable from the ubiquitous smooth material of the central and southern terrae (figure 3).

Few subjacent crater forms can be recognized within 150 km of Montes Apenninus, but they are more abundant and better preserved farther away from the basin. These relationships indicate that a blanket of material with distinctive topographic characteristics surrounds Mare Imbrium and that the blanket thins, becomes smoother, and generally covers older craters less deeply as the distance from Mare Imbrium increases[4]. Large fault-controlled blocks, 50 to 60 km in length and 10 to 15 km in width, are present in the Montes Apenninus region, their maximum elongation being radial to the basin. Farther from Mare Imbrium, deformation is less intense; individual structural blocks are smaller, grading finally into subdued radial lineaments. Most lunar workers have recognized the existence of the blanket, including Gilbert[3], Dietz[5], Baldwin[6], Urey[7], Kuiper[8], and Shoemaker[1], and have interpreted it to consist of ejecta derived by impact from the Imbrium basin. Regardless of its origin, it constitutes an excellent regional stratigraphic marker horizon in the north and central parts of the visible hemisphere and provides a means of distinguishing materials and events predating and postdating formation of the blanket.

Shoemaker and Hackman[2] included these hummocky materials in the Imbrian System, a time-stratigraphic unit inferred to have been deposited in a very short interval of time during the formation of the Imbrium basin. The Imbrian System was later redefined[9,10] to include two time-stratigraphic divisions called series. The lower unit was called the Apenninian Series for the type area in Montes Apenninus and included the rough hummocky blanket material surrounding Mare Imbrium. The upper unit was called the Archimedian Series for the crater Archimedes at the southeastern edge of the Imbrium basin. This unit included the numerous individual

FIGURE 2 The Imbrium basin with north at top. This convention applies to all succeeding photographs. Rough, hummocky-to-blocky topography of the Imbrium rim best seen at lower right. Same general characteristics seen on the north side of basin, southeast of the large mare-filled crater Plato. Large ray crater, Copernicus, approximately 100 km in diameter is at lower left of photograph and Eratosthenes at lower center. Archimedes is the large mare-filled crater on the Apennine bench northwest of the scarp at the front of Montes Apenninus. [Mt. Wilson Observatory photograph]

deposits of crater rim material superimposed on the Apenninian Series but overlapped by mare material of the Procellarian System. The Imbrian System, by addition of the Archimedian Series, therefore represented a significantly longer segment of lunar history than was originally included. This twofold breakdown of the Imbrian System was used in the two earliest published U.S. Geological Survey lunar geological maps, those of the Kepler[10] and Letronne[11] regions, but has since been further modified.

Procellarian System. The next youngest major time-stratigraphic unit was called the Procellarian System; it included the dark, relatively smooth mare material that fills the major lunar basins as well as smaller isolated topographic depressions. The mare clearly embays and locally covers materials of both the Apenninian and Archimedian Series and is, therefore, younger. The name is taken from Oceanus Procellarum, the

FIGURE 3 Hummocky material of Montes Apenninus also showing pronounced structure radial to Mare Imbrium. Apennine scarp at north; large crater Conon, 22 km in diameter at upper left. The coarse hummocky material grades to smooth material in the south as the distance from Mare Imbrium increases. [After Wilhelms[22]]

largest continuous exposure of mare material in the west-central part of the visible hemisphere. The type area of the Procellarian System, by general agreement but not formal definition, was in the western part of the Kepler region[10].

The mare surfaces were interpreted to be of approximately the same age where exposed on the visible hemisphere. The supposition that the maria were everywhere about the same age and that the surface of the Procellarian represented a well-defined time-stratigraphic horizon was based on preliminary crater counts of eight different large mare areas[12]. Later work, however, showed that the crater density over small parts of the mare surface does vary significantly and that those parts with a lower crater density are generally darker; these differences were interpreted to mean that the surface of the Procellarian System is divisible into many units of different ages[13, 14]. Its base also cannot be effectively defined in terms of a single time horizon. Part of the mare material at the surface may be older than some Archimedian crater materials, and material beneath the surface in the pre-Imbrium basins may be older than the Apenninian. The term Procellarian System was dropped, therefore, by later investigators. Materials of morphology and albedo similar to those originally designated as the Procellarian System were assigned to the Procellarum Group—a rock-stratigraphic unit whose top by definition was to represent the top of the Imbrian System. In accordance with this modification, the Imbrian System includes (i) the ejecta blanket surrounding Mare Imbrium (Apenninian Series), (ii) the craters superimposed on this blanket and overlain by mare material (Archimedian Series), and (iii) all mare material similar to that in the western part of the Kepler region (Procellarum Group).

Eratosthenian System. Two distinct types of craters are superimposed on the maria: (i) craters with associated rays and rim materials that are generally brighter than the mare, and (ii) craters without readily detectable rays and with rim materials of albedo similar to the mare[1]. The Eratosthenian System originally included only the crater materials associated with the rayless craters superposed on the maria that are younger than the materials of the Imbrian and Procellarian Systems. The ray materials are frequently observed to overlie rayless craters as in the type area—the crater Eratosthenes about 220 km northeast of Copernicus (figure 2). The craters included in the Eratosthenian System are presumed to be older than those with rays. The processes inferred to be responsible for ray and rim darkening are prolonged micrometeorite bombardment and solar radiation effects.

The absence of rays does not, however, necessarily indicate that a crater is Eratosthenian in age. Many dark-rimmed rayless craters on the maria interrupt rays and are, therefore, younger in age. Carr[15] has pointed out the similarity in form between these dark craters and those generally mapped as Eratosthenian. It is also recognized that the presence or absence of rays may be a function of the albedo and cohesiveness of the bed rock in which craters form. Furthermore, it is difficult to detect faint rays on many parts of the lunar surface, particularly the terrae, because of the brightness of the background material. In fact, recent photography has revealed that Eratosthenes, itself, has faint rays. A further problem in the terrae is that fresh-appearing, rayless craters cannot be restricted to the Eratosthenian System because of their indeterminate position with respect to the mare material; by current mapping convention, they are designated as Eratosthenian to Imbrian in age, an unsatisfactory stratigraphic practice. The Eratosthenian System, therefore, is not an effective lunar-wide, time-stratigraphic unit. It is satisfactory in some areas for large craters but becomes less workable with smaller craters and at larger mapping scales. It has been decided, however, to retain the name Eratosthenian System without rigorous time-stratigraphic definition of its top or bottom in the 1:1 000 000 scale mapping program for the sake of consistency with the already published maps.

Copernican System. The Copernican System, stratigraphically the highest and therefore the youngest of the original lunar time-stratigraphic units, includes several mappable units. The most extensive in the vicinity of the crater Copernicus, the type area (figure 2), are the rays, rim, and floor units of the fresh-appearing craters superimposed on the materials of all other systems. Also included are the numerous small, generally irregular secondary craters that are concentrated within radial rays and ray loops around Copernicus and other large ray craters. It was mainly the analysis of the distribution pattern of these secondary craters that led Shoemaker[1] to the conclusion that most of the large lunar craters are of impact origin.

The albedo of Copernican materials ranges from intermediate to high; it is generally higher than that of materials of the other systems. The system also includes material of very high albedo present on slopes generally exceeding 20°; most of this material occurs on the inner walls of Copernican and some older craters, but it is also present on steep noncrater scarps. The correlation between high albedo and steep slopes is interpreted to mean that bright fresh material is being continuously or intermittently exposed on these slopes by mass movement. The dark-halo craters that appear to crosscut the rays and rim deposits of Copernicus and several other large craters of similar age, such as Langrenus on the eastern limb of the Moon, are also mapped as Copernican. The dark craters are interpreted by most workers to be volcanic features of the maar type. Their close spatial association with large Copernican craters suggests that they may be the product of impact-triggered volcanism[2, 16]. Some could, however, be young impact craters that simply have quarried dark material from the subsurface.

Subsequent Systematic Geological Investigations

Rock-stratigraphic units of the Imbrium basin

The early geological work that led to the establishment of the original lunar time scale in the Copernicus area was followed by systematic work in four nearby regions: Kepler, Montes Riphaeus, Letronne, and Montes Apenninus. In these regions, the stratigraphic concepts of Shoemaker and Hackman[2] were applied without basic modification. During this later work, however, it was found desirable to define formally several rock-stratigraphic units—groups, formations, and members—within the existing time-stratigraphic framework, following, as closely as possible, the recommendations in the code of stratigraphic nomenclature[17]. This procedure of defining local rock-stratigraphic units in each newly mapped region to portray specific relationships has been followed by all later investigators. Many of these units have been formally defined as formational units on published maps and reports.

Fra Mauro Formation. Work in the Montes Riphaeus and Montes Apenninus regions[18, 19] led to the establishment of the Fra Mauro Formation. This unit, as defined by Eggleton[20], consists essentially of the hummocky ejecta blanket surrounding Mare Imbrium, previously identified in time-stratigraphic terms as the Apenninian Series of the Imbrian System. Its present designation as a rock-stratigraphic unit assures that it will be mapped by physical criteria independently of time and genetic assumptions. According to Eggleton[20], it includes two members: (i) a *hummocky member* with the type area from 0° S to 2° S, and from 16° W to 18° W, and (ii) a *smooth member* with the type area from 6° S to 7° S, and from 16° W to 17° W (figure 4). The boundary between the members is gradational, however, and members were not differentiated on the published map of the Montes Riphaeus region. These units have proved useful in studies elsewhere in the equatorial region, and they have appeared on several preliminary maps. Wilhelms[21, 22], while mapping the Mare Vaporum and Julius Caesar regions, recognized material believed to be correlative with the Fra Mauro Formation of Eggleton[20] and amplified the definition of the smooth member. A correlative of Eggleton's smooth member is present in the area south of Mare Vaporum some 600 km from the edge of the Montes Apenninus scarp. Eggleton's identification of the smooth member as part of the Fra Mauro is based on the fact that it mantles subjacent cratered topography and is laterally continuous with the hummocky member of the Fra Mauro. In addition, Wilhelms[22] has described vague, subdued braided ridges similar in form to the more pronounced ridges seen in the hummocky Fra Mauro. This characteristic distinguishes the unit from material

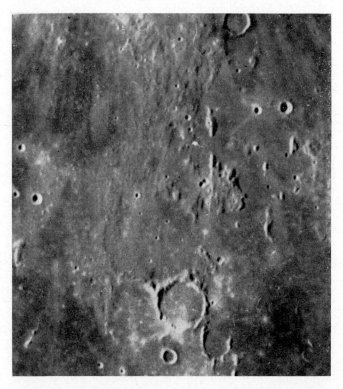

FIGURE 4   Type area of the Fra Mauro Formation. The broad shallow crater in the center is Fra Mauro, about 100 km in diameter. The hummocky member is present at the top of the photograph, the smooth at the bottom. [Mt. Wilson Observatory photograph]

with a very smooth flat surface previously included by some investigators in the smooth Fra Mauro but assigned by Wilhelms to another, as yet unnamed, formation. The relatively smooth, subtly lineated facies of the Fra Mauro may owe its distinctive texture to subjacent structures, rather than to a difference in depositional mechanism.

The stratigraphy of the Fra Mauro Formation in the eastern hemisphere is complex, and work is continuing in an attempt to unravel detailed relationships, particularly with respect to the other basins present in this area. As yet, no major basin-related units have been formally defined in the eastern part of the Moon. Elston[23], however, in the course of work in the Colombo quadrangle has proposed a preliminary and informal pre-Imbrian stratigraphic sequence around the Nectaris and Tranquillitatis basins which will not be reviewed here since mapping in this area is not yet complete.

Apennine Bench Formation. Materials with smooth-to-rolling topography and intermediate albedo located on the bench at the foot of the Apennine scarp are called the
Apennine Bench Formation (figure 2) by Hackman[24]. The unit was included in the
Apenninian Series and it appears locally to overlie the Fra Mauro Formation. It may
be a much later volcanic unit unrelated to the Imbrium impact or a contemporaneous
facies of the Fra Mauro Formation. The unit, as originally defined, has not been used
by workers outside the Apennine region because of its limited extent and difficulties
in meaningful correlation.

Plains-forming materials of the terrae. The very extensive, relatively smooth terra
material of intermediate to high albedo that fills local depressions, such as the floors of
deformed craters and irregular structural troughs, was informally designated as plains-
forming material by Milton[25] as a result of work in the Theophilus quadrangle. This
unit is not laterally continuous with the Fra Mauro Formation but rather appears to
occur in patches primarily within local basins throughout the terrae. Wilhelms[21,22]
later amplified its description in the vicinity of the crater Cayley and extended the
unit in the Julius Caesar and Mare Vaporum quadrangles. In these regions it locally
contains numerous small superimposed pits and some larger craters and is embayed
by mare material. It also appears to partially subdue or in some cases completely
mantle the radial lineaments and faults related to the Imbrium basin so that it can be
assigned a post-Imbrium basin (Apenninian) pre-mare age. Where Imbrium radial
structure is completely absent and the unit is not in contact with the mare, as in the
extreme southern hemisphere, its age range cannot be so restricted. In these areas, the
plains-forming materials are assigned a pre-Imbrian to Imbrian age. The origin of the
unit is not known, but its location in large terra depressions has led Wilhelms to
suggest that it may be of local origin. It may consist either of volcanic flows, ash-flow
tuff deposits, or both, or it may be material eroded from adjacent highland areas.
The unit as now mapped probably does not represent a time-stratigraphic horizon but
may range widely in age from place to place on the lunar surface.

Stratigraphy and structure of the Orientale and Humorum basins

Mapping in the Hevelius and Mare Humorum regions of the western and southwestern parts of the Moon by McCauley[26] and Titley[27] led to the description of two
new major rock-stratigraphic units. The first unit surrounds the Orientale basin, the
center of which lies about 2800 km from the center of Mare Imbrium, on the extreme
leading edge of the Moon. The second unit surrounds the Humorum basin in the
southwestern part of the visible hemisphere, the center of which lies some 2000 km
from the center of Mare Imbrium. These units, like the Fra Mauro Formation,
have proved to be useful marker horizons for regional stratigraphic studies.

Hummocky material surrounding Mare Orientale. The structure surrounding Mare
Orientale was described by Hartmann and Kuiper[28] and later by Hartmann[29]
with emphasis on four prominent concentric scarps. The highest scarp in the
Montes Cordillera has approximately 6000 m of local relief. It is comparable in height
with the Montes Apenninus scarp surrounding the southeastern part of Mare Imbrium. Study of excellent rectified photographs in these papers, additional unpublished
photographs provided to the author by Hartmann, and discussions with Marshall,

formerly of the U.S. Geological Survey, led to the recognition of a previously un-described stratigraphic unit[26] on the eastern side of Mare Orientale (figure 5). Its morphology and distribution are similar to that of the Fra Mauro Formation sur-rounding Mare Imbrium. In the Montes Cordillera, it consists of rough hummocky material with individual hummocks from four to six kilometers across (the limiting recognition resolution of the rectified limb photography). Like the Fra Mauro, the

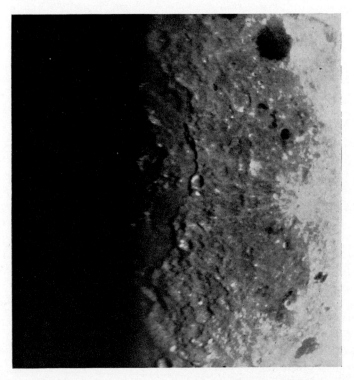

FIGURE 5   Eastern edge of the Orientale basin. Cordillera scarp at left of photo. Crater Eichstadt, approximately 50 km in diameter, near center superimposed on scarp. The hummocky texture of the Cordillera Formation is not resolvable. [Lunar and Planetary Laboratory, Tucson, Arizona, rectified photograph]

hummocks become smaller as the radial distance from the basin increases, and on its outer margins, about 500 to 600 km from the basin center, the unit is indistinguishable from terra plains-forming material. In Montes Cordillera, few subjacent crater forms can be seen, but about 200 km from the edge of the basin, partially buried, but otherwise well-preserved craters such as Rocca, Riccioli, and Darwin are present (figure 6). The unit, on the basis of this evidence, is interpreted to be thick close to the highest scarp and thinner farther from the basin.

   Blocks of rectangular outline, typically 30 to 60 km in length, are abundant; their maximum elongation is in the radial direction. Pronounced radial faults, along with a well-developed system of concentric faults, outline most of the blocks. In the best available photographs, the top surfaces of these blocks appear to have a vague hum-mocky texture similar to that of most of the surrounding terrain.

The blanket, the concentric scarps, the radial structure, and the Orientale basin itself are thought to be the products of impact by an asteroidal-sized body. Although inferred to be genetically similar to the Imbrium basin, the Orientale radial structure is not as well developed as the radial Imbrium structure. The 'Imbrium sculpture' is,

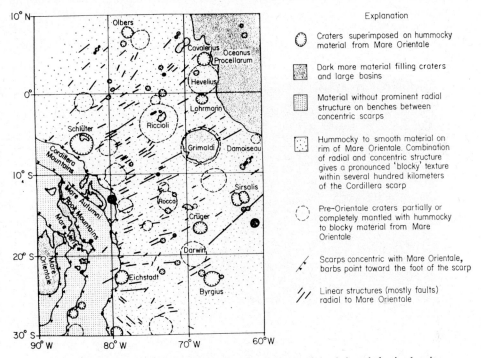

Explanation

⊙ Craters superimposed on hummocky material from Mare Orientale

▨ Dark mare material filling craters and large basins

▢ Material without prominent radial structure on benches between concentric scarps

⋯ Hummocky to smooth material on rim of Mare Orientale. Combination of radial and concentric structure gives a pronounced 'blocky' texture within several hundred kilometers of the Cordillera scarp

◌ Pre-Orientale craters partially or completely mantled with hummocky to blocky material from Mare Orientale

⤪ Scarps concentric with Mare Orientale, barbs point toward the foot of the scarp

∕∕ Linear structures (mostly faults) radial to Mare Orientale

FIGURE 6 Geologic sketch map of the northeastern part of the Orientale basin showing the recognizable extent of the hummocky rim material and the most prominent radial structures. A number of large pre-basin craters such as Riccioli, Hevelius, and Darwin are outlined along with the prominent concentric scarps and mare-filled areas

however, coincident with structure that is both older and younger than the basin and is, at least in part, unrelated to the Imbrium impact. The radial structure of the Orientale basin may, therefore, be more typical of that developed solely by impact around large lunar basins.

The unique character of the Orientale basin. A particularly important feature of the Orientale basin is that much of what is inferred to be the original crater floor can be seen because of limited flooding by mare material (figure 7). The Soviet *Zond III* photograph of the far side of the leading edge of the Moon taken July 20, 1965 shows, despite its relatively poor resolution, that the floor material of the inner basin has a gross texture similar to that of the benches and outer rim. In contrast, the other major lunar basins, such as Imbrium and Humorum, are more deeply filled with mare material, and their floors are completely buried. In fact, the position of the inner basin within Mare Imbrium and Humorum can only be inferred from the presence of isolated islands and mare ridges that follow a circular pattern[28]. The nature of the floor material and the thickness of mare filling, therefore, cannot be determined for these basins. The relatively small amount of mare filling within the Orientale basin provides, therefore, an important clue to the original configuration of the other large basins.

The Orientale basin, in its present configuration, consists of a broad, depressed central plain some 300 km in diameter, partially flooded by mare material and encircled by a series of outward-tilted benches. The Cordillera scarp, at the inner face of the highest of these, makes a ring approximately 900 km in diameter, and the maximum estimated depth of the partially flooded floor below the level of the terra surrounding this scarp is of the order of 15 000 m. The Orientale basin is, therefore, quite

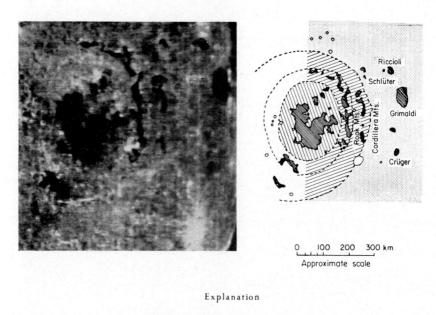

0   100   200   300 km

Approximate scale

Explanation

▨	Mare areas
▧	Inner basin floor material
▨	Bench material
▢	Hummocky to blocky rim material
O	Prominent post-basin craters
- - -	Approximate location of prominent concentric scarps

FIGURE 7   Part of a Soviet *Zond III* photograph of the Orientale basin and a geologic sketch map of the same area. The surrounding concentric scarps and the extent of the dark mare material within the inner basin are shown

shallow in comparison with its diameter; it does, however, fall on the depth-to-diameter curve of the larger lunar craters (>10 km radius) determined by Quaide, Gault, and Schmidt[30]. Immediate gravitative transfer of material from the rim and inner walls has been suggested[28] as the principal mechanism responsible for the shallow configuration of the large lunar craters. Fallback of impact debris and isostatic rebound of the crater floor sometime after formation are also probably involved in decreasing crater depth[31,32]. The important consideration here is that the same shallow pre-mare configuration may be inferred for the other major impact basins.

The total thickness of mare material, even in the central parts of these basins, then, is probably of the order of thousands of meters rather than hundreds of kilometers. Mare material may be, therefore, volumetrically a minor constituent of the lunar crust.

Rock-stratigraphic units of the Humorum basin. A subdued discontinuous, somewhat asymmetrical blanket of hummocky material surrounding Mare Humorum has been described by Titley and Eggleton[33], Titley[34], and Trask and Titley[35]. The photographic evidence for its existence is, however, not as clear as in the Imbrium and

FIGURE 8   The Humorum basin. The large, relatively shallow crater on the north rim of the basin is Gassendi, approximately 100 km in diameter. [Lick Observatory photograph]

Orientale areas; it is seen best to the northwest of the basin for a radial distance of about 350 km (figure 8). It has been named the Vitello Formation after the crater at the southern edge of the basin. Like the other blankets, it is also interpreted to be of impact origin (figure 9).

The Humorum basin is surrounded by discontinuous scarps which are considerably lower than those surrounding the Orientale and Imbrium basins. The relative relief on the Vitello is also less than on the other blankets, and it is more densely cratered. Concentric structure is well developed, but radial structure is not. In addition to the

Vitello Formation, a unit consisting of large, smooth-textured blocks has been mapped. The unit is interpreted by Trask and Titley to consist of uplifted segments of pre-basin bedrock that were areas of nondeposition of Vitello or areas where the Vitello has since been texturally modified or eroded away. A group of craters younger than the Vitello Formation, but overlapped by mare material of the Procellarum Group, are also recognized and termed the Gassendi Group. They are analogous stratigraphically

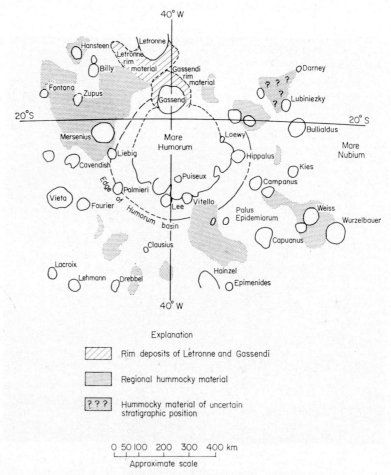

Explanation

▨ Rim deposits of Letronne and Gassendi

▢ Regional hummocky material

▢?? Hummocky material of uncertain
stratigraphic position

0 50 100 200   300   400 km
Approximate scale

FIGURE 9   Geologic sketch map of the Humorum basin showing the approximate
extent of the surrounding hummocky blanket. [By Titley[25]]

to the craters of the Archimedian Series of the Imbrium basin, that is they are later than the basin ejecta and earlier than the mare.

Relative ages of the Orientale, Imbrium, and Humorum basins. The relative ages of the major circular basins in the western hemisphere of the Moon can be established with a fair degree of certainty because of the presence of reasonably well-defined surrounding stratigraphic units and structural features. The comparative frequency of craters superimposed on each ejecta blanket (if we assume that most of these are of impact origin), overlap relationships among the blankets, and the relative freshness of the primary textures and associated structures are the principle age criteria.

Comparison of the relative frequency of craters superimposed on areas of approximately equal extent on the inferred ejecta blankets around the Orientale, Imbrium, and Humorum basins indicate that Orientale has the lowest crater density (figure 10). The Imbrium curve is parallel to that of Orientale but shows a crater frequency averaging about a factor of 2 greater. The Humorum rim exhibits an even greater crater frequency and a distinctive size distribution, as seen by its lower slope. These data are interpreted to indicate that Orientale is the youngest of these three basins and that Humorum is the oldest, that is pre-Imbrian. The distinctive cumulative frequency curve for craters younger than the Humorum basin is similar to the curve for the older terrae of Dodd, Salisbury, and Smalley[13], which may mean (i) the size–frequency distribution of bodies striking the Moon was different during the time interval between the formation of the Humorum and Imbrium basins, or (ii) that selective destruction

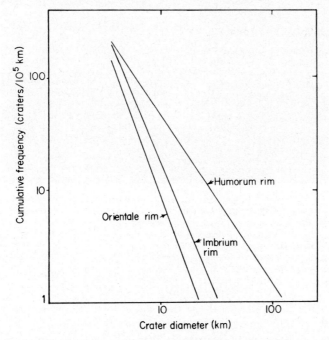

FIGURE 10   Comparison of the cumulative crater frequencies on the rims of the Orientale, Imbrium, and Humorum basins. [By A. R. Kelly]

or burial of smaller craters has occurred under constant flux conditions because of saturation bombardment of the more ancient Humorum rim. An alternate possibility is that volcanism or other depositional processes occurred in post-Humorum time, burying large numbers of the smaller craters. The present telescopic data are insufficient to test these different hypotheses.

In the Grimaldi region, relatively smooth materials of intermediate albedo interpreted to be Orientale ejecta appear to overlie darker rougher Humorum ejecta north of the crater Fontana[14]. In the Montes Riphaeus region, a similar superposition relation may exist between Imbrium- and Humorum-related material[33]; present photography is not, however, good enough for confirmation. No superposition relations between Orientale and Imbrium have been observed because the two basins are so widely separated, and the intervening area is covered by younger mare material of Oceanus Procellarum.

The relative youth of the Orientale basin is also suggested by the freshness of the concentric structures, their great relative relief, and the preservation of hummocky

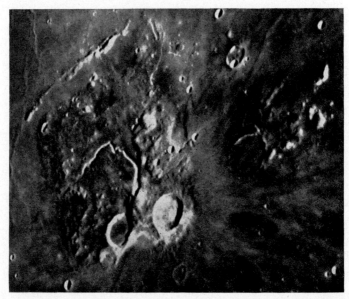

FIGURE 11   The Aristarchus area (Aristarchus is the large crater in the center, about 40 km in diameter). Features of probable volcanic origin include the craters and associated rilles in the Montes Harbinger area on the eastern edge of the photo and on the dark plateau north of Aristarchus. The most spectacular of these are the Cobra Head and Vallis Schröteri. Other probable volcanic features are the numerous small domes, the smooth patches of very dark material, and the cratered cone at the northeastern edge of the plateau. [Lunar and Planetary Laboratory, Tucson, Arizona, photograph]

texture on the structural blocks of the rim; in contrast, the structural blocks of the Humorum rim are quite smooth and appear somewhat rounded or eroded. The lack of a significant amount of mare material in the central regions of the Orientale basin, in contrast with the degree of filling of the other major basins, suggests that the basin may have formed after the major episode of lunar volcanism when the supply of mare-forming magmatic material was limited.

Noteworthy volcanic features

Whereas the earliest investigations in the region around Mare Imbrium (Copernicus, Kepler, Letronne, and Montes Apenninus regions) tended to emphasize the geology of impact-related units, particularly those of regional extent such as the Fra Mauro Formation, features such as dark plains-forming mare units, chain craters, and dark-halo craters were also mapped and interpreted to be of volcanic origin. Subsequent investigations elsewhere in the equatorial belt over the past four years have led to the recognition of an even greater variety of possible volcanic features attesting to a longer and more complicated history of lunar magmatic activity than previously realized. Brief descriptions of several of the best-documented examples are given below.

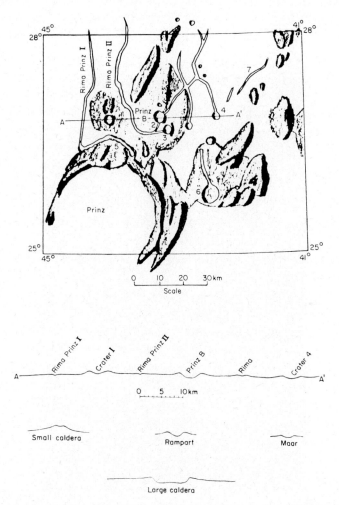

FIGURE 12   Sketch map of the Montes Harbinger area (top) about 130 km northeast of Aristarchus showing the association between small craters and sinuous rilles. Profiles at bottom show the comparison in form between the craters of the Montes Harbinger area along section AA′ and selected terrestrial volcanic features. [By Moore]

Montes Harbinger. A possible volcanic complex in the Montes Harbinger area has been described by Moore[36]. The complex was noted while he was mapping the Aristarchus region (figure 11). It is characterized by an unusual group of craters with associated sinuous rilles. The albedo of these craters is similar to the surrounding mare. The craters are usually located on the crests and flanks of hills but sometimes occur in relatively flat terrain. The rilles commonly originate in the craters, a relationship that cannot be easily explained by the impact theory. Four basic morphologic associations are recognized: (i) hills with apical or flank craters and associated rilles, (ii) hills with apical craters without associated rilles, (iii) craters in gently sloping to flat terrain with associated rilles, and (iv) isolated rilles in flat terrain. Moore finds close agreement between the profiles of these features and selected terrestrial volcanic structure (figure 12). Although the craters in this area compare in form and scale with terrestrial volcanic analogs, interpretation of the sinuous rilles presents a

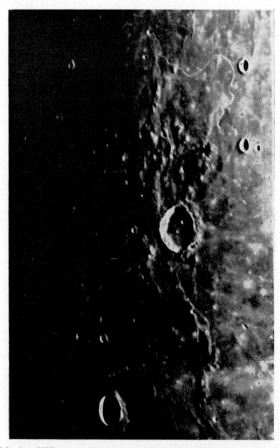

FIGURE 13   Marius Hills area (Marius is large mare-filled crater at right of photo, about 42 km across). Numerous domes, both of the low and steep type, can be seen along with several rimless depressions and rilles just to the north of Marius. [Lick Observatory photograph]

unique problem. They have many of the characteristics of terrestrial erosion channels, and Cameron[37] has suggested that they may be the product of nuée-ardente-type volcanic eruptions, but convincing terrestrial analogs in support of this concept are lacking. Kuiper, Strom, and LePoole[38] have, on the other hand, suggested that they may be drained lava channels and have presented a number of small terrestrial examples that do compare closely in form but not in scale.

A number of additional features also of probable volcanic origin are present in this general region, particularly near Aristarchus[39]. Included are the well-known Cobra Head and Vallis Schröteri, the largest of the sinuous lunar rilles; the numerous very smooth patches of dark material surrounding many of the rilles, and the small clustered domes present throughout the Aristarchus plateau.

Marius Hills. The Marius Hills (informal selenographic name) volcanic complex consists of a large (35 000 km²) southward-dipping plateau, several hundred meters above the surrounding mare but of similar albedo. It is located in the northeastern part of the Hevelius region and is named for the large mare-filled crater Marius at the eastern edge of the complex[40, 41]. Numerous closely spaced domes, three to ten kilometers wide, are superimposed on the smooth-to-undulating parts of the plateau

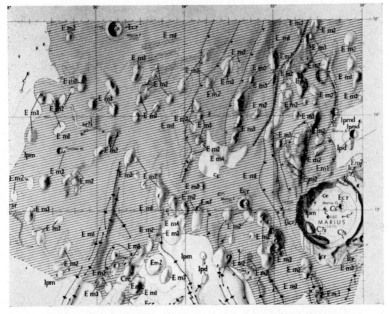

FIGURE 14   Part of the geologic map of the Hevelius region showing the extent of the Marius Group and the distribution of the two types of volcanic domes (Em2, Em3)

surface (figure 13). Two distinctly different types of domes are recognized. The most common are broad, relatively low features of several hundred meters relief with convex-upward profiles, similar in form to mare domes. Half as abundant are steeper sided, higher domes that exhibit as much as 1000 m of local relief. They are locally superimposed on the low type and often have concave-upward flanks (figures 14 and 15). Both types have small summit pits that can be resolved at a large aperture telescope under good seeing conditions.

The complex is considered to be a rock-stratigraphic unit called the Marius Group[38]. Although the albedo of the Marius Group is similar to that of the surrounding mare, the crater density is markedly lower, so that the unit is believed to be significantly younger than the adjacent plains-forming mare material of the Procellarum Group of Imbrian age. It is overlain by rays traceable to Kepler and Aristarchus and is, therefore, older than these Copernican craters. For these reasons and because of its

C_s

Slope material

Characteristics
Albedo very high; typically 0·13–0·14; greater than adjacent crater floor or rim material. Present mostly on relatively smooth interior crater slopes ranging from 20–40 degrees.

Interpretation
Partly sorted, relatively fresh rock fragments ranging in size from dust to large blocks. Derived principally by slumping and spalling of the steep inner walls of craters.

C_{re}

Reiner Gamma Formation

Characteristics
Albedo intermediate, typically about 0·08–0·09. Appears superposed on surrounding units with no topographic expression of its own. Occurs in three patches: the largest has an irregular outline and surrounds two crescent-shaped areas of mare material; the others are linear and trend northeastwards. Type area is Reiner γ 7 1/2° N, 58° W.

Interpretation
The unit is unique on the visible hemisphere of the moon, and no certain Earth analogues are known. It could represent a felsic glowing avalanche (nuee ardente) deposit that originated in the Marius Hills area.

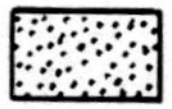

Ray material

Characteristics
Albedo generally high (>0·10); detectability depends on the albedo of the background material. Distribution generally patchy. Appears superposed on all other units with no discernible topographic expression of its own.

Interpretation
Small, telescopically unresolvable, closely spaced, secondary craters with fresh, bright materials on the inner walls. The integrated effect of these bright patches of slope material gives the rays a higher albedo than that of surrounding less cratered material or of older stabilized cratered surfaces.

Copernican System

FIGURE 15 Explanation of geologic map of the Marius Hills area (units not critical to the interpretation omitted)

Ecr

Crater rim material, undifferentiated

Characteristics
Albedo low and uniform, typically 0·06–0·08. Ecr generally around craters less than 20 km in diameter, where topography appears smooth.

Interpretation
The rim materials are genetically similar to Ccr. The concentric ridges of Ecr are interpreted to be the surface expression of slices thrust radially outward from the crater during its formation by impact.

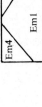

Marius Group

Em4, material of small dome clusters
Em3, material of steep domes
Em2, material of low domes
Em1, smooth undulating material

Characteristics
Occurs on south-dipping plateau surface several hundred meters higher along its northern edge (in the adjacent Seleucus region) than the adjacent maria. Em1 consists of smooth undulating terrain with ridges, small scarps, and plateaus present locally; albedo low and uniform. Em2 consists of domes of convex profile and gentle slopes, typically 2–3 degrees, similar in general form to mare domes (Ipd). Em3 consists of domes having a concave profile and fairly steep slopes, typically 6–7 degrees; several are superimposed on the lower Em2 domes. Many domes of both types are elongated NNE–SSW and some appear to be steeper on the east side. Many domes have small summit pits (some too small to plot on the map) and fine rille-like structures on the flanks. Em4 consists of clusters of domes appear to be similar in form to Em2 domes. Type area is within 150 km west and north of the genetically unrelated crater Marius, from which the name is derived.

Interpretation
Complex series of volcanic flow materials intercalated with some pyroclastic deposits, both derived from the pits at the crests of many of the domes. The difference in form between Em2 and Em3 domes may result from a difference in composition, with Em2 materials mafic and Em3 intermediate to possibly felsic, or from a difference in eruptive processes with lavas of the same composition. The ring of Em2 and Em3 domes directly west of the crater Marius may result from collapse along ring fractures with the subsequent formation of rim volcanoes, the deposits from which nearly fill the original depression. Em1 is the oldest unit, and Em2 is older than Em3 where these units are in contact. The relation of Em4 to Em2 and Em3 is indeterminate.

Eratosthenian System

FIGURE 15 contd. Explanation of geologic map of the Marius Hills area (units not critical to the interpretation omitted)

Imbrian System

Ipmd — Mare material, dark

Characteristics
Albedo typically very low (<0·06); lower than that of Ipm. Topographic characteristics are similar to those of Ipm except for a lower frequency of domes. Generally exhibits a lower crater density and a lower incidence of superposed ray material than Ipm. Occurs along the west margins of Oceanus Procellarum and in small isolated patches in the northeastern part of the region.

Interpretation
Similar genetically to Ipm but probably forms a thin blanket of younger material (possibly Eratosthenian or in part Copernican) covering the older Ipm. Locally, however, it could be contemporaneous with Ipm but be composed of darker, more mafic material.

Ipd / Ipm — Procellarum Group

Ipd, mare dome material
Ipm, mare material

Characteristics
Albedo generally low and uniform; indeterminate where rays are superposed. Ipm forms extensive relative smooth dark areas marked by elongate broad low ridges; terminates abruptly against higher topographic features. Ipd occurs as domes generally elliptical in plan, 3–15 km across and as high as 300 meters; small craters occur on the flanks of many domes; some domes exhibit a cleft along their crests with a small crater at one end.

Interpretation
Ipm is a thick complexly overlapping series of volcanic materials locally covered by a discontinuous thin layer of relatively fine-grained material formed by impact; the wide extent and low relief suggest either mafic flows or ash-flow deposits (ignimbrites) as the principal materials. Ipd domes may be small shield volcanoes of mafic composition, consisting mostly of volcanic flows but perhaps include intercalated volcanic ash.

Icr — Crater rim material

Characteristics
Topography and albedo similar to Eratosthenian and Eratosthenian or Imbrian crater material. The crater floors are generally buried and the rim units embayed by Ipmd.

Interpretation
Impact crater material genetically similar to that of Copernican and Eratosthenian craters. Overlain by dark mare material of late Imbrian (Ipm) or possible post-Imbrian (Ipmd) age.

Contact — Long-dashed where approximately located; queried where indefinitely located; short-dashed where gradational.

(Iplcw)
(Iplcr)
Concealed contact — Formation concealed by younger deposits indicated by symbols in parentheses.

Fault — Bar and ball on apparent downthrown side. Dashed where approximately located; dotted where concealed.

Lineament — Gentle linear scarp or depression. Interpretation: fault or surface expression of buried fault or graben.

Ridge — Line marks crest. Arrow indicates tapered end. Dotted where concealed.

Scarp — Line marks base. Barb points downslope.

C Crater — Crater whose position has been noted on photographs but whose form cannot be determined. Mostly 1–2 km in diameter. Interpretation: may be small nonrayed primary impact crater or satellite crater.

Rille and chain-crater material — Material in straight to gently curving narrow depressions with crater-like enlargements as much as 5 km in diameter along their length. Albedo low to intermediate. Interpretation: volcano-tectonic depressions and craters.

Sinuous rille — Narrow depressions, commonly with a meandering pattern; in places have associated small craters. Albedo of inner walls intermediate to high. Interpretation: may be erosion channels cut by fluidized volcanic ejecta.

Concealed ficrater — Symbol marks rim crest.

Slump block — Arrows show direction of movement.

Rimless depression — Irregular to circular. Interpretation: collapse feature or landslide scar.

FIGURE 15 contd. Explanation of geologic map of the Marius Hills area (units not critical to the interpretation omitted)

stratigraphic superposition on the adjacent mare of the Procellarum Group, the Marius Group has been assigned an Eratosthenian age.

The differences in morphology of the domes may reflect changes in the composition of the magmatic material from which they were formed. The steeper domes, by analogy to numerous terrestrial examples, such as those of northern California[42], may have formed from more viscous material of higher silica content than the earlier low type. In the terrestrial case, the change in form and composition of features of this type is generally attributed to differentiation in the magma chamber with time. This region, then, presents an interesting petrogenic problem and is considered important for an understanding of lunar igneous processes.

Young dark blanketing units. During the early geological investigations[1], numerous dark-halo craters that interrupt or truncate rim material and rays of Copernican craters were noted. These were interpreted to mean that volcanism had occurred up through the most recent period of lunar history. Later workers have discovered many examples of dark smooth units that blanket subjacent surfaces of considerable relief. These dark units commonly surround craters or rilles near the major concentric scarps or faults on the margins of the large lunar basins. They either show a markedly lower crater density than the Imbrian Procellarum Group or are superposed on or intersect stratigraphic units of Eratosthenian to Copernican age. They are interpreted to be of volcanic origin, and, because of their mantling characteristics, to consist mostly of pyroclastic material.

Carr[43], mapping in the southern part of Mare Serenitatis, noted a number of areas with very low albedo around rilles, such as the Sulpicius Gallus system (figure 16). The dark materials appear to overlap both the terrae and the adjacent maria but to have little or no intrinsic relief. They have been interpreted as being young pyroclastic deposits formed after the major mare-basin-filling episode in this area.

A volcanic unit of very low albedo, the Cavalerius Formation, surrounding the site of the Soviet surface probe, *Luna 9* (figures 17 and 18), has recently been mapped by McCauley[41]. The unit also has no intrinsic topographic expression but rather is draped over a cratered terra surface of considerable local relief (ACIC measurements, LAC 56, indicate a maximum of about 1000 m in this area). Subjacent units include (i) most of the rim of a partially ruined, unnamed Imbrian crater north of Cavalerius, (ii) the northern part of the rim of Cavalerius, of probable Eratosthenian age, and (iii) the adjacent mare which in this area is darker and less cratered than the mare of the Procellarum Group and, therefore, of questionable Imbrian age. The Cavalerius Formation appears to truncate rays from Olbers A, a Copernican crater some 200 km to the west, and has been assigned a Copernican age. The manner in which it blankets a topographically and genetically varied underlying surface suggests a pyroclastic origin.

Regional Nature of the Lunar Surface

Meaningful absolute time correlations between the rock units related to each of the basins discussed in this chapter are not yet possible; their relative ages are, however, reasonably well established. Separate stratigraphic columns for each basin have been developed and materials that predate the basin, materials essentially contemporaneous with the formation of the basin itself (the major ejecta blankets such as the Fra Mauro Formation), and materials that clearly postdate basin formation are mapped. From the distribution of these materials, a generalized picture of the geologic history of the western hemisphere can be constructed.

The ejecta blanket of each basin was deposited on a surface characterized by an

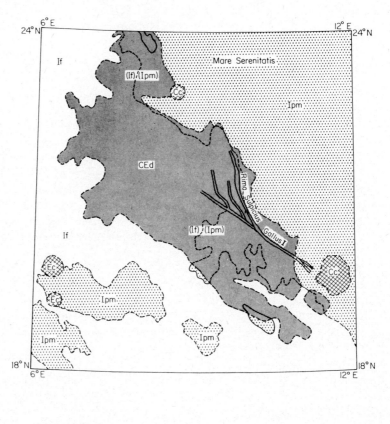

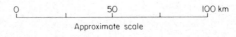

Approximate scale

FIGURE 16   Geologic sketch map showing the extent of smooth dark blanketing material on the southwest margin of Mare Serenitatis. CEd is the dark blanketing material; Ipm, mare material of the Procellarum Group: If, Fra Mauro Formation; Cc, Copernican crater materials; Ec, Eratosthenian crater materials. [By Carr[43]]

abundance of very large (100 to 200 km in diameter) but relatively shallow, closely spaced to overlapping craters. The basins, then, demonstrably postdate an earlier episode of large-crater formation. Filling of these basins probably began shortly after formation by impact, climaxed in the Humorum and Imbrium basins at the end of Imbrian time with deposition of mare material of the Procellarum Group. Formation of the Orientale basin apparently postdated the magmatic climax, as evidenced by the small quantity of mare material present in the inner basin. Many of the dark mare plains-forming units peripheral to the major basins and located near rilles or

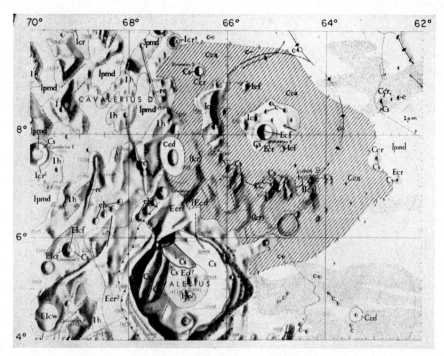

FIGURE 17   Part of the geologic map of the Hevelius region showing the extent of some
of the dark blanketing material (Cca) near the western edge of Oceanus Procellarum.
The *Luna 9* landing site is within this unit

other tectonic features formed in early post-Imbrian time. Several good examples of post-Imbrian constructional volcanic features exist, such as those in the Montes Harbinger area and in the Marius Hills. Several dark blanketing units, some of which overlie the mare–terra contacts, can be shown to be of Copernican age since they interrupt recognizable Copernican crater materials. A long interval of impact cratering followed the formation and filling of the major basins. The older of these topographically fresh craters have lost detectable rays either by micrometeorite bombardment or by solar radiation darkening. The younger ones, however, show well-developed radial ray patterns which are locally superimposed on all other lunar stratigraphic units.

In summary, systematic geological investigations of the lunar equatorial belt have led to the recognition that the lunar crust has a very complex geological history. The major processes responsible for its present configuration are impact and volcanism. Both of these processes have played significant roles from the earliest days of decipherable lunar history, and the inferred products of each can be mapped and arranged in relative age sequences. Fundamental unresolved problems, such as the method of emplacement of the inferred volcanic materials, their composition, and the details of the impact process are among the many unanswered questions that will have to await larger-scale unmanned and manned surface investigations. The mapping program described is but a prelude to this effort.

Cca Cavalerius Formation

Characteristics
Albedo very low (<0·06). Present on flanks of Cavalerius, where it subdues but does not conceal subjacent topography; extends over parts of the adjacent mare surface. Has no intrinsic relief. Appears to truncate rays radial to the Copernican crater Olbers A, approximately 250 km northwest of Cavalerius. Type area is north flank of crater Cavalerius, 7° N, 66° W.

Interpretation
Pyroclastic material for the most part, but may include flows on the mare plain.

Cs Slope material

Characteristics
Albedo very high; typically 0·13–0·14 and greater than adjacent crater floor or rim material. Present mostly on relatively smooth interior crater slopes ranging from 20–40 degrees.

Interpretation
Partly sorted, relatively fresh rock fragments ranging in size from dust to large blocks. Derived principally by slumping and spalling of the steep inner walls of craters.

Ccr Crater rim material

Characteristics
Albedo generally high (>0·10); detectability depends on the albedo of the background material. Surrounds craters 2–3 km in diameter; topography appears smooth at the limit of resolution. Rim material grades outward from some craters to small patches of ray material.

Interpretation
Impact crater ejecta. Poorly sorted crushed rock possibly containing scattered large blocks. Block size and thickness are maximum near the crater rim.

Ray material

Characteristics
Albedo generally high (>0·10); detectability depends on the albedo of the background material. Distribution generally patchy. Appears superposed on all other units with no discernible topographic expression of its own.

Interpretation
Small, telescopically unresolvable, closely spaced, secondary craters with fresh, bright materials on the inner walls. The integrated effect of these bright patches of slope material gives the rays a higher albedo than that of surrounding less cratered material or of older stabilized cratered surfaces.

Cd Dark-halo crater material

Characteristics
Albedo very low, same as that of Cca. Forms craters and surrounding halos or aprons having little or no detectable relief. Appears to interrupt Copernican rays.

Interpretation
Volcanic craters surrounded by pyroclastic ejecta.

Copernican System

FIGURE 18   Explanation of the geologic map of the *Luna 9* landing area (units not critical to the interpretation omitted)

| Ecr | Ecf | Ecp |

Crater material

Ecr, rim material, undifferentiated
Ecf, floor material
Ecp, peak material

Characteristics

Albedo low and uniform, typically 0·06–0·08. Ecr generally around craters less than 20 km in diameter, where topography appears smooth; hummocky and radial topography and possible faint rays not differentiated in Ecr around Cavalerius. Ecf is smooth to slightly hummocky. Ecp forms smooth but steep hills near center of crater.

Interpretation

The rim materials are genetically similar to Ccr. The concentric ridges of Ecr are interpreted to be the surface expression of slices thrust radially outwards from the crater during its formation by impact, and parts of Ecr consist of ballistically deposited ejecta. Ecf is brecciated bedrock and fine impact ejecta that has fallen back into the crater and may also include slumped wall material; breccia may form a relatively deep lens beneath the crater. Ecp may consist of brecciated bedrock uplifted during or after impact or may be volcanic material produced later than the crater. Crater Cavalerius may be of Copernican age if nearby rays are derived from it.

Contact

Long-dashed where approximately located; queried where indefinitely located; short-dashed where gradational.

(Icr) ········· (Ecr)
Concealed contact

Formation concealed by younger deposits indicated by symbols in parentheses.

Fault

Bar and ball on apparent downthrown side. Dashed where approximately located; dotted where concealed.

Lineament

Gentle linear scarp or depression. Interpretation: fault or surface expression of buried fault or graben.

Thrust fault

Saw teeth on upper plate. Interpretation: sole of blocks thrust from crater at low angle and thinly buried by ballistically deposited ejecta.

Ridge

Line marks crest. Arrow indicates tapered end. Dotted where concealed.

Concealed crater

Symbol marks rim crest.

Slump block

Arrows show direction of movement.

Rimless depression

Irregular to circular. Interpretation: collapse feature or landslide scar.

ch
Chain-crater material

Rimless to low-rimmed aligned craters, 6 km in diameter or less, that either overlap or are closely spaced. Interpretation: volcanic craters of the maar type, collapse depressions, or possibly satellitic craters.

Ⓒ Crater

Crater whose position has been noted on photographs but whose form cannot be determined. Mostly 1–2 km in diameter. Interpretation: may be small nonrayed primary impact crater or satellitic crater.

rc
Rille and chain-crater material

Material in straight to gently curving narrow depressions with crater-like enlargements as much as 5 km in diameter along their length. Albedo low to intermediate. Interpretation: volcano-tectonic depressions and craters.

FIGURE 18 contd.   Explanation of the geologic map of the *Luna 9* landing area (units not critical to the interpretation omitted)

Icr Icf

Crater material

Icr, rim material
Icf, floor material

Characteristics
Topography and albedo, except for Icf, similar to Eratosthenian and Eratosthenian or Imbrian crater material. Icf is rough, densely cratered, and has numerous small rilles; it occupies the central tumescence of the large, mostly flooded crater north of Cavalerius. The crater floors are generally buried and the rim units embayed by Ipmd.

Interpretation
Impact crater material genetically similar to that of Copernican and Eratosthenian craters. Includes all crater material overlying the Hevelius Formation (Ih) and overlain by dark mare material of late Imbrian (Ipm) or possible post-Imbrian (Ipmd) age.

Ih

Hevelius Formation

Characteristics
Relatively smooth material with a fine hummocky to braided texture (hummocks less than 1/2 km across); texture is progressively coarser in the direction of Mare Orientale (the center of which lies about 1000 km to the southwest of the Hevelius region). Fine texture, including numerous small pits, best seen visually, but coarser hummocky texture about 100 km to the southwest is photographically resolvable. Albedo not uniform; generally intermediate to high. Type area is western part of the floor of the crater Hevelius near 2° N, 68° W.

Interpretation
Ejecta from the impact that formed the Orientale Basin. Consists of poorly sorted crushed rock with scattered blocks less than 1/2 km in size. May contain patches of smooth material of local derivation in small depressions; mantles the crater Hevelius.

Ipmd

Mare material, dark

Characteristics
Albedo typically very low (>0·06); lower than that of Ipm. Topographic characteristics are similar to those of Ipm except for a lower frequency of domes. Generally exhibits a lower crater density and a lower incidence of superposed ray material than Ipm. Occurs mostly along the west margins of Oceanus Procellarum.

Interpretation
Similar genetically to Ipm but probably forms a thin blanket of younger material (possibly Eratosthenian or in part Copernican) covering the older Ipm. Locally, however, it could be contemporaneous with Ipm but be composed of darker, more mafic material.

Ipm

Mare material

Characteristics
Albedo generally low and uniform; indeterminate where rays are superposed. Ipm forms extensive relatively smooth dark areas marked by elongate broad low ridges; terminates abruptly against higher topographic features.

Interpretation
Ipm is a thick complexly overlapping series of volcanic materials locally covered by a discontinuous thin layer of relatively fine-grained material formed by impact; the wide extent and low relief suggest either mafic flows or ash-flow deposits (ignimbrites) as the principal materials.

Imbrian System

FIGURE 18 contd.   Explanation of the geologic map of the *Luna 9* landing area (units not critical to the interpretation omitted)

Acknowledgements

The author wishes particularly to acknowledge the efforts of his colleagues, D. E. Wilhelms, N. J. Trask, and M. H. Carr, who contributed significantly to this chapter by means of discussion and careful technical review. A. R. Kelly prepared the crater frequency curves and many of the illustrations. The cooperation of the many authors whose work is cited is also gratefully acknowledged. Conclusions and figures not accompanied by a specific reference are the work of the author.

References

1. E. M. Shoemaker, 'Interpretation of lunar craters', in *Physics and Astronomy of the Moon* (Ed. Z. Kopal), Academic Press, New York, 1962, pp. 283–359.
2. E. M. Shoemaker and R. J. Hackman, 'Stratigraphic basis for a lunar time scale', in *The Moon, Intern. Astron. Union Symp., 14th* (Eds. Z. Kopal and Z. K. Mikhailov), Academic Press, London, 1962, pp. 289–99.
3. G. K. Gilbert, *Phil. Soc. Wash.*, **9**, 241–92 (1893).
4. R. E. Eggleton, *U.S. Geol. Astrogeological Studies Ann. Progr. Rept., August 25, 1961, to August 24, 1962*, 19–30 (1963).
5. R. S. Dietz, *J. Geol.*, **54**, 359–75 (1946).
6. R. B. Baldwin, *The Face of the Moon*, University of Chicago Press, Chicago, 1949.
7. H. C. Urey, *Geochim. Cosmochim. Acta*, **1**, 209–77 (1951).
8. G. P. Kuiper, *Proc. Natl. Acad. Sci. U.S.A.*, **40**, 1096–112 (1954).
9. E. M. Shoemaker, R. J. Hackman, R. E. Eggleton, and C. H. Marshall, *U.S. Geol. Surv., Astrogeologic Studies Semiann. Progr. Rept., February 26, 1961, to August 24, 1961*, 113–6 (1962).
10. R. J. Hackman, *U.S. Geol. Surv. Misc. Geol. Invest. Map I-355* (1962).
11. C. H. Marshall, *U.S. Geol. Surv. Misc. Geol. Invest. Map I-385* (1963).
12. E. M. Shoemaker, R. J. Hackman, and R. E. Eggleton, *Advan. Astronaut. Sci.*, **8**, 70–89 (1962).
13. R. T. Dodd, J. W. Salisbury, and V. G. Smalley, *Icarus*, **2**, 466–80 (1963).
14. J. F. McCauley, *U.S. Geol. Surv., Astrogeologic Studies Ann. Progr. Rept., July 1, 1963, to July 1, 1964*, Pt. A, 28–32 (1964).
15. M. H. Carr, *U.S. Geol. Surv., Astrogeologic Studies Ann. Progr. Rept., August 25, 1962, to July 1, 1963*, Pt. A, 9–23 (1964).
16. M. H. Carr, *U.S. Geol. Surv., Astrogeologic Studies Ann. Progr. Rept., July 1, 1963, to July 1, 1964*, Pt. A, 52–66 (1964).
17. American Commission on Stratigraphic Nomenclature, *Bull. Petrol. Geologists*, **45**, 645–65 (1961).
18. R. E. Eggleton, *U.S. Geol. Surv. Misc. Geol. Invest. Map I-458* (1965).
19. R. J. Hackman, *U.S. Geol. Surv. Misc. Geol. Invest. Map I-463* (1966).
20. R. E. Eggleton, *U.S. Geol. Surv., Astrogeologic Studies Ann. Progr. Rept., August 25, 1962, to July 1, 1963*, Pt. A, 46–63 (1964).
21. D. E. Wilhelms, *U.S. Geol. Surv., Astrogeologic Studies Ann. Progr. Rept., July 1, 1963, to July 1, 1964*, Pt. A, 1–16 (1964).
22. D. E. Wilhelms, *U.S. Geol. Surv., Astrogeologic Studies Ann. Progr. Rept., July 1, 1964, to July 1, 1965*, Pt. A, 13–27 (1965).
23. D. P. Elston, *U.S. Geol. Surv., Astrogeologic Studies Ann. Progr. Rept., August 25, 1962, to July 1, 1963*, Pt. A, 99–109 (1964).
24. R. J. Hackman, *U.S. Geol. Surv., Astrogeologic Studies Ann. Progr. Rept., August 25, 1961, to August 25, 1962*, Pt. A, 2–10 (1963).
25. D. J. Milton, *U.S. Geol. Surv., Astrogeologic Studies Ann. Progr. Rept., July 1, 1963, to July 1, 1964*, Pt. A, 17–27 (1964).

26. J. F. McCauley, *U.S. Geol. Surv., Astrogeologic Studies Ann. Progr. Rept., August 25, 1962, to July 1, 1963*, Pt. A, 86–98 (1964).
27. S. R. Titley, *U.S. Geol. Surv., Astrogeologic Studies Ann. Progr. Rept., August 25, 1962, to July 1, 1963*, Pt. A, 64–73 (1964).
28. W. K. Hartmann and G. P. Kuiper, *Commun. Lunar Planetary Lab., Ariz. Univ.*, **1**, 51–72 (1962).
29. W. K. Hartmann, *Commun. Lunar Planetary Lab., Ariz. Univ.*, **2**, 175–92 (1964).
30. W. L. Quaide, D. E. Gault, and R. H. Schmidt, *Ann. N. Y. Acad. Sci.*, **123**, 563–72 (1965).
31. H. Masursky, *U.S. Geol. Surv., Astrogeologic Studies Ann. Progr. Rept., July 1, 1963, to July 1, 1964*, Pt. A, 102–34 (1964).
32. Z. F. Daněs, *U.S. Geol. Surv., Astrogeologic Studies Ann. Progr. Rept., July 1, 1964, to July 1, 1965*, Pt. A, 81–100 (1965).
33. S. R. Titley and R. E. Eggleton, *U.S. Geol. Surv., Astrogeologic Studies Ann. Progr. Rept., July 1, 1963, to July 1, 1964*, Pt. A, 85–9 (1964).
34. S. R. Titley, *U.S. Geol. Surv. Misc. Geol. Invest. Map I-495* (1966).
35. N. J. Trask and S. R. Titley, *U.S. Geol. Surv. Misc. Geol. Invest. Map I-485* (1966).
36. H. J. Moore, *U.S. Geol. Surv., Astrogeologic Studies Ann. Progr. Rept., July 1, 1963, to July 1, 1964*, Pt. A, 42–51 (1964).
37. W. S. Cameron, *J. Geophys. Res.*, **69**, 2423–30 (1964).
38. G. P. Kuiper, R. G. Strom, and R. S. LePoole, 'Interpretation of the *Ranger* records', in *Ranger VIII and IX, Jet Propulsion Lab. Tech. Rept. No.* 32-800, Pt. II, 35–248 (1966).
39. H. J. Moore, private communication.
40. J. F. McCauley, *U.S. Geol. Surv., Astrogeologic Studies Ann. Progr. Rept., July 1, 1964, to July 1, 1965*, Pt. A, 115–22 (1965).
41. J. F. McCauley, *U.S. Geol. Surv. Misc. Geol. Invest. Map I-491* (1966).
42. C. A. Anderson, *Calif. Univ. Publ. Geol. Sci.*, **25**, 347–422 (1941).
43. M. H. Carr, *U.S. Geol. Surv., Astrogeologic Studies Ann. Progr. Rept., July 1, 1964, to July 1, 1965*, Pt. A, 35–43 (1965).

9

G. FIELDER

University of London Observatory
Mill Hill Park
London, England

Evidence for volcanism and faulting on the Moon

Lunar and Terrestrial Craters Compared

Terrestrial features which resemble the so-called 'craters' of the Moon are of many different types. Geologists recognize, among others, lava sink holes, maars, impact craters, volcanic craters, calderas, and volcano-tectonic depressions, classed in order of increasing size. A thorough study of the morphology and positioning of the sub-circular features on the Moon leads to the conclusion that they are dispersed, in similar fashion to the terrestrial objects, through a whole spectrum of some forty types[1]. Furthermore, the lunar features do not grade uniformly from the largest mare to the smallest crater. Therefore it is most unlikely that they shared a common origin.

Comparison of the measured profiles of lunar and terrestrial features may be used to demonstrate that the large circular objects on the Moon (figure 1) are remarkably

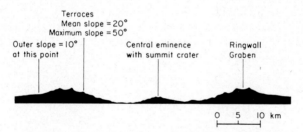

FIGURE 1   Typical profile of a large lunar ring structure

similar to certain types of volcanic structure such as the Niuafo'ou ring caldera (figure 2) in the Pacific. Fielder[1] has listed eighty named igneous structures on the Earth larger than 5 km in diameter, and these are comparable with the large lunar objects, whereas the relatively few established terrestrial impact craters (which are, in addition, all smaller than 5 km in diameter) are similar only to some of the smaller lunar features.

Cone volcanoes are inconspicuous to the casual lunar observer, but individual 'positive' volcanic structures, nevertheless, exist on the Moon. There are many lunar shields, or domes, with approximately circular summit craters—for example, near to Cauchy—some of which have been discussed by McCauley (see section VIII, chapter 8

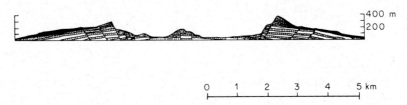

FIGURE 2 Section across the volcanic structure Niuafo'ou (drawn with the vertical scale twice the horizontal scale)

of this book). Many mountain peaks—for instance the two peaks near to Archimedes X in Mare Imbrium—carry summit craters, too.

The word 'peak' is misleading since these objects commonly slope at only 10° or 20° to the horizontal and, when near to the terminator, their pointed shadows suggest steeply inclined faces rather than gentle rises. It is important to note this difference, because invariably the hill or mountain top crater is found at the very highest point, even though the total area of peak where an impact crater could have formed is considerable. Statistical arguments based on present data on summit craters neither support nor preclude the impact hypothesis and, for the reasons given, it is probable that the majority of the summit craters are volcanic.

With the improved surface resolution afforded by the *Ranger* photography the incidence of known summit craters per unit of the Moon's surface has increased. A clear-cut crater 250 m in diameter appears (figure 3) on the rim of a 1·3 km crater in frames of the *Ranger 9*, series B, and there is an apron of material extending from the smaller crater into the larger one. The volume of matter in this apron is so large that it cannot possibly have been generated by the displacement of rim material from the larger crater during an impact process which, one may presume, formed the smaller crater. Rather, it seems that the excess of material must have been generated by volcanic forces, and that the smaller crater caps a lunar volcanic cone.

There are other probable volcanoes in the same region. The statement that the lunar craters and rings are quite unlike terrestrial volcanic features is an argument which is demonstrably incorrect.

Elliptical Craters on the Moon

Elliptical, oval, elongated, or contiguous craters perched at the highest points along the axis of a narrow lunar ridge lineament, or set in the axis of a rille, demonstrate the extent and significance of the volcanic process on the Moon. Elliptical craters on ridges are commonplace and always occur with their longest axis in line with the axial trend of the ridge. No impact phenomenon is capable of producing this particular configuration. The relation is observed, however, in certain terrestrial volcanic regions and has its explanation in the extrusion of materials from a controlling fissure, with subsequent induration of a layered lava ridge.

Although known to lunar observers, few of these elliptical ridge-crest craters have been photographed. One recorded by *Ranger 7* is reproduced in figure 4, and elliptical rille craters, photographed by *Ranger 9*, are shown in figure 5. The latter are almost certainly collapse craters (see p. 468). Some of the elliptical rille craters in Alphonsus

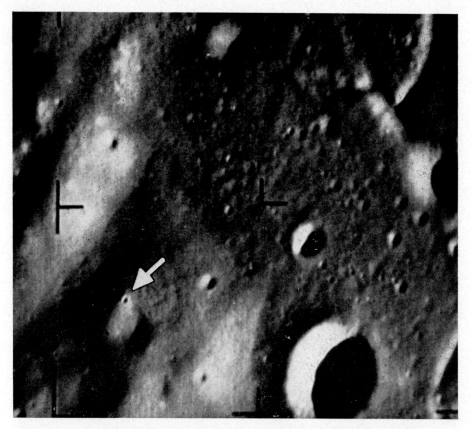

FIGURE 3   A probable lunar cone volcano with a crater 250 m in diameter. The volcano is situated on the rim of a larger crater 1·3 km in diameter. [*Ranger 9* photo]

FIGURE 4   An elliptical ridge-crest crater photographed by *Ranger 7*

FIGURE 5   Rille craters in Alphonsus demonstrating collapse [*Ranger 9* photo]

are surrounded by dark patches, and the evidence points to their being aerial deposits. Light, rather than dark, rays are associated, on the other hand, with probable impact craters.

In addition to the craters on ridges and those in rilles, elliptical craters and elliptical rings (figure 6) occur in the maria. In the majority of cases it may be shown that their major axes lie in directions that parallel established tectonic trends, so that their production by glancing impacts is most improbable.

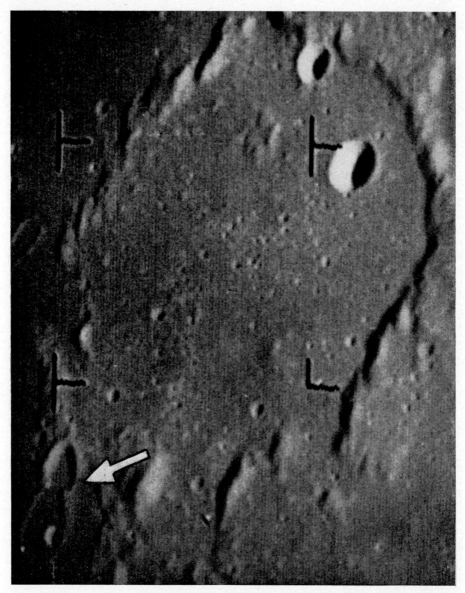

FIGURE 6 Elliptical crater rings near Guericke in Mare Nubium [*Ranger 7* photo]

Analysis of a Cluster of Craters Photographed by *Ranger 7*

A remarkable cluster of craters was recorded on one of the later A frames of *Ranger 7* (figure 7). Several of the craters in the group are elongated or contiguous, forming chains. The distribution of circular crater centres in the region is definitely non-random, and primary impacts would not be expected to have such a distribution unless the meteoroids were travelling together in a compact family. There is no independent evidence that meteoroids travel in groups, and it has been argued that the

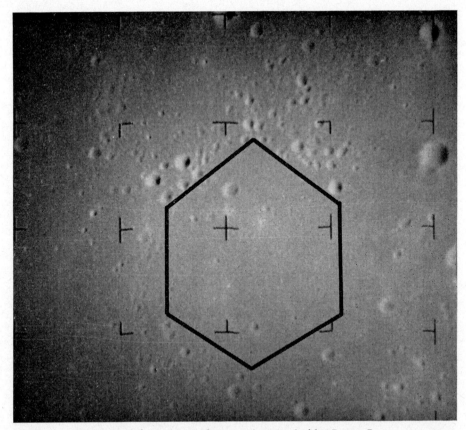

<figure>FIGURE 7   A cluster of craters photographed by *Ranger 7*</figure>

'clumpiness' of the crater distribution is a result of secondary impacts produced by throw-out from a primary impact (or volcanic) crater such as Tycho or Copernicus.

An answer to this question derives from a statistical analysis of the azimuths of the major axes of elongated objects and chains of craters visible in the *Ranger 7* photographs. The position angles of 136 such lineaments in an area of 20×20 km^2 around the impact point were measured on a rectified chart prepared by the Aeronautical Chart and Information Center of the U.S. Air Force (ACIC) and, again, in a control zone having outer bounds measuring 56×56 km^2 around this impact area. Both frequency diagrams (figure 8) showed strong maxima in the meridional direction and peaks, separated from the north–south direction by lacunae, trending approximately 40° east and west (astronomical convention) of the meridian.

The directions of possible primary craters which might have been responsible for secondary craters in the impact area are due north (Copernicus) and 15° west of south (Tycho). Evidently, Copernicus is a possible source of elongated secondary craters trending meridionally but the direction of Tycho is not coincident with any of the three directions that are strongly represented in figure 8. However, the frequency pattern does correlate closely with the trends of regional lineaments, and this suggests that the majority of the elongates and chains of craters are controlled by endogenic factors.

Tycho

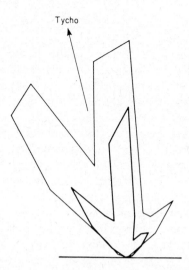

FIGURE 8   Frequency diagrams of lineaments in the region covered by figure 7. The inner pattern reflects trends in the 'impact zone' and the outer pattern (thinner lines) refers to the 'control zone'. The direction of Tycho is indicated

To recapitulate there are, in this cluster, (i) subcircular craters which are very significantly grouped together, and (ii) elongates and chains with preferred directions. Broadly speaking, the circular craters are more sharply defined than the smooth-rimmed elongated craters. One may superimpose a regular hexagon upon the group of craters in figure 7 such that the crater density outside the bounds of the hexagon is in every direction greater than the crater density within it, and the cluster of craters under discussion avoids the region within the imaginary hexagon. This region has a different reflectivity from the terrain outside the hexagon. It is pertinent to ask why, if the elongated craters were produced by secondary ejecta from Copernicus, they should have formed in exactly the same peculiarly and closely defined region as the more circular craters.

Secondly, on the secondary ejecta hypothesis (which may, in any case, account only for the north–south peak on the frequency diagram) the more sharply sculptured circular craters would have to be considerably younger than the shallower elongates. Did ejections from Copernicus occur at widely separated times and still give rise, each time, to the very specially defined distribution observed? This would be implausible in the extreme, and all these reasons seem sufficient to reject the secondary impact hypothesis and label the cluster of craters as predominantly of internal origin.

One of two hypotheses is preferred here. In either case, it is thought that the cluster marks a region of weakness in the lunar crust. The different forms of the craters could be a result of their being of different type; or spasmodic activity could have given rise to craters of different ages.

Many of the lunar ring structures are hexagonal and, in particular, the line joining the centre of the hexagon to a vertex makes an angle of $60n$ degrees with the meridian, where $n = 0, 1, \ldots, 5$. The hexagon discussed here also has this property, so it is tempting to suggest that *Ranger 7* photographed a hexagonal ring structure in the earliest stages of development, following the anagenetic process proposed by Fielder[1].

Field Lineaments

Experimenters who first examined the last p frames (those giving the highest ground resolution) of *Ranger 7* were puzzled by an apparent striation of the terrain on a scale of a metre or so. Elongated craters with their longest axes set in the same direction as the overall trend prompted the suggestion that the motion of the cameras prior to impact had produced a blurred image of the landscape; yet calculations showed that this effect was insufficient to account for the observations and, in any case, some circular—apparently undistorted—craters were present in the same field. It was decided that the lineamentation of the terrain was real.

Even more striking sets of fine, parallel lineaments are in evidence on the last A frames of *Ranger 9* on the 10-metre scale (figure 9). These lineaments take the form of ridges, crater alignments, and depressions and seem to occur everywhere on the Moon.

The larger-scale components have been known to telescopic observers for a long time[2] and the entire system of lunar lineaments has been described as the lunar grid system. In some parts of the Moon one set of parallel topographic markings predominates; elsewhere equally developed intersecting sets of lineaments may be found.

At pre-*Ranger* resolution the lunar lineaments are known to be related to crustal faults or at least to underlying fractures, and the faults and fractures are the result of shearing or tension. It has been argued[3] that the underlying cause of the shear stresses is a crustal drag originating in the particular mode of convection in the body of the Moon that Runcorn[4] proposed in order to account for the differences in the Moon's principal moments of inertia. This solution provides an adequate explanation of the very particular boundary condition imposed by the observed pattern of Moon-wide lineaments, and no other explanation has been proposed. It is probable, therefore, that the fine, lineamented structure observed at the metre scale on the *Ranger* photographs is controlled by underlying fractures or shear faults.

Of great significance is the fact that this structure, which gives the Moon's surface a 'raked-over' appearance—but punctured also with parallel rows of tiny craters—cannot have been formed exogenically. In the first instance, glancing encounters with meteorites or secondary ejecta would not produce uniform rows of furrows and circular craters in strongly preferred directions considerably inclined to the Moon's equator. Secondly, the fine lineaments form the natural extrapolation to smaller sizes from the coarser lineaments that are known to have an internal origin (see p. 462). One would indeed expect the craters forming chains parallel to the principal trend in any given region to be of internal origin; but the surprising observation that one is forced to draw from the *Ranger* photography is that the incidence of meteoritic impacts producing craters of metre size and larger is so low that the character of the terrain that was impressed in the first instance by endogenic factors has not been destroyed. We are looking not so much at the haphazardly distributed 'meteor slag' of Sytinskaya[5] as at the ordered effects of activity originating within the Moon itself.

Lunar Collapse Craters

All three *Ranger* vehicles provided pictures of a number of funnel-shaped craters, each with very little or no raised rim. Because of their shape, the shadows cast within

FIGURE 9   Rake-like markings on the last A frame of *Ranger 9*

them are characteristically different from those in craters of more common profile. Some of the funnels appear to come to a point at the base, whilst others are dimple shaped (figure 10).

Funnel-shaped depressions can be produced by explosions (or meteorites) in a medium that behaves like a gravel[6]. However, numerous craters of more conventional shape are found in their immediate vicinity on the Moon and one would be in difficulty to explain why there should be abrupt changes in the texture of the lunar materials only in those places where the funnel craters occur. The objects are, however, characteristic of the sink holes found in terrestrial lava fields such as the Mauna Loa flows in Hawaii or the New Mexico flows recorded by Kuiper[7].

Rilles are known to be collapse features and the association between normal rilles and crater chains, into which many rilles degenerate, has been studied for years— particularly by Warner[8]. Figure 5 shows that the crater progression associated with one of the rilles in Alphonsus is one of depressions without raised rims, and craters of this

M.E.—16

FIGURE 10   A dimple crater photographed by *Ranger 8*

form are generally regarded to be of collapse origin. It is therefore no surprise that they link with a rille.

Finally, *Luna 9* recorded at least three depressions, each of the order of 10 m across, which are similar to the somewhat larger pits, or calderas, that form a chain along the eastern rift zone of Hawaii. Like the Hawaiian collapse pits, these *Luna 9* features appear to have no rims raised above the surrounding country. The undoubted presence of craters of collapse on the Moon speaks independently for a terrain shaped by underlying fissures and volcanism.

The Origin of the Lunar Craters

The long controversy over the origin of the circular lunar surface features is surely winding to an end. The question is no longer whether the lunar craters are volcanic or impact features. Even Baldwin[9], the leading advocate of the impact hypothesis, acknowledges that at least some of the smaller craters on the Moon are of internal origin. As the author sees it, the question now concerns the *proportion* of internal to impact craters. It is important, therefore, to develop methods for discriminating between endogenic and impact craters in order to form ratios of numbers of each type within convenient size brackets. Some exploratory methods and provisional results will be discussed briefly.

Present-day asteroidal data have been used by Fielder[1] to estimate the cumulative number of asteroidal impact craters expected on the Moon in its lifetime. Kiang[10] corrected asteroid counts for incompleteness of observation and, using his corrected data, it may be shown that possibly ten per cent of the lunar craters larger than 6 km in diameter are of impact origin. This does not prove that most of the large lunar rings are endogenic, for the space density of interplanetary debris may have exceeded its present value in the past. On the other hand, there may have been fewer objects available for collisions with the Moon in the past. All the results show, therefore, is that the suggestion that most of the lunar circular objects are of internal origin is not inconsistent with what we know about asteroidal impacts. This is a necessary, but not sufficient, condition to rule that endogenic craters and rings on the Moon outnumber lunar impact craters.

Of 157 of the craters between 1·5 km and 3·8 km in diameter that lie in the southern floor of Ptolemaeus (photographed by *Ranger 9*), some 40% of them are members of well-defined crater chains. Furthermore, the chains run in strongly preferred directions[11], that correlate well with the trends of tectonic lineaments mapped by Strom and Palm[12] outside, but in the immediate vicinity of, Ptolemaeus. Therefore it appears that at least 40% of the craters counted are of internal origin.

Kuiper[13] has counted the numbers of craters with and without raised rims in the *Ranger 9* photographs of the floor of Alphonsus and has concluded that as many as 80% to 90% of the craters are rimless craters of collapse, and that the remainder are impact craters.

In an earlier chapter McCauley (see section VIII, chapter 8 of this book) has described some of the results now emerging from the extensive selenological mapping programme of the U.S. Geological Survey. Using rim-profile and stratigraphic criteria to define the type and geological period of a crater, he has estimated that at least 25% of the craters in Alphonsus are of internal origin and at least 25% are of impact origin.

Analyses along these lines will no doubt become more refined in the future, and the actual figures arrived at may depend quite critically on the size interval of the craters under consideration. For the moment, it is encouraging to observe that the trend of ideas is converging: the impact crater is being relegated to assume a less important role than in the past, and internally formed craters are assuming an increasing importance in discussions of the lunar surface.

Acknowledgements

This work was supported by a Research Grant from the S.R.C. and from the N.E.R.C.

References

1. G. Fielder, *Lunar Geology*, Lutterworth Press, London, 1965.
2. G. Fielder, *J. Brit. Astron. Assoc.*, **67**, 315–8 (1957).
3. G. Fielder, *Geophys. J.*, **10**, 437–43 (1966).
4. S. K. Runcorn, *Jet Propulsion Lab. Tech. Rept. No.* 32-529 (1963).
5. N. N. Sytinskaya, *Astron. Zh.*, **36**, 315–21 (1959).
6. G. Fielder, *Monthly Notices Roy. Astron. Soc.*, **123**, 15–26 (1961).
7. G. P. Kuiper, *Jet Propulsion Lab. Tech. Rept. No.* 32-800 (1966).
8. B. Warner, *J. Brit. Astron. Assoc.*, **71**, 116–9 (1961).

9. R. B. Baldwin, *The Measure of the Moon*, University of Chicago Press, Chicago, 1963.
10. T. Kiang (1965), quoted in reference 1.
11. G. Fielder, *Monthly Notices Roy. Astron. Soc.*, **132**, 413–22 (1966).
12. R. G. Strom and A. Palm, *Space Sci. Lab., Univ. Calif., Ser. 3, No. 24* (1962).
13. G. P. Kuiper, *Roy. Soc. Conf. on the Moon, London, 1965*.

10

L. B. RONCA

Lunar-Planetary Research Branch
Space Physics Laboratory
Air Force Cambridge Research Laboratories
L. G. Hanscom Field
Bedford, Massachusetts, U.S.A.

Minor lunar tectonics

Introduction

The study of tectonism is the branch of geology which contributes to the knowledge of the nature of the underlying mantle of a planet. A high degree of tectonic activity on the surface of a planet would indicate an active mantle with an intense energy transfer, probably through convection currents, while a lack of tectonism would indicate a stable mantle.

In the case of the Moon, a complete determination of the amount of tectonism will be available only when the origin of lunar craters is unquestionably known. If the craters are completely or at least predominantly volcanic, the lunar mantle must have been in a state of extensive activity. On the other hand, if meteoritic impact has been the predominant agent in shaping the lunar surface, it is possible that the lunar mantle has always been a stable unit. The presence of tectonism, at least to a lesser degree, can be proved, however, by studies of such minor characteristics as linear features and the shape of craters. Although these studies cannot establish whether the tectonism was extensive enough to cover the surface with volcanic craters, they can show that tectonism existed, thus rejecting the possibility that the mantle has always been inactive.

Linear Elements of Mare Humorum

The azimuthal frequencies of linear elements of and around Mare Humorum were studied[1]. The azimuths of rilles, rays, and wrinkle ridges were measured. The azimuths of slightly curved elements were measured by considering them to be the sum of a discrete number of straight lines. The rays are actually elongated areas of higher albedo than the surroundings, lacking the common radial pattern of the normal rays. For this reason the term 'vitta' (plural vittae, Latin for ribbon) was proposed, as the term ray implies a radial pattern. Figure 1 shows the frequency distribution of the azimuths of the three types of linear features. Rather than a common histogram, a three-point-moving-average frequency diagram is presented. This treatment avoids the problems common to histograms, which stem from the question of how narrow can the chosen interval be without losing any real structure and also without being affected by the statistically low number of points. Also a three-point-moving-average

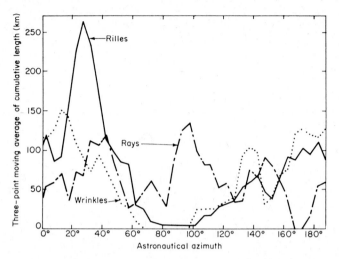

FIGURE 1   Cumulative length against azimuth of rilles, wrinkle ridges, and vittae (rays):
full curve, rilles; dotted curve, wrinkles; chain curve, rays

extends the importance of each interval to the bordering intervals, thus correcting for the unavoidable errors in the measurement.

The following facts about the frequency diagram can be considered. The linear features are not randomly oriented, but are arranged in four preferred orientations, at approximately 30°, 95°, 140°, and 175°. The 95° preferred azimuth is displayed only by the vittae.

It is most surprising to find that not only the wrinkle ridges and rilles, but also the vittae have similar preferred orientations. The correspondence is not so close as in the case of the wrinkle ridges and rilles, primarily because the strong east–west preferred orientation of the vittae is not matched by the other features. This discrepancy may be more apparent than real, however, owing to the relative invisibility of linear topographic elements perpendicular to the terminator. If this is the case, there is sufficient correlation of the orientation of all linear features on Mare Humorum to suggest a related origin. Because wrinkle ridges and rilles are most certainly endogenous, some or all of the vittae may be endogenous as well.

Another fact points toward an endogenous origin of the vittae of Mare Humorum: the frequency of the number of craters on the vittae as against the number of craters on the surroundings. Of the 330 craters measured, the density ratio is as follows. For all craters there are 9 times more craters on the vittae as on the surroundings, for craters larger than 3 km in diameter 10 times more craters on the vittae, for craters larger than 4 km 17 times more craters on the vittae, for craters larger than 6 km 24 times more craters on the vittae, and the two craters larger than 10 km are both on the vittae. If the vittae are rays produced by the ejection of material from an impact site, the craters on the vittae would be secondary. However, it can be easily shown that this cannot be true. Let us assume that the craters are secondary, produced by a primary crater the size of Copernicus. The volume of the crater Copernicus was measured to be approximately $5 \cdot 6 \times 10^{18}$ cm^3. To ensure that this is a maximum value the figure can be doubled to $1 \cdot 1 \times 10^{19}$ cm^3. The density of lunar material is probably less than $3 \cdot 3$ g/cm^3, making the mass removed from Copernicus less than $3 \cdot 7 \times 10^{19}$ g.

Gault, Shoemaker, and Moore[2] present a correlation between the mass of the largest fragment ejected and the total mass ejected from an impact. An extrapolation of one order of magnitude is necessary; this is justified since the linear correlation holds valid over 20 orders of magnitude. The largest fragment ejected from the primary impact has a mass of less than $4\cdot5 \times 10^{14}$ g, which can be further increased to 10^{15} g. If we assume the maximum possible velocity, the lunar escape velocity, the maximum energy of such a fragment would be less than $2\cdot8 \times 10^{25}$ erg. By using Baldwin's equations[3], the maximum diameter of the craters produced by such a fragment would be less than five kilometers.

The conclusion of this study seems inescapable: the area of Mare Humorum and surroundings was affected by tectonic directions of weakness which resulted in wrinkle ridges, rilles, and vittae. The detailed nature of each of these features has been postulated elsewhere[4]; for the purpose of this chapter, suffice it to say that these features are likely to be the result of tectonic forces which probably resulted from processes operating extensively in depth.

The Circularity of Lunar Craters

Another area of study which furnishes indications of the existence of tectonic processes on the lunar surface is the frequency of the circularity index of lunar craters[5]. There are several ways by which the shape of a crater can be described, the most common being roundness, polygonality, ellipticity, and circularity. Roundness has to do with the sharpness of the edges and corners. The mathematical formula requires the exact identification of the edges and corners of the figure, which is difficult or impossible in the case of lunar craters. Polygonality and ellipticity work very well for craters having definite polygonal or elliptical outlines, but are not very satisfactory for intermediate figures, which are actually the most common. After testing many formulae, it was found that circularity gives the most generalized results. Circularity measures the amount of deviation from a circle, and is independent from the general outline of the figure, which can be rectangular, polygonal, elliptical, or anything in between. Mathematically, a circularity index is given by

$$\rho = \frac{4A}{\pi d_m^{\,2}}$$

where ρ is the circularity index, A is the area of the figure, and d_m is the diameter of the minimum circumscribed circle. Lunar craters were measured from Aeronautical Chart and Information Center of the U.S. Air Force (ACIC) LAC charts available at the time. Figure 2 shows the area covered. All craters satisfying the following requirements were measured: (i) the approximate average diameter must be larger than 25 km, and (ii) no more than 60° of arc must be missing from the circumference, or obviously be influenced by a nearby crater. Missing parts of the rim were filled in in such a way that the circularity index is the highest possible.

Figure 3 shows the frequency distribution of the circularity indices off the 84 measured craters. Again a three-point-moving-average plot is used. The frequency function is bimodal, that is, it is composed of two peaks. Each peak is similar to a

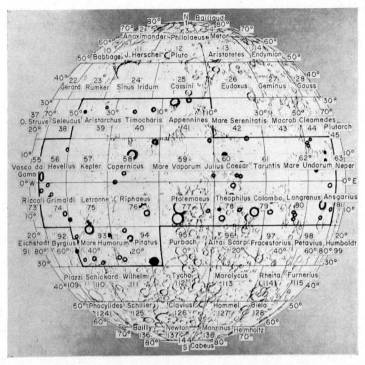

FIGURE 2   Location of the craters for which the circularity index was measured. Circular craters are shown by open circles, subcircular craters by closed circles

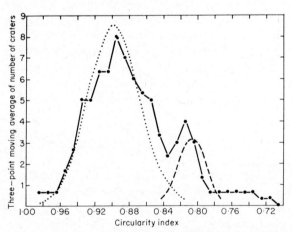

FIGURE 3   The frequency of the circularity indices. Full line connects the experimental data; dotted and broken lines represent two Gaussian distributions

Gaussian distribution, represented by a dotted and a broken line in figure 3. The mean of the circular group is 0·8984, with the interval between 0·8908 and 0·9060 being a 95% confidence interval for the mean. The mean of the subcircular group is 0·8097 (excluding the values below 0·7600), with the 95% confidence interval between 0·8008 and 0·8186. The standard deviation, calculated with the assumption that each group is Gaussian, is 0·0288 for the first group, with 0·0244 to 0·0348 being the 95% confidence interval, and 0·0151 for the second group, with 0·0236 to 0·0107 being the 95% confidence interval. In figure 2, the craters belonging to the circular group are shown as open circles, and the craters of the subcircular group as closed circles.

Figure 4 shows a plot of the circularity indices of the craters against their average diameter. No functional relation is apparent.

The frequency distribution curve of the index of circularity for the measured craters appears to be bimodal, with a gap at approximately $\rho = 0·83$. The existence of this gap could be explained in one of the following ways.

(i) The gap is not real, but is the result of a systematic error of the ACIC chartographers. Undoubtedly, the absolute values of the measured indices are affected by

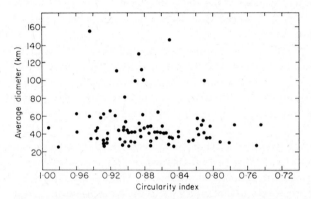

FIGURE 4   Average diameter of craters against their circularity indices

errors in the map-making process. However, it is difficult to understand why the error should result in a gap in the frequency distribution. It would be more plausible to expect a symmetrical error curve which would broaden the real distribution curve, but not introduce a gap. The same considerations apply to errors introduced in measuring the indices.

It is important to realize that the indices of circularity are probably noticeably in error when their absolute values are considered. For this reason a three-point-moving-average curve is particularly adapted to giving a graphic representation. However, error due to the chartography and the measurements should be symmetrical, and thus unable to explain the gap.

(ii) It is possible that the gap is real, and that it is the result of the fact that two different populations of craters occur on the Moon. This interpretation is substantiated by the similarity of the frequency distribution curve to the sum of two Gaussian distributions.

If we accept the second possibility as a working hypothesis—that there are indeed two crater populations on the lunar surface—then we must explain this phenomenon. It could be explained in the five following ways.

(*a*) If all craters were produced by meteorite impact, then those meteorites striking the lunar surface at very shallow angles might produce subcircular craters, despite their hypervelocity. Such a hypothesis demands, however, two populations of meteorites, one of which has a remarkable tendency of striking the surface of a sphere at shallow

M.E.—16*

angles, no matter what the location of the impact. This hypothesis appears very unlikely.

(*b*) It might be that two populations of impacting bodies exist, one of which has less than hypervelocity. In such a case, subcircular craters would commonly be produced by the lower-velocity impacts. This is exactly what happens with low-velocity ejecta thrown out of hypervelocity impact craters. There is, however, a limit to the size of secondary craters of approximately five kilometers, as shown above; thus this possibility is excluded.

(*c*) Rather than being a function of the impacting body, it is possible that the circularity of craters is a function of the target material, i.e. that some areas of the lunar surface are under stress or are particularly densely jointed, so that craters with distorted outlines result even from a hypervelocity impact. Such a situation appears unlikely, however, because circular and subcircular craters appear literally side by side on the Moon. Figure 2 shows that there is no preferential area of one population with respect to the other.

(*d*) Another possibility is that the two populations were formed by two different processes. Thus, the circular craters might be of impact origin and the subcircular craters of volcanic origin. This possibility seems unlikely, as two fundamentally different processes as impact and volcanism would produce two populations of craters with differences greater than those shown by their circularity index, which is a minor characteristic.

(*e*) It is also conceivable that a second process has acted upon some of the craters (whatever their origin) after their formation to distort their shape. Here one might call upon lunar forces to reduce the circularity of craters by transverse faulting. Several cases of such horizontal movement along faults have been identified[6, 7].

In order to understand their origin better, relative ages were determined for the craters. It was found that they are not random in age, but have a particular place in the context of lunar history. Unlike the circular craters, which are both pre-mare and post-mare, all subcircular craters are pre-mare (pre-Procellarian). Such an age relationship suggests that there may have been a particular time in lunar history when the subcircular craters were formed.

If this hypothesis is correct, it indicates that lunar tectonism not only existed, but went through at least one maximum of activity in the pre-mare time.

Conclusion

The previous studies, restricted in areal extent and in object, can present only a small aspect of all the possible manifestations of lunar tectonics. The study of the linear elements of and around Mare Humorum indicates that regional preferred orientations exist in that area, along which energy supplied from the substratum was expended in different surface manifestations. As far as the lunar mantle is concerned, such a study indicates that the mantle was sufficiently active to perform some work on the lunar surface. The study of the frequency of the circularity indices of lunar craters confirms the above theory and adds to it the theory that the activity of the lunar mantle was changing through time, showing at least one maximum in the remote geological past.

Although this sort of study cannot solve the fundamental question of the origin of lunar craters, it can disprove the theory that the Moon has always been a dead planet.

References

1. J. W. Salisbury, V. G. Smalley, and L. B. Ronca, *Nature*, **206**, 385 (1965).
2. D. E. Gault, E. M. Shoemaker, and H. J. Moor, *NASA* (*Natl. Aeron. Space Admin.*), *Tech. Note*, TN–D–1767 (1963).
3. R. B. Baldwin, *The Measure of the Moon*, University of Chicago Press, Chicago, 1963, p. 162.
4. L. B. Ronca, *Icarus*, **4**, 390 (1965).
5. L. B. Ronca and J. W. Salisbury, *Icarus*, **5**, 130 (1966).
6. G. Fielder, *Planetary Space Sci.*, **8**, 1 (1961).
7. L. B. Ronca, *Nature*, **209**, 182 (1966).

IX

Thermal convection in planets

A. Observational clues

1. The World rift system and its bearing on possible processes in the mantle (R. W. GIRDLER) . . . 483

2. The spherical harmonic analysis of major tectonic
   features (A. M. COODE) 489

B. Laboratory experiments

3. Laboratory analogies for convection problems (M. J.
   GROSS) 499

4. Geophysical implications of laboratory experiments on
   convection with internal heat generation (D. J.
   TRITTON and M. N. ZARRAGA) 505

C. Theories

5. Convection in the Earth's mantle (D. W. ALLAN, W. B.
   THOMPSON, and N. O. WEISS) 507

6. Convection in the planets (S. K. RUNCORN) . . 513

7. Thermal turbulence and its role in the Earth's mantle
   (J. W. ELDER) 525

D. Heat flow

8. A review of terrestrial heat flow (R. W. GIRDLER) . 549

1

R. W. GIRDLER

Department of Geophysics and Planetary Physics
School of Physics
University of Newcastle upon Tyne
England

The World rift system and its bearing on possible processes in the mantle

Introduction

Since its discovery ten years ago[1,2], the World rift system has been thought by many to be related to subcrustal movements. The World rift system was located by plotting the epicentres of shallow earthquakes[1] and was found to be continuous on a World-wide scale[2] occasionally being deflected along old fracture zones.

The rift system is mostly found in the ocean floor. As the oceanic crust is thin (11 km including 4·5 km of water for the standard oceanic section) and the focal depths of the earthquakes extend to 70 km, it is clear that the rift system is related to tectonic processes in the upper mantle. Further, horizontal crustal displacements are found associated with the rifts and these lead to the recognition of horizontal motions in the upper mantle. It is difficult to explain these without invoking some kind of mantle convection; the World rift system therefore provides some indications as to the possible nature of mantle convection patterns. This chapter lists various factors which must be considered when the World rift system is used to explore the possible nature of mantle convection.

The Nature of the World Rift System

The location of the World rift system is shown in figure 1. The following features are noted.

(i) Most of the rift system is located near the centres of ocean basins. There are four places where it intersects the continental crust: the Gulf of California, the Gulf of Aden, the mouth of the River Lena (Siberia), and the south island of New Zealand.

(ii) The rift often changes direction. For example, around Africa there is a change of direction of 180°.

(iii) The rift is associated with a ridge or rise several thousand kilometres in width. In continental areas such as western North America and Africa it is associated with block faulting and frequently basaltic volcanism.

(iv) Gravity data indicate that the rifts are in approximate isostatic equilibrium[3,4]. No large deviations from equilibrium have been found.

(v) Large magnetic anomalies are often found over the rift suggesting the presence of basic igneous intrusions[3]. Smaller anomalies are found on either side and these are in zones parallel to the large rift anomaly.

(vi) The seismic velocities for subcrustal material in rift regions are low, ranging from 7·0 to 7·7 km/sec instead of the more usual 8·1 km/sec. Talwani, Le Pichon, and Ewing[5] from a combined study of gravity and seismic refraction data find that the low-velocity (and hence low-density) material spreads out under the associated ridge beneath normal mantle material.

(vii) There are frequently zones of high heat flow associated with the axis of the ridge[6].

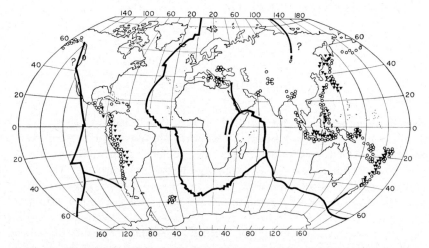

FIGURE 1   The location of the World rift system (full line, shallow seismicity). The location of deep-focus (denoted by closed triangles) and intermediate-focus (denoted by open circles) earthquakes are also shown

(viii) It seems likely that new oceanic crustal material is forming along the seismically active zone[4] by intrusion of basic igneous material and associated volcanism.

(ix) There is increasing evidence that the age of the rift zone increases outwards from the centre. This is observed to be so for Iceland[7], is likely to be so for oceanic regions[8,9], and is found to be so from geological mapping of the rift in northern Kenya[10].

In addition, if we look at parts of the World rift system in detail, there is evidence for both translational and rotational crustal movements associated with the rifting. An example is the movement of Arabia and the formation of the Red Sea and Gulf of Aden.

Translation and Rotation of Arabia

A detailed summary of the evidence for a northward movement and anticlockwise rotation of Arabia and the implications of this movement to Red Sea–Gulf of Aden rifting has been given by the author[11]. A brief resumé is given here.

Evidence for translational movement of Arabia

Freund[12] has presented several different lines of geological evidence which indicate a transcurrent motion of 90 km along the Dead Sea rift, the direction of motion being consistent with a northward movement of Arabia. The evidence involves measurements of the displacements of two separate facies types of the Turonian, marine Jurassic strata, Cambrian limestone facies, Pre-Cambrian igneous rocks, manganese and copper deposits, and various tectonic features. As the displacements of the Pre-Cambrian and Cambrian strata are found to be of the same magnitude as the displacement of the Lower Turonian strata, the Dead Sea rift must have formed since Upper Cretaceous times.

Evidence for rotational movement of Arabia

Some of the evidence for an anticlockwise rotation of Arabia may be seen in figures 2 and 3. The main Red Sea fault trough widens towards the south and measurements north of 24° N where the margins are straight give a divergence of 7°. A similar figure is obtained from various features (figure 2) of the bottom topography in the

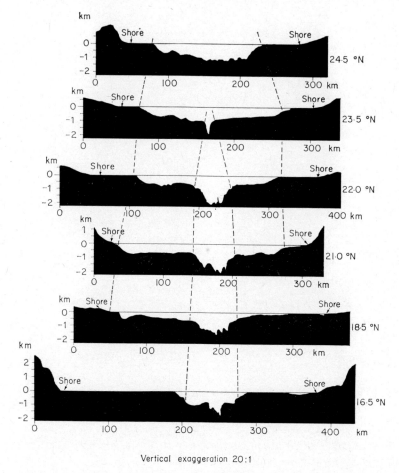

Vertical exaggeration 20:1

FIGURE 2   Bottom topography of the Red Sea [after Drake and Girdler[13]]

northern and central parts of the Red Sea. (In the southern part, the main structures are obscured by recent volcanism, by the accumulation of large thickness of evaporites, and by the build up of coral reefs.) Further evidence is obtained from the Gulf of Aden which widens in a similar way towards the east.

The regions of large magnetic anomalies which have been found over the centres

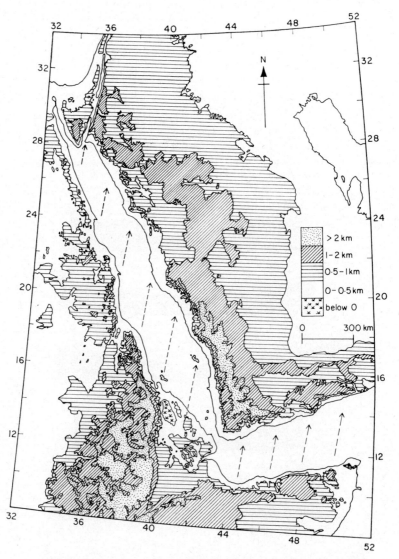

FIGURE 3   Map of the Red Sea area. The lengths of the arrows represent the amount of crustal separation, on the assumptions of a northward translation of Arabia of 100 km and an anticlockwise rotation of 7°

of the Red Sea and Gulf of Aden also widen towards the south and east respectively, in a way consistent with the anticlockwise rotation.

Lastly, palaeomagnetic measurements on the Aden volcanic rocks[14] give a mean declination of N 6·9° W ± 3·8°, a result which is also consistent with an anticlockwise rotation of Arabia subsequent to the cooling of the rocks through their Curie temperature.

There is therefore a considerable amount of evidence for the northward translation (by 90 km) and anticlockwise rotation (by 7°) of the Arabian Peninsula. This represents a rotational movement of a very large portion of continental crust involving rifting and crustal separation along the Red Sea and Gulf of Aden.

Possible Nature of Mantle Convection Patterns

The various features described on pp. 483–6 enable some conditions to be placed on the possible nature of mantle convection currents.

First, various geophysical data indicate that the rifts are tensional features and it is therefore reasonable to suppose that they are associated with uprising, diverging convection currents.

Secondly, the fact that the rift often changes direction (e.g. by 180° around Africa) restricts the geometry of the convection pattern. For example it makes simple cylindrical convection cells very unlikely.

Thirdly, the presence of translational and rotational movements such as described in the previous section further suggests that subcrustal movements must be more complex than a simple divergence along the axis of the rift.

Fourthly, the uprising currents cannot be entirely confined to the ocean basins as the rift system sometimes intersects the continents.

A consideration of these points leads to the conclusion that the World rift system lies over and connects a series of regions of uprising convection which are roughly circular or elliptical in plan. In this way, the tensional nature of the rifts can still be explained and the translational and rotational movements will be expected near the margins of the regions of uprising convection. The areas between regions of uprising will be where most shear occurs and where the rift system changes direction.

The question remains as to the location of the regions of uprising convection which give rise to the World rift system. Runcorn[15] has made the interesting suggestion that these may be determined from satellite gravity data, the regions of uprising convection giving rise to regions of negative gravity owing to their higher temperature and lower density. A consideration of the World rift system (figure 1) and the satellite gravity data suggest that there are at least four regions of uprising convection. These are located under the eastern Pacific Ocean, under the mid-Atlantic Ocean, under the Indian Ocean and India, and under the Pacific–Antarctic Ocean south of New Zealand. It is likely that the rift system lies over and connects these regions of upwelling.

The location of possible regions of descending convection has been discussed by the author[4] and the suggestion is made that these are located in regions where deep seismicity occurs.

References

1. J. P. Rothé, *Proc. Roy. Soc.* (*London*), *Ser. A*, **222**, 387 (1954).
2. W. M. Ewing and B. C. Heezen, *Am. Geophys. Union Monograph No.* 1, 75 (1956).
3. R. W. Girdler, *Quart. J. Geol. Soc. London*, **114**, 79 (1958).
4. R. W. Girdler, *Phil. Trans. Roy. Soc. London, Ser. A*, **258**, 123 (1965).
5. M. Talwani, X. Le Pichon and W. M. Ewing, *J. Geophys. Res.*, **70**, 341 (1965).
6. R. P. Von Herzen and S. Uyeda, *J. Geophys. Res.*, **68**, 4219 (1963).
7. G. Bodvarsson and G. P. L. Walker, *Geophys. J.*, **8**, 285 (1964).
8. H. H. Hess, *Proc. Roy. Soc.* (*London*), *Ser. A*, **222**, 341 (1954).
9. F. J. Vine and D. H. Matthews, *Nature*, **199**, 947 (1963).
10. J. Walsh, Ph.D. Thesis, University of London (1965).
11. R. W. Girdler, *Intern. Upper Mantle Symp.*, *Ottawa*, *1965*.
12. R. Freund, *Geol. Mag.*, **102**, 189 (1965).
13. C. L. Drake and R. W. Girdler, *Geophys. J.*, **8**, 473 (1964).
14. E. Irving and D. H. Tarling, *J. Geophys. Res.*, **66**, 549 (1961).
15. S. K. Runcorn, *Nature*, **200**, 628 (1963).

2

A. M. COODE

Department of Geophysics and Planetary Physics
School of Physics
University of Newcastle upon Tyne
England

The spherical harmonic analysis
of major tectonic features

The major tectonic features of the Earth's surface are formed by processes in the mantle. It is desirable to describe them analytically to see whether their distribution offers any clue to their origin. If tension and compression features can be shown to be related and each set of features shown to have the same degree of symmetry, then some form of convection may be present. On the other hand, if the symmetry for each set either did not exist or were not similar and there was no apparent relationship between tension and compression, it would be difficult to invoke convection and redress may have to be made to an expanding or contracting Earth. Analyses of topography have, in the past, been criticized on the grounds that the coefficients reflect the size and distribution of the continents and these mask the tectonic features. Of course, the distribution of the continents will reflect the mantle forces and this is desirable, but there does not seem to be any reliable way to separate this contribution from that of their size. An analysis of tectonic features may be a better way to approach this problem.

The two most important features thought to be formed by compression are the fold belts or mountain systems of continents and oceanic trenches. Oceanic ridges and continental rift valleys have been shown to be part of one continuous feature and, as the Red Sea[1] at one place and Iceland[2] at another are shown to be in tension, it seems fair to interpolate that the ridges are in tension. A lot of the work in discovering these ridges was facilitated using shallow earthquake epicentres which were found at the crest of ridges in fair numbers. Later work has shown that they are also associated with high heat flow and anomalous gravity observations. There are some ridges, however, which are not connected to the continuous system. These are not only fragmented and apparently unrelated to the continuous, World system, but they seem much less active. There is no evidence of abnormal seismic activity. Their shape in cross section is much more peaked, with steeply rising sides, than the continuous system. It is assumed, for simplicity, that these passive ridges are scars on the ocean floor formed contemporaneously from past tension. Their present location may, or may not, reflect their old positions. Presumably, some degree of fragmentation has occurred with continental drift, but if their analysis fits into a theoretical model with the active tectonic features then their inclusion will be of value.

All these features may be regarded as linear. The active ridges, for example, extend

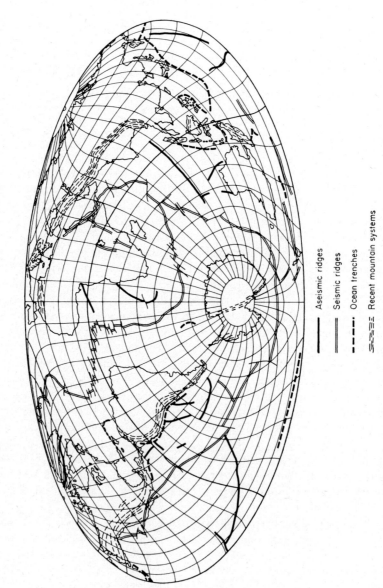

Aseismic ridges

Seismic ridges

Ocean trenches

Recent mountain systems

FIGURE 1   Distribution of the major tectonic features used in this analysis

for 50000 km and have an average cross section of one to two thousand kilometres; the oceanic trenches and continental mountain systems have similar length to breadth ratios. As the analysis will smooth these features, at the twelfth degree the topography will be smoothed to a function whose wavelength is 30° and, as the superficial irregularities of the topography are not important, smoothing before analysis will not be harmful. A function is needed that is zero wherever there are no tectonic features, that can express the linear nature of these features, and whose low-degree harmonics will approximate the coefficients of an analysis of tectonic features. The function should, when integrated along the features, give the length S. The cross section can be expressed analytically by fitting a polynomial every 10° across the features. This is arduous and a suitable, arbitrary function fitted everywhere would give as much information. If a Dirac δ function is used, the low-degree harmonics will approximate the true coefficients and its integral will be unity, therefore giving equal weight to all parts of the features. Let $F(\theta, \phi)$ be the function which describes the features, then

$$\int_0^{2\pi} \int_0^{\pi} F(\theta, \phi) \sin \theta \, d\theta \, d\phi = S$$

If we normalize this using $f(\theta, \phi) = F(\theta, \phi)/S$, then (1) holds true. Data cannot be

$$\int_0^{2\pi} \int_0^{\pi} f(\theta, \phi) \sin \theta \, d\theta \, d\phi = 1 \tag{1}$$

taken continuously along the ridge; there must, for convenience, be a discrete interval between two data points. Consequently the function $f(\theta, \phi)$ becomes a line of two-dimensional δ functions on the surface of the sphere and is given by (2).

$$f(\theta, \phi) = \frac{1}{g} \sum_{i=1}^{g} \delta(\theta_i, \phi_i) \tag{2}$$

Let

$$(\theta, \phi) = \sum_{n=0}^{\infty} \sum_{m=0}^{n} \{\bar{a}_n^m \cos(m\phi) + \bar{b}_n^m \sin(m\phi)\} \bar{P}_n^m (\cos \theta)$$

where the associated Legendre polynomials are fully normalized, i.e.

$$\frac{1}{4\pi} \int_0^{2\pi} \int_0^{\pi} \left[\bar{P}_n^m (\cos \theta) \begin{Bmatrix} \cos \\ \sin \end{Bmatrix} m\phi \right]^2 \sin \theta \, d\theta \, d\phi = 1$$

and then the coefficients $\bar{a}_n^m$ and $\bar{b}_n^m$ can be found by integration[3] to be (3), and $\bar{b}_n^0$

$$\begin{Bmatrix} \bar{a}_n^m \\ \bar{b}_n^m \end{Bmatrix} = \frac{1}{g} \sum_{i=1}^{g} \bar{P}_n^m (\cos \theta_i) \begin{Bmatrix} \cos \\ \sin \end{Bmatrix} (m\phi_i) \tag{3}$$

will be zero, for all n, and $\bar{a}_0^0$ unity. The coefficients $\bar{A}_n^m$ and $\bar{B}_n^m$ of all tension and compression features are found from a weighted contribution of their individual analyses. For a total of g positive δ functions used to calculate the coefficients $\bar{a}_n^m$ and $\bar{b}_n^m$ of the ridges, and a total of γ negative δ functions for the coefficients $\bar{\alpha}_n^m$ and $\bar{\beta}_n^m$ of the trenches and mountain systems, then (4) is true. If, on the other hand, all δ

$$\begin{Bmatrix} \bar{A}_n^m \\ \bar{B}_n^m \end{Bmatrix} = \frac{1}{g + \gamma} \left[g \begin{Bmatrix} \bar{a}_n^m \\ \bar{b}_n^m \end{Bmatrix} + \gamma \begin{Bmatrix} \bar{\alpha}_n^m \\ \bar{\beta}_n^m \end{Bmatrix} \right] \tag{4}$$

functions were positive then equation (5) holds. The relation between the ridges and

$$\begin{Bmatrix} \bar{A}_n^m \\ \bar{B}_n^m \end{Bmatrix} = \frac{1}{g + \gamma} \left[g \begin{Bmatrix} \bar{a}_n^m \\ \bar{b}_n^m \end{Bmatrix} - \gamma \begin{Bmatrix} \bar{\alpha}_n^m \\ \bar{\beta}_n^m \end{Bmatrix} \right] \tag{5}$$

the trench and mountain systems can be tested using (4) and (5). If positive δ functions are used for each of the individual analyses and $\bar{A}_n^m$ and $\bar{B}_n^m$ are calculated from (4) and (5), it should be possible to tell whether the symmetries of the individual analyses have been preserved or destroyed in the combination. On the assumption that ridges are formed by tension and trenches and mountain systems by compression, then by using (4) the symmetries should disappear; by using (5), if the symmetries are preserved, then tension and compression are related but, if the symmetries should disappear, then tension and compression features are not related. Naturally, if the relationship should be shown to exist, it would not mean that convection existed but it would be evidence in its favour.

The axis of rotation may, or may not, play a significant part in upper mantle processes, so some quantity is needed that is independent of the coordinate axes. Such a function is the harmonic content which is defined by

$$\sigma_n = \left[(\bar{A}_n^0)^2 + \sum_{m=1}^{n} \{ (\bar{A}_n^m)^2 + (\bar{B}_n^m)^2 \} \right]^{1/2}$$

It is a function of degree alone for any given data set. Plotting it against degree will show where symmetries exist.

As a test of the significance of this analysis a set of δ functions were placed one degree of latitude apart, from the North Pole to the South Pole, and 72° of longitude apart from 72° to 360° and each δ function was weighted by a factor M_i, where

$$M_i = \bar{P}_5^5(\cos \theta_i)$$

so that

$$\begin{Bmatrix} \bar{a}_n^m \\ \bar{b}_n^m \end{Bmatrix} = \frac{3\sqrt{154}}{16g} \sum_{i=1}^{g} \sin^5 \theta_i \, \bar{P}_n^m(\cos \theta_i) \begin{Bmatrix} \cos \\ \sin \end{Bmatrix}(m\phi_i)$$

Over a regular grid, with continuous functions, $\bar{a}_n^m$ and $\bar{b}_n^m$ are derived by the integration of two orthogonal functions so that one might expect

$$\bar{a}_n^m = \bar{b}_n^m = 0 \qquad \text{for all } m \text{ and } n$$

except

$$\bar{a}_5^5 = 1$$

but because of the nature of the δ functions this condition is not fully satisfied. Two factors contribute to the amplitude of $\bar{a}_n^m$ and $\bar{b}_n^m$. The first is due to the weighting factor M_i which is zero at the North Pole and South Pole and $3\sqrt{154}/16$ at the equator and is always positive, so that there will be a contribution to the $\bar{a}_2^0$ term and, to a lesser extent, to the $\bar{a}_4^0$ term. Secondly, coefficients, whose degree and order is a product of the fundamental harmonic, will appear. Hence the terms $\bar{a}_{10}^{10}$ and $\bar{a}_{15}^{15}$ will contribute to the analysis. Figure 2 shows this clearly. The small peak at $n = 12$ is solely due to $\bar{a}_{12}^{10}$ but it is three times smaller than $\bar{a}_5^5$ and $\bar{a}_{10}^{10}$. Of course, if an analysis is conducted where the fifth and tenth harmonic are reproduced, it is not possible to differentiate between mathematical or physical causes. Other evidence must be reviewed to do this.

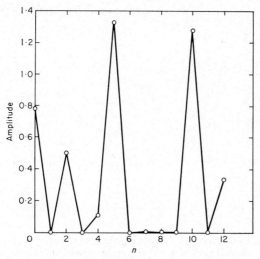

FIGURE 2   Amplitude of the harmonic content up to the twelfth degree for the weighted
δ functions of P_5^5 (cos θ), showing the fundamental peak at $n = 5$ and the secondary
at $n = 10$

In the analyses of tectonic features δ functions were placed one degree of latitude
apart, as in the test, but no weighting was added. This distribution gives equal weighting
to all parts of a section and all tectonic features. To test the effect on the analysis of an
undiscovered section of ridge, the seismically active ridges were separated into two

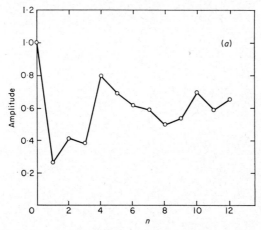

FIGURE 3(a)   Harmonic content of the active ridges without the east African and Red
Sea rift (574 δ functions)

groups. The first included all features (652 δ functions) and the second omitted the
east African and the Red Sea rift system (574 δ functions). The difference in length
between these two is 78° of latitude; the uncertainty in location of the δ functions is
less than 2°. Combining this with an undiscovered ridge 78° long, one finds a maximum error of 20% at the fourth degree (see figures 3(a) and 3(b)). It is more probable
that ridges of 10° or 20° may not have been found so the harmonic content can be
determined to within 5%.

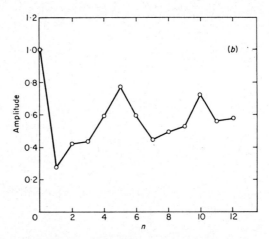

FIGURE 3(*b*)   Harmonic content of all active ridges (652 δ functions) showing the fundamental peak at $n = 5$ and the secondary at $n = 10$

The active ridges peaked at the fifth degree, with a clear secondary at the tenth—
the analysis was taken to the twelfth degree to establish this. The passive ridges
peaked at the fourth degree (figure 3(*c*)) and, if these ridges are the scars of tensions
in the past, the symmetry of the global tension-generating mechanism has changed
from a fourth degree to a fifth. The presence of a fourth-degree peak is not surprising

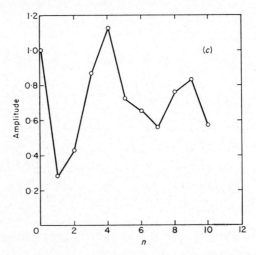

FIGURE 3(*c*)   Harmonic content of the passive ridges showing the fundamental peak
at $n = 4$

even if continental drift is assumed to have taken place. Let us take, for example, the
polynomial $\bar{P}_5^0$, which has five zeros between the North Pole and South Pole, and the
polynomial $\bar{P}_4^0$, which has four zeros. The zeros of $\bar{P}_4^0$ will be separated from each
other by the zeros of $\bar{P}_5^0$. Similarly the fourth-degree ridges will be separated by those
of the fifth degree, so that σ_n will show the dominant harmonic of the aseismic ridges
in the past, but the distribution of these ridges will be distorted under the influence

of the more recent distribution, which may account for the ninth harmonic peak. This reinforces Runcorn's[4] view that convection in the mantle has recently changed from a fourth- to a fifth-degree cell pattern.

The harmonic content of the trenches and mountain systems peaks at the fifth degree and again at the ninth (figure 3(d)). The distribution of σ_n for this system is less well defined than that derived from the active ridges; there is a small peak at the second degree, which is probably due to the ring of compression features surrounding

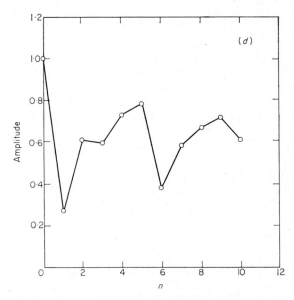

FIGURE 3(d) Harmonic content of the compression features, oceanic trenches, and recent mountain systems. The symmetry is similar to that of the oceanic ridges

the Pacific, and the amplitude of σ_4 is almost as large as the amplitude of σ_5. This spread in the fundamental peak may give rise to the secondary at the ninth harmonic. If the generating mechanism has changed from a fourth- to a fifth-degree symmetry, as has been suggested above, then the continents may still retain a memory of the fourth-degree symmetry giving rise to the large amplitude in σ_4.

Combining all the tectonic features using only positive δ functions and equation (4) one finds the symmetries lost (see figure 4(a)), as was expected. But if equation (5) is used, so that ridges are assumed to be formed by tension and trenches and mountain systems by compression, the symmetries are almost perfectly retained (figure 4(b)). It is fair to conclude, therefore, that the tension and compression features are related and are formed by the same generating mechanism.

There are several theories of the origin of tectonic features: some invoke a contracting Earth and satisfactorily explain mountain building but not the tension features, while some expand the Earth and explain the oceanic ridges but not the compression features. Neither of these theories offers a relation between tension and compression nor do they explain the strangely linear manner in which the tectonic features seem to be distributed. Of the current theories only convection relates both tension and compression on the globe and expects them to be linear.

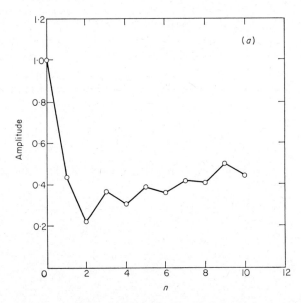

FIGURE 4(*a*) Harmonic content of all active tectonic features assuming that they are
all formed by compression. No peaks appear and the distribution must be almost
random

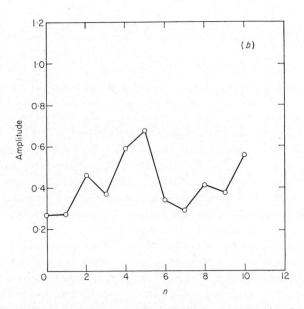

FIGURE 4(*b*) Harmonic content of all active tectonic features assuming that the ridges
are formed by tension and the trenches and mountain systems by compression. Symmetry
is preserved, showing that tension and compression features are formed by the same
mechanism

Runcorn[5] has suggested that the mantle might be regarded as viscous compared with the crust and that convection acts as shear stresses below the crust for long periods of time. The stresses generated should be proportional to the gradient of $f(\theta, \phi)$. The north and east component will then be proportional to

$$\frac{\partial f(\theta, \phi)}{\partial \theta} \quad \text{and} \quad \frac{1}{\sin \theta} \frac{\partial f(\theta, \phi)}{\partial \phi}$$

Using the coefficients of tension and compression (figure 4(*b*)), the author has computed a sixth-degree stress pattern, taken over a 10° grid (figure 5). This compares

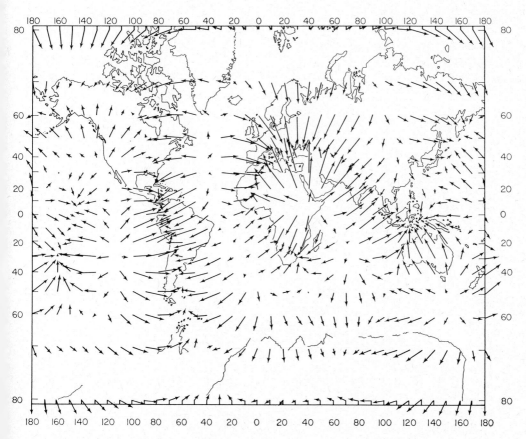

FIGURE 5   Flow pattern of the sixth degree derived from an analysis of all active tectonic features

favourably with the flow pattern obtained by Runcorn[5] from an analysis of the geoid.

In conclusion, we can say that the passive ridges have a fourth-degree symmetry and that the modern tectonic feature have a fifth-degree symmetry. A study of tension and compression features indicates they are related and formed by the same mechanism. An analysis of tectonic features, therefore, does not seem to deny the existence of convection but strengthens it.

Acknowledgements

The author would like to thank the *Geophysical Journal* for the use of figures 1 and 3–5.

References

1. R. W. Girdler, *Quart. J. Geol. Soc. London*, **114**, 79 (1958).
2. G. Bodvarsson and G. P. L. Walker, *Geophys. J.*, **8**, 285 (1964).
3. A. M. Coode, *Geophys. J.*, **12**, 55 (1966).
4. S. K. Runcorn, in *Continental Drift* (Ed. S. K. Runcorn), Academic Press, London, 1962.
5. S. K. Runcorn, *J. Geophys. Res.*, **69**, 4389 (1964).

3

M. J. GROSS

Department of Geophysics and Planetary Physics
School of Physics
University of Newcastle upon Tyne
England

Laboratory analogies for convection problems

Introduction

Preliminary investigations have been started into the possibilities of setting up laboratory analogies of fluid flow under gravitational convection. The incentives for doing this come from the difficulties of solving equations of flow for almost any convective flow problem. A reference to the literature or Chandrasekhar's book on hydrodynamic and hydromagnetic stability[1] shows that usually it is only feasible to make predictions about the *onset* of convective flow. In geophysics we should be at least as interested in the actual form of the flow pattern as in the initial values of various parameters at its onset, and in particular we should like to know what sort of flows we might expect in a gravitating body having a free outer surface, a dense liquid core, and a self-heating mantle.

In such a system, corresponding to present views of some of the larger planets, the gravitational field is very nearly radially symmetric about the centre of mass. There is good reason to believe that the average temperature, density, and pressure of regions large compared with the fine scale variations, but nevertheless very much smaller than planet size, must also be closely radially symmetric.

By calculation and analogy with the Bénard convection one may expect that, when the temperature increases with depth sufficiently rapidly, such a system will be unstable and will exhibit free convection. However, the form of the flow pattern once convective flow has established itself has not yet been calculated. This makes it desirable to construct a model in which the flow could be observed in a radial force field.

Gravitational forces have four characteristics in the present context. Firstly, they obey an inverse square-law variation, as do also electrostatic and magnetostatic forces. Secondly, they are equivalent to an acceleration as Eötvös, Mach, and Einstein have assured us. Thirdly, they are very weak for interactions between laboratory-sized objects compared with commonly encountered forces, and, fourthly, they apparently cannot be screened or shielded.

Electrostatic forces appear to offer an opportunity to construct radially symmetric body force fields which could be conveniently manipulated on a laboratory scale. Magnetostatic systems appear less convenient, although a subject called ferrohydrodynamics has recently come into being.

The streaming of dielectric fluids containing free charges in electric fields is widely known, but the difficulties of controlling the charge density led to the choice of an insulating dielectric liquid without free charge for some of the present experiments.

Theory

Only the underlying equations will be presented here as there are some difficulties, and many approximations must be made to obtain useful equations.

The electrical body force in an uncharged dielectric fluid is found by the principle of virtual work[2], or thermodynamics[3], to be

$$\mathbf{f} = - \operatorname{grad} p_0 + \frac{1}{8\pi} \operatorname{grad} \left\{ E^2 \rho \left(\frac{\partial \varepsilon}{\partial \rho} \right)_T \right\} - \frac{E^2}{8\pi} \operatorname{grad} \varepsilon \tag{1}$$

where $\mathbf{E}$ is the electric field (c.g.s. units), ρ the density, ε the dielectric permeability or so-called dielectric constant, and $p_0 = p_0(\rho, T)$ the hydrostatic pressure due to the electric stresses. If the fluid is uncharged, and the electric field derived from a potential difference,

$$\operatorname{div} \varepsilon \mathbf{E} = 0 \tag{2a}$$

and
$$\operatorname{curl} \mathbf{E} = 0 \tag{2b}$$

If the liquid is of uniform composition, and ε is assumed to be a function of ρ and T only (and not E), equation (1) can be rearranged to give (1a).

$$\mathbf{f} = - \operatorname{grad} p_0 + \frac{\rho}{8\pi} \operatorname{grad} \left\{ E^2 \left(\frac{\partial \varepsilon}{\partial \rho} \right)_T \right\} - \frac{E^2}{8\pi} \left(\frac{\partial \varepsilon}{\partial T} \right)_\rho \operatorname{grad} T \tag{1a}$$

For non-polar insulators the term $(\partial \varepsilon / \partial \rho)_T$ can be estimated by the Clausius–Mossotti equation[4,5] as $(\partial \varepsilon / \partial \rho)_T = \frac{1}{3}(\varepsilon + 2)(\varepsilon - 1)$. However, as we are interested in the forces causing convection, which disappear when T is constant throughout,

$$\operatorname{grad} p_0 = \frac{\rho}{8\pi} \operatorname{grad} \left\{ E^2 \left(\frac{\partial \varepsilon}{\partial \rho} \right)_T \right\}$$

so the remaining terms are responsible for the motion of the fluid to the first order when T varies slightly (provided $(\partial \rho / \partial T)_p$ and $\partial^2 \varepsilon / \partial T \, \partial \rho$ are small). Equating this to the other stresses in a slowly moving incompressible Stokesian fluid gives equation (3).

$$-\rho(\mathbf{v} . \nabla)\mathbf{v} - \nabla p + \eta \nabla^2 \mathbf{v} = \frac{E^2}{8\pi} \left(\frac{\partial \varepsilon}{\partial T} \right)_\rho \operatorname{grad} T \tag{3}$$

The continuity equations for fluid and heat, on the assumption of incompressible steady slow motion with negligible viscous heating, are given by (4) and (5).

$$\operatorname{div} \mathbf{v} = 0 \tag{4}$$

$$\mathbf{v} . \operatorname{grad} T = \frac{\kappa}{\rho C_p} \nabla^2 \tag{5}$$

where $\kappa / \rho C_p$ is the thermal diffusivity.

Equations (1) to (5) determine the steady motion of the fluid. That the force **f** represented by these equations can produce a circulation follows from taking the curl of equation (1):

$$\mathbf{curl\ f} = \frac{1}{8\pi} \mathbf{grad}\ \varepsilon \times \mathbf{grad}\ E^2 \tag{6}$$

so that in general only when these gradients are parallel (or zero) will there be no net circulatory force.

In the event of there being a space charge q present in the liquid, equations (1) and (1a) have an additional term $q\mathbf{E}$ on their right-hand side, and (2a) becomes

$$\text{div}\ \varepsilon\mathbf{E} = 4\pi q$$

Equation (6) then becomes

$$\mathbf{curl\ f} = \frac{1}{8\pi} \mathbf{grad}\ \varepsilon \times \mathbf{grad}\ E^2 + \mathbf{grad}\ q \times \mathbf{E} \tag{6a}$$

but now the equations do not form a complete set, without additional relations for the charge density. (A fuller discussion of these complexities will be reported elsewhere.)

Experiments

The difficulties associated with solving equations (1) to (5) are considerable even for plane geometry. Because of this the following situation is suggestive: two plane layers of dielectric of different permeability ε_1 and ε_2 lying between two equipotential planes are in equilibrium with the electric field perpendicular to the planes and the plane interface between the dielectrics (figure 1(a)). However, the equilibrium is unstable

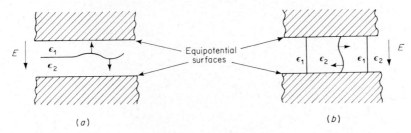

$$(a) \qquad\qquad\qquad\qquad (b)$$

FIGURE 1   (*a*) Unstable equilibrium (perturbations grow); (*b*) stable equilibrium

and any slight perturbation of the interface will cause the two dielectrics to rearrange their positions into columns so that the interface is parallel to the now uniform electric field (figure 1(*b*)), this being the position of stable equilibrium (cf. equation (6)).

In the actual experiments only one dielectric, carefully purified transformer oil, was used so, except for a few confirmatory experiments with an air–oil interface, oil filled the region between a metal plate and a transparent conducting film on glass (figure 2).

The upper plate was heated electrically to a few degrees Celsius above ambient, giving rise to a thermally stable temperature gradient in the absence of the electric

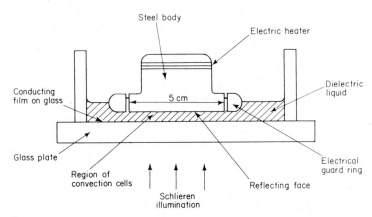

FIGURE 2   Scheme of apparatus for convection with plane geometry

field, and then a voltage 300–1000 v was applied to the plates which were typically separated by 1 mm. Within about one or two seconds a well-developed convection pattern (figure 3) would become visible via the schlieren system. Switching off the voltage caused the pattern to gradually disappear in a few seconds.

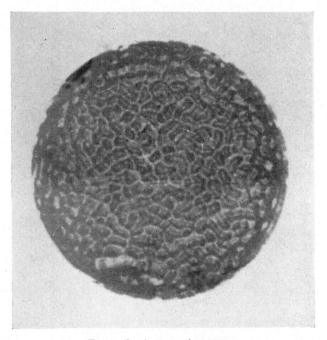

FIGURE 3   A convection pattern

The leakage current density was typically 2×10^{-11} A/cm^2, but the absence of convection cell formation with alternating e.m.f.'s of similar voltage (and other observations) leads the author to conclude that the effects shown are due to space charges in the liquid, the field **E** acting directly on the charges. These charges accumulate non-uniformly, not by local emission from roughness of the electrode surfaces which were highly polished, but because the oil used (typical of commercial insulating oils) decreases its resistivity by a factor of about ten times for a temperature increase of 50 degc, the corresponding change of permittivity being only a few per cent ($\sim 2 \cdot 5\%$).

The non-uniform charge density gives rise to a circulatory force in accordance with the right-hand term of equation (6a).

A fuller description will be reported elsewhere[6].

References

1. S. Chandrasekhar, *Hydrodynamic and Hydromagnetic Stability*, Clarendon Press, Oxford, 1961.
2. J. Jeans, *The Mathematical Theory of Electricity and Magnetism*, Cambridge University Press, London, 1925, Chap. 7.
3. L. D. Landau and E. M. Lifshitz, *Electrodynamics of Continuous Media*, Pergamon Press, Oxford, 1960, Chaps. 2, 15.
4. B. Bleaney and E. Bleaney, *Electricity and Magnetism*, Clarendon Press, Oxford, 1959, Chap. 18.
5. J. B. Birks, *Modern Dielectric Materials*, Heywood, London, 1960, Chaps. 1, 3.
6. M. J. Gross and J. E. Porter, *Nature*, **212**, 1343 (1966).

D. J. TRITTON
and
M. N. ZARRAGA

Department of Geophysics and Planetary Physics
School of Physics
University of Newcastle upon Tyne
England

Geophysical implications of laboratory experiments on convection with internal heat generation

An experimental investigation has been made of a configuration related to the classical Bénard situation (our knowledge of which has been the starting point for many discussions of convection within the mantles of the Earth and other planets). In the Bénard configuration, a horizontal layer of fluid is heated from below and cooled from above. In the present experiments, the heating was uniformly distributed throughout the fluid (water). The bottom surface was thermally insulating; the top was again held at a constant temperature. Thus, as in the Bénard case, the fluid came into motion through instability of a vertical temperature profile.

A detailed account of the experiments and their results is being published elsewhere[1]. Here, we just wish to draw attention to the main geophysical implications of the experiments. Since a likely source of energy for mantle convection is radiogenic heating within the mantle itself, the observations are perhaps more nearly relevant to the geophysical situation than those drawn on previously.

The sequence of events observed as the Rayleigh number is increased (i.e. as the amount of internal heat generation is increased with all other parameters held constant) is in many respects similar to that observed in the Bénard situation (see, for example, Silveston[2]). In two respects, however, there are striking differences, and it is these that have important implications for the mantle convection problem.

The first difference concerns the horizontal size of the convection cells. This can be much larger than in the Bénard case. This 'elongation' is most marked for the higher Rayleigh numbers, when a typical distance between upgoing and downgoing currents is five times the depth of the layer. Even greater elongation might have been observed but for the finite horizontal extent of the apparatus.

This result bears on the controversy about how much of the mantle is convecting. Models such as that of Runcorn[3] show convection extending throughout the mantle; Tozer[4] and others have argued that convection may be confined to the upper part of

506   *Thermal convection in planets*

the mantle (e.g. the upper 700 km) because of high viscosity and perhaps subadiabatic temperature gradients elsewhere*. A powerful argument for the former point of view has seemed to be provided by the horizontal scale of the surface features that might be manifestations of the convection. On the supposition that convection cells tend to be of comparable scale vertically and horizontally, it was argued that the depth of the convecting layer should be of the same order as the width of the oceans—and this is of the order of the depth of the mantle. The present experiments invalidate this argument, and thus, at least in a negative sense, support the second point of view.

The other relevant feature of the experiments is that the convection has the falling currents at the centres of the cells and the rising currents at the peripheries—the opposite way round from Bénard convection in water. The direction of circulation normally depends on the way in which the viscosity varies with temperature, but in the present case is probably a consequence of the heating being over a volume and the cooling over a surface. This may mean that, in mantle convection, the downgoing currents are strong and concentrated whilst the upgoing ones are weaker and more diffuse. One ought perhaps to pay more attention to tectonic features that could be associated with the former; the tendency hitherto has been the opposite.

* This oversimplifies what is really a many-sided controversy into a two-sided one.

References

1. D. J. Tritton and M. N. Zarraga, to be published (1967).
2. P. L. Silveston, *Forsch. Gebiete. Ingenieurw.*, **24**, 29, 59 (1958).
3. S. K. Runcorn, *Nature*, **193**, 311 (1962).
4. D. C. Tozer, *Phil. Trans. Roy. Soc. London, Ser. A*, **258**, 252 (1965).

5

D. W. ALLAN

Department of Mathematics
King's College, London
England

and

N. O. WEISS

Department of Applied Mathematics and Theoretical Physics
University of Cambridge
England

W. B. THOMPSON

Department of Physics
University of California at San Diego
La Jolla, California, U.S.A.

Convection in the Earth's mantle

Introduction

There are three distinct mechanisms that might give rise to convection in the Earth's mantle. Rayleigh–Bénard convection will take place if the superadiabatic gradient exceeds a critical value[1]; this has been discussed by Hales[2] and Knopoff[3]. Alternatively, convection may be ascribed to the presence of internal heat sources[4]. Both these effects grow from unstable perturbations to a static equilibrium; but no such equilibrium is possible if horizontal temperature gradients are present. We shall discuss this third mechanism only.

If we adopt a straightforward model of the temperature distribution in a static mantle[5] with radioactive sources concentrated under continents and a uniform heat flux at the surface, then isotherms must be more closely spaced in oceanic regions. In fact, MacDonald finds that the temperature at a depth of 150 km is about 100 degc higher under the oceans than under continents. The associated density gradients inevitably cause mass motions whose pattern is governed by the distribution of continents: currents rise under the oceans, flow towards continental regions, and then sink under them[6]. If this convection is to be associated with continental drift, can the requisite velocities (1 cm/year) be attained?

Pekeris[7] and Bernstein[8] have treated the problem in a spherical Earth, using a method due to Oberbeck[9]. Pekeris assumed a Newtonian viscosity, constant throughout the mantle and with the value derived from Fennoscandian uplift. Recent investigations[10] show that at low stresses diffusion creep is the only mechanism available for deformation and that it does indeed act as a Newtonian viscosity. However, the non-hydrostatic equatorial bulge measured by satellites implies a much higher viscosity in the lower mantle. We shall adopt McKenzie's model, with a kinematic viscosity $v \sim 10^{21}$ s in the upper mantle, while $v \sim 10^{26}$ s in the lower mantle, below 700 km depth. So far as convection is concerned, the lower mantle is effectively rigid and we need only consider motions in a shallow layer. Since the effects of curvature are negligible, we shall first discuss a simple model of two-dimensional convection in a bounded plane layer for which precise results can be obtained. These criteria will then be applied to the mantle.

Convection Driven by Horizontal Temperature Gradients

We consider an incompressible fluid to which the Boussinesq approximation may be applied. Then its motion is governed by the Navier–Stokes equation

$$\rho_0 \left\{ \frac{\partial \mathbf{u}}{\partial t} + (\mathbf{u} \cdot \nabla) \mathbf{u} \right\} = -\nabla P + \rho \mathbf{g} + \rho_0 \nu \nabla^2 \mathbf{u} \tag{1}$$

and $\nabla \cdot \mathbf{u} = 0$, where $\mathbf{u}$ is the velocity and ν the kinematic viscosity. If T_0 and ρ_0 are the mean temperature and density respectively, then

$$T = T_0 + T' \tag{2}$$

$$\rho = \rho_0 + \rho' = \rho_0(1 - \alpha T') \tag{3}$$

where α is the volume coefficient of expansion. We eliminate the pressure P by taking the curl of (1) and so obtain an equation for the vorticity ω.

$$\frac{\partial \omega}{\partial t} + \text{curl} \, (\omega \times \mathbf{u}) = \frac{1}{\rho_0} \nabla \rho \times \mathbf{g} + \nu \nabla^2 \omega \tag{4}$$

If there is any variation of ρ along an equipotential, equation (4) shows that it must generate vorticity and so produce convection. For slow, steady motions (4) simplifies to

$$\nabla^2 \omega = -\frac{1}{\nu \rho_0} \nabla \rho \times \mathbf{g} = \frac{\alpha}{\nu} \nabla T \times \mathbf{g} \tag{5}$$

The equation of heat flow has the form

$$\frac{\partial T}{\partial t} + \mathbf{u} \cdot \nabla T = \kappa \nabla^2 T + \varepsilon \tag{6}$$

where the thermometric conductivity κ is assumed constant and εc_p is the rate of generation of energy per unit mass. We now *assume* that κ is large and that the heat flow is therefore dominated by conductivity; we also drop ε and simply impose the horizontal variation of temperature as a boundary condition. Then

$$\nabla^2 T = 0 \tag{7}$$

and T is given at the surface $y = 0$.

We adopt Cartesian coordinates with the y axis vertical and consider the two-dimensional problem in which all motion is confined to the xy plane and nothing varies in the z direction. The system is linear, so we need only consider a single Fourier component in the x direction and let

$$T' = \theta \cos kx \quad \text{at} \quad y = 0 \tag{8}$$

The velocity is described by a stream function ψ, where

$$\mathbf{u} = \left(\frac{\partial \psi}{\partial y}, -\frac{\partial \psi}{\partial x}, 0 \right)$$

and

$$\boldsymbol{\omega} = (0, 0, \zeta) = (0, 0, -\nabla^2 \psi)$$

Then

$$\nabla^2 \zeta = -\frac{g\alpha}{v} \frac{\partial T}{\partial x} = -\nabla^4 \psi \tag{9}$$

We assume a rigid upper boundary at $y = 0$, so that $u_y = 0$ and $\psi = 0$, say. Another boundary condition is necessary: we could take either (i) a 'fixed' boundary, with no tangential velocity, for which

$$\frac{\partial \psi}{\partial y} = \psi = 0 \tag{10}$$

or (ii) a 'free' boundary, at which the tangential stress vanishes and

$$\frac{\partial^2 \psi}{\partial y^2} = \psi = \zeta = 0 \tag{11}$$

Bottomless layer

If the fluid occupies the half-space $y < 0$ then

$$T' = \theta \cos kx \, e^{ky} \tag{12}$$

The solution for a fixed boundary at $y = 0$ was obtained by Babcock[11]. However, we are interested in the free boundary conditions (11), for which

$$\psi = -\frac{g\alpha\theta}{8k^2 v} \sin kx \, (ky^2 - y) \, e^{ky} \tag{13}$$

Hot fluid rises at the 'hot spot' where $x = 0$ and sinks at $|x| = \pi$. At $y = 0$, the horizontal velocity u_x is

$$u_x = \frac{g\alpha\theta}{8k^2 v} \sin kx \tag{14}$$

Bounded layer

The upper mantle is a shallow layer and we want to investigate the effect of the lower boundary. Let us therefore consider a system confined between a free boundary at $y = 0$ and a fixed rigid boundary at $y = -L$. For simplicity, we assume also that the temperature variation vanishes at the lower boundary. Then

$$T' = \theta \cos kx \, \frac{\sinh ky_1}{\sinh \eta} \tag{15}$$

where

$$y_1 = y + L \quad \text{and} \quad \eta = kL$$

M.E.—17*

while

$$\psi = -\frac{g\alpha\theta}{8k^2\nu}\frac{\sin kx}{\sinh \eta}\left\{ky^2 \sinh ky_1 - y \cosh ky_1\right.$$

$$\left.+\frac{P\ ky \cosh ky - Q \sinh ky}{k(\eta - \sinh \eta \cosh \eta)}\right\} \tag{16}$$

where

$$P = (\eta^2 - 1) \sinh \eta + \eta \cosh \eta$$

$$Q = \eta^2(\eta \cosh \eta + \sinh \eta)$$

At the upper surface $y = 0$, from (16),

$$u_x = \frac{g\alpha\theta}{8k^2\nu} (\sin kx)F(\eta) \tag{17}$$

where

$$F(\eta) = \frac{\eta^3 \cosh \eta - \sinh^3 \eta}{\sinh \eta(\eta - \sinh \eta \cosh \eta)} \tag{18}$$

Comparison of (17) with (14) shows that the imposition of a lower boundary decreases the velocity by a factor F. Table 1 shows F as a function of η. For a layer of infinite

TABLE 1   Effect of finite depth

η	F	η	F
0·0	0	1·0	0·084
0·1	0·0001	1·5	0·230
0·2	0·0008	2·0	0·417
0·4	0·0062	3·0	0·748
0·6	0·0202	4·0	0·918
0·8	0·0456	5·0	0·978

depth, F is of course unity; its value drops to 0·5 when $\eta = 2\cdot2$ and for $\eta \ll 1$

$$F = \tfrac{1}{10}\eta^3 + O(\eta^5) \tag{19}$$

The velocity in a shallow layer is critically dependent on its depth. That F should vary as η^3 is dimensionally inevitable but the constant of proportionality is important. To be sure, this constant is affected by the assumptions in our model; nevertheless, it is small. (For example if the lower boundary condition on T is relaxed, so that (15) is replaced by (12), then $\tfrac{1}{10}$ goes over to $\tfrac{2}{9}$.)

Convection in the Mantle

Static equilibrium is impossible if horizontal temperature gradients are present in the mantle. On the other hand, the speed U of the motion is restricted by the shallowness of the layer. Does the resulting convection have geophysical significance? That is to say, what temperature difference θ is required to produce a velocity of the magnitude suggested for continental drift ($U \sim 3 \times 10^{-8}$ cm/sec)? Let us adopt for the moment the model discussed in the last section, with the following properties: $g = 10^3$ cm/sec², $\alpha = 2 \times 10^{-5}$ degc^{-1}, $\kappa = 3 \times 10^{-2}$ cm²/sec, $v = 10^{21}$ cm²/sec. Table 2 then

TABLE 2   Temperature difference to produce a speed of 1 cm/year

	$\frac{1}{2}\lambda$ (km)	L (km)	η	F	θ (degc)
(i)	6000	∞	∞	1	0·3
(ii)	6000	3000	1·5	0·23	1·3
(iii)	6000	600	0·3	0·0027	110
(iv)	6000	500	0·25	0·0015	200
(v)	3000	500	0·5	0·012	100
(vi)	800	500	2·0	0·42	45

shows values of θ that correspond to various horizontal and vertical length scales.

Consider first an infinite half-space, for which

$$\theta = \frac{8k^2 v}{g\alpha} U \qquad (20)$$

from (14). As an estimate of the horizontal scale, suppose that three wavelengths span the Earth's circumference; then the half-wavelength ($\frac{1}{2}\lambda$) is 6000 km. This is case (i) of table 2: $\theta = 10^7 U$ and so a temperature difference of only 0·3 degc, over a distance of 6000 km, would suffice to produce velocities of 1 cm/year. Horizontal gradients are effective.

Now consider a bounded layer. If convection extended through the whole mantle (case (ii)), the temperature difference would rise to 1·3 degc. But the convecting region is bounded by the bottom of the crust and, say, the level of the deepest earthquakes, so η is correspondingly low. The relation between θ and U then depends critically on the layer depth. For $L = 600$ km the temperature difference is about 100 degc but for $L = 500$ km θ rises to 200 degc, which is excessive.

This discussion shows the crucial significance of the layer depth. A more realistic procedure is to keep L fixed and to vary k, i.e. to find what horizontal scale of temperature variation is likely to be effective. If λ is halved, then the required motion can be maintained by a temperature difference of 100 degc, while the optimum horizontal scale has a half-wavelength of about 800 km, over which θ need only be about 45 degc.

Thus it appears that horizontal temperature differences of 100 degc will just suffice to produce velocities of 1 cm/year over distances of up to 3000 km. That is to say, the static mantle proposed by MacDonald[5] is unrealistic. Significant motion would take place. Free convection driven by horizontal temperature gradients in the mantle is probably more important than the forced convection caused by internal heat generation or heating from below*. Moreover, any analysis of stability in the mantle

* Professor L. Knopoff[12] has used similar arguments to reach the same conclusion (see also Tozer[13]).

should be based on perturbations to a steady flow rather than a static equilibrium.

The model we have discussed incorporates various assumptions. In particular, it is valid only if the non-linear terms can be neglected. Now the Reynolds number

$$R = \frac{UL}{v} \sim 10^{-21}$$

which is comfortably less than unity. The equation of motion (5) is therefore adequate. The thermal decay time for the upper mantle is less than 10^8 years, so the region could reach thermal equilibrium. However, the thermal Reynolds (or Péclet) number is large:

$$R_t = \frac{UL}{\kappa} \sim 1$$

Thus the non-linear term in (6) cannot be disregarded, nor can it even be treated as a perturbation. In order to gain a proper understanding of convection in the mantle, we must solve (5) and (6) together, incorporating both advection and non-uniform generation of heat. Elder[14] has performed some relevant experiments but such a problem, incorporating interactions between instabilities and the basic motion, really has to be tackled on a computer.

Acknowledgements

We owe thanks to Dr. D. P. McKenzie for discussions which delivered us from error. Computations were done at the Culham Laboratory, Abingdon, Berkshire.

References

1. S. Chandrasekhar, *Hydrodynamic and Hydromagnetic Stability*, Clarendon Press, Oxford, 1961.
2. A. L. Hales, *Monthly Notices Roy. Astron. Soc., Geophys. Suppl.*, **3**, 372 (1935).
3. L. Knopoff, *Rev. Geophys.*, **2**, 89 (1964).
4. D. C. Tozer, *Phil. Trans. Roy. Soc. London, Ser. A*, **258**, 252 (1965).
5. G. J. F. MacDonald, *Rev. Geophys.*, **1**, 587 (1963).
6. E. C. Bullard, *Quart. J. Geol. Soc. London*, **120**, 1 (1964).
7. C. L. Pekeris, *Monthly Notices Roy. Astron. Soc., Geophys. Suppl.*, **3**, 343 (1935).
8. V. A. Bernstein, *Izv. Akad. Nauk SSSR, Ser. Geofiz.*, **1959**, No. 9, 1278.
9. A. Oberbeck, *Ann. Physik*, **7**, 271 (1879).
10. D. P. McKenzie, *J. Geophys. Res.*, **71**, 3995 (1966).
11. R. W. Babcock, *Phys. Rev.*, **7**, 271 (1930).
12. L. Knopoff, private communication.
13. D. C. Tozer, (Ed.), 'Non-elastic processes in the mantle', *Geophys. J.*, in press (1966).
14. J. W. Elder, *Bull Volcanol.*, **29**, 327 (1966).

6

S. K. RUNCORN
Department of Geophysics and Planetary Physics
School of Physics
University of Newcastle upon Tyne
England

Convection in the planets

A decisive advance in any science is made when it becomes possible to move from qualitative to quantitative reasoning. Yet a fair account of the development of a science should stress the vital importance of those ideas which result from the application of reason and intuition, but which are not yet ready for mathematical development. An illustration of this is the controversy about the age of the Earth and the Sun. The biologists, developing an understanding of the process of evolution, concluded that all the complicated developments which they saw in life on the Earth indicated that the latter had a much greater age than that Kelvin had calculated, tens of million years, from his study of the cooling of the Earth. Some biologists had even drawn the inference that an unknown source of energy must exist within the Earth and Sun, which they were of course not able to specify. The mathematician's discussion of the age of the Earth was quantitative, elegant, and seemingly complete, but it had had to leave out the most important physical idea of all, that is that there could be a spontaneous generation of heat within the Earth. Quantitative determination of the radioactivity of rocks and meteorites has now made possible various mathematical models of the thermal history of the Earth. These, which suppose conduction to be the only cause of heat transfer, are again elegant but have left out an essential physical process, convection, first proposed to explain geological data.

Holmes[1] was among the first to postulate the existence of convection currents in the Earth's mantle, but his discussion was not quantitative and was in fact quite sketchy. He suggested that convection in the mantle might be a very useful mechanism for bringing about the compression in the crust necessary in the development of geosynclines and mountain building, and he was clearly led to this idea by two qualitative reasons. The first was that geologists had demonstrated that the horizontal displacements in mountain belts reached hundreds of kilometres, and seemed too great to be explained by the contraction of the Earth by cooling. Jeffreys[2] had shown that cooling is only appreciable in the upper few hundred kilometres of the mantle and the cooling in the whole of the Earth's life below this amounts only to a few degrees, providing that thermal convection is the only effective method of heat transfer. Holmes' second reason for his conclusion, that convection was a very important mechanism in the interior of the Earth, arose from his study with radioactivity. He knew that the heat flow through the surface of the Earth represented an energy much greater than any other terrestrial one and, on the other hand, he saw the tectonic processes at the surface of the Earth as the expression in geology of the Earth's internal energy. Tectonic processes involve movement and Holmes saw convection as the natural heat engine within the Earth: it is difficult to think of another which leads from heat to motion. But the discussion of convection given by Holmes and the geologists were qualitative—even realistic order-of-magnitude calculations were unavailable: by contrast the mathematical discussion of the conduction of heat within a sphere was complete and impressively detailed. Yet convection within the Earth's mantle was always a sound idea, both physically and geologically.

If we now examine the position at the present time, the palaeomagnetic evidence for continental drift is most striking support for flow in the Earth's mantle. The horizontal motions of the continents are an order of magnitude greater than those

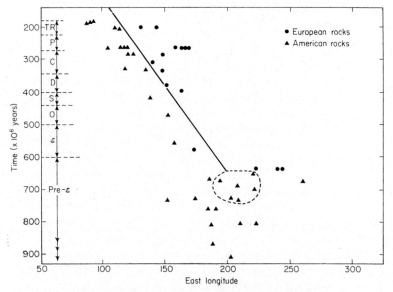

FIGURE 1   Longitudes of pole positions from American and British rocks. TR, Triassic; P, Permian; C, Carboniferous; D, Devonian; S, Silurian; O, Ordovician; ε, Cambrian; Pre-ε, Pre-Cambrian. [From Creer, Irving, and Runcorn[4]]

the geologists require for mountain building. Thus the physicist concludes that continental drift is the fundamental problem to be explained and mountain building involving compressional movements of one or two hundred kilometres is a second-order effect. Thus it is hardly to be expected that the right answer to the major problem of geology, that is tectonics, will emerge unless this much larger movement is investigated and a theory for it formulated. Wegener[3] himself saw this vaguely, when he drew attention to a possible causal relation between the Andes and the Rockies on the west side of North America and South America and the westward movement of these continents. Again one may criticize this wholly unquantitative model in which the mechanical behaviour of the upper layers of the crust are not specified by any physical laws. Wegener's intuition, that the crumpling of these mountain belts which has occurred in the last hundred or two hundred million years was the result of these continents being pushed westwards, was a more pregnant idea that Jeffreys[2] admits.

The palaeomagnetic argument for continental drift is that the divergence between the polar wandering paths calculated from measurements of remanent magnetization for the various continents is a real physical phenomenon. This discrepancy demonstrates that another hypothesis must be introduced into the interpretation of the palaeomagnetic data to bring contemporaneous poles obtained from different continents into agreement. This hypothesis is continental drift and it satisfactorily removes the discrepancies. Figure 1 shows the discrepancy between the longitudes of the European and American pole positions plotted against geological time. The separation, despite the scatter of points, which is to be expected from inadequate sampling

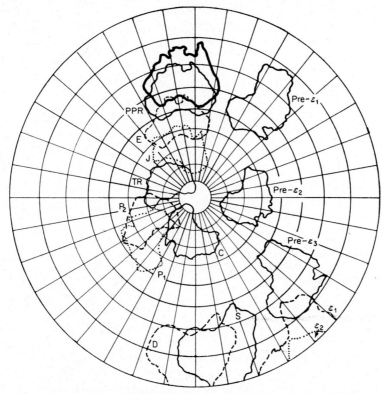

FIGURE 2   Palaeopositions of Australia determined by palaeomagnetism. PPR, Pliocene, Pleistocene, and present; E, Eocene; J, Jurassic; TR, Triassic; P_1, P_2, Permian; C, Carboniferous; D, Devonian; S, Silurian; ε_1, ε_2, Cambrian; Pre-ε_1, Pre-ε_2, Pre-ε_3, Pre-Cambrian. [From Creer and others[5]]

and imperfections in dating, is clear except in the Pre-Cambrian Period where the inaccuracy of correlations would be expected to give a pattern difficult to interpret.

   It is very instructive to use another way of representing palaeomagnetic results by plotting the position of the continent in different geological periods relative to the ancient pole. In figure 2 this is done for Australia. The pole is fixed at the centre of the stereographic projection. This method makes clear one of the strongest arguments in favour of the reality of the palaeomagnetic measurements, that the movements, both in this diagram and in the polar wandering diagram, are not random but are progressive with geological age. This was always a strong reason for the interpretation

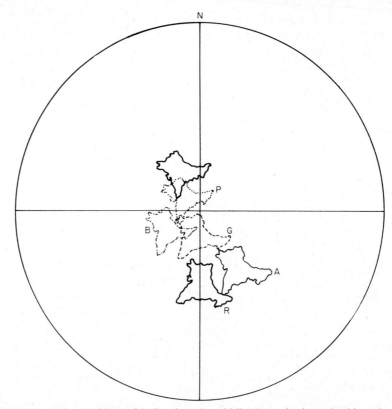

FIGURE 3   Palaeopositions of India, since the middle Mesozoic, determined by palaeomagnetism. P, Upper Pavagadh; B, Nipani upper, Amba upper, Lower Pavagadh;
G, Lower Ghats; A, Nipani lower, Amba lower, Linga, Khandala; R, Rajmahal traps

made in the early development of this subject, that the magnetic directions recovered
from the rocks were caused by a planetary phenomenon and not by physical or
chemical processes of local origin. A further powerful reason for accepting the assumption of palaeomagnetism is illustrated also by figure 2. The data show that Australia
was close to the South Pole in the Permo-Carboniferous Period and again in a certain
part of the late Pre-Cambrian. These positions fit with the palaeoclimatic evidence
because widespread glaciations are found in Australia during the Permo-Carboniferous
Era and in the Pre-Cambrian Era. Figure 3 is a similar map for India. The palaeomagnetic data for the continent have been put in the form of a movement of India
relative to the pole on a meridional stereographic projection. This shows that India
has moved northwards in the Mesozoic and the Tertiary Periods (figure 2 also shows
that in the last hundred or two hundred million years Australia has moved north-
wards).

    Figure 4 shows Creer's palaeolatitude curve for South America, which again
shows the high latitudes which South America occupied in the Permo-Carboniferous
Period, again in agreement with the palaeoclimatic evidence. Thus all the palaeomagnetic results from the southern continents fit in a broad way with Wegener's idea
that South America, Australia, India, and Africa were close together near the South
Pole in the Permian and Carboniferous times, a reconstruction which he thought was

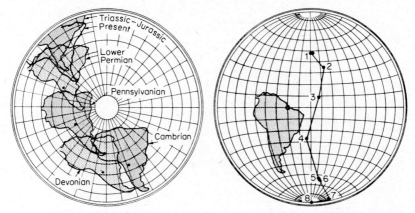

FIGURE 4 Palaeolatitudes of South America determined by palaeomagnetism [from Creer[6]]

reasonable, especially in view of the Permo-Carboniferous glaciation evidence. These broad outlines of the continental drift reconstructions and the consequent movements of the continental blocks in the last 100–200 million years must be borne in mind in discussing the pattern of convection. After Holmes' original suggestion of the idea of convection currents in mountain building, Vening-Meinesz[7] made use of the convection mechanism to explain the Java Trench and the associated negative gravity anomaly by the down-warping of the ocean floor near the East Indies. The paradox that compression in the continents produces mountains and in the ocean floor trenches has been a great stumbling block to the acceptance of the idea that there are both compressional features and tensional features in the Earth's crust. Vening-Meinesz introduced one further important point into the discussion that Wegener had anticipated, that isostasy was likely to be a key in understanding the mechanism of drift, for it suggested that some of the properties of a fluid might be attributed to the mantle—in its simplest interpretation the continental blocks are floating in the mantle.

Vening-Meinesz took the further step of suggesting that the convection currents would have a tendency to drive the continents to places where the convection currents were descending. There is no doubt that in a general way this has in recent years been proved. It explains why the great compressional features produced by the down-going convection currents tend to occur in the continents more frequently than tensional ones. Thus the classical geophysicist thought that compressional features were the most important aspect of the tectonics of the Earth that had to be explained. He was therefore naturally led to suppose that the Earth was contracting as a whole and attempted to explain this by the theory of a cooling Earth. Figure 5 shows a summary of the tectonic features of the globe and demonstrates how this view of the World has changed with the recognition that the oceanic ridges are tensional features and are a phenomenon comparable in scale with the great Tertiary mountain belts. Thus in some parts of the crust there is tension and in some parts compression and both may be explained by the theory of convection. For just a short time after the discovery was made that the ocean ridges were tensional features there were one or two geophysicists, particularly Egyed and Heezen, who thought that these tensional features were much more important and they therefore assumed that the Earth was expanding.

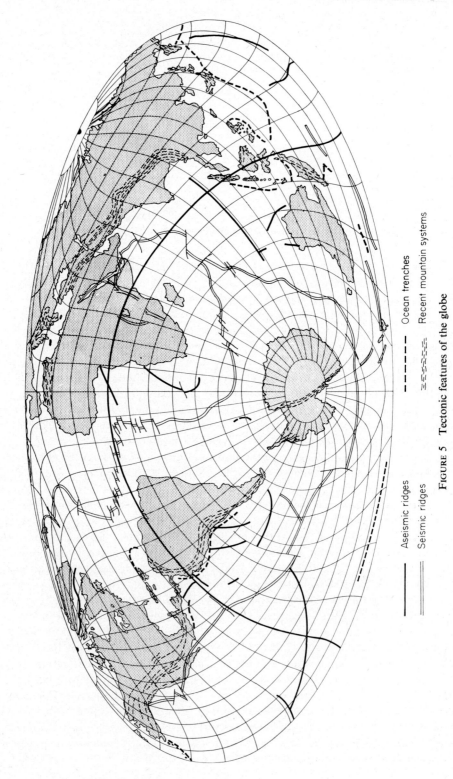

FIGURE 5   Tectonic features of the globe

Aseismic ridges ———   Ocean trenches - - - - -
Seismic ridges ═══   Recent mountain systems ≈≈≈≈≈

But the theory that both the tensional and compressional features have a common physical cause has been strengthened by the spherical analysis of tectonic features on the globe[8]. This is a first step in the development of a mathematical method of discussing the real, but qualitative, notion that there is a planetary distribution of tectonic features. Coode's analysis suggests strongly that the physical process causing tension in the Earth's crust is the same physical process as that causing compression. Coode takes the positions of the seismically active ridges, that is those thought to be tensional features, and describes their position on the globe by a distribution of Dirac delta functions spaced uniformly along them. A distribution of delta functions along the ridges and nowhere else can be expanded in a spherical harmonic series. The root-mean-square of the coefficients summed for every order in each degree, termed the harmonic content, can be plotted against the degree. It is independent, of course, of the axis of coordinates and therefore is a physically meaningful account of the global distribution. Coode made a similar analysis for the compressional features, the mountain building belts on the continents and the ocean trenches, both of which are associated with deep-focus earthquakes, suggestive of a common origin. Coode shows that the harmonic content diagrams for both compressional and tensional features are similar and are greatest at the fifth degree. It is logical to suppose that this is strong evidence that the physical process underlying mountain building and the oceanic trenches, on the one hand, and the process causing tension in the crust are the same. Perhaps one should put the conclusion even more cautiously and say that it would be very remarkable if the tensional features were caused by one mechanism and the compressional features by another, when both of them are analysed by these harmonic content diagrams and show a similar global distribution. Coode argues that the processes of compression and tension can be considered as one. If positive delta functions are used to represent the compressional features and negative the tensional features, the resulting harmonic content diagram obtained from the spherical harmonic analysis of the tectonic features of the globe ought to describe the distribution of the physical forces in the mantle which are causing them. Whether this is convection is not of course to be concluded from such a mathematical analysis.

Vening-Meinesz[7] had previously argued that the position of the continents themselves would indicate the places where the convection currents were descending and that therefore the topography of the Earth, analysed into a spherical harmonic series, should describe the distribution of convection currents. If the heights of the continents above sea level and the depths of the ocean floors are represented by negative numbers, these quantities can be expanded in a spherical harmonic series. Vening-Meinesz found that the harmonic content was a maximum about the third, fourth and fifth degrees, in addition to the peak at the first degree which arises from the continents being largely in one hemisphere. This work of Vening-Meinesz was an important, though very subtle, argument for convection and it was perhaps not accorded the attention it deserved. However, the fact that the continents cover a big area and that they are probably still moving—he did not in the early discussions entertain the idea of continental drift—complicates the question, which he was really wanting to solve, that is the pattern of the convection currents. Coode's harmonic content diagrams are more sharply peaked than Vening-Meinesz's and we conclude that they describe better than his the present convection current distribution.

This attempt to infer the pattern of flow in the Earth's mantle from geophysical and geological evidence seems to be sounder at this stage in the study of convection than attempts to calculate from theoretical ideas, or from analogies with experiments, the distribution of currents or even to conclude whether or not convection is occurring within the Earth. It follows from the arguments above that the pattern changed about one or two hundred million years ago. Now the indication, both from Vening-Meinesz's work and from Coode's work, is that the present system of convection currents in the Earth's mantle is described by harmonics, in which the fifth degree is very strong and perhaps dominant. In order to explain what has happened in the Earth's mantle in the last 100–200 million years, it is essential to recognize that a remarkable redistribution of the continents has occurred in the last few per cent of the Earth's lifetime. Therefore an event has to be postulated which sets off continental drift and which could reasonably have happened so recently in the Earth's history. The present author has suggested that such a change in the convection pattern is reasonable because convection is an unstable process which could have been changed by a small external influence[9]. He argues that the distribution of the continents before 'Wegenerian' continental drift took place must have been a simpler one than the present. The palaeomagnetic evidence shows that the southern continents were around the South Pole and this was, of course, Wegener's conception of Gondwanaland. There is plenty of evidence, both palaeoclimatic and palaeomagnetic, for Europe and North America having been lower latitudes than they occupy at the present time. If one adopts Vening-Meinesz's idea that the continents do, approximately, reflect the distribution of convection currents in the mantle, the dispersion of Gondwanaland and the movement north of Australia and India and the parting of Europe and North America suggest that the convection currents in the mantle have become more complicated in the last one or two hundred million years. The present author therefore has suggested that what may have happened is that a dominantly fourth-degree convection pattern has been changing into a fifth-degree one. One group of continents near a pole and the other group at the equator would fit a simple four-cell pattern in which the continents are positioned above the descending currents. To follow this line of speculation it is natural to think that possibly in the earlier history of the Earth there was a predominantly three-cell pattern and before that a two-cell pattern and before that a single-cell pattern. To suggest that a one-cell pattern originally existed is equivalent to supposing that the continents were once a single mass, and it has been suggested that the absence of continents from a whole hemisphere of the Earth today is a possible consequence of the existence of a single-cell convection pattern in its early history. That the convection pattern was essentially of fourth degree before Wegenerian continental drift took place is supported by Coode's analysis of the aseismic ocean ridges, which are thought to be the oceanic rifts of former times. The harmonic content of these had a peak at the fourth degree. The only evidence we really have of tectonic activity in the earlier part of the Earth's existence is the existence of igneous and metamorphic rocks of the shield areas of the World. It now seems generally agreed that there is strong tendency for the rocks of the shields to have ages strongly distributed around 2600 and 1800 and 1000 million years. The rocks, on which measurements have been made, are metamorphic and igneous and thus come from the depths of the crust. Thus the histograms of radioactive ages are really reflections of relative amounts of tectonic activity. This grouping of ages around similar values in Canada, in Europe, in Australia, and in Africa suggests that there were World-wide epochs of enhanced crustal movement or tectonic activity. The author has suggested that each of these peaks of activity might be associated with the successive changes in the convection pattern.

By making use of the theory of marginal stability, he has also suggested that one might in a general way explain this evolution of the convection pattern in the Earth's mantle by adopting Urey's[10] idea of a growing core. One may then obtain an empirical curve relating the growth of the core to these radioactive age peaks. From this curve the dependence of the moment of inertia of the Earth with time can be calculated. The gradually decreasing moment of inertia on the growing core hypothesis would indicate a change in the length of the day, in addition to that caused by the tides raised by the Sun and Moon, but of opposite sign. This long chain of speculation may now be capable of being put to experimental test, for these are possibilities of measuring the rate of rotation of the Earth in the geological past by the analysis of the growth rings on fossil corals[11].

Because the earlier discussions of convection were qualitative and the more recent discussions have been necessarily speculative, it is most satisfactory that it now appears that a physical measurement is being made which will really prove the existence of convection in the Earth's mantle at the present time and which will determine the distribution of convection currents. Extremely important and beautiful data, being obtained from the analysis of satellite orbits, are giving the geoid of the Earth. The author believes this is the key to the distribution of convection currents in the Earth's mantle. Figure 6 shows the geoid of Guier and Newton[12]; the highs and lows represent differences of gravity of one part in 10^5. If we suppose that the sources of these anomalies are distributed throughout the mantle, the results indicate that in the deep mantle there are variations of density of the same order, one part in 10^5. The explanation in terms of convection is controversial and it is interesting to enquire why it is so. If one ignores the evidence for continental drift and if one supposes that flow is impossible in the mantle, then of course it is possible to say that these satellite gravity observations simply reflect differences in density of the mantle which were caused at the origin of the Earth or continents and which have been retained because of the finite strength of the mantle. This theory cannot be taken very seriously: it is not plausible in solid-state physics to take such a simple view of the non-elastic behaviour of the mantle. The present author has postulated that the non-hydrostatic shape of the Earth and, of course, the non-hydrostatic shape of the Moon, arise from hydrodynamic behaviour—the variations of density associated with motion. As the buoyancy forces on the density variations drive the convection currents, the author argues that the satellite geoid can be used to derive the distribution of convection currents in the Earth's mantle. It is interesting to compare geoids based on different data. Guier and Newton[12] determined a geoid which is based on coefficients up to and including the eighth degree—the highest so far reached. But even the earlier workers agree in finding a negative anomaly in the Indian Ocean, the western Atlantic, and the east Pacific. As geoids based on coefficients of higher degree are determined, a more obvious correlation has emerged between the highs and lows of the potential and the tectonic features discussed above. For example, all workers obtained a large positive anomaly over the tropical west Pacific. But Guier and Newton show that, when higher-degree terms are included, it divides into three more or less separate highs, one very close to the Tonga Trench and the associated deep-focus earthquakes, one

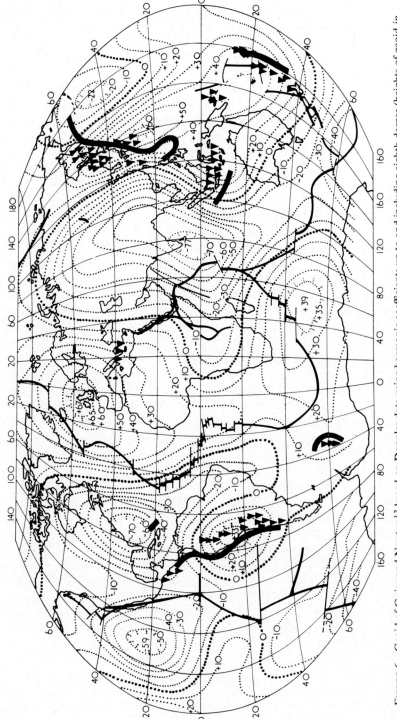

FIGURE 6   Geoid of Guier and Newton[12] based on Doppler data using harmonic coefficients up to and including eighth degree (heights of geoid in metres). Thin lines are the oceanic ridge systems, thick lines the oceanic trenches; triangles are the deep-focus earthquakes

close to the east Indian compressional zone, and another elongated one closely parallel to the Mariana and Japan Trenches. Positive anomalies cover Europe and the Alps and also the Andes, and the Peru–Chile Trench associated with the deep-focus earthquakes. The gravity anomalies are about one part in 10^5. On the convection hypothesis the material in the mantle below the positive anomalies is denser and there-fore falling. These regions therefore ought to be regions of compression and the author believes the proximity of these positive anomalies to the Andes, the Alps, and the ocean trenches in the west Pacific are in rather strong support of the idea that satellite gravity observations are explained by convection. The Rockies are on a north–south high in the geoid between lows in the west Atlantic and east Pacific. Thus the Rockies represent regions of falling convection currents and therefore North America is being compressed. The palaeomagnetic data demonstrate that India is being pushed north-wards against the mass of Asia and the negative anomaly in the Indian Ocean indicates an uprising current which is thrusting India northwards. On the earlier maps of the geoid there was no feature correlating with the Scotia arc, but on Guier and Newton's map of the geoid there is a suggestion of a high around the Scotia arc. This is a very small feature, of course, which would only convincingly emerge if harmonic co-efficients to perhaps the tenth or twelfth degrees were obtained.

The negative anomalies lie in the Indian Ocean, near the Carlsberg Ridge in the Atlantic, displaced west of the Atlantic Ridge but similar in trend and in the east Pacific not too far from the East Pacific Rise. It seems to me there is a reasonable case for saying that these negative anomalies, which indicate rising currents and therefore cause tension in the crust, give a reasonable explanation for the rift valleys in the centre of the East Pacific Rise, in the Atlantic Ridge, and in the Carlsberg Ridge in the Indian Ocean floor. The east African rift valleys too are tensional features. The earlier satellite gravity observations show no feature suggestive of correlation with the east African rift valleys, yet on Guier and Newton's map of the geoid the beginning of the formation of a negative anomaly in east Africa is seen. There is a very large negative anomaly which goes right through Asia and correlates with the Russian suggestion that Lake Baikal represents a line of rifts—a similar tensional feature to the east Africa rift valleys. An elongated negative anomaly is quite close to the Indian Antarctic Ridge.

Qualitatively this explanation of the satellite geoid by convection is reasonable. The density differences necessary to drive currents in the mantle at a rate of a few centi-metres a year, which is what is necessary to explain continental drift, are about 1 part in 10^5 and this is of course what is needed to explain in order of magnitude the ob-served anomaly. A mathematical discussion is now possible[13].

The possibility that convection is occurring in the Moon and in other planets has only been considered recently[14]. No evidence in favour of this from the study of surface tectonics is likely to be compelling. However, the Moon's moments of inertia differ from each other by an order of magnitude greater than if it were in hydrostatic equilibrium. Unless its interior is so cold that even creep rates less than 10^{-20} sec^{-1} have not occurred under stress differences of 50 b, a convection current of second degree must be present[14,15] with density differences corresponding to a temperature excess of the rising over the falling currents of 50 degc.

We see in this book that Mars may also be out of hydrostatic equilibrium if the optical determination of the ellipticity of its surface is correct. Mercury and Venus must also be out of hydrostatic equilibrium if the explanations of their rotation rates given in this book are correct. Consequently the possibility of convection in all the terrestrial planets must be at least entertained. This hypothesis drastically alters the thermal history of these bodies. Convection would also play a role in the chemical differentiation of their interiors. Convection may thus be of key importance in under-standing the evolution of the planets, as it is of the Earth's evolution. Further, the possibility of convection makes a careful study of planetary surfaces for indications (however different from those on the Earth's surface) of internal activity, volcanic or tectonic, even of the most feeble kind, of great scientific significance.

References

1. A. Holmes, *Trans. Geol. Soc. Glasgow*, **28**, 559 (1931).
2. H. Jeffreys, *The Earth*, Cambridge University Press, London, 1952.
3. A. Wegener, *Geol. Rundschau*, **3**, 276 (1912).
4. K. M. Creer, E. Irving, and S. K. Runcorn, *Phil. Trans. Roy. Soc. London, Ser. A*, **250**, 144 (1957).
5. K. M. Creer, E. Irving, A. E. M. Nairn, and S. K. Runcorn, *Ann. Geophys.*, **14**, 492 (1958).
6. K. M. Creer, *Phil. Trans. Roy. Soc. London, Ser. A*, **258**, 27 (1965).
7. F. A. Vening-Meinesz, *Koninkl. Ned. Akad. Wetenschap., Proc., Ser. B*, **54**, 212 (1951).
8. A. M. Coode, *Geophys. J.*, **12**, 53 (1966).
9. S. K. Runcorn, *Phil. Trans. Roy. Soc. London, Ser. A*, **258**, 228 (1965).
10. H. C. Urey, *The Planets*, Yale University Press, New Haven, 1952.
11. S. K. Runcorn, *Nature*, **204**, 823 (1964).
12. W. H. Guier and R. R. Newton, *J. Geophys. Res.*, **70**, 4613 (1965).
13. S. K. Runcorn, *Geophys. J.*, **13**, in press (1967).
14. S. K. Runcorn, *Nature*, **195**, 1150 (1962).
15. S. K. Runcorn, *Proc. Roy. Soc. (London), Ser. A*, **296**, 270 (1967).

7

J. W. ELDER

Department of Applied Mathematics and Theoretical Physics
University of Cambridge
England

Thermal turbulence and its role in the Earth's mantle

Introduction

The spatial variation and temporal variability in the geological record clearly requires a dynamical model of the Earth's interior. The possibility of producing an elastic model to describe the very wide spectrum of these variations seems remote. Convection, however, has many of the qualitative features required. The reluctance of many geophysicists to accept the convective hypothesis seems to arise from a lack of appreciation of the very wide range of known convective phenomena. In particular, the peculiar time-dependent behaviour of convection, when the motion is sufficiently rapid for non-linear effects to be predominant, may be the key to the underlying mechanisms of many geological processes. The bulk of this chapter emphasizes these effects as observed in the laboratory, but provides sufficient discussion to show that a strongly convecting mantle is qualitatively compatible with many of the puzzling geological data.

The discussion first considers, in the next section, the problem of formulating a dynamical model of the mantle, largely to indicate the theoretical difficulties of even the simplest models and suggest models for future investigation. A particular aspect of the problem, the non-steady convective motions found in strongly unstable systems, is outlined on p. 529. Some of these observations are then considered in relation to the Earth's mantle by means of a sequence of simple models. Finally, a number of proposals suggested by the theory are sketched on p. 546. The point of view is similar to that of Knopoff[1], Tozer[2], and Elder[3,4] but with emphasis on those features of the problem which call for time-varying phenomena.

Formulation of the Dynamical Problem

Studies of the gross shape of the Earth show, to an accuracy of about 1 in 10^5, that the Earth behaves like a self-gravitating mass of inviscid slightly compressible fluid in uniform rotation. Departures from this state of uniform rotation can arise from imbalanced density variations, considered here to be produced by variations of temperature which arise because the Earth is not in thermodynamic equilibrium. A first approximation to a description of such effects by means of a dynamical theory is to consider the fluid viscous. This approximation is a good one, provided the stresses in the fluid are sufficiently small, and will therefore apply nearly everywhere throughout the Earth except possibly in earthquake and vigorous tectonic regions.

Let us consider for a moment the dimensional analysis of the convective motion of a homogeneous fluid sphere of mass M, radius R, spinning at the angular rate Ω, initial available energy per unit volume Q, whose decay constant is λ. Let the fluid have density ρ, specific heat c, kinematic viscosity v, thermal diffusivity κ, and coefficient of cubical expansion γ. If we make the Boussinesq approximation (see below) and note that the acceleration due to buoyancy has the form $\gamma g \Delta T$ with $g \sim GM/R^2$, where G is the gravitational constant, and $\Delta T \sim QR^2/\rho c \kappa$, the problem is defined by

$$v, \kappa, \gamma g \Delta T, \Omega, \lambda, R$$

These six quantities involve only length and time, so that four dimensionless quantities are required to specify the system. A convenient choice is the following:

$$
\begin{aligned}
A &= \gamma g \Delta T R^3/\kappa v && \text{Rayleigh number}\\
\sigma &= v/\kappa && \text{Prandtl number}\\
\mathcal{R} &= 2\Omega R^2/v && \text{Coriolis parameter}\\
\Lambda &= \lambda R^2/\kappa && \text{decay parameter}
\end{aligned}
$$

Inserting typical values

$$\gamma = 10^{-5}\ \text{degc}^{-1}, \quad g = 10^3\ \text{cm/sec}^2, \quad \Delta T = 10^3\ \text{degc}, \quad R = 6 \times 10^3\ \text{km}$$

$$\kappa = 10^{-2}\ \text{cm}^2/\text{sec}, \quad v = 10^{20}\ \text{cm}^2/\text{sec}, \quad \Omega = 7 \times 10^{-5}\ \text{rad/sec}, \quad \lambda = 10^{-9}\ \text{year}^{-1}$$

we find

$$A \sim 10^9, \qquad \sigma \sim 10^{22}, \qquad \mathcal{R} \sim 10^{-2}, \qquad \Lambda \sim 10^{-1}$$

These values indicate the following points: convection will be important, convective inertial effects will be negligible, Coriolis effects will be very small, and the energy sources decay more rapidly than the body would cool by only thermal conduction. Since most of the discussion refers to the mantle, it is preferable to choose the thickness of the mantle H as the length scale, rather than R. To discuss the problem in more detail let us consider the system of equations relative to axes fixed in the Earth describing the conservation of mass, momentum, energy, and a single solute; these are given by (1)–(4) where (5)–(7) apply. We write the velocity as $\mathbf{q}$, pressure p, temperature

$$\frac{d\rho}{dt} = -\rho \nabla \cdot \mathbf{q} \tag{1}$$

$$\frac{d\mathbf{q}}{dt} + 2\Omega \times \mathbf{q} = -\frac{1}{\rho}\nabla p + \mathbf{g} + \mathbf{F}(v, \mathbf{q}) \tag{2}$$

$$\rho c \frac{dT}{dt} = \nabla \cdot K \nabla T + Q(C, \mathbf{q}, \rho) \tag{3}$$

$$\frac{dC}{dt} = \nabla \cdot D \nabla C + J(C) \tag{4}$$

$$\rho = \rho(p, T) \tag{5}$$

$$\mathbf{g} = -\frac{Gm\hat{r}}{r^2} \tag{6}$$

$$m = \int_{V(r)} \rho \, dV \tag{7}$$

relative to the reference state (see below) T, concentration of solute C, angular velocity $\boldsymbol{\Omega}$, viscous body force $\mathbf{F}$, rate of generation of heat Q, rate of generation of solute J, specific heat c, thermal conductivity K, solute diffusion coefficient D, and m is the total mass inside a sphere of radius r and volume V. The time derivatives are those following the motion, and the centrifugal pressure $\frac{1}{2}(\boldsymbol{\Omega} \times \mathbf{r})^2$ has been included in the pressure p.

Implicit in the argument below is the suggestion that in (5) the effects of p and T can be separated, for example into a form like

$$\rho = \rho_0(1 + n\chi_0 p)^{1/n}\{1 - \gamma(T - T_0)\}$$

where χ_0 is the compressibility at zero pressure and the term $\gamma(T - T_0) \ll 1$. For the Earth $n \simeq 3$ and apart from the crust $\chi_0 \simeq 7 \cdot 6 \times 10^{-13} \text{ cm}^2/\text{dyn}$ and $\rho_0 \simeq 3 \cdot 26 \text{ g/cm}^3$ are constant throughout the mantle. Thus, since the departures from uniform rotation are small, the system of equations can be conveniently considered in two portions, a static part and a dynamic part. Thus relative to the reference state $t \to \infty$ in which $\mathbf{q} \to 0$ we write $p_0 = p_\infty + p'$, $\rho = \rho_\infty + \rho'$, etc., where it is important to note that p_∞, ρ_∞, etc., are functions of position and p', ρ', etc., arise solely from temperature variations. Hence from (2) we find (8) and (9), where we neglect the very small term

$$0 = -\frac{1}{\rho_\infty}\nabla p_\infty + \mathbf{g}_\infty \tag{8}$$

$$\frac{d\mathbf{q}}{dt} + 2\boldsymbol{\Omega} \times \mathbf{q} = -\frac{1}{\rho}\nabla p' + \frac{\rho'}{\rho}\mathbf{g}_\infty + \mathbf{F}(v, \mathbf{q}) \tag{9}$$

$\rho'\mathbf{g}'/\rho$. For considerations solely of the present day, a preferable reference state would be that corresponding to an adiabatic temperature distribution appropriate to the lower mantle. We notice that the only term producing motion is the acceleration due to buoyancy $\rho'\mathbf{g}_\infty/\rho$ (external pressures are ignored here). In the laboratory a very good approximation due to Boussinesq[5] is to ignore density variations except in so far as they produce buoyancy. This is not such a good approximation for the mantle, since ρ varies by a factor of about 2. Nevertheless profound errors are not forseeable if we make the Boussinesq approximation in the mantle. Thus we write $\rho = \rho_0$ and note that (1) becomes $\nabla \cdot \mathbf{q} = 0$. At the same level of approximation $\mathbf{g}_\infty \simeq g\hat{r}$ with $g \simeq 10^3 \text{ cm/sec}^2$. The three molecular processes, diffusion of momentum, heat, and solute, with diffusivities v, $\kappa = K/\rho c$, D, are functions of both temperature and pressure. Theoretical methods for coping with these variations are almost non-existent. Laboratory experience suggests, however, that variations of several orders of magnitude are necessary to produce qualitatively significant effects. Probably the most important variation in the mantle is for v. For the discussion below we ignore variations in κ and D, remembering that this assumption is a very poor one, but we retain some discussion of the effects of variations of v.

The major difficulty for this model is the resistive terms $\mathbf{F}(v, \mathbf{q})$. There are two simple possibilities. The first and usual one is $\mathbf{F} = \nabla \cdot v\nabla\mathbf{q}$, corresponding to a simple viscous fluid. A more recent suggestion is that the mantle behaves like a porous medium with a small amount of melt between an immobile granular matrix. In this case we write $d\mathbf{q}/dt \equiv 0$ and $\mathbf{F} = -v\mathbf{q}/k$, where v is the kinematic viscosity of the melt and k is the permeability of the matrix. An important consequence of this approximation is that there can be convection of the mantle without continental drift. The difficulty in both cases is that v is not constant but is generally a function of p and T. However, since for the mantle $\sigma \gg 1$, there is a powerful simplification of the equations. Let us make the equations dimensionless by choosing units of length H, velocity κ/H, and time H^2/κ, so that for a viscous fluid (9) becomes (10),

$$\frac{1}{\sigma}\frac{d\mathbf{q}}{dt} + \mathscr{R}\hat{k} \times \mathbf{q} = -B\nabla p + A\theta\hat{r} + \nabla \cdot \xi\nabla\mathbf{q} \tag{10}$$

where $\xi = v/v_0$ (v_0 being the smallest value of v), $\sigma = v_0/\kappa$ the Prandtl number, $\mathscr{R} = 2\Omega H^2/v_0$ a Reynolds number based on the Coriolis force, $B = gL^3/\kappa v_0$, and $A = (\Delta\rho/\rho)gH^3/\kappa v_0$ the Rayleigh number. For the mantle $\sigma \gg 1$, so that the inertia term $(1/\sigma)(d\mathbf{q}/dt)$ can be neglected. Recent studies show that this is an excellent approximation for the gross features of the flow[6] provided $\sigma \gtrsim 1$. The Coriolis parameter $\mathscr{R}$ is small. For example for the mantle, if $v \sim 10^{20}$ cm^2/sec, $\mathscr{R} \sim 10^{-7}$. If, however, in the deep mantle $v \sim 10^{14}$ cm^2/sec, $\mathscr{R} \sim 0\cdot 1$ and may be sufficiently large to weakly constrain the largest eddies.

The heat source term Q involves three possible effects: viscous dissipation, radioactive heating, and release of gravitational energy by gross reorganizations of the Earth's interior such as formation of the core (which we ignore here). Thus in dimensionless variables (3) becomes (11) where $\mathscr{H}$ and $\mathscr{P}$ are given by (11a) and (11b). The

$$\frac{dT}{dt} = \nabla^2 T + \mathscr{H}\left(\frac{\partial q_i}{\partial x_j} + \frac{\partial q_j}{\partial x_i}\right)^2 + \mathscr{P}C \tag{11}$$

$$\mathscr{H} = \kappa v/2cH^2\Delta T = \tfrac{1}{2}(\gamma gH/c)/A \tag{11a}$$

$$\mathscr{P} = H^2C_0/\rho c\kappa\Delta T \tag{11b}$$

dissipation parameter $\mathscr{H} \sim 3 \times 10^{-2}$, for $v \sim 10^{20}$ cm^2/sec and $\kappa \sim 10^{-2}$ cm^2/sec, is by no means negligible. But, if $v \sim 10^{14}$ cm^2/sec in the deep mantle, $\mathscr{H}$ can be neglected. The value of $\mathscr{P}$ is somewhat uncertain; probably $\mathscr{P} \sim 10^2$–10^3.

The generation of solute term $J(C)$ for a radioactive solute is simply $J = -\lambda C$, where λ is the decay constant. Hence in dimensionless variables (4) becomes (12),

$$\frac{dC}{dt} = d\nabla^2 C - \Lambda C \tag{12}$$

where $d = D/\kappa$ and $\Lambda = \lambda H^2/\kappa$.

Theoretical studies of systems with an equation such as the above are at the moment largely confined to two-dimensional problems with constant coefficients. We then can write, in Cartesian coordinates, equations (13)–(16), where the stream function ψ is

$$\nabla^2\omega = -A\theta_x \tag{13}$$

$$\nabla^2\psi = \omega \tag{14}$$

$$\frac{\partial \theta}{\partial t} = \nabla^2 \theta - \partial(\psi, \theta) + \mathscr{P}C \qquad (15)$$

$$\frac{\partial C}{\partial t} = d\nabla^2 C - \partial(\psi, C) - \Lambda C \qquad (16)$$

defined by $\mathbf{q} = (-\psi_z, 0, \psi_x)$, the vorticity $\boldsymbol{\omega} = \nabla \times \mathbf{q} = -\hat{j}\omega$, and $\partial(\psi, \theta) = (\psi_x\theta_z - \psi_z\theta_x)$ is the advection of heat. It should be noted that, for the porous medium approximation, equation (13) is replaced by $\omega = A\theta_x$. Analytical studies are largely restricted to the case when ψ is sufficiently small for the advection to be negligible so that the problem is linear. However, such studies are of considerable value, since the form of the flow generally persists well into the non-linear region. For non-linear problems recent progress with numerical studies indicates considerable promise.

Experimental Studies of Thermal Turbulence in a Fluid of Large Prandtl Number*

In everyday speech the meaning of 'thermal turbulence' is clear. We refer to the more or less chaotic motion produced by heating a large body of fluid. However, a more precise definition is difficult. There is no problem with the word 'thermal', although the word 'buoyancy' is possibly preferable. We consider motions generated by buoyancy forces, namely forces which arise from spatial variations of an otherwise uniform imposed force field. It is simplest to consider the case in which these variations arise from spatial variations of density in a uniform acceleration field. As Jeffreys[8] pointed out these variations should be measured relative to a reference state in which there is no motion and the entropy is independent of position. Further, a powerful simplification of the description of the flow field is possible with the so-called Boussinesq approximation in which density variations relative to the reference state are ignored except in so far as they generate buoyancy forces. This approximation may still be a good one even if in the reference state there are large relative variations in the density field. There are three effects of the temperature field in this approximation: vorticity is generated by the gradients of the buoyancy forces normal to the applied force field, temperature is advected by the flow, and diffused by molecular processes. On the other hand, the word 'turbulence' poses a difficult and contentious problem. At the outset one requires a definition of turbulence and a specification of the circumstances under which it is present. While there can be little doubt that the turbulence generated in a shear flow is fundamentally different from laminar or quasi-laminar flows, the distinction for turbulence generated by buoyancy forces is not so clear. Nevertheless, studies of a horizontal layer of fluid uniformly heated from below do show a remarkable change in the flow between a Rayleigh number of 10^6 to 10^7. Flows at higher Rayleigh numbers exhibit the property of 'continuous instability', proposed as a suitable definition of turbulence by Hasselmann.

Let us consider the motions which develop in a body of fluid of large Prandtl number and of large horizontal extent, uniformly heated from below, as the Rayleigh number is very slowly increased from zero. Below a critical Rayleigh number

---

* This section is an outline of work to be published elsewhere in more detail[7]. The reader is also referred to the work by Townsend[16], Deardorf and Willis[24,29], and Priestley[28].

$A_c = 1700$ there is no motion and any small imposed disturbance dies away. The theoretical value of A_c has been given by Reid and Harris[9] to be 1707·762. The first careful experimental value of $1770 \pm 8\%$ was given by Schmidt and Milverton[10]. Silveston[11] finds $1700 \pm 3\%$. A_c is found both experimentally and theoretically to be independent of σ. A little above 1700 a steady cellular motion very slowly develops. Chandra[12] has given some nice photographs, but the observations of Silveston[11] are notable. A study of this régime is still a difficult and contentious problem, in spite of

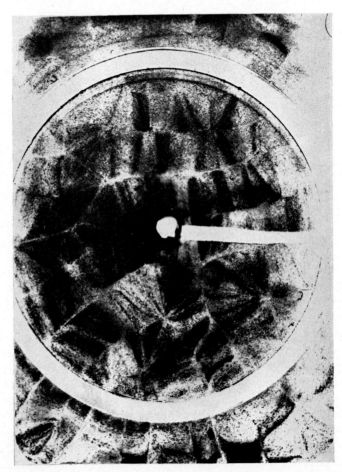

FIGURE 1   Cellular convection at $A = 2·6 \times 10^4$. Photograph of the midhorizontal plane. Depth of fluid, 1·0 cm; internal diameter of ring, 10·0 cm; outer container diameter 20·95 cm; 20 centistoke fluid. (HSL a12, exposure 1 sec)

the considerable work done since the fundamental studies of Rayleigh[13], Jeffreys[8], and Pellew and Southwell[14]. The problem is theoretically difficult because the flow is soon dominated by the non-linear advection of heat and momentum. Figure 1 is a photograph of the cellular régime.

The cellular pattern remains to Rayleigh numbers of the order of 10^6 but there are pronounced changes. Already at a Rayleigh number about 5000 the flow field in each cell is dominated by boundary layers on the walls and thin plumes in the middle of the cells. Further, as the Rayleigh number increases the cell boundaries are seen to be no longer stationary but to move slowly and occasionally to be annihilated while others are formed. This tendency becomes very pronounced at Rayleigh numbers of the order of 10^6. One observes that near $A = 10^4$ the time of adjustment of cell boundaries is very long compared with the orbit time of a fluid particle. Near $A = 10^6$ these times are comparable. Nevertheless, the heat transfer coefficient remains proportional to $A^{1/4}$, indicating that the motion is still laminar and dominated by the combined processes of diffusion and advection in the boundary layers and plumes. Because of the now rapid drifting of the cells, measurements with temperature or velocity probes will indicate a strongly varying signal and one may be tempted to call the motion turbulent.

At a Rayleigh number somewhat above 10^6, however, one observes a remarkable and pronounced change in the system (see figures 2 and 3). Regular or quasiregular cellular motion in the body of the fluid disappears, and buoyant elements are seen rising from the hot lower wall and falling from the cold upper wall in a random

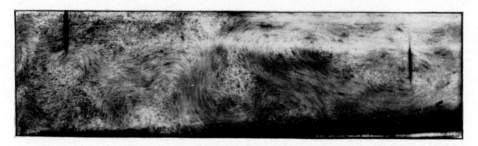

FIGURE 2 Turbulent convection at $A = 2.5 \times 10^7$. Photograph of the midvertical plane. Depth of fluid, 6·0 cm; diameter of container, 20·95 cm; 20 centistoke fluid. (HSA 9, exposure 1 sec)

manner. These buoyant elements were noted by Ramadas and Malurkar[15] and emphasized by Townsend[16]. They have been incorporated, as an essential feature, into a recent theoretical study by Howard[17]. All evidence of 'cellular' motion is not, however, lost, for it is found to persist in the sublayers on the hot and cold walls (see figure 4). These observations are confirmed by studies of the temperature and velocity spectra.

For a body cooling from above, at the highest A the motions are seen to be rapid and of small length scale. As the body cools and A falls—very slowly, owing to the large thermal capacity of the body compared with the rate of heat loss—the motions become slower and the length scale increases. The pattern is continually changing, cell boundaries disappearing, others growing, and upwelling sites changing position. All this is strikingly similar to observations of the solar granules. The length scales are found to correspond to a marginally stable sublayer, viz. $A(\delta) \sim 10^3$, where δ is the sublayer thickness. If the same apparatus is viewed horizontally, it is seen that the coherent motions of length scale δ in the sublayer only exist to a depth of order δ; below this depth the motion is fully turbulent.

The gross features of the various flow régimes can be deduced from measurements of heat transfer characteristic $N(A)$, where N, the Nusselt number, is defined by (17)

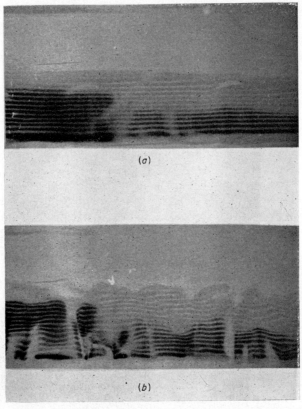

(*a*)

(*b*)

FIGURE 3   Visualization of the temperature distribution (cf. figure 2). (*a*) The initia
appearance of blobs, (*b*) the final state

$$f = NK\Delta T/H \tag{17}$$

and f is the mean heat flux. In the range $10^4 < A < 10^6$ the motion is laminar or
quasilaminar and (18) applies. At rather higher values of A the motion is observed

$$N = 0 \cdot 24 A^{1/4} \tag{18}$$

to be highly irregular and (19) then applies. (See Jakob[18], based on measurements

$$N = 0 \cdot 06 A^{1/3} \tag{19}$$

by Mull and Reiher; see also de Graaf and van der Held[19], Malkus[20], Globe and
Dropkin[21].) The $\frac{1}{3}$ power law of (19) implies that the heat transfer is independent of H.
Since the corresponding motion is observed to be highly irregular, a suitable experimental test for turbulence would be that the properties of the motion are independent
of H. It is convenient to write (19) in the form (20), where θ is the temperature drop

$$f = \rho c \kappa \theta / \delta \tag{20}$$

across the sublayer, so that then we obtain (21).

$$\delta = S\theta^{-1/3}, \qquad S \simeq 8(\kappa v/\gamma g)^{1/3} \tag{21}$$

FIGURE 4   The sublayer. Photograph of the free surface of a cooling layer of MS200/100 centistoke oil of depth 15 cm. $A \simeq 10^8$. The width of the above area is 20 cm. (VP 19)

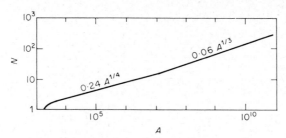

FIGURE 5   Heat transfer characteristic for free convection between horizontal planes. Nusselt number N against Rayleigh number A. [After Silveston[11], Jakob[18], and Malkus[20]]

The distribution of mean temperature $\theta(z)$ is given in figures 6 and 7. $\theta(z)$ has a similar form to that found in a vertical slot[22]: a linear region near the wall, a mixing region for which $(\theta - \theta_m)z^{-1/3} \simeq$ constant, and a uniform core.

An elaborate study of the temperature fluctuations in thermal turbulence in air has been made by Thomas and Townsend[23], Townsend[16], and Deardorff and Willis[24]. A few of the authors' measurements in water and oil are presented below. They show the same qualitative features as the above air measurements. The temperature at a fixed point as a function of time is shown in figure 8. The five traces at $z^* = 1, 2, 3, 4,$ 5 cm are for the turbulent core. They reveal three obvious features: (i) pronounced quiescence for times of order 10 sec, the temperature being close to 0·5, (ii) spikes or bursts of cold fluid of duration of order 1 sec, and (iii) similar bursts of hot fluid. The record at $z^* = 3$ cm has nearly equal numbers of nearly equal hot and cold spikes. But at $z^* = 4, 5$ cm the proportion and amplitude of the cold spikes increases. Clearly these correspond to plumes of cold fluid falling out of the upper sublayer. It should

M.E.—18

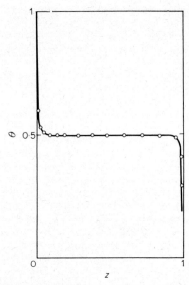

FIGURE 6   Sketch of mean temperature profile. $A \sim 10^9$

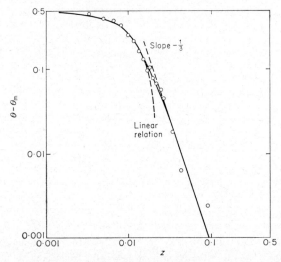

FIGURE 7   Mean temperature profile $\theta(z)$ near the lower surface for thermal turbulence at $A = 1.4 \times 10^8$. Obtained with water in a square prism of width 30.0 cm and depth 6.0 cm. $\theta_m = 0.5$ is the midlevel mean temperature

be noticed that even at $z^* = 5$ cm the spikes appear merely to be superimposed on the background temperatures of about 0.5. Similar remarks apply to the hot spikes which predominate for $z^* < 3$ cm. There is considerable evidence that the strongest plumes can completely cross the turbulent interior, e.g. there is evidence of the remnant of a cold subplume in the $z^* = 0.2$ cm trace.

The four traces at $z^* = 0.02, 0.05, 0.1, 0.2$ cm are for the lower wall region. The appearance is now dominated by the hot plumes and there are no longer noticeable periods of quiescence. The inmost trace $z^* = 0.02$ is well within the sublayer. Here

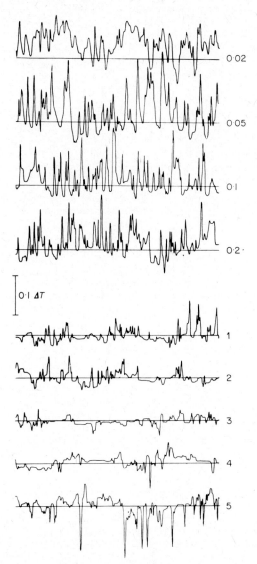

FIGURE 8   Temperature traces $\theta(z, t)$ at stated value of z cm. Width of record 100 sec.
Parameters as in figure 7

the fluctuations are more symmetrical and no longer suggest that substantial portions
of this fluid are moving out of the layer.

The observations are made clearer in the data of figure 9 which show $P(\theta)$, the
probability distribution of temperature. $P(\theta)$ is symmetrical—closely Gaussian—
within the sublayer and the interior. Otherwise $P(\theta)$ shows considerable skewness.
This is clearly due to the transport of heat into the interior by the buoyant elements.

Figure 10 shows temperature spectra corresponding to the data of figure 8. The
spectra have been obtained from series of 4096 readings taken at intervals of 0·5 sec
by computing the correlation for 100 lags and taking the cosine transform using the

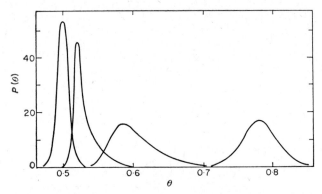

FIGURE 9   Temperature probability distribution $P(\theta)$ at $A = 2\cdot4 \times 10^8$. Obtained with MS 200/20 centistoke silicon oil; diameter of circular container, 20·95 cm; fluid depth, 10·0 cm

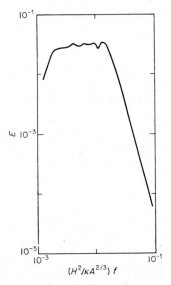

FIGURE 10   Temperature spectrum $E(f)$ in the cavity interior. $\theta(t)$ is normalized to have zero mean and unit variance. Parameters as in figure 9

programme of Bullard and others[25]. Instrumental noise is at the level 10^{-5} in figure 10.

The spectrum shows three distinct regions. Above 0·2 c/s the rapid fall is undoubtedly due to the role of thermal diffusion acting as a dissipative mechanism. From 0·2 c/s to 0·04 c/s the spectrum is nearly white. Below 0·04 c/s the behaviour is somewhat uncertain but appears to be falling. This is to be expected in a finite apparatus.

Our theoretical understanding of these phenomena is very limited. The most elaborate attempt at a self-consistent theory is that of Malkus[20,26-28] who invoked the hypothesis that under certain constraints the mean heat flux is a maximum and that the sublayers are marginally unstable. Although the theoretical predictions do not agree with experiment in the interior of the flow, the idea of a marginally stable sublayer seems a good one. Priestley[28] suggested that the mixing region was dominated by advection and deduced $(\theta - \theta_m)z^{-1/3} = \text{constant}$, which agrees rather well with certain meteorological data and the laboratory measurements. A number of discussions of these theories are to be found in the literature, that by Townsend[16] being notable. A more recent development has been attempts to simulate thermal turbulence with numerical models. Some fascinating results have been reported by Deardorff[29,30] and his colleagues. A summary of a somewhat similar study by the author is presented

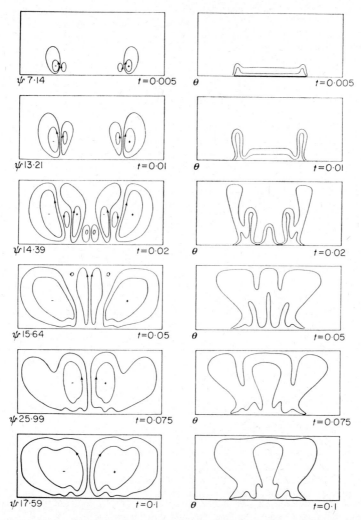

FIGURE 11   Stream function and temperature distributions at various times in a 2:1 box suddenly heated over half the base at Rayleigh number $A = 400$. Porous medium. The contours show 0·2 and 0·6 of the maximum value. (PM275)

below. The numerical techniques have been reported elsewhere. The study presented is largely for the porous medium approximation.

When the layer of fluid is suddenly heated from below at $t = 0$ the subsequent development of the flow is as shown in figure 11. A number of eddying motions grow above the heated region but after a time $t > 0·1$ settle down to two large steady eddies. This development is summarized in figure 12 which shows the maximum value of the

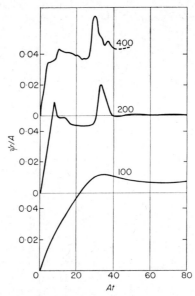

FIGURE 12   Maximum value of the stream function for the problem of figure 11 at
$A = 100, 200, 400$. (PM 224, 242, 275)

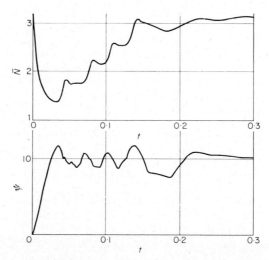

FIGURE 13   Nusselt number and maximum value of the stream function at various times
for a 10:1 box heated over the central 90% of the base at $A = 200$

stream function as a function of time for three values of the Rayleigh number. The
feature of note is that, whereas at low Rayleigh numbers the development is smooth,
the development at higher Rayleigh numbers, for which the non-linear terms are
dominant, is spiky with periods of quiescence. A more pronounced example of this
behaviour is shown in figure 13 for a long heated section. We note that a characteristic
feature of strongly non-linear problems is not only the spiky nature of the spatial
field (boundary layers and plumes) but the spiky nature of the time development.

These flows, nevertheless, develop in a regular manner towards a final steady state.

If, however, we introduce a small amount of noise (e.g. putting $\theta = 1 + \varepsilon(x)$ on the heated surface, where ε is a random function of the order of 10^{-2}) the development is no longer so regular (see figure 14). The eddies and the isotherms grow in a rather irregular way so that throughout the interval $t < 0.1$ the flows are in detail markedly different. We note that a small amount of noise in a high-gain non-linear system leads to qualitative differences of behaviour.

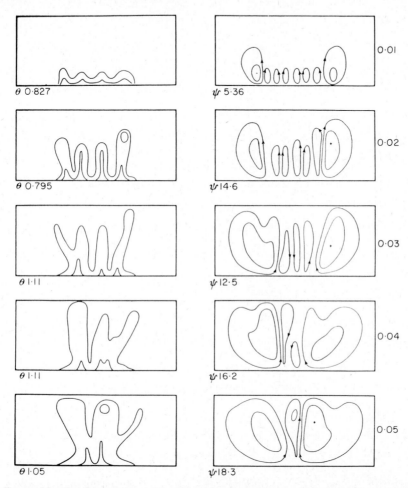

FIGURE 14   The flow of figure 11 with random temperature noise of amplitude 10% over the heated area

If these two processes, advection and noise, are combined in a very unstable system, the consequent flow has many of the features of thermal turbulence. Figure 15 shows the development of such a system. The initial development is the growth of a set of eddies on the hot and cold walls into fairly regular plumes. The final state corresponds to growth of thin plumes at random positions on the walls. The development of the mean temperature profile is shown in figure 16. After the pronounced irregularities of the initial period the profile rapidly settles down to a form similar to that found in the laboratory. The time development is summarized in figure 17 which shows $\theta(z, t)$,

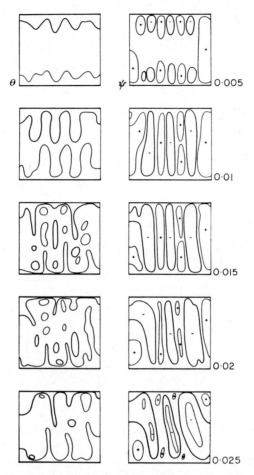

FIGURE 15   Temperature and stream-function distributions at various times for two-dimensional simulation of thermal turbulence

the temperature on the centre line, as a function of time. The thin boundary layers and the intermittency of the flow in the interior is well represented.

The features discussed above are qualitatively the same whether or not there is advection or diffusion of vorticity. Hence in a dynamical model which is dominated by convection the use of either a porous medium or a viscous fluid approximation are equivalent.

Zero-dimensional Model

Because of our inability to solve the system of equations presented on p. 526 it is necessary to consider a number of model problems. The simplest such problem is to consider the zero-dimensional problem obtained by integrating the equations over the entire volume of the Earth. The shape of the Earth is required only to specify the ratio of surface area to volume. Hence in dimensional variables (22) holds, where

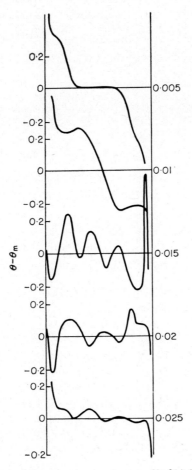

FIGURE 16 Development of the mean temperature profile $\theta(z)$ for the flow of figure 15

$$\dot{\theta} = -\frac{3\kappa}{R}\frac{\theta}{\delta} + \frac{C}{\rho c} \tag{22}$$

$C = C_0 e^{-\lambda t}$ and θ, C are mean values over the volume. The terms are the rate of change of internal energy, the total surface power loss, and the total internal power. We assume that convection is the dominant heat transfer mechanism, δ representing the sublayer thickness.

If $C_0 = 0$ so that the only source of energy is the original thermal energy of the Earth we find, using (21), that (23) is true. An immediate difficulty is apparent since

$$t = \frac{RS}{\kappa}\left(\frac{1}{\theta^{1/3}} - \frac{1}{\theta_0^{1/3}}\right) \tag{23}$$

the value of S involves the uncertain v. If, for example, the original mean temperature was 4000 °K, the time to cool to 2000 °K with a corresponding $v \sim 10^{14}$ cm^2/sec is of the order of 10^7 years. Clearly this is much too small. This difficulty is partially resolved in the one-dimensional model below, but here there is no alternative to requiring $C_0 \neq 0$.

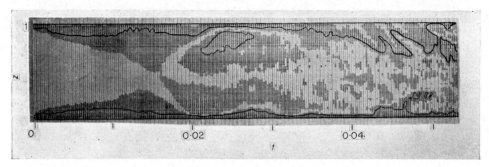

FIGURE 17   The time development on the vertical centre line. The lines represent
$\theta = 0, \, 0{\cdot}15, \, 0{\cdot}85, \, 1$

If at the other extreme the rate of change of internal energy is sufficiently small so that nearly all the energy arises from radioactive decay, $f = \frac{1}{3}CR$. Estimates of C are so poor that we cannot say how closely this relation is satisfied but it is not inconsistent with present data. We can, however, integrate (22) to give (24), where we have taken δ

$$\theta = \theta_0 \, e^{-st} + \frac{C_0}{\rho c (\lambda - s)} (e^{-st} - e^{-\lambda t}) \tag{24}$$

to be constant and write $s = 3\kappa/R\delta$. This expression is reasonably consistent with present data. Taking $\theta \sim 1500$ degc, $\kappa \sim 10^{-2}$ cm^2/sec, and $f \sim 10^{-6}$ μcal/cm^2 sec we find $1/s \sim 10^{10}$ years, $\delta \sim 150$ km. Further, if $1/\lambda \sim 10^9$ years, $t \sim 5 \times 10^9$ years, and $C_0 \sim 5 \times 10^{-13}$ cal/cm^3 sec which is consistent with a present-day value $C \sim 5 \times 10^{-15}$ cal/cm^3 sec. The term $C_0/\rho c(\lambda - s) \sim 1500$ degc. These are reasonable values. It should be noted that the time constant for cooling by thermal conduction alone $0{\cdot}1R^2/\kappa \sim 10^{11}$ years. Since that is an order of magnitude greater than $1/s$ we are justified in ignoring the role of thermal conduction.

One-dimensional Model

If the field equations are integrated over the surface of spheres of radius r, we obtain the equations of a time-dependent problem in which only variations in the radial direction are considered. The Earth is therefore considered to be spherically symmetrical.

The major change in the properties of the Earth with depth occurs at the core-mantle boundary. There will be sublayers both at the base of the mantle and the top of the core attached to this boundary. For the purpose of evaluating the internal thermal energy of the core a good approximation is that it is nearly adiabatic. From (20) the temperature drop across the core sublayer is given by (25), where f is the heat flux

$$\theta \sim 8 \left(\frac{\kappa \nu}{\gamma g} \right)^{1/4} \left(\frac{f}{K} \right)^{3/4} \tag{25}$$

from the core. An upper bound for θ is obtained by assuming that all the Earth's heat loss arises from the core so that $f = 4$ μcal/cm^2 sec and that $\nu \sim 10^{10}$ cm^2/sec, a value too high to prevent the transmission of shear waves. Thence using $\kappa \sim 1$ cm^2/sec. $\gamma \sim 10^{-5}$ degc^{-1}, we have $\theta \lesssim 1$ degc.

The greatest uncertainty in the properties of the mantle is in the value of v. The expression (26) proposed by the author[3] is based on data from volcanic rocks. Its

$$v = 10^8 \exp\left(3 \times 10^4/T \, °\text{K}\right) \text{cm}^2/\text{sec} \tag{26}$$

greater weakness is the neglect of a pressure effect. In the upper portion of the mantle, however, the values are reasonable. The value at 300 degK is 10^{51} cm^2/sec (very rigid!). The Fennoscandian uplift gives 10^{21} cm^2/sec, corresponding to about 10^3 degK and a depth of 50 km. The value below 300 km is 10^{14} cm^2/sec. An estimate of the value of v at the bottom of the mantle can be made in the following way. If the dynamo hypothesis is correct, there must be a net heat loss from the core. Further, if the core–mantle boundary is static—that is f is not obtained by freezing the core to make the mantle or some such process, a not unlike possibility—then f must be transmitted through the mantle. We now use (25) to estimate v by taking $\kappa \sim 10^{-2}$ cm^2/sec, $\gamma = 10^{-5}$ degC^{-1}, and $f \sim 1$ μcal/cm^2 sec representing a quarter of the Earth's net heat loss. With $v \sim 10^{14}$ cm^2/sec, $\theta \sim 25$ degC which is quite undetectable by seismic techniques. A value $v \sim 10^{20}$ cm^2/sec requires $\theta \sim 800$ degC which is a detectable value. There is very weak evidence for a $\theta \sim 300$ degC from seismic data. This requires $v \lesssim 10^{18}$ cm^2/sec. Hence a pressure effect raising the coefficient in (26) from 3×10^4 to about 5×10^4 at the base of the mantle is possible.

Thus if v near the core–mantle boundary is sufficiently small and there is no need to consider latent heat effects at the core–mantle boundary, we can ignore the small temperature drops in the sublayers and consider the temperature adiabatic from the midmantle to the centre of the Earth. Only the upper sublayer need therefore concern us and the above expression for $v(T)$ can be used with somewhat more confidence.

The large variation of v through the mantle, in particular the large values near the surface, suggest that even if the deep mantle is rapidly convecting the surface layers are not. Two possible constraints on the thickness h of the upper mantle come to mind. Firstly, the Rayleigh number $A(h) \sim 10^3$, a state of marginal stability. Even if $A(h) \gg 10^3$, however, flow may not occur unless the temperature fluctuation at the base of the upper mantle persists for a time t_1 sufficient for convection in the upper mantle to be established. It has been shown[4] that t_1 is determined by requiring that the region heated from the temperature fluctuation, the initial heat transfer in the upper mantle being by thermal conduction, produces a region of thickness $\delta \sim 2(\kappa t_1)^{1/2}$ such that $A(\delta) \gtrsim 10^3$. Hence (27) holds true. If, for example, the

$$\min(t_1) \simeq \frac{25(h^2/\kappa)}{A(h)^{2/3}} \tag{27}$$

temperature fluctuations have a typical life of $t_1 \sim 10^4$ years, we require $A(h) \sim 10^9$ and therefore $h \sim 200$ km.

Thus we envisage a layer of depth of order 10^2 km, the upper mantle, which is sufficiently viscous to be in a state of marginal convective stability under the action of finite-amplitude temperature fluctuations in the lower mantle. Slow convective motions will still be possible in the upper mantle but the dominant heat transfer mechanism will be thermal conduction, except in regions where lithothermal systems are possible. The upper portion of the lower mantle will be similar to laboratory sublayers, with an upper layer in which molecular processes are important, a mixing region dominated by the rapid advection in buoyant plumes, and an adiabatic lower region. Temperature gradients will be a maximum in the upper portion and temperature fluctuations will be a maximum in the mixing region.

Direct evidence for this model is not available. However, let us consider figure 18 which shows $\chi(\rho)$, the compressibility, obtained from seismic travel-time curves. We note that $\chi\rho^3 \simeq$ constant throughout the mantle except for the upper 400 km (in Bullen's[31] model A data). Rather than interpret this as a phase change we may

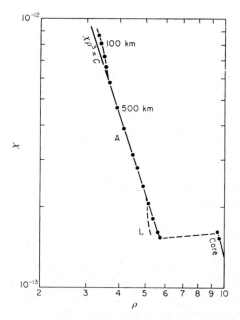

FIGURE 18   The compressibility $\chi(\rho)$ for the Earth's mantle. [After Bullen (A) and Landisman and others (L)]

consider the higher values of ρ to arise, because in this region temperatures will depart from adiabatic because the layer is being cooled. A temperature change of order 10^3 degc is indicated. The data suggest that the upper sublayer extends from 100 to 400 km. A recent analysis by Landisman, Sato, and Nafe[32], which takes into account the free vibration data, further suggests a density loss of order 0.2 g/cm^2 at the base of the mantle, in contrast with Bullen's compilation. One views this result with suspicion since the fit to the vibration data is not much better than Bullen's model A. If taken at face value the evidence suggests a similar sublayer at the base of the core, the lower densities arising from the excess temperature (produced by heat loss from the core). The rather larger sublayer thickness suggests from (21) that the viscosity in the lower sublayer could be as much as 10^2 times as great as that in the upper sublayer.

A simple model, compatible with present data, has already been presented by the author[3]. A number of more elaborate models are at present under investigation and will be published shortly.

Two-dimensional Model

By averaging the field equations around the polar axis we obtain a problem in two space dimensions. Since the upper mantle is thin compared with the Earth's radius, it is possible to ignore the Earth's curvature except for the largest eddies. A schema of the mantle is presented in figure 19. This shows the very turbulent, nearly adiabatic core, the turbulent mantle, and the very slow movements of the upper mantle. The variation of mean (with respect to time) temperature is nearly adiabatic except in the sublayers. Possible variation of root-mean-square temperature fluctuations are

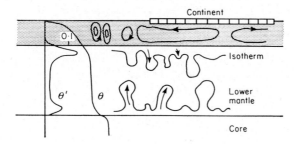

FIGURE 19 Schema for the mantle

shown with a maximum in the mixing region and a rapid fall-off in the upper mantle. The motions suggested in the upper mantle are quasicellular patterns, roughly square in oceanic regions but strongly elongated horizontally under continents, and litho-thermal systems in volcanic regions. It is important to note that h is not sharply defined and, even so, will vary greatly with position.

It is necessary to emphasize that the upper mantle provides a very low pass filter in transmitting temperature and velocity fluctuations from the lower mantle to the surface. Thus, if continents drift at about 10^{-7} cm/sec, corresponding to a shear stress of order 1 b, in view of (26) and on the assumption that the shear stress is independent of depth, the velocity at the base of the upper mantle needs to be 10^4 or more times greater. Further, variations of 1 degc of the mean temperature with depth, $\theta_m(x, y)$, in the mantle are sufficient to support the bumps on the geoid. With any laminar convective model of the mantle, variations in θ_m will greatly exceed 1 degc. In the turbulent model, however, the contributions to the largest scales of θ_m from the lower mantle will be quite small; the bulk of the contribution will arise from the penetration by thermal conduction of sublayer fluctuations into the upper mantle. Variations of temperature from this mechanism could be about 10 degc, sufficient to have produced the bumps on the geoid. Should this expectation prove inadequate, some mechanism for organizing the largest eddies of the lower mantle must be sought. There are already two such mechanisms known, but no thorough investigation is yet available. The first is the role of the Coriolis force in principally tending to produce a zonal flow (i.e. about the axis of rotation). The second is the non-uniform mean surface temperature of the Earth—the equator–pole difference is of order 40 degc. This is small, and influences the lower mantle through the upper mantle filter. Never-theless, laboratory studies of thermal turbulence show that systematic non-uniformities of the order of 0.1% in the boundary conditions lead to variations of θ_m of 1%, i.e. for the mantle as a whole variations of 10 degc. It is worth noting that both of these effects would produce effects principally in the form of an equatorial bulge.

Conclusions and Proposals

It is hoped that it has become clear to the reader that the bulk of the discussion is very speculative. Undoubtedly most of the details will need modification when a more complete range of data becomes available. Nevertheless, the qualitative features of the model are those that would be required for a dynamical basis for physical geology. A number of characteristic features of the model suggest a field search for certain data.

(i) Intermittency is perhaps the most striking feature of turbulence. There should be widespread evidence in the gross features of the geological record—as there is. These features need not be correlated over large distances and will be considerably muted by the viscous and thermal damping of the upper mantle.

(ii) The broad white spectrum of the temperature fluctuations suggests that the spectrum of bumps in the geoid, allowance being made for geometrical factors, will be white over perhaps a 10^3:1 range. Data at present available are compatible with this suggestion.

(iii) The variations of temperature in the white part of the spectrum range from periods of about 10^3–10^6 years/cycle. While rather slow by human standards, small changes might be detected with the most sensitive instruments over an interval of 10 years or so. It would be desirable to set up very long period gravimeters in stable regions to search for this effect.

(iv) Perhaps a more sensitive test would be (if we note the sensitivity of seismic velocities to temperature changes) to set seismic arrays around a suitable great circle, sites having been chosen to sample as much of the top of the lower mantle as possible, and to explode a kiloton bomb once a year from the same water-filled pit. The pit could be calibrated by means of a surrounding array of smaller pits. Travel times accurate to about 1 msec would be possible with present-day techniques. Noticeable changes should be found over an interval of 10 years.

If we are to remove much of the speculation about the Earth's interior, it will be necessary to collect very precise data for many years from permanent stations. Until such data are available our case rests only on circumstantial evidence.

References

1. L. Knopoff, *Rev. Geophys.*, **2**, 89 (1964).
2. D. C. Tozer, *Phil. Trans. Roy. Soc. London, Ser. A*, **258**, 252 (1965).
3. J. W. Elder, in *Terrestrial Heat Flow* (Ed. W. H. K. Lee), *Am. Geophys. Union Monograph No.* 8 (1965).
4. J. W. Elder, *Bull. Volcanol.*, **29**, 347 (1966).
5. J. Boussinesq, *Theorie Analytique de la Chaleur*, Vol. 2, Gauthier-Villars, Paris, 1903, p. 172.
6. J. W. Elder, *J. Fluid Mech.*, **24**, 823 (1966).
7. J. W. Elder, *Proc. Australian Conf. on Fluid Mech.*, 2nd, 1966.

8. H. Jeffreys, *Proc. Roy. Soc.* (*London*), *Ser. A*, **118**, 195 (1928).
9. W. H. Reid and D. L. Harris, *Phys. Fluids*, **1**, 102 (1958).
10. R. J. Schmidt and S. W. Milverton, *Proc. Roy. Soc.* (*London*), *Ser. A*, **152**, 586 (1935).
11. P. L. Silveston, *Forsch. Gebiete Ingenieurw.*, **24**, 29, 52 (1958).
12. K. Chandra, *Proc. Roy. Soc.* (*London*), *Ser. A*, **164**, 231 (1938).
13. Lord Rayleigh, *Phil. Mag.*, **32**, 529 (1916).
14. A. Pellew and R. V. Southwell, *Proc. Roy. Soc.* (*London*), *Ser. A*, **176**, 312 (1940).
15. L. A. Ramadas and S. L. Malurkar, *Indian J. Phys.*, **7**, 1 (1932).
16. A. A. Townsend, *J. Fluid Mech.*, **5**, 209 (1959).
17. L. Howard, *Proc. IUTAM Munich Conf., 1964.*
18. M. Jakob, *Heat Transfer*, Wiley, New York, 1949.
19. J. G. A. de Graff and E. F. M. van der Held, *Appl. Sci. Res., Sect. A*, **3**, 393 (1953).
20. W. V. R. Malkus, *Proc. Roy. Soc.* (*London*), *Ser. A*, **225**, 185 (1954).
21. S. Globe and D. Dropkin, *J. Heat Transfer*, **81**, 24 (1959).
22. J. W. Elder, *J. Fluid Mech.*, **23**, 77 (1965).
23. D. B. Thomas and A. A. Townsend, *J. Fluid Mech.*, **2**, 473 (1957).
24. J. W. Deardorff and G. E. Willis, *NCAR Rept.*, 140 (1966).
25. E. C. Bullard, W. H. Oglebay, W. H. Munk, and G. R. Miller, *A System of Programmes for the Analysis of Time Series*, University of California Press, San Diego, 1964.
26. W. V. R. Malkus, in *Theory and Fundamental Research in Heat Transfer* (Ed. J. A. Clark), Macmillan, London, 1963.
27. D. J. Tritton, *J. Fluid Mech.*, **16**, 282 (1963).
28. C. H. B. Priestley, *Turbulent Transfer in the Lower Atmosphere*, University of Chicago Press, Chicago, 1959.
29. J. W. Deardorff and G. E. Willis, *J. Fluid Mech.*, **23**, 337 (1965).
30. J. W. Deardorff and G. E. Willis, *J. Atmos. Sci.*, **22**, 419 (1965).
31. K. E. Bullen, *An Introduction to the Theory of Seismology*, Cambridge University Press, Cambridge, 1953.
32. M. Landisman, Y. Sato, and J. Nafe, *Geophys. J.*, **9**, 439 (1965).

8

R. W. GIRDLER

Department of Geophysics and Planetary Physics
School of Physics
University of Newcastle upon Tyne
England

A review of terrestrial heat flow

Introduction

No work on the mantle of the Earth is complete without reference to the flow of heat from the Earth's surface. There are now about 2000 measurements of heat flow, but unfortunately they are somewhat unevenly distributed and of varying quality. There tends to be some oceanic regions which are well covered whilst for vast areas of Africa, Asia, and South America there are no observations. Even so, it has been possible to draw some general conclusions on the variations of heat flow over the Earth's surface. For instance, Lee and Uyeda[1] find that the arithmetic means for oceans and continents do not differ significantly, and that heat flow observations are well correlated with geological features on land and sea—for example heat flow tends to be low over deep sea trenches and high over oceanic ridges. Such conclusions are of importance when considering possible processes which may be taking place in the mantle.

For upper mantle studies, it is often of interest to compare the heat flow over a large region of the Earth's surface (10^6 to 10^8 km² in extent) with that of another region of comparable size. Such a case arises in looking for possible correlations between heat flow and the satellite free-air gravity anomalies. Runcorn[2] (see also section IX, chapter 6 of this book) has suggested that the satellite gravity anomalies may be interpreted in terms of convection in the mantle. The wavelengths of the low-harmonic gravity anomalies suggest that they are due to lateral density variations in the mantle. These density variations could be due to material differences or temperature differences. It is therefore of interest to compare the satellite gravity and heat flow data. This involves looking at large regions of the Earth's surface which often cover various physiographic and geologic provinces.

Lee and MacDonald[3] and Lee and Uyeda[1] have made spherical harmonic analyses of the measurements of terrestrial heat flow for the whole World and have compared these analyses with recent satellite geoid determinations. They find a correlation such that regions of negative free-air gravity are associated with high heat flow and regions of positive free-air gravity are associated with low heat flow. This work has been followed up by Wang[4] who supports the correlation. Strange[5], however, finds no significant correlation between satellite gravity data and heat flow. It is important to resolve this in view of the current interest in interpreting the satellite gravity anomalies in terms of temperature differences in the mantle.

The spherical harmonic analyses of heat flow data could be misleading as they are based on measurements which are unevenly distributed over the sphere. There is a tendency for such analyses to produce anomalies where there are no observations. For example, the map of Lee and Uyeda[1] (p. 152) shows the largest positive anomaly to be over north central Africa where there are no observations. Much of this region is Pre-Cambrian shield and, by analogy with other shield areas, there is a possibility that this may be a region of low heat flow.

In this chapter, emphasis is given to the problem of comparing the heat flow over large regions of the Earth's surface. Readers are referred to the very comprehensive review by Lee and Uyeda[1] for discussions of the reliability of data, distributions of heat flow by geological provinces for both continental and oceanic areas, and for the spherical harmonic analysis of heat flow. Recent reviews of techniques for measuring heat flow on land have been given by Beck[6] and of techniques for measuring heat flow at sea by Langseth[7] and by Von Herzen and Langseth[8].

Throughout this chapter, the data used are the observations listed in the appendix of Lee and Uyeda[1] and classified as 'good value', 'fair value', and 'average value of a given range of heat flow values'. Use has also been made of a later list issued on July 24, 1966, and kindly supplied by Mr. W. H. K. Lee.

The Nature of Heat Flow Distributions

When histograms are plotted of the measurements of terrestrial heat flow over large regions they commonly show positive skew distributions. Examples are shown in figure 1 in which histograms are given for measurements for all continental areas and all oceanic areas. The heat flow values range from 0 to greater than 10 μcal/cm^2 sec with modal values in the class interval 1·0 to 1·2 μcal/cm^2 sec. The arithmetic means are consequently higher than the modes. For example, Lee and Uyeda[1] give an arithmetic mean for the whole World of 1·58 μcal/cm^2 sec (for 1150 measurements) whereas the mode is about 1·1 μcal/cm^2 sec.

This type of distribution seems to be very common. The review by Lee and Uyeda[1] shows many histograms, and most of these show positive skew distributions. Examples include heat flow values for the Atlantic Ridge, for Indian Ocean Ridges, for Pacific Ocean Ridges, for the whole World, for the Atlantic, Indian and Pacific Oceans separately, and for oceanic 'other areas'.

Histograms of heat flow values for ocean basins and for Pre-Cambrian shield areas are more symmetrical and closer to normal distributions. This is probably because these tend to be regions of more uniform geology.

It is of interest to look for possible reasons for the nature of the histograms, and espesially for the positive skew character such as shown in figure 1. For oceanic regions, the high heat flow values are usually associated with the mid-oceanic rift system. A detailed study of the East Pacific Rise by Von Herzen and Uyeda[9] shows that there are narrow strips of unusually high heat flow a few hundred kilometres wide near the crest of the Rise. These local highs are superimposed on a broader high with some local regions of low heat flow on the flanks. The local highs can be explained by regions of unusually high temperature at a depth of about 10 km beneath the sea floor and a few tens of kilometres wide[9]. As the oceanic rift system is often associated with volcanicity and igneous intrusions[10-12], it seems likely that the high heat flow regions are due to bodies such as igneous dykes. The regions of low heat flow on either side of the Rise have values about half the normal oceanic average. As the high values are sometimes six to eight times the oceanic average, they have a much greater effect on the nature of the histograms than do the low values.

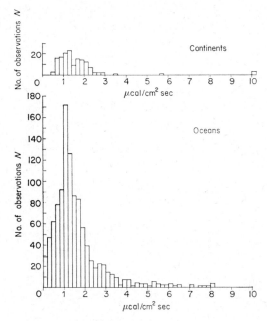

FIGURE 1   Histograms of heat flow observations for continents and oceans

For the purpose of comparing the heat flow over *large* regions it is desirable to find statistical techniques which reduce the effect of the *localized* high values. Attempts have been made to reduce the effects of high values and the concentration of measurements on the ridges by local averaging[8], but even these local averages give rise to positive skew distributions. Lee and Uyeda[1] also show histograms of grid averages (9×10^4 square nautical miles per grid) of heat flow for the whole World, for all oceanic areas, and for the individual oceans and these also show positive skew distributions. A further technique for reducing the effect of local high values is described in the next section.

Statistical Treatment

In this chapter, the arithmetic means, standard deviations (σ) and standard error of the means ($\sigma/\sqrt{n}$) are given first, on the assumption that the observations are normally distributed. With the present status of heat flow observations this seems to be true only for the ocean basins and Pre-Cambrian shield areas, i.e. regions of relatively uniform geology.

When the region to be examined extends over various physiographic and geologic provinces, it seems desirable to look at a statistical distribution which takes some account of the positive skew nature of the observations (e.g. figure 1). The histograms of figure 1 and those of Lee and Uyeda[1] suggest that the logarithmic normal distribution may be better than the normal distribution for heat flow observations over large regions. This involves computing the geometric mean (G) which, for a set of observations H_1, H_2, H_3, etc., is given by

$$G = (H_1 \times H_2 \times H_3 \times \ldots)^{1/n}$$

or

$$\log G = \frac{1}{n}(L_1 + L_2 + L_3 + \ldots)$$

where $L_1 = \log H_1$, etc. The standard deviation of the log values, σ_L, is calculated from

$$\sigma_L{}^2 = \frac{1}{n}\sum (L - \bar{L})^2$$

where $\bar{L}$ is the arithmetic mean of the logarithmic values. The normal frequency curve may be fitted to the log values using

$$y = \frac{n}{\sigma_L(2\pi)^{1/2}} \exp\left\{\frac{-(x - \bar{L})^2}{2\sigma_L{}^2}\right\}$$

The standard error of the arithmetic mean of the logarithmic values is given by $\sigma_L/\sqrt{n}$. Owing to the asymmetry of the distribution of natural values, it is not possible to give a standard error of the geometric mean, the positive error being larger than the negative error. Here, the positive error is calculated, which may be looked upon as the *maximum* standard error of the geometric mean.

The statistical data are presented in tables 1 to 4. These include the number of observations (N), the arithmetic mean with the standard deviation and standard error of the arithmetic mean, the arithmetic mean of the log values with the standard deviation and standard error of the arithmetic mean of the log values, and the geometric mean and maximum standard error of the geometric mean.

Histograms of logarithmic values with normal frequency curves are given in figures 2, 3, 4, 5, 7, and 8. The corresponding natural values are in units of $\mu\text{cal}/\text{cm}^2$ sec. Histograms of the natural values are not given, as most of these can be found in the paper by Lee and Uyeda[1].

It will be seen that the logarithmic heat flow values give distributions closer to normal than the natural values, and it is suggested that geometric means should be considered as well as arithmetic means before making deductions concerning the heat flow over large areas of the Earth's surface.

Continents, Oceans, and the Whole Earth

The histograms for the logarithmic values for heat flow for all continental areas and all oceanic areas are shown in figure 2. These may be compared with figure 1, the histograms for the corresponding natural values. It is seen that the logarithmic values are much more nearly normally distributed than are the natural values.

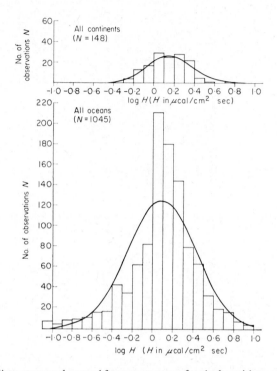

FIGURE 2   Histograms and normal frequency curves for the logarithms of the heat flow values for all continental areas and all oceanic areas (cf. figure 1). In this and succeeding figures, the natural values corresponding to the logarithmic values have units of μcal/cm^2 sec

The histogram for the logarithms of the heat flow values for the whole World is given in figure 3.

The numerical data corresponding to figures 2 and 3 are given in table 1, together with the arithmetic means and their standard deviations and standard errors. It is seen that, for each set of observations, the geometric means are smaller than the corresponding arithmetic means. The geometric means are, of course, much closer to the modal values in each case.

Reference to the histograms shows the distribution to be fairly symmetrical about the geometric mean. The normal frequency curves give reasonably good fits except for the strong peaking near the geometric mean. This is due to the strong peaking at the mode (figure 1). The fact that the distribution is reasonably symmetric about the geometric mean suggests that the geometric mean might be a useful statistic to be considered in addition to the arithmetic mean.

TABLE 1 Heat flow statistics for continents, oceans, and the whole Earth

	(1)	(2)	(3)	(4)	(5)	(6)	(7)	(8)	(9)
all continental areas	148	1·69	±1·67	±0·14	+0·150	±0·224	±0·018	1·41	±0·06
all oceanic areas	1045	1·56	±1·16	±0·04	+0·087	±0·335	±0·010	1·22	±0·03
whole Earth	1193	1·57	±1·23	±0·04	+0·095	±0·324	±0·009	1·24	±0·03

Column (1), number of observations N; column (2), arithmetic mean (μcal/cm^2 sec) with standard deviation (3) and standard error of the arithmetic mean (4); column (5), arithmetic mean of log values with standard deviation (6) and standard error of mean of log values (7); column (8), geometric mean (μcal/cm^2 sec) with maximum standard error of geometric mean (9).

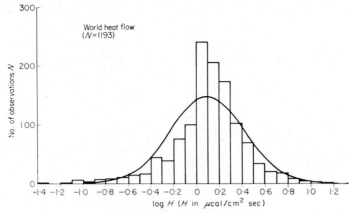

FIGURE 3   Histogram and normal frequency curves for the logarithms of the heat flow
values for the whole Earth

It is seen that the geometric mean for continental areas ($1 \cdot 41 \pm 0 \cdot 06$ μcal/cm^2 sec)
is slightly *higher* (by 15%) than the geometric mean for oceanic areas ($1 \cdot 22 \pm 0 \cdot 03$
μcal/cm^2 sec), whereas the corresponding difference for the arithmetic means is
only 8%.

The geometric mean heat flow for the whole Earth is $1 \cdot 24 \pm 0 \cdot 03$ μcal/cm^2 sec
compared with an arithmetic mean of $1 \cdot 57 \pm 0 \cdot 04$ μcal/cm^2 sec.

Individual Oceanic Areas

Histograms of the logarithmic values of heat flow for the Atlantic, Indian, and
Pacific Oceans are shown in figure 4. The statistics are given in table 2, which for

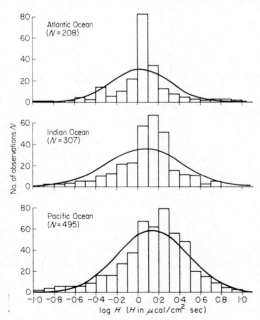

FIGURE 4   Histograms and normal frequency curves for the logarithms of the heat
flow values for the Atlantic, Indian, and
Pacific Oceans

TABLE 2   Oceanic regions

	(1)	(2)	(3)	(4)	(5)	(6)	(7)	(8)	(9)
Atlantic Ocean	208	1·28	±1·00	±0·07	+0·025	±0·275	±0·019	1·06	±0·05
Indian Ocean	307	1·42	±0·94	±0·05	+0·046	±0·365	±0·021	1·11	±0·05
Pacific Ocean	495	1·79	±1·32	±0·06	+0·139	±0·339	±0·015	1·38	±0·05
Arctic Ocean	30	1·20	±0·35	±0·06	+0·056	±0·160	±0·029	1·14	±0·08
Mediterranean Sea	3	1·45	±0·95	±0·55	+0·097	±0·296	±0·171	1·25	±0·60
Red Sea	2	2·62	±2·21	±1·56	+0·323	±0·421	±0·298	2·10	±2·07

Column (1), number of observations N; column (2), arithmetic mean (μcal/cm² sec) with standard deviation (3) and standard error of the arithmetic mean; column (5), arithmetic mean of log values with standard deviation (6) and standard error of mean of log values (7); column (8), geometric mean (μcal/cm² sec) with maximum standard error of geometric mean (9).

completeness also includes data for the Arctic Ocean and the Mediterranean and Red Seas. For the last two the values of N are small.

Atlantic Ocean

Of the three large oceans, the Atlantic shows the strongest peaking at the mode, and the geometric mean 1·06 μcal/cm^2 sec is close to the modal value.

Indian Ocean

This ocean has the most uniform and complete coverage of observations[8]. The histogram of the logarithmic values is somewhat similar to that of the Atlantic Ocean. The geometric mean is 1·11 μcal/cm^2 sec.

Pacific Ocean

There are 2·4 times as many heat flow observations in the Pacific Ocean as in the Atlantic Ocean and 1·6 times as many as in the Indian Ocean. However, the Pacific Ocean is larger in area than the Atlantic by a factor of 2 and larger than the Indian Ocean by a factor of 2·3. Both the arithmetic mean (1·79 μcal/cm^2 sec) and geometric mean (1·38 μcal/cm^2 sec) are higher than the corresponding arithmetic and geometric means for the Atlantic and Indian Oceans. This may be due to the rather large number of observations over the East Pacific Rise which show many high values. The observations are well represented by the normal frequency curve for the logarithmic values.

Arctic Ocean

The observations are from two areas, north and northwest of Canada, and are unlikely to be representative of the Arctic Ocean.

Mediterranean Sea

There are three reliable measurements in the Mediterranean Sea and the statistics are included in table 2 for the sake of completeness.

Red Sea

There are two reliable measurements in the Red Sea which are of special interest, as the Red Sea is part of the World rift system where high values are found.

Figure 4 shows that the histogram for the Pacific Ocean is somewhat different from the histograms for the Atlantic and Indian Oceans. It will be interesting to see whether this difference persists as the number of observations increases. No attempt is made in this chapter to make separate analyses for different oceanic provinces such as ridges, basins, and margins. This has been done[1, 8], and Von Herzen and Langseth[8] plot percentiles of heat flow as a function of distance from the axes of ridges. For the Mid-Atlantic Ridge the half-width of the high heat flow zone is found to be about 200 km, whilst for the East Pacific Rise the half-width is more than twice this value. This phenomenon, together with the large number of measurements over the East Pacific Rise, may partly explain the different nature of the histogram for the Pacific Ocean (figure 4).

Individual Continental Regions

The number of heat flow measurements in individual continental regions is often small and hence the statistics may be unreliable. They are given here only for the sake of completeness. The different regions include North America, Europe, Australia, Japan, Asia without Japan, and Africa. Japan was treated separately because of the relatively large number of measurements over what is a small part of an island arc region.

The histograms for the logarithmic values of heat flow for various continental regions are given in figure 5 and the corresponding numerical data in table 3.

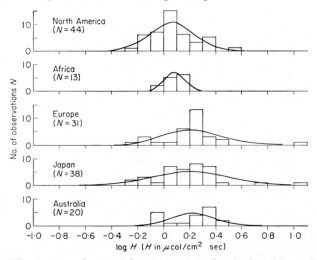

FIGURE 5   Histograms and normal frequency curves for the logarithms of heat flow
values for various continental regions

North America

The number of observations is the largest for any continental region, and measurements have been made in regions of widely differing geology, ranging from the Canadian Shield to the Basin and Range Province of western U.S.A. The arithmetic mean heat flow is 1·26 μcal/cm^2 sec and the geometric mean is 1·16 μcal/cm^2 sec.

Africa

The data are from South Africa and are unlikely to be representative of Africa as a whole.

Europe

The data are widely spaced and include measurements from Great Britain, Switzerland, Austria, Hungary, Czechoslovakia, France, Italy, Germany, and the U.S.S.R. The arithmetic mean (1·91 μcal/cm^2 sec) is considerably higher than the geometric mean (1·62 μcal/cm^2 sec) and the logarithmic values are well fitted by the normal frequency curve.

Japan

Although the number of observations (38) is fairly large, the histogram of figure 5 shows a different character from the histograms for other regions. The dispersion,

TABLE 3 Continental regions

	(1)	(2)	(3)	(4)	(5)	(6)	(7)	(8)	(9)
North America	44	1·26	±0·57	±0·09	+0·065	±0·169	±0·025	1·16	±0·07
Africa	13	1·20	±0·21	±0·06	+0·074	±0·077	±0·021	1·19	±0·06
Europe	31	1·91	±1·70	±0·30	+0·208	±0·224	±0·040	1·62	±0·16
Japan	38	2·21	±2·73	±0·44	+0·209	±0·293	±0·048	1·62	±0·19
Australia	20	1·76	±0·62	±0·14	+0·215	±0·170	±0·038	1·64	±0·15
Asia without Japan	2	0·76	±0·15	±0·11	−0·120	±0·085	±0·060	0·76	±0·11

Column (1), number of observations N; column (2), arithmetic mean ($\mu cal/cm^2$ sec) with standard deviation (3) and standard error of the arithmetic mean (4); column (5), arithmetic mean of log values with standard deviation (6) and standard error of mean of log values (7); column (8), geometric mean ($\mu cal/cm^2$ sec) with maximum standard error of geometric mean (9).

and hence standard deviation, of the logarithmic values is large. This presumably reflects the varied geology of Japan which includes regions of active volcanism. The arithmetic mean (2·21 μcal/cm^2 sec) is high compared with the geometric mean (1·62 μcal/cm^2 sec). The normal frequency curve still gives a reasonably good fit to the logarithmic values.

Australia

The data are mainly from western and southeast Australia. The heat flow tends to be low over the shield areas of the west and higher in the east.

Asia without Japan

Only two values are available (India and Iran) and are included merely for the sake of completeness.

Examination of table 3 shows that the geometric means are always less than the corresponding arithmetic means, and hence closer to the modal values. The differences between arithmetic and geometric means are largest when there are larger numbers of observations. This is probably due to the fact that, when n is large, a greater variety of regions of different geology has been sampled.

Heat Flow and Satellite Gravity Anomalies

The same statistical procedure is used to investigate the possible correlation between the satellite free-air gravity anomalies and terrestrial heat flow.

The latest satellite gravity map[13] is shown in figure 6. The map shows four main regions of negative free-air gravity (geoid depressions) and four main regions of positive free-air gravity (geoid elevations). The negative regions are centred over the eastern Pacific, the western Atlantic, the north Indian Ocean, and the Antarctic Ocean, and are numbered 1 to 4 in figure 6. The positive regions are centred over the western Pacific and southeast Asia, the Andes, northwest Europe, and southeast of Africa and are numbered I to IV in figure 6.

The heat flow values were assigned to their appropriate regions, and the arithmetic and geometric means were computed for each region, together with the arithmetic means and standard deviations of the logarithmic values. The statistics were also obtained for all regions of negative gravity and all regions of positive gravity together.

The object is to see if the heat flow over regions of positive and negative gravity differ. For this, it is especially important to try to reduce the effect of localized high heat flow values, as there is a tendency for the regions of negative gravity to be located over the oceans where the high values are found. For example, region 1 has many localized high values associated with the East Pacific Rise, in contrast, for example, with region II. The use of logarithmic normal curves and geometric means helps to reduce the effect of the high values, and hence it is more difficult to argue that, if the heat flow is found to be higher over the regions of negative gravity, it is due to the local anomalies over the ridges.

A further advantage of the method is that the heat flow values are assigned directly to the regions of positive and negative gravity without any previous assumptions. We have seen that the use of spherical harmonic analysis without an even distribution of observations can be misleading and it is desirable at present to supplement the type

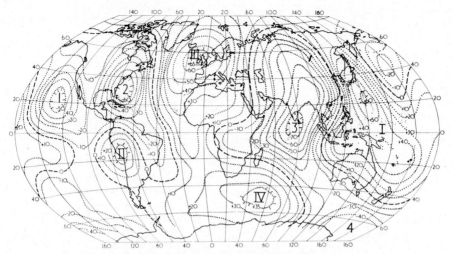

FIGURE 6   The satellite-geoid map of Guier and Newton[13] with contour interval at 10 m

of analyses as carried out in the papers by Lee and Uyeda[1], Lee and Macdonald[3], and Wang[4], all of which make use of heat flow maps produced by spherical harmonic analyses.

All regions of positive gravity and all regions of negative gravity

The heat flow distributions for all regions of positive gravity and all regions of negative gravity are shown in logarithmic form in figure 7. The arithmetic mean of the

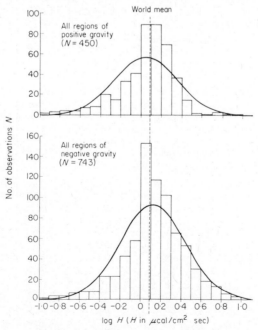

FIGURE 7   Histograms and normal frequency curves of the logarithmic values of heat flow for all regions of negative gravity and all regions of positive gravity for Guier and Newton's[13] satellite geoid of figure 6

M.E.—19*

TABLE 4 Regions of positive gravity and regions of negative gravity

	Geoid height (m)	(1)	(2)	(3)	(4)	(5)	(6)	(7)	(8)	(9)
Regions of positive gravity										
all regions		450	1·33	±0·83	±0·04	+0·041	±0·309	±0·015	1·10	±0·04
region I (west Pacific)	+60	220	1·36	±0·60	±0·04	+0·077	±0·252	±0·017	1·19	±0·05
region II (Andes)	+33	36	1·40	±1·11	±0·18	−0·003	±0·410	±0·068	0·99	±0·17
region III (northwest Europe)	+67	127	1·43	±1·13	±0·10	+0·059	±0·293	±0·026	1·15	±0·07
region IV (south of Africa)	+39	67	1·05	±0·54	±0·07	−0·087	±0·405	±0·049	0·82	±0·17
Regions of negative gravity										
all regions		743	1·67	±1·22	±0·04	+0·121	±0·322	±0·012	1·32	±0·04
region 1 (east Pacific)	−59	304	1·97	±1·44	±0·08	+0·189	±0·319	±0·018	1·54	±0·07
region 2 (west Atlantic)	−70	156	1·37	±0·93	±0·07	+0·071	±0·234	±0·019	1·18	±0·05
region 3 (north Indian Ocean)	−77	249	1·48	±1·02	±0·06	+0·065	±0·359	±0·023	1·16	±0·06
region 4 (Antarctic)	−40	34	1·69	±0·94	±0·16	+0·151	±0·300	±0·051	1·41	±0·18

Column (1), number of observations N; column (2), arithmetic mean (μcal/cm^2 sec) with standard deviation (3) and standard error of the arithmetic mean (4); column (5), arithmetic mean of log values with standard deviation (6) and standard error of log values (7); column (8), geometric mean (μcal/cm^2 sec) with maximum standard error of geometric mean (9).

logarithmic values for the whole World is shown as a broken line (corresponding to a geometric mean of $1\cdot24\ \mu\text{cal}/\text{cm}^2$ sec). The geometric mean heat flow for regions of negative gravity is seen to be higher than the World mean, and the geometric mean for regions of positive gravity is seen to be lower than the World mean.

Full numerical statistics are given in table 4, which tabulates arithmetic means, standard deviations and standard errors of the arithmetic means, arithmetic means, standard deviations and standard errors of the arithmetic means of the logarithmic values, and the geometric means and maximum errors of the geometric means for all regions of negative gravity and all regions of positive gravity and for all the individual regions.

The arithmetic mean heat flow, for all regions of negative geoid height, is found to be 22% higher than the arithmetic mean for all regions of positive geoid height. The corresponding difference for the geometric means is 18%.

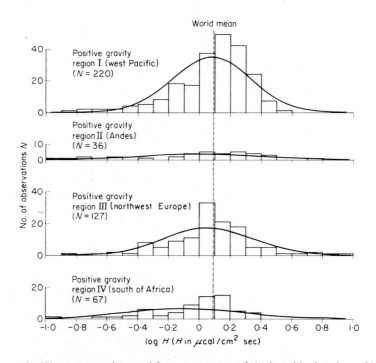

FIGURE 8   Histograms and normal frequency curves of the logarithmic values of heat flow for individual regions of positive gravity of Guier and Newton's[13] satellite geoid

Individual regions of positive gravity

For all four regions of positive gravity anomaly the arithmetic and geometric means are found to be less than the arithmetic and geometric mean heat flows for the whole World. The histograms of the logarithmic values are given in figure 8.

Region I. The region includes much of the west Pacific and southeast Asia. A large proportion of the observations are in and around Japan. The arithmetic and geometric means are respectively $0\cdot18\ \mu\text{cal}/\text{cm}^2$ sec and $0\cdot04\ \mu\text{cal}/\text{cm}^2$ sec *less* than the corresponding means for the whole World.

Region II. This region is centred over the Andes of western South America. Compared with other regions there are few measurements (37), but both arithmetic and geometric means are *less* than the corresponding means for the whole World.

Region III. This region covers much of northwest Europe and the northeast Atlantic. The arithmetic mean is 0·11 μcal/cm² sec *less* than the World arithmetic mean and the geometric mean is 0·08 μcal/cm² sec *less* than the World geometric mean.

Region IV. This region is centred southeast of Africa, and both the arithmetic and geometric means for 67 measurements are considerably *less* than the arithmetic and geometric means for the whole World.

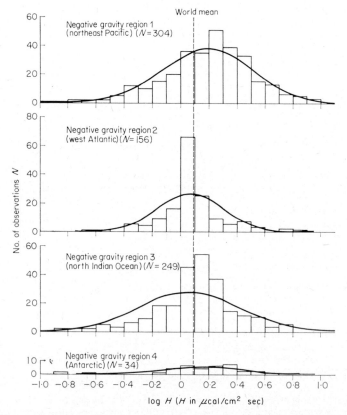

FIGURE 9   Histograms and normal frequency curves of the logarithmic values of heat flow for individual regions of negative gravity of Guier and Newton's[13] satellite geoid

Individual regions of negative gravity

For two of the four regions of negative gravity the arithmetic and geometric means are found to be higher than the arithmetic and geometric means for the whole World. For the other two regions the arithmetic and geometric means are lower than the corresponding World means, but the geometric means are not significantly lower than the World geometric mean. The histograms for the logarithmic values are shown in figure 9.

Region 1. This region covers the northeast Pacific. It has the largest number of measurements (304), many of which are over the East Pacific Rise. The arithmetic mean heat flow is 0·43 μcal/cm^2 sec *higher* than the World arithmetic mean and the geometric mean is 0·31 μcal/cm^2 sec *higher* than the World geometric mean.

Region 2. This region is mainly over the western Atlantic Ocean and eastern North America, and does not include the Mid-Atlantic Ridge. Both arithmetic and geometric means are less than the corresponding World means, but the geometric mean is not significantly less (table 5).

Region 3. This region is centred over the northern Indian Ocean where there are many measurements and includes much of Asia where there are virtually no measurements. The arithmetic and geometric means are barely significantly less than the corresponding means for the whole World.

Region 4. The region is centred southeast of Australia and only has 34 observations, but both arithmetic and geometric means are higher than the World means.

Table 5 summarizes the difference of the arithmetic and geometric means for all the regions from the arithmetic and geometric means for the whole World. It is seen

TABLE 5   Differences of arithmetic (dA) and geometric (dG) mean heat flows (μcal/cm^2 sec) from the corresponding World mean for various satellite geoid regions[13]

	dA	dG
Regions of positive gravity		
for all regions	$-0\cdot21 \pm0\cdot05$	$-0\cdot13 \pm0\cdot05$
region I (west Pacific)	$-0\cdot18 \pm0\cdot05$	$-0\cdot04 \pm0\cdot06$
region II (Andes)	$-0\cdot14 \pm0\cdot18$	$-0\cdot24 \pm0\cdot17$
region III (northwest Europe)	$-0\cdot11 \pm0\cdot10$	$-0\cdot08 \pm0\cdot08$
region IV (southeast of Africa)	$-0\cdot49 \pm0\cdot07$	$-0\cdot41 \pm0\cdot16$
Regions of negative gravity		
for all regions	$+0\cdot13 \pm0\cdot05$	$+0\cdot09 \pm0\cdot05$
region 1 (east Pacific)	$+0\cdot43 \pm0\cdot08$	$+0\cdot31 \pm0\cdot08$
region 2 (west Atlantic)	$-0\cdot17 \pm0\cdot08$	$-0\cdot05 \pm0\cdot06$
region 3 (north Indian Ocean)	$-0\cdot06 \pm0\cdot07$	$-0\cdot07 \pm0\cdot07$
region 4 (Antarctic)	$+0\cdot15 \pm0\cdot16$	$+0\cdot18 \pm0\cdot18$

that all regions of positive gravity have heat flow *less* than the World mean and two out of four regions of negative gravity have heat flow *higher* than the World mean. One region is doubtful and one region of negative gravity (the western Atlantic) has *low* heat flow.

The analysis therefore tends to support the hypothesis that regions of negative geoid height are associated with high heat flow and regions of positive geoid height with low heat flow. The one notable exception is region 2 over the west Atlantic. This may be due to poor determination of the longitude terms of the satellite geoid, as this region is not centred over the oceanic rise and rift, unlike the other regions of negative gravity. It will be of interest to repeat the analysis for future satellite gravity maps as more heat flow measurements become available.

Conclusions

(i) It is suggested that the logarithmic normal distribution should be examined as well as the normal distribution for heat flow over large regions of the Earth's surface, which cover a variety of physiographic and geological provinces.

(ii) The arithmetic mean and geometric mean heat flow for the whole Earth are, respectively, 1.57 ± 0.04 $\mu cal/cm^2$ sec and 1.24 ± 0.03 $\mu cal/cm^2$ sec.

(iii) The arithmetic and geometric means for all continental areas are *higher* than the corresponding means for all oceanic areas by 8% and 15% respectively.

(iv) The hypothesis that regions of negative geoid height are associated with high heat flow and regions of positive geoid height with low heat flow tends to be supported. For the satellite map of Guier and Newton[13] the heat flow over all regions of negative gravity is significantly higher than the heat flow over all regions of positive gravity, the difference being 22% for the arithmetic means and 18% for the geometric means. There is one notable exception: the region of negative gravity to the west of the Atlantic ridge has lower heat flow than the World mean.

(v) It is felt that the analyses carried out here lend further support to the hypothesis that the undulations of the geoid are due to temperature differences in the mantle.

Acknowledgements

The author is indebted to several members of the Upper Mantle Symposium in Ottawa, 1965, and especially to Mr. W. H. K. Lee for lively discussion on the origin of the World rift system, which stimulated this work. My sincere thanks are extended to Professor S. K. Runcorn for his continued interest, to Dr. R. D. Von Herzen and Mr. W. H. K. Lee for their helpful comments by correspondence, and to Dr. L. Molyneux, Dr. D. H. Tarling, and Miss M. Hillaby for help with the computations which were carried out on the KDF 9 computer of the Newcastle University Computing Laboratory.

Note added in proof. Since this chapter was written, a paper by Kaula[14] has appeared in which a cross covariance analysis of heat flow and free-air gravity is made. This also supports the correlation discussed here.

References

1. W. H. K. Lee and S. Uyeda, *Am. Geophys. Union Monograph No. 8*, 87–190 (1965).
2. S. K. Runcorn, *Nature*, **200**, 628–30 (1960).
3. W. H. K. Lee and G. J. F. MacDonald, *J. Geophys. Res.*, **68**, 6481–92 (1963).
4. C. Wang, *J. Geophys. Res.*, **70**, 5629–34 (1965).
5. W. E. Strange, *Trans. Am. Geophys. Union*, **46**, 544 (1965).
6. A. E. Beck, *Am. Geophys. Union Monograph No. 8*, 58–77 (1965).
7. M. G. Langseth, *Am. Geophys. Union Monograph No. 8*, 24–57 (1965).
8. R. P. Von Herzen and M. G. Langseth, *Phys. Chem. Earth*, **6**, 365–407 (1965).
9. R. P. Von Herzen and S. Uyeda, *J. Geophys. Res.*, **68**, 4219–50 (1963).
10. R. W. Girdler, *Bull. Volcanol.*, **26**, 37–57 (1963).
11. C. L. Drake and R. W. Girdler, *Geophys. J.*, **8**, 473–95 (1964).
12. G. Bodvarsson and G. P. L. Walker, *Geophys. J.*, **8**, 285–300 (1964).
13. W. H. Guier and R. R. Newton, *J. Geophys. Res.*, **70**, 4613–26 (1965).
14. W. M. Kaula, *Am. Geophys. Union Monograph No. 9*, 58–67 (1966).

Author Index

This author index is designed to enable the reader to locate an author's name and work with the aid of the reference numbers appearing in the text. The page numbers are printed in normal type in ascending numerical order, followed by the reference numbers in brackets. The numbers in italics refer to the pages on which the references are actually listed.

Adams, J. C. 225(2), *228*
Adler, I. 23(32), *33*
Agrell, S. O. 17(14), 18, *32*
Ahmad, F. 373(21), *381*
Alexander, W. M. 63(3), 65(2), 67(2), *73*, 394(16), *410*
Alfvén, H. 213(1), 214(3, 4), 215(3, 4, 5, 6, 7), *218*, 229(3), *234*, 235(1, 2, 3, 4, 5, 6, 7, 8), *239*, *240*, 242(4), *249*
Allan, R. R. 153(10), *161*
Allen, C. W. 133(27), *138*, 216(8), *218*
Allen, J. D. 408(25), *411*, 419(24), *424*
Aller, L. H. 45(34), *47*, 253(11, 12, 13, 14), 254(11, 12, 13, 14), *260*
Alley, C. O. 99(5), *106*
American Commission on Stratigraphic Nomenclature 438(17), *459*
Anderle, R. J. 147(15), 148(15), *150*, 151(1, 5), 153(1, 7, 15), 154(16), 157(1), 161(15), *161*, *162*
Anders, E. 10, 12(13, 15, 22), 13, *14*, 17(8), 21, 25(8, 38, 39), 26(25, 41), 28, 30(8), 32(25), *32*, *33*, 35(2), 36(4), 40(4, 17), 42, 43, 44(4, 17, 31, 32), 45(4, 17, 32), *47*, 49(1, 2, 3), 50(1, 2, 3), 59(3), *60*
Anderson, C. A. 21(26), 30(26), *32*, 453(42), *460*
Anderson, D. L. 115(2, 3), 116(4), 124(14), *126*, 134(28), *138*
Angerth, B. 236(9), *240*
Arnold, J. R. 53(38, 39), 58(38, 39), *60*, *61*, 252(9, 10), *260*
Arthur, D. W. G. 418(7), *424*
Ashbrook, J. 430(8), *430*
Athavale, R. N. 361(31), *382*

Babcock, R. W. 509(11), *512*
Babkine, J. 306(6), *316*
Bain, G. W. 347(18), *349*
Balashov, Yu. A. 267(1, 2, 3), *282*
Baldwin, R. B. 174(10), 175(10), 176(10), 177(10), *180*, 418(6, 19), 419(19), 422(6), *423*, *424*, 435(6), *459*, 470(9), *471*, 475(3), *479*

Bando, Y. 18(21), *32*
Bassett, W. A. 17(5), *32*
Bate, G. L. 53(30), *60*
Baur, H. 22(28), *32*
Beck, A. E. 341(12), *349*, 550(6), *566*
Begemann, F. 50(11), *60*
Beiser, E. 53(35), *60*
Bellomo, E. 196(12, 13), 199(12, 13), 200(12, 13), 205(12, 13), 206(12, 13), 207(12, 13), *211*
Bemmelen, R. W. van 248(20), *250*
Bender, P. L. 99(5), *106*
Benioff, H. 383, *383*
Berg, O. E. 65(2), 67(2), *73*
Berlage, H. P. 242(10), 243(10, 13), 245(10, 13, 15), 247, 248(15, 16, 23), *250*
Bernstein, V. A. 507(8), *512*
Berthelot, M. 271(19), *283*
Best, G. T. 63(1), *73*
Bieri, R. 53(37), 54(37), *60*
Binder, A. B. 413(5), *416*
Binns, R. A. 31(54), *33*, 299(17), *304*, 306(8), *316*
Birch, F. 120(12, 13), 124(13), *126*
Birks, J. B. 500(5), *503*
Birtill, J. *110*
Black, R. F. 337(11), *349*
Blagg, M. A. 174(13), *180*
Bleaney, B. 500(4), *503*
Bleaney, E. 500(4), *503*
Bleibtreu, K. 323(6), *328*
Block, L. 236(9), *240*
Blundell, D. J. 362(33), *382*
Bodvarsson, G. 484(7), *488*, 489(2), *498*, 551(12), *566*
Boer, J. de 131(23), *138*
Borovskii, I. B. 17(11), *32*
Boström, K. 40(25), 42(25), 44(25), *47*
Boussinesq, J. 527(5), *546*
Bowen, N. L. 309(15), *316*
Boyd, F. R. 306(10), 308(13), *316*
Brock, A. 356(26), *381*
Brouwer, D. 85(1), 91(1), *92*, 129(12), *138*, 143(1, 3), *150*, 205(14), *211*
Brown, E. W. 99(7), 100(11), *106*

Brown, H. 12(20), *14*, 27(45), *33*, 420(31), *424*
Bullard, E. C. 348(19), *349*, 363(5), *381*, 507(6), *512*, 536(25), *547*
Bullen, K. E. 128(1, 2, 3, 4, 5, 11), 130(2, 20, 21), 131(3, 25), 132(20), 133(20, 30), 136(29), 137(20), *138*, 261(3), *264*, 544(31), *547*
Bundy, F. P. 17(7), *32*
Burnett, D. S. 56(44, 48), *61*
Burnham, C. W. 309(19), *316*
Burton, H. E. 77(3), *84*

Cain, D. L. 397(17, 18, 19), *410*, 428(5), *430*
Cameron, A. G. W. 13(24), *14*, 251(2), *260*
Cameron, E. N. 17(9), *32*
Cameron, W. S. 447(37), *460*
Camichel, H. 129(16), *138*
Carpenter, E. W. *110*
Carpenter, R. L. 194(8), *211*
Carr, M. H. 437(15, 16), 453(43), 454(43), *495*, *460*
Carter, J. C. 315(28), *317*
Cattala, L. 346(16), *349*
Chamalaun, F. H. 332(2), *349*, 366(11, 12), 367(11, 12), *381*
Chandra, K. 530(12), *547*
Chandrasekhar, S. 499(1), *503*, 507(1), *512*
Chase, J. W. 267(12), 268(12, 17), 282(17), *282*, *283*
Chodos, A. 27(45), *33*
Clark, H. K. 99(6), *106*
Clark, S. P. 23(36), 24(36), *33*, 307(12), 308(12), *316*
Clemence, G. M. 85(1), 91(1), *92*, 101(12), *106*, 129(12), *138*, 143(1), *150*
Clendenen, R. L. 17(6), *32*
Cohen, C. J. 153(7), *161*
Coleman, P. J. Jr. 297(22), 392(6, 7), *410*
Collée, A. L. G. 324(11), *328*
Collinson, D. W. 341(14), *349*
Colombo, G. 193(5, 6, 7), 195(6, 7), 196(6, 7, 12, 13), 199(12, 13), 200(12, 13), 204(6, 7), 205(6, 7, 12, 13), 206(12, 13), 207(12, 13), *211*
Compston, W. 53(34), *60*
Conqueré, F. 306(6), *316*
Coode, A. M. 491(3), *498*, 519(8), *524*
Cook, A. H. 144(5), *150*
Cook, G. E. 144(5, 6), 145(9, 11), 146(5, 11), *150*, 153(9), *161*
Coryell, C. D. 267(12), 268(12, 17), 282(17), *282*, *283*
Craig, H. 38(15), *47*
Crasty, R. L. 55(41), *61*
Creer, K. M. 332(2), 345(15), *349*, 351(1), 355(2), 356(2, 9, 17, 23), 365(1, 6, 7, 8, 9), 366(9, 11), 367(11), 368(2, 6, 9, 17, 18), 374, 375(17), 379(36), *381*, *382*, 514(4), 515(5), 517(6), 519(7), *524*
Cross, W. 323(9), *328*
Crozier, W. D. 70(23), *74*
Cruikshank, D. P. 413(5), *416*

Daněs, Z. F. 443(32), *460*
Darwin, G. H. 227(9), *228*, 229(4), 232(4), *234*
Datta, A. N. 261(4), *264*
Dauben, C. H. 268(13), *282*
Davis, B. T. C. 311(21), *317*
Davis, G. S. 386(3), *410*
Davis, L. Jr. 297(22), 392(6, 7), *410*
Davis, R. Jr. 57(49), *61*
Deardorff, J. W. 529(24, 29), 533(24), 537(29, 30), *547*
DeCarli, P. 52(17), *60*
Derge, G. 3(5), *14*
Deutch, E. R. 361(32), *382*
Dicke, R. H. 99(5), *106*, 341(13), *349*
Dietz, R. S. 248(22), *250*, 435(5), *459*
Dodd, R. T. 418(18), *424*, 436(13), 444(13), *459*
Doerner, H. A. 271(*18*), *283*
Dole, S. H. 237(11), *240*
Dollfus, A. 87(4), 89(5, 6), 90(6, 7, 8, 9), 91(7), *92*, 193(3), *211*, 413(2, 6), *416*
Domen, H. 334(8), *349*
Donahoe, F. J. 239(15), *240*
Donlin, T. J. 389(4), *410*
Donn, B. D. 248(21), *250*
Donn, W. C. 248(21), *250*
Drake, C. L. 485(13), *488*, 551(11), *566*
Drake, F. D. 397(17), *410*
Drickamer, H. G. 17(6), *32*
Dropkin, D. 532(21), *547*
Drummond, R. D. 414(9), *416*
Du Fresne, E. R. 36(4), 40(4), 42(4), 43(4), 44(4), 45(4), *47*
Duke, M. B. 39(16), 41(16), *47*
Duncumb, P. 20(23), *32*
Dwornik, E. J. 23(32), *33*
Dyce, R. B. 193(1, 2), *211*

Eaton, J. P. 28ε(9), *304*
Eberhardt, P. 50(8), 51(12, 13), 52(12, 13, 28), *60*
Eckels, A. 153(6), *161*
Eckert, D. 98(3), 100(3), *106*
Eckert, W. J. 94(4), *95*, 98(3, 4), 99(4, 6), 100(3, 4, 8, 9, 10), 101(4), 102(4), 105(4), *106*
Eggleton, R. E. 418(16), *424*, 435(4), 436(9, 12), 438(18, 20), 443(33), 445(33), *459*, *460*
Elder, J. W. 512(14), *512*, 525(3, 4), 528(6), 529(7), 533(22), 543(4), 544(3), *546*, *547*
Elston, D. P. 438(23), *459*
Embleton, B. 367(16), *381*
Engel, A. E. J. 293(11, 12), 294(12), 295(12, 14), *304*, 314(27), 315(27), *317*
Engel, C. E. 293(11, 12), 294(12), 295(12, 14), *304*, 314(27), 315(27), *317*
England, J. C. 306(10), 308(13), *316*
Eninger, J. 235(10), *240*
Epstein, S. 39(16), 41(16), *47*
Ernst, T. 323(5, 8), *328*
Eshleman, V. R. 397(17, 20), *410*
Eugster, O. 52(28), *60*
Everett, J. E. 348(19), *349*, 363(5), *381*

Ewing, E. *384*, 483(2), 484(5), *488*
Ezer, D. 13(24), *14*

Fahleson, U. 236(9), *240*
Fairbairn, H. W. 53(35), *60*
Faller, J. E. 99(5), *106*
Fan, C. Y. 393(12), *410*
Fechtig, H. 53(36), 54(36), *60*
Feel, H. W. 68(13), *73*
Feller-Kniepmeyer, M. 17(13), *32*
Fielder, G. 248(18), *250*, 418(8, 9), *424*, 461(1),
    467(1), 468(2, 3), 469(6), 471(1, 11), *471*,
    478(6), *479*
Fireman, E. 71(26), 72(26), *74*
Fish, R. A. 12(22), 13(22), *14*
Fitch, F. 44(31), *47*
Fjeldbo, G. 397(17, 20), *410*
Fleischer, R. L. 12(16), *14*
Flinn, E. A. *110*
Földvari-Vogl, M. 44(30), 45(30), *47*
Forbes, R. B. 306(4), *316*
Foster, M. D. 306(5), *316*
Fowler, W. A. 56(45), *61*, 117(5), 125(5), *126*
Frank, L. A. 392(8), 397(23), *410, 411*
Franken, P. A. 99(5), *106*
Franz, J. 173(2, 7, 8), 177(2, 7), 179(8), *180*
Fredriksson, K. 36(6), 37(7, 10), 38(7), 40(25),
    42(25), 44(25), *47*, 51(16), 52(17), *60*
Freund, R. 485(12), *488*
Frey, F. A. 267(7, 9), 269(7, 9), 270(7, 9),
    271(9), 272(9), 274(9), 282(7), *282*
Friend, J. F. 68(13), *73*
Frondel, C. 56(44), *61*
Fullam, E. F. 66(8), *73*
Fuller, M. D. 334(5), 336(5), *349*

Garfinkel, B. 149(25), 150(28), *150*
Gault, D. E. 443(30), *460*, 475(2), *479*
Gehl, M. A. 267(10), 272(10), *282*
Geiss, J. 50(8), 51(12, 13), 52(12, 13, 28), *60*
Gentner, W. 53(36), 54(36), *60*
Gerstenkorn, H. 213(2), 216(2), *218*, 229(1, 2),
    234, 238(12), *240*, 242(2), *249*, 251(5), *260*
Gilbert, G. K. 433(3), 435(3), *459*
Girdler, R. W. 484(3, 4, 11), 485(13), 487(4),
    488, 489(1), *498*, 551(10, 11), *566*
Gliozzi, J. 70(22), *74*
Globe, S. 532(21), *547*
Gloeckler, G. 393(12), *410*
Goebel, K. 57(52), *61*
Gold, T. 193(4), *211*, 258(25), *260*
Goldberg, E. D. 268(15), *283*
Goldberg, L. G. 45(34), *47*, 253(12), 254(12), *260*
Goldreich, P. 211(17, 18), *211*, 251(4), *260*
Goldstein, J. I. 6(3), 7(3, 7, 8), 8(8), *14*, 17(16,
    17), 18(22), 21(16), 23(33), 24(33), 29(49),
    30(16), *32, 33*
Goldstein, R. M. 194(9), 206(15), *211*
Goles, G. G. 12(22), 13(22), *14*
Gonyer, F. A. 322(1), *328*
Gordon, R. B. 428(6), *430*
Goudas, C. L. 170(1, 2, 3), *171*, 177(17),
    179(17), *180*

Gough, D. I. 356(26, 28), *381*
Graff, J. G. A. de. 532(19), *547*
Graham, K. W. T. 356(27), *381*
Gray, B. 171(4), *172*
Greenewalt, D. 334(6), *349*
Grjebine, T. 68(15), 69(18, 19, 20), 70(21),
    72(29), 73(31), *73, 74*
Grögler, N. 51(12, 13), 52(12, 13), *60*
Gross, M. J. 503(6), *503*
Guier, W. H. 145(12), 147(12), 148(12), *150*,
    151(4), *161*, 521(11), *524*, 560(13), 561(13),
    563(13), 564(13), 565(13), 566(13), *566*
Gutenberg, B. 128(10), *138, 383*

Habibulin, Sh. T. 94(3), *95*
Hackman, R. 418(16), *424*, 432(2), 433(2),
    434(2), 435(2), 436(9, 10, 12), 437(2),
    438(2, 19), 439(24), *459*
Hales, A. L. 356(27), *381*, 507(2), *512*
Hall, A. 77(1), 83(1), *84*
Halley, E. 225(1), *228*
Hamaguchi, H. 53(29), *60*
Hamilton, D. C. 309(19), *316*
Hanneman, R. E. 7(7), *14*, 29(49), *33*
Hansen, M. 21(27), *32*
Hapke, B. W. 259(26), *260*
Harris, D. L. 530(9), *547*
Harris, E. P. 40(19, 20), *47*
Harris, P. G. 278(31, 33), *283*, 305(1, 2),
    307(1), 309(17), 311(17), 314(25),
    316, 317
Hartmann, W. K. 248(19), *250*, 418(20, 21),
    424, 440(28, 29), 443(28), *460*
Haskin, L. 267(7, 8, 9, 10), 269(7, 9), 270(7, 9),
    271(9), 272(9, 10), 274(9), 282(7), *282*
Hausdorff, F. 68(10), *73*
Havens, R. G. 293(12), 294(12), 295(12), *304*,
    314(27), 315(27), *317*
Hayatsu, R. 35(2), *47*
Hayn, F. 173(3, 4), 179(3, 4), 180(3, 4),
    180
Hays, E. E. 294(13), *304*
Heezen, B. C. 483(2), *488*
Heier, K. S. 315(28), *317*
Held, E. F. M. van der 532(19), *547*
Helsley, C. E. 336(10), 337(10), *349*
Hemenway, C. L. 65(5), 66(6, 7, 8), *73*
Henderson, E. P. 12(18), *14*, 23(35), *33*
Hennessy, D. J. 36(5), 40(5), 44(5), *47*
Hess, H. H. 287(5, 7), 289(7), 298(7), 299(7, 18),
    300(7), *303, 304*, 484(8), *488*
Hey, M. H. 15(1), 16(2), 27, *32*
Heymann, D. 17(8), 25(8), 30(8), *32*, 52(25),
    57(50), *60, 61*
Higuchi, S. 18(21), *32*
Hills, H. K. 397(23), *411*
Hilten, D. van 336(9), 341(9), *349*
Hintenberger, H. 50(11), 51(14), 52(26), 57(51),
    60, 61
Hodge, P. W. 70(24), *74*
Holland, H. D. 272(21), *283*, 285(8), *304*
Holmes, A. 290(10), *304*, 513(1), *523*

Hopmann, J. 174(14), 175(14), 177(16), *179*, 180(14, 18), *180*, *181*
Hoskins, W. M. 271(18), *283*
Howard, L. 531(17), *547*
Hoyle, F. 56(45), *61*, 117(5), 125(5), *126*
Huizenga, J. R. 53(30), *60*
Hurley, P. M. 53(35), *60*
Hutchins, W. *110*

Ilyin, N. P. 17(11), *32*
Irving, E. 331(1), 333(1), 337(1), 339(1), 342(1), 343(1), 345(1), *349*, 351(1), 356(14), 357(14), 358(14), 359(14), 360(14), 361(14), 362(14), 365(1, 7, 14), 366(14), 368(14), *381*, 486(14), *488*, 514(4), 515(5), *523*
Irving, J. 322(1), *328*
Ito, H. 334(7), *349*
Izsak, I. G. 147(14), 149(14), *150*, 151(2), *161*

Jakob, M. 532(18), 533(18), *547*
James, J. N. 385(1), *410*
Jaschek, C. R. O. 418(13), *424*
Jeans, J. 500(2), *503*
Jeffreys, B. 150(29), *150*
Jeffreys, H. 93(1, 2), 94(1), *95*, 103(13), *106*, 128(8), 130(19), 131(19), *138*, 227(6), *228*, 261(1), *264*, 513(2), 514(2), *523*, 529(8), 530(8), *547*
Jones, D. E. 392(6, 7), 397(22), *410*
Jones, R. 99(6), *106*

Kachi, S. 18(21), *32*
Kaiser, W. 52(23), *60*
Kalsbeck, F. 325(12), *328*
Kant, E. 225(3), *228*
Kaufman, L. 18(20), 26(44), *32*, *33*
Kaula, W. M. 147(13), 150(30), *150*, 151(3), 153(13), *161*, *162*
Kawai, N. 334(7), *349*
Keen, C. G. *110*
Keil, K. 36(6), 37(7), 38(7), 42(7), 45(7), *47*, 50(11), 51(16), *60*
Kempe, W. 56(47), *61*
Ken Knight, C. E. 259(28, 29), *260*
Kerridge, J. F. 37(8), 38(13), 41(8), 42(8), 43(8), 44(8), *47*
Key, F. A. *110*
Kiang, T. 471(10), *471*
Kigoshi, K. 53(31), *60*
Kilston, S. D. 414(9), *416*
King, L. C. 372(20), *381*
King, R. F. 377(22), *381*
King-Hele, D. G. 144(5, 9), 145(9, 11), 146 (5, 11), *150*, 153(9), *161*
Kirsten, T. 52(21), 53(21), 54(21), *60*
Kliore, A. 397(17, 18, 19), *410*, 428(5), *430*
Klock, B. L. 98(2), *106*
Knopoff, L. 507(3), 511(12), *512*, 525(1), *546*
Knorring, O. von 306(9), 308(9), *316*
König, H. 50(11), 52(26), *60*
Koide, M. 268(15), *283*
Kommel, A. R. 3(5), *14*

Kopal, Z. 103(14), *106*, 242(5), *250*
Korringa, J. 131(23), *138*
Kovach, R. L. 115(3), 116(4), *126*, 134(28), *138*
Kovalenko, G. V. 334(3, 4), *349*
Kozai, Y. 143(2), 144(6), 145(6), *150*, 153(8), *161*
Krankowsky, D. 52(21, 27), 53(21), 54(21), *60*
Kreiter, T. J. 418(14), *424*
Krey, P. W. 68(13), *73*
Krimigis, S. M. 232(8), 393(15), 395(15), 397(23), *410*
Kronig, R. 131(23), *138*
Kuhn, W. 131(22), *138*
Kuiper, G. P. 245(14), *250*, 435(8), 440(28), 443(28), 447(38), 453(38), *459*, *460*, 469(7), 471(13), *471*
Kulp, J. L. 272(21), *283*
Kuno, H. 278(28), *283*, 306(4), 311(22), *316*, *317*
Kunr, S. 334(7), *349*
Kuroda, P. K. *12*(17), *14*
Kushiro, I. 278(28), *283*, 311(20, 22), *316*, *317*, 327(14), *328*
Kvasha, L. G. 40(22), *47*

Labeyrie, J. 70(21), *74*
Lämmerzahl, P. 53(36), 54(36), 56(46), 57(46), 58(46), *60*, *61*
La Gow, H. E. 63(3), *73*
Lal, D. 72(30), *74*
Lambert, G. 70(21), *74*
Landau, L. D. 500(3), *503*
Landisman, M. 128(6), *138*, 384, 544(32), *547*
Langseth, M. G. 550(7, 8), 551(8), 557(8), *566*
Larsen, E. S. 322(1), *328*
Lash, J. E. 267(4), 268(4), 269(4), 273(4), *282*
Lee, W. H. K. 549(1, 3), 550(1), 551(1), 552(1), 557(1), 561(1, 3), *566*
Lehmann, I. 128(9), *138*
Leighton, R. B. 408(25, 26), *411*, 419(24), *424*
LePichon, X. 484(5), *488*
LePoole, R. S. 447(38), 453(38), *460*
Levin, B. J. 40(18), *47*
Levin, B. Yu. 11(14), *14*
Levy, G. S. 397(17, 18, 19), *410*, 428(5), *430*
Lifshitz, E. M. 500(3), *503*
Lighthill, M. J. 263(5), *264*
Link, F. 67(9), 68(9, 11, 12), *73*
Lippolt, H. J. 56(48), *61*
Lipschutz, M. E. 17(8), 25(8, 38, 39), 26(41), 30(8), *32*, *33*
Little, S. 253(13), 254(13), *260*
Liu, Y. K. 18(19), *32*
Long, J. V. P. 17(14), 18(14), *32*
Lotze, F. 346(17), *349*
Lovering, J. F. 26(42), 27(45), 29(48), *33*, 53(32), *60*
Low, A. H. 128(5), *138*
Lubimova, H. 117(7), 118(7), *126*
Lüst, R. 243(12), *250*
Lyot, B. 87(3), *92*
Lyttleton, R. A. 129(13), 135(13), *138*, 252(6), *260*

Ma, T. Y. H. 227(11), *228*
McAllister, G. T. 149(25), *150*
McCauley, J. F. 436(14), 440(26), 441(26), 445(14), 448(40, 41), 453(41), *459, 460*
McCord, T. 238(13), *240*
McCracken, C. W. 65(2), 67(2), *73*, 394(16), *410*
McCrea, W. H. 217(9), *218*
MacDonald, G. A. 323(10), *328*
MacDonald, G. J. F. 114(1), 117(5, 6, 8), 118(8), 125(5), *126*, 130(18), 134(18), *138*, 226(5), *228*, 233(5, 6), *234*, 238(14), *240*, 242(3), *249*, 251(3), *260*, 507(5), 511(5), *512*, 549(3), 561(3), *566*
MacDonald, T. L. 417(1, 2, 3), 422(27), *423*
McGillem, C. D. 418(7), *424*
McIntire, W. L. 272(26), 274(26), *283*
McKenzie, D. P. 507(10), *512*
Magnitskii, V. A. 278(41), *283*
Malkus, W. V. R. 532(20), 533(20), 536(20, 26), *547*
Manning, G. K. 17(4, 12), *32*
Marchukova, I. D. 17(11), *32*
Marcus, A. H. 418(10, 11, 12, 23), 419(10, 11, 12, 23, 27, 28, 29, 30), 420(12, 34), 422(30), *424*
Mariner Mars 1964 Project Report, Mission & Spacecraft Development, Technical Report 32-740, Vol. II, Appendixes 409(30, 31, 32, 33, 34, 35), *411*
Maringer, R. E. 17(4, 12), *32*
Marsden, B. G. 83(8), *84*, 129(14), *138*
Marshall, C. H. 436(9, 11), *459*
Marshall, P. O. *110*
Marti, K. 50(8), 52(28), *60*
Mason, B. 35(3), 38(12), 40(24), *47*
Massalski, T. B. 21(24), *32*
Massevich, A. 179(21), *181*
Masuda, A. 268(14), 272(14), 274(14), *282*
Masursky, H. 443(31), *460*
Matsui, Y. 268(14), 272(14), 274(14), *282*
Matthews, D. H. 484(9), *488*
Mayeda, T. 8(9), *14*
Mead, J. 272(23), *283*, 312(24), 313(24), *317*
Meinschein, W. G. 36(5), 40(5), 44(5), *47*
Meisenholder, G. W. 386(3), *410*
Melville, R. 372(19), 379(19), *381*
Mercy, E. L. P. 308(14), *316*
Merrihue, C. 50(7), 55(40), *60, 61*
Merson, R. H. 143(4), *150*
Meyer, D. L. 173(1), 174(1), 175(1), 176(1), 177(1), *180*
Michael, I. 413(4), *416*
Migdisov, A. A. 267(1), *282*
Miller, B. P. 418(17), *424*
Miller, G. R. 536(25), *547*
Miller, J. A. 55(41), *61*
Milton, D. J. 439(25), 445(25), *459*
Milverton, S. W. 530(10), *547*
Minami, E. 274(43), *283*
Mitchell, R. L. 274(27), *283*
Montgomery, J. *110*
Moore, H. J. 446(36), 447(39), *460*, 475(2), *479*

Morgan, J. W. 53(32), *60*
Mosen, A. W. 267(4), 268(4), 269(4), 273(4), *282*
Mowat, W. M. H. *110*
Müller, E. A. 45(34), *47*, 253(12, 15), 254(12, 15), *260*
Mueller, G. 37(9), 44(9), *47*
Müller, K. 174(13), *180*
Müller, O. 50(5), 51(5), 55(43), 56(43), *60, 61*
Mullard, J. E. *110*
Muller, P. 87(2), *92*
Munk, W. H. 226(5), *228*, 536(25), *547*
Murata, K. J. 288(9), *304*
Murray, B. C. 408(25), *411*, 419(24), *424*
Murthy, V. R. 53(34), *60*
Mutschlecner, J. P. 253(15), 254(15), *260*
Myers, A. T. 306(5), *316*

Nafe, J. 128(6), *138*, 544(32), *547*
Nagy, B. 36(5), 40(5), 44(5), *47*
Nairn, A. E. M. 356(29), 367(15), *381, 382*, 515(5), *523*
Nalwalk, A. J. 294(13), *304*
Nazarova, T. N. 63(4), *73*
Nernst, W. 271(20), *283*
Neumann, H. 272(22, 23), *283*, 312(24), 313(24), *317*
Newton, R. R. 145(12), 147(12), 148(12), *150*, 151(4), *161*, 521(11), *524*, 560(13), 561(13), 563(13), 564(13), 565(13), 566(13), *566*
Nichiporuk, W. 27(45), *33*
Nicholls, G. D. 286(4), 287(6), 288(6), 290(6), 294(4, 13), 295(4), *303, 304*
Nicks, O. W. 409(23), *411*
Nielson, B. 17(8), 25(8), 30(8), *32*
Nininger, H. H. 25(37), *33*
Nixon, P. H. 306(9), 308(9), *316*
Null, G. 397(2), *410*

Oberbeck, A. 507(9), *512*
Öpik, E. J. 83(9), *84*, 242(8), *250*, 252(7, 8), *260*, 263(6), *264*, 418(15), 419(26), *424*
O'Gallagher, J. J. 393(11, 13, 14), 397(24), *410, 411*
Ogilvie, R. E. 6(3), 7(7, 8), 8(8), *14*, 17(14, 16), 18(14, 22), 21(16), 23(33), 24(33), 29(49), 30(16), *32, 33*
Oglebay, F. E. 536(25), *547*
O'Hara, M. J. 308(14), *316*
O'Keefe, J. A. 153(6), *161*
Olehy, D. A. 267(4, 5), 268(4), 269(5), 269(4), 273(4, 5), 274(5), 275(5), *282*
O'Mara, B. J. 253(13), 254(13), *260*
Opdyke, N. D. 356(24, 25, 28), *381*
Osborn, E. F. 309(19), *316*
Ostic, R. G. 256(20), *260*
Owen, E. A. 18(19), *32*

Palm, A. 471(12), *471*
Park, F. R. 21(24), *32*
Patterson, C. 53(33), *60*
Peale, S. J. 193(4), 211(17, 18), *211*
Pekeris, C. L. 507(7), *512*

Pellew, A. 530(14), *547*
Pepin, R. O. 50(6), 52(18), *60*
Perry, S. H. 3(6), 12(18), *14*, 23(35), *33*
Pettengill, G. H. *189*, 193(1, 2), 194(11), *211*
Petterson, H. 68(16), *73*
Pfann, W. G. 278(32), 279(42), *283*, 314(26), *317*
Phan, K. D. 306(6), *316*
Phaneuf, J. P. 413(4), *416*
Piggott, B. A. M. 148(22), *150*
Pinson, W. H. Jr. 53(35), *60*
Piotrowski, S. 420(32), *424*
Pisani, F. 40(21), *47*
Platt, D. C. *110*
Plotkin, H. H. 99(5), *106*
Plummer, H. C. 148(24), *150*
Poldervaart, A. 286(2), 288(2), *303*
Porter, J. E. 503(6), *503*
Potratz, H. A. 53(30), *60*
Potter, H. J. 179(19), *181*
Price, P. B. 12(16), *14*
Priestley, C. H. B. 529(28), 536(28), *547*

Quaide, W. L. 443(30), *460*

Rabe, E. 83(7), *84*
Radhakrishnamurty, C. 361(30, 31, 32), *382*
Rakos, K. D. 83(10), *84*
Ramadas, L. A. 531(15), *547*
Ramdohr, P. 44(29), 45(29), *47*
Ramsden, A. R. 17(9), *32*
Ramsey, W. H. 131(24), *138*, 261(2), *264*
Randall, J. C. 389(4), *410*
Rayleigh, Lord 530(13), *547*
Reay, A. 278(31), *283*, 305(1), 307(1, 11), 309(17), 311(17), *316*
Reed, G. W. 53(29, 31), *60*
Reed, S. J. B. 8(10), *14*, 17(18), 20(18), *32*, 23(34), 24(34), 31(52, 54), *33*
Reid, W. H. 530(9), *547*
Reiff, G. A. 385(1), *410*
Report Mission and Spacecraft Development, Technical Report 32-740, Vol. I 409(29), *411*
Reynolds, J. H. 13(23), *14*, 52(18), *60*
Richter, C. F. *383*
Ringwood, A. E. 18(20), *32*, 26(40, 44), 31(51), *33*, 37(10), *47*, 253(16), 254(16, 17), *260*, 278(29, 30), *283*, 307(12), 308(12), *316*
Ritter, H. 183(1), *186*
Rittmann, A. 131(22), *138*
Roche, A. 346(16), *349*
Roever, W. P. de 327(13), *328*
Ronca, L. B. 415(13), *416*, 473(1), *479*, 475(4, 5), 478(7), *479*
Ronov, A. B. 267(1), *282*, 286(3), *303*
Rooke, J. M. 306(9), 308(9), *316*
Rose, M. E. 149(27), *150*
Rosen, J. M. 68(14), *73*
Rosenberg, D. L. 259(28, 29), *260*
Ross, C. S. 306(5), *316*
Rothé, J. P. 483(1), *488*

Rowe, M. W. 12(17), *14*
Rubey, W. W. 286(1), 287(1), 288(1), 289(1), *303*
Ruffin, B. W. 173(1), 174(1), 175(1), 176(1), 177(1), *180*
Runcorn, S. K. 170(4), *171*, 228(14), *228*, 228, 257(22), *260*, 341(14), *349*, 351(1), 365(1, 7), *381*, 429(7), *430*, 468(4), *471*, 487(15), *488*, 495(4), 497(5), *498*, 505(3), *506*, 514(4), 515(5), 520(9), 521(11), 523(13), *523*, *524*, 549(2), *566*
Ruskol, E. L. 239(16), *240*, 242(6, 7), *250*
Rutsch, W. 53(37), 54(37), *60*
Ryabchikov, I. D. 272(25), *283*

Sacks, I. S. 128(7), *138*
Sagan, C. 413(4, 8), 414(9), *416*
Sahastrabudhe, P. W. 361(31, 32), *382*(31, 32)
Salisbury, J. W. 414(10, 11), *416*, 418(18), *424*, 436(13), 444(13), *459*, 473(1), 475(5), *479*
Satô, Y. 128(6), *138*, 544(32), *547*
Schadler, D. 323(7), *328*
Schaeffer, O. A. 57(49, 50), *61*, 71(27), 72(27, 28), *74*
Schairer, J. P. 311(21), *317*
Schilling, J. G. 267(11), 269(11), 272(11), *282*
Schmidt, R. A. 70(25), *74*
Schmidt, R. H. 443(30), *460*
Schmidt, R. J. 530(10), *547*
Schmitt, R. A. 267(4, 5, 9), 268(4, 15), 269(4, 5, 9), 270(9), 271(9), 272(9), 273(4, 5), 274(5, 9), *282*, *283*
Schneiderman, D. 385(1), *410*
Schnetzler, C. C. 53(35), *60*
Schrutka, G. 173(5, 6, 9), 174(9, 12), 175(9, 12), 176(9, 12), 177(12, 16), 179(12, 16), 180(9), *180*
Schütz, D. 323(3), 324(3), *328*
Schultes, H. 57(52), *61*
Schultz, L. 52(26), *60*
Schutz, F. L. 389(5), *410*
Schwarcz, H. P. 44(31), *47*
Scott, D. K. 98(2), *106*
Scott, D. W. 144(9), 145(9, 11), 146(11), *150*
Scrutton, C. T. 228(13), *228*
Scull, J. R. 386(2), *410*
Secretan, L. 65(2), 67(2), *73*
Shapiro, I. I. 193(2, 6, 7), 194(10, 11), 195(6, 7), 196(6, 7, 12, 13), 199(12, 13), 200(12, 13), 204(6, 7), 205(7, 12, 13), 206(12, 13, 16), 207(10, 12, 13), *211*
Sharanov, V. V. 413(3), *416*
Sharp, R. P. 408(25), *411*, 419(24), *424*
Sharpless, B. P. 77(5), *84*
Shimazu, Y. 278(37, 38, 39, 40), *283*
Shoemaker, E. M. 257(21), *260*, 418(16, 22), *424*, 432(1, 2), 433(2), 434(2), 435(1, 2), 436(1, 9, 12), 437(1, 2), 438(2), 453(1), *459*, 475(2), *479*
Short, J. M. 21(26), 30(26), *32*
Signer, P. 50(6, 10), *60*
Silver, L. T. 39(16), 41(16), *47*
Silveston, P. L. 505(2), *506*, 530(11), 533(11), *547*

Simpson, J. A. 393(11, 12, 13, 14), 397(24), *410, 411*
Sinton, W. M. 413(1), *416*
Siscoe, G. L. 392(7), *410*
Sitte, K. 60(55), *61*
Sitter, W. de 106(15), *106*
Skrivanek, R. A. 66(8), *73*
Slichter, L. B. 227(8), *228*
Sloan, R. K. 408(25), *411*, 419(24), *424*
Smalley, V. G. 418(18), *424*, 436(13), 444(13), *459*, 473(1), *479*
Smith, A. G. 348(19), *349*, 363(5), *381*
Smith, C. S. 17(3), *32*
Smith, D. E. 144(7), 145(10), *150*
Smith, E. J. 297(22), 392(6, 7), *410*
Smith, H. F. Jr. 100(8, 9), *106*
Smith, R. H. 267(4, 5, 9), 268(4, 15), 269(4, 5, 9), 270(9), 271(9), 272(9), 273(4, 5, 9), 274(5), 275(5), *282, 283*
Soberman, R. K. 65(5), 66(6, 7, 8), *73*
Soop, K. 236(9), *240*
Southwell, R. V. 530(14), *547*
Spar, J. 68(13), *73*
Spencer-Jones, H. 226(4), *228*
Squires, R. K. 153(6), *161*
Stoenner, R. W. 55(42), 57(49), *61*
Strange, W. E. 549(5), *566*
Strom, R. G. 447(38), 453(38), *460*, 471(12), *471*
Strong, H. M. 119(10), 122(10), *126*
Strong, J. 413(1), *416*
Struve, H. 77(2), *84*
Stubbs, P. M. 366(10, 13), *381*
Studier, M. H. 35(2), *47*
Stulov, N. N. 17(10), *32*
Suess, H. E. 50(10), 52(19), *60*
Superintendent of Documents, U.S. Government Printing Office, Washington, D.C. 409(27), *411*
Sykes, L. R. *384*
Sytinskaya, N. N. 468(5), *471*
Sztrokay, K. I. 44(30), 45(30), *47*

Takashi, T. 17(5), *32*
Talwani, M. 484(5), *488*
Tarling, D. H. 486(14), *488*
Taylor, G. I. 227(7), *228*
Taylor, H. P. 39(16), 41(16), *47*
Taylor, S. R. 315(30), *317*
Templeton, D. H. 268(13), *282*
Ter Haar, D. 118(9), *126*
Thiel, E. 373(34), *382*
Thirlaway, H. I. S. *110*
Thomas, D. B. 533(23), *547*
Thomas, R. N. 12(19), *14*
Thomson, J. H. *189*
Tilley, C. E. 119(11), *126*, 295(15), 298(16), 299(16, 19), 300(15), *304*, 310(18), 311(18), *316*, 322(2), 327(2), *328*
Titley, S. R. 440(27), 443(33, 34, 35), 445(27, 33), *460*
Tobin, D. G. *384*
Toit, A. du 363(4), *381*
Tolnay, V. 44(30), 45(30), *47*

Towell, D. G. 267(6), 268(6), 282(6), *282*
Townsend, A. A. 529(16), 531(16), 533(16, 23), 537(16), *547*
Tozer, D. C. 505(4), *506*, 507(4), 511(13), *512*, 525(2), *546*
Tracking & Data Acquisition Support for *Mariner* Mars 1964, Cruise to Post-Encounter Phase 410(36), *411*
Trask, N. J. 443(35), *460*
Tritton, D. J. 505(1), *506*, 536(27), *547*
Tropin, Yu. D. 334(3), *349*
Tschermak, G. 38(14), *47*
Turanskaya, N. W. 267(1, 3), *282*
Turkevich, A. 53(29, 31), *60*
Turner, F. J. 312(23), *317*
Turner, G. 52(18), 55(40, 41), *60, 61*
Tyutyunov, I. A. 415(14), *416*

Uhlig, H. H. 17(13), 26(43), *32, 33*
Urey, H. C. 3(1), 8(9), 10(12), 12(1, 21), *14*, 35(1), 38(15), 44(28), *47*, 133(26), *138*, 228(12), *228*, 248(17), *250*, 255(18, 19), 258 (23, 34), 259(27), *260*, 413(7), 416(7), *416*, 427(3), 428(3), *430*, 435(7), *459*, 521(9), *524*
U.S. Army Map Service 174(11), 175(11), 176(11), 177(11), *180*
Uyeda, S. 484(6), *488*, 549(1), 550(1, 9), 551(1, 9), 552(1), 557(1), 561(1), *566*

Vaile, R. B. Jr. 420(33), *424*
Valentine, W. G. 248(21), *250*
Van Allen, J. A. 392(8), 393(9, 10, 15), 395(15), 397(23), *410, 411*
Van den Bosch, C. A. 83(6), *84*
Van Tassel, R. A. 414(11), *416*
Vasilevskis, J. 267(4), 268(4), 269(4), 273(4), *282*
Vaucouleurs, G. de 129(15), *138*, 427(4), *430*
Veiss, G. 153(11), *162*
Vening-Meinesz, F. A. 517(6), *524*
Venkatavaradam, V. S. 72(30), *74*
Verhoogen, J. 312(23), *317*
Vilcsek, E. 51(14), *60*
Viliminot, J.-C. 306(6, 7), *316*, 328(15), *328*
Vincent, E. A. 315(29), *317*
Vine, F. J. 484(9), *488*
Vinogradov, A. P. 52(24), *60*, 278(34, 35, 36), *283*
Vitaliano, C. J. 272(23), *283*, 313(24), *317*
Vlasov, A. Ya. 334(3, 4), *349*
Vogel, A. 163(1, 2, 3, 4), *163*
Vogel, R. 22(28, 29, 30, 31), *32*
Volfovsky Spirn, R. 267(6), 268(6, 16), 272(16), 282(6), *282, 283*
Von Herzen, R. P. 484(6), *488*, 550(8, 9), 551(8, 9), 557(8), *566*
Voshage, H. 57(51, 53), 58(53), *61*

Wänke, H. 51(14), 52(19, 20, 22), 60(26), *60, 61*
Wager, L. R. 274(27), *283*
Wagner, C. A. 148(20, 21), *150*

Walker, G. P. L. 484(7), *488*, 489(2), *498*, 551(12), *566*
Walker, M. J. 98(3), 100(3), *106*
Walker, R. M. 12(16), *14*
Walsh, J. 484(10), *488*
Walton, A. 68(13), *73*
Wang, C. 549(4), 561(4), *566*
Warner, B. 469(8), *471*
Wasserburg, G. J. 56(44, 48), *61*, 117(5), 125(5), *126*
Wasson, J. T. 27(46), *33*
Watson, G. N. 148(23), 149(23), *150*
Watts, C. B. 97(1), *106*, 179(20), *181*
Wedepohl, K. H. 323(4), *328*
Wegener, A. 363(3), *381*, 514(3), *523*
Wehner, G. K. 259(28, 29), *260*
Weimer, Th. 175(15), *180*
Weizsäcker, C. F. von 243(11), 244(11), *250*
Wells, J. W. 227(10), *228*
Weston, C. R. 414(12), *416*
Whipple, F. L. 46(35), *47*, 242(9), *250*
White, A. J. R. 315(30), *317*, 328(16), *328*
White, I. G. 305(1), 306(3), 307(1, 3), *316*
Whiteway, F. E. *110*
Whittaker, E. T. 148(23), 149(23), *150*
Wigner, E. P. 149(26), *150*
Wiik, H. B. 43(26), *47*
Wilcox, J. M. 215(7), *218*, 235(2), *239*
Wildeman, T. R. 267(8), *282*
Wildt, R. W. 70(24), *74*
Wilhelms, D. E. 435(22), 438(21, 22), 439(21, 22), *459*
Wilkins, G. A. 426(2), *430*
Wilkinson, D. T. 99(5), *106*
Willis, G. E. 529(24, 29), 533(24), 537(29, 30), *547*

Wilshire, H. G. 299(17), *304*, 306(8), *316*
Winchester, J. W. 267(6, 11, 12), 268(12, 17), 269(11), 272(11), 282(17), *282*, *283*
Wise, D. U. 241(1), *249*, 251(1), *260*
Wlotska, F. 50(11), 52(19), *60*
Wöhler, F. 40(19, 20), *47*
Wolff, F. C. 43(27), *47*
Wollenhaupt, W. R. 153(12), *162*
Wood, J. A. 3(2), 5(2), 6(4), 7(2, 4), 8(2, 4), 9(4, 11), 10(11), 11(2), *14*, 17(15), 21(15), 22(15), 26(15), 30(15), 31(53), *32*, *33*, 37(11), 39(11), 45(33), 46(11), *47*
Woolard, E. W. 77(4), *84*, 129(17), *138*, 426(1), *430*
Woollard, G. P. 373(35), *382*

Yaskawa, K. 334(7), *349*
Yavnel, A. A. 17(11), 28(47), 31(50), *32*, *33*
Yionoulis, S. M. 147(16, 17), 148(18), *150*, 153(14), *162*
Yoder, H. S. 119(11), *126*, 295(15), 300(15), *304*, 309(16, 18), 310(18), 311(18), *316*, 322(2), 327(2), *328*
Young, J. 417(4, 5), *423*

Zachariasen, W. H. 40(23), *47*
Zacharov, I. 68(17), *74*
Zadorozhny, I. K. 52(24), *60*
Zähringer, J. 49(4), 50(5, 9), 51(5, 15), 52(21, 22, 23, 27), 53(21, 22), 54(21, 22), 55(42, 43), 56(43, 46, 47), 57(46, 52), 58(46), 59(22), *60*, *61*
Zarraga, M. N. 505(1), *506*
Zeller, E. J. 415(13), *416*
Zijl, J. S. V. van 356(27), *381*

Subject Index

Africa,
    geoid 155, 158–161
    heat flow 549, 550, 558, 559
    Madagascar 346
    Mozambique,
        Cretaceous–Jurassic volcanic rocks 335
        red siltstones 335
    palaeomagnetism 335, 516
        data 356
    polar wandering 352, 370–372, 375–377
    rift system 493, 523
        basaltic volcanism 483
        block faulting 483
        gravity anomaly 523
        in Kenya 484
    shield, age 520
Albite 293, 327
America, North,
    California 299, 453, 483
    heat flow 558, 559
    Florida Bay 272
    movement 514
    palaeomagnetism 331–349
        data 337, 360, 369
        pole positions 514
    polar wandering 341–345, 354, 369–371,
        376–378
    rift system,
        basaltic volcanism 483
        block faulting 483
    Rockies 514
        gravity anomaly 523
    seismic arrays 109
America, South,
    Andes 514
        gravity anomaly 523, 560
    geoid 155, 158–161
    heat flow 549
    palaeoclimates 516, 517
    palaeomagnetism 516
        data 356
    palaeopositions 516, 517
    Peru–Chile Trench 523
    polar wandering 345–347, 352, 371, 372,
        375–377
    Venezuela 271
Amphibole 308
Andesite 322, 323
    formation 315
Anorthite 327
Antarctica,
    palaeomagnetism, data 362

polar wandering 373, 375, 378
    weathering 415
Antarctic Ocean,
    convection currents 486
    gravity anomaly 565
Arabia,
    Gulf of Aden 483–487
    palaeomagnetism, data 486
    Red Sea,
        crustal segregation 486
        formation 484
        heat flow 556, 557
        map 486
        rift system 493
        tension 489
        topographic profiles 485
    rotation 484–487
    translation 484, 485
Arctic Ocean, heat flow 556, 557
Ariel 237, 247
Ascension 319
Asia,
    gravity anomaly 523, 560
    heat flow 549, 558, 559
    Lake Baikal 523
    palaeomagnetism 341–349
        data 339
Asteroids,
    Ceres, radius 22
    chondrites 35, 59, 60
    density 216, 243
    formation 45, 46, 214, 215
    iron meteorite, origin 1, 15, 58
    masses 213
    moment of inertia 216
    origin 214, 215
    rotation 213–217
        period 213, 216
    structure, internal 216
Atlantic Ocean 241
    convection currents 487
    geoid 155, 158–161
    gravity anomaly 521, 523, 560
    heat flow, 550, 555–557
    Mid-Atlantic Ridge 269–282, 523
        heat flow 308, 550
        serpentinites 298–300
        tholeiites 269, 270
Australia,
    Delegate eclogite 275, 277
    heat flow 558–560
    movement 520

Australia—*contd.*
  New South Wales 299
  palaeoclimates 515
  palaeomagnetism 515, 516
    data 357
  palaeopositions 515
  polar wandering 353, 372, 374–377, 515
  seismic array 109
  shield, age 520

Basalts,
  alkaline 292, 321, 322
    jadeite–orthoenstatite, stability 322
    lead isotope ratios 319
  analyses, oceanic 315
  ankaramite 269
  cohenite 25
  dolorite 322
  eclogite, melt 327, 328
  formation,
    fractional crystallization 272–276, 310,
      313, 315
    fractional melting 277, 278, 315
    partial melting 276, 277, 328
    zone melting 278–280, 314
  from Greenland, Disko Island 26
  from Hawaii 268, 269
  from Mars 316
  from Mid-Atlantic Ridge 269, 270, 281,
    282
  from Moon 316
  from Tristan da Cunha 296
  from West Germany 321–328
  magma, origin 297, 327, 328
  melting curve 309, 310
  nepheline–melilite 269
  nepheline, normative 293, 294, 297, 298
    occurrence 293
    potassium content 295
    vesicular 297
  nepheline–olivine–albite 269
  norm 293
  oceanite 311
  olivine nodules 298, 299, 305, 306,
    321–328
  olivine tholeiite 269, 275, 276, 281, 311
  orthopyroxene 293, 308, 327
  orthopyroxene, normative,
    composition 294
    occurrence 293
  orthopyroxene–olivine–albite 293
  peridotite,
    melt 310, 321, 327
    nodules 322
  phlogopite 297
  picrite 311
  tholeiite 293–295, 298, 311, 314–316
    crystallization 311, 312
    mineralogy 295, 311
    potassium content 295
    titanium content 295
  trace elements 312

Callisto 237, 247, 249
Canada,
  Mt. Albert 271
  palaeomagnetism, data 337, 360
  Scotia arc 523
  seismic array 109
  shield, age 520
Canary Islands, Tenerife 319
Clinopyroxene 307, 311
Continental drift 347, 348, 351, 507, 511, 521
  and continental fits 348, 363
  in Pacific Ocean 348
  onset time 363–376, 520
  palaeomagnetic evidence 331–349, 514, 515
  palaeopositions, determinations 351
    palaeolatitudes 351, 363, 377, 517
    palaeolongitudes 351, 355
  reality 377–379
  reconstructions 355, 363, 370, 371, 379, 516
    of Gondwanaland 368, 371–375, 520
    of Laurasia 368, 370–374
Convection 483–566
  analogues, laboratory 499–503
  Bénard 499, 505, 506
  Coriolis force 526, 528, 545
  decay parameter 526
  experiments 501–503, 504, 505, 529–540
  gravitational 499
  Nusselt number 531, 538
  patterns, experimental 502
    cellular 530, 531
    turbulent 531
  Péclet number, *see* Convection, Reynolds
    number
  Prandtl number 526, 528, 529
  Rayleigh number 505, 526–530, 537–540, 543
  Reynolds number 512, 528
  temperature gradient, horizontal,
    in mantle 510–512
    theory 508–510
  uprising currents 486
Corals,
  month, length 228
  rugose, Devonian 227
    epitheca ridges 227, 228
  year, length 228
Core, Earth's,
  composition 119, 132, 251
  depth 119
  formation 114, 120, 270, 308, 520
  hydrogen, postulate 131
  mantle,
    coupling 163, 226, 430
    mass ratio 130, 131, 273
Core, Jupiter's 429
Core, Mars' 131–134, 428–430
Core, Moon's 94
Core, Venus' 116, 132, 261
Cosmic dust 63–74
  accretion rate 63–74
    atmospheric determination 66–70
    ground collection 70, 71
    in Pleistocene 73

Cosmic dust—*contd.*
  in Pliocene 73
  in Tertiary 71
    radioactive determination 63–67
    space determination 63–67
  iron to nickel ratio 69
  origin 71–73
Crust, Earth's,
  composition 314
  continental 315
  formation 248, 315
  Moho 239
  ocean 286–291, 298, 315
  origin 239
  uranium content 117
Crust, Moon's 257, 466
  tektites 249

Deimos 77–84, 129, 246, 247, 425–427
  discovery 77
  orbit 77–80
  perturbations 78
  precession 77, 427
  rotation 78
Dione 237, 247, 249
Dunite 326

Earth,
  accretion rate 63–74
  age 513
  angular momentum 230, 248
  as Maxwell body 231
  atmosphere,
    origin 286
    original 239
  caldera 461, 462
  composition, chondritic 114, 267, 275, 281, 305
  cooling 513, 517
  core 114, 119, 120, 131, 132, 251, 270, 308, 430,
    520
  crust 117, 239, 248, 286–291, 298, 314, 315
  day, length 226, 228, 230, 241, 248
  deceleration 225, 226, 241
  density 85, 242, 246
    internal 127–137
  differentiated 114, 119
  dust ring 245, 248
  earthquakes, *see under* Seismology
  energy, internal 514
  Fennoscandian uplift 507
  figure 101, 102
  fumaroles 287
  geoid 143, 146, 147, 151–162, 521, 545,
    546, 566
  geomagnetic field 226, 351
  geosyncline, development 573
  Gerstenkorn event 239
  gravitational potential 141–150, 153
  gravity anomalies 487, 521–523, 549, 560–566
  heat flow 114, 308, 484, 513, 549–566
  homogeneous 109

hydrosphere, origin 286
hydrostatic state 141–163, 165, 523
mantle 111, 285–328, 485–489, 507–512,
  525–546
mass, mantle–core ratio 130, 131, 273
models 127–138
  Bullen's A 128, 129
  Bullen's B 128, 129
moment of inertia 128
Moon 101, 102, 225–264
motion, orbital 194
non-hydrostatic state 141–163
oblateness 144
oceans 285–304, 550
pressure 128
radiative conductivity 117
radioactive abundances 114
radius 22
rare-earth distribution 270–282
red clay 272
red soils 414
ridges, oceanic 489–498, 549–551
rift system 483–487
seismology 109, 111, 114, 128, 163, 483,
  484, 487, 523
shields, Pre-Cambrian,
  age 520
  heat flow 308, 550, 552
tectonics 489–498, 506, 514, 518–523
tektites 249
temperature, initial 113, 118–126
thermal history 113–126
thorium to uranium ratio 117
tidal friction 225–234
tidal potential 229
topography 519, 520
trenches, oceanic 298, 489–498, 517, 523
uranium content 117
Venus 194
volcanic gases 287–291
volcanic lavas, composition 292–298
Eclogite 277, 327
Enceladus 237, 247, 249
England,
  Derbyshire, Carboniferous sediments and
    lavas 335
  geoid 155, 158–161
  Lizard, Cornwall 271
Europa 237, 247, 249
Europe,
  Alps 523
  gravity anomaly 560
  heat flow 558, 559
  palaeomagnetism,
    data 339, 358, 359, 364
    pole positions 515
  polar wandering 341–345, 353, 354, 365,
    368, 370, 371, 376, 377
  shield, age 520

Ganymede 237, 247, 249
Geoid, Earth's 143, 146, 147, 151–162, 521,
  545, 546, 566

Germany, West 321, 324
Globigerina, rare-earth abundances 272
Gough 319
Granite 314, 315
Granodiorite 315
Greenland,
    Disko Island 26
    palaeomagnetism 336

Hawaii,
    cosmic dust 68
    Kilauea 68, 268, 269, 272
    Mauna Loa 453
    Puu Anahulu 272
    tholeiites 268, 269, 275, 276, 281
    trachyte 269, 272, 281
    volcanic gases 287, 288
Heat flow 114, 308, 484, 513, 549–566
    continents 553–555, 558–560
    geological correlations 549, 550
    gravity, comparison 549, 550
    log normal distribution 551–566
    oceans 551, 553–557
    spherical harmonic analysis 549, 550
Hyperion 237, 247, 249

Iceland,
    Pleistocene–Tertiary rocks,
        lead isotope ratios 319
        strontium isotope ratios 319
    rift system 484, 489
Igneous rocks, differentiated 280
Imp II 393, 394
India,
    convection currents 487
    geoid 155, 158–161
    heat flow 550, 555–557
    movement 523
    palaeoclimates 516
    palaeomagnetism 523
        data 361
    palaeopositions 516
    polar wandering 355, 373, 375
    seismic array 109
Indian Ocean,
    Antarctic Ridge 523
        gravity anomaly 523
    Carlsberg 523
        gravity anomaly 523
    convection currents 487
    gravity anomaly 521
    heat flow 550, 555–557
Io 237, 247, 249

Japan 523, 558
    geoid 155, 158–161
    heat flow 558, 559
    Ichinomegata 299
Japetus 237, 247, 249
Java 517
Jupiter 216, 429, 430
    core 430

density 216, 243, 249
magnetic field 429, 430
mass 101, 249
moment of inertia 216
Moon 101
red spot 430
rotation 216, 430
satellites 235, 237, 245–249
    Callisto 237, 247, 249
    Europa 237, 247, 249
    Ganymede 237, 247, 249
    Io 237, 247, 249

Kimberlites 306, 308
    formation depths 306
    nodules 308
    xenoliths 306
Krakatoa 69

Leonid meteor shower 69
Leucite 297
Luna 9 258, 418, 453, 455, 456, 470
Luna 10 179, 251, 259

Magmatic processes 267–284
Manganese nodules 268
Mantle, Earth's,
    as Einstein solid 111
    basaltic fraction 285–298
    composition 285–317, 319, 321–328
    compressibility 544
    convection currents 287, 289, 308, 348,
        485–487, 489, 505, 507–513, 520–547
    core,
        coupling 163, 226, 430
        mass ratio 130, 131, 273
    creep 428
    degassing 285, 286, 288, 289
    density 127–137
    formation 272
    heat, sources 116, 117, 308, 309
    k 129, 137
    magmatic processes 267–284
    melting 308–312
    melts 310–313
    mineralogy 307, 308
    models 114, 128, 131, 132
    origin 113, 248
    physical properties, depth dependency 117
    potassium to uranium ratio 117
    radioactive abundances 116, 117
    recycling 291
    residual fraction 298–301
    segregation processes 312, 313
    serpentinite, fraction 285, 289–292
    specific heat 117
    stress pattern 495
    temperature distribution 114, 507
    thermal experiments 529–540
    thermal history 113–126
    thermal turbulence 525–547

Mantle, Earth's—*contd.*
  thorium to uranium ratio 117
  uranium content 117
  volatiles 285–287, 289, 291, 292, 301, 302
  zone refining 314
Mantle, Mars' 128–137
  density 133
  iron content 133–135
  olivine 134
Mariana Trench 523
Mariner II 385, 393
Mariner IV,
  Atlas–Agena 385, 389
  communications 387
  cosmic dust 393–385
    detector 390
  cosmic-ray telescope 390
  distance of closest approach 389
  experiments 390
  ionization chamber 390
  launching 389
  light pressure 388
  magnetic measurements 390, 392
  Mars 385–411
    mass 83, 426
  occultation 392, 394
  photography 91, 397, 428
  radiation belts 397
  Ranger 385
  solar electrons 383–395
  solar flares 393
  solar panels 386, 389
  solar plasma probe 390
  solar protons 394
  solar wind 392
  star tracker 386
  surface density 137
  telemetry 394
  television system 390, 399, 400
  temperature, internal 388
  trajectory 387, 392
  trapped radiation detector 390
  weight 389
Mars,
  accretion rate 118
  atmosphere 89–92, 395, 396, 401, 413,
    414, 428
    composition 395
  ballistic energy curve 386
  blue clearing phenomena 392
  chondrites 60
  composition, chondritic 114
  convection 429
  core 131–134, 428–430
  cosmic-ray production 397
  craters 401, 402, 408, 417–423
  density 85, 116, 133, 134, 137, 216, 413, 427
    internal 127–137
    surface 137
  diameter 85–92, 428
    measurement 85–89
  differentiated 114
  Electris–Mare Chronium 395

  ellipticity 77–92, 129–137, 165, 425–429
  Emden equation 135
  equation of state 135
  figure 425–430
  frost 428
  gravitational potential 425–427
  homogeneous 114
  hydrostatic state 130, 426–428, 523
  ionosphere 394–397
  k 137
  limonite 413, 414
  magnetic field 116, 397, 429
  mantle 128–137
  Mare Acidalium 396
  maria, nature 421–423
  Mariner IV 387–411, 428
  mass 77, 84, 91, 101, 115, 116, 129, 132,
    133, 137, 397, 427
    mantle–core ratio 130–132
  models 128, 131–138
  moment of inertia 115, 116, 129, 130, 132,
    216, 428
  Moon 101, 398, 408
  oppositions 89, 385, 397, 398
  orbit 385, 386
  photography 397–416
    Mariner IV 403–407, 413–416
  pressure centre 128
  radiation belts 397, 429
  radius 77, 80, 129–137, 397, 427
  refractivity 395, 396
  rotation, period 214, 216, 430
  satellites,
    Deimos 77–84, 129, 246, 247, 425–427
    Phobos 77–84, 129, 246–248, 425–427
  soil 92
  solar wind 397
  surface 429
    age 407
    conditions 414–416
  temperature,
    initial 118, 120–126
    internal 124
    surface 395, 396
  thermal history 114, 126
  tholeiite 316
  viscosity 428, 429
  volume 91
  weathering 415
  yellow haze 413
Mediterranean Sea, heat flow 556, 557
Mercury,
  atmosphere 191
  density 116, 246
  Earth 226
  ellipsoid 193, 195
  figure 165
  hydrostatic state 524
  iron to silicon ratio 253
  mass 116
  moment of inertia 195
  non-hydrostatic state 165
  rotation,

Mercury—*contd.*
  period 165
  rate 189, 191, 193, 214
  sense 189
  theory 195–211, 214, 219
  thermal history 115, 116
Meteorites,
  achondrites 12, 31, 50, 53–55, 226, 270,
    273–275, 281, 282
  age 49, 51–58
  ataxites 16, 17, 26–28
  carbonaceous 35–46
    mineralogy 37–45
  chondrites 29–31, 34–46, 50, 52–55, 267,
    268, 274–276, 305
    mineralogy 8–10, 28, 31, 37–45
  composition 15–33, 35–44
  cooling rates 7, 8, 10, 11, 21, 22, 28, 30,
    31, 37
  exposures ages, cosmic-ray 56–60
  formation 3–7, 18–23, 30, 35–41, 44–46, 245
  gallium–germanium groups 27, 28
  hexahedrites 16, 17, 23, 27, 28
  iron content 38, 46, 51
  irons 3–13, 14–32, 55, 56
    mineralogy 16–33
    phosphorus content 22–25
  iron to nickel ratio 3, 4, 16–20, 26, 69
  octahedrites 3–8, 10, 11, 16, 17, 20–24, 27, 28
  origin 8, 10, 18, 31, 32, 35–46, 58–60
  parent bodies 3, 8, 10–34, 46, 52, 55
    nature 28–32
    pressure 22, 25–28
  radioactivity 10–13
  rare-earth abundances 267–270
  rare-gas isotopes 49–59
  thermal history 3–12, 52
  Widmanstätten structure 3–5, 16–24, 26, 31
Mimas 237, 247, 249
Miranda 237, 247
Moon,
  acceleration 225, 226, 241
  accretion rate 118
  angular momentum 230
  ash flows 258, 259, 439
  basins 180, 439–446, 455
  bulge 165–172, 181, 182
  capture 241, 242, 252, 253
  chondrites 58–60
  composition 94, 181, 252, 253, 255
    chondritic 124
    iron to silicon ratio 124, 253
  convection, theory 95, 172, 257, 468, 521, 523,
    524
  Copernican System 433, 436, 437, 450, 456
  core 94
  craters,
    age 478
    circular 467
    cluster analysis 465–467
    collapsed 468–471
    densities 436, 444–446, 474
    Earth craters, comparison 418, 461

    elliptical 462–466
    formation 248, 442, 478
    origin 58, 241, 417, 420, 421, 467–471,
      474, 477, 478
    rilles 464, 474
    shapes 468–470, 475–478, 486
    statistics 417–421
  crust 249, 257, 466
  density 93–95, 104, 124, 242, 246, 249
  diameter 93
  distance from Earth 98, 248
  dust ring 242
  Earth 98–106, 221, 225–264, 418, 461
  eclipse 226, 227
  ellipticity 167, 172
  Eratosthenian System 433, 436, 451, 453, 457
  evolution, internal 248, 249, 256
  faults 440, 461–471
  field lineaments 468, 473–475
  figure 93–95, 101–104, 165–186
  gamma spectroscopy 259
  geological mapping 431–460
  heat flow 125, 126
  heights 166–168, 176–182
  Humorum basin 182, 439, 443–446,
    473–475, 478
  hydrostatic state 94, 165–167
  Imbrian System 433, 434, 436, 452, 458
  Imbrium basin 182, 248, 433–441, 462
  lavas 257, 258, 439
  libration 103
  Luna 9 258, 418, 453, 455–458, 470
  Luna 10 181, 251, 259
  maria 182, 433–446, 453–455, 462, 473–475,
    478
    formation 248, 423
  Mariner IV 249, 419
  Mars 239
  mass 249
    distribution 102, 103
  Mercury 225
  moment of inertia 93–106, 165, 166, 180, 523
  montes 433–447, 455
  month, length 98, 228, 248
  moons, other 235, 247, 248, 256
  motion,
    anomalistic 98
    centennial 100
    diagrammatic 166
    discrepancies 105, 106
    laws 165
    libration 166
    perigee 96–106
    perturbations 100, 101
    precession 99, 105, 165
    relativity 99, 105
    theory 99–106
  occultation 97
  orbit 93–106
    inclination 93, 103, 221
    retrograde 242
  Orientale basin 439–443, 445, 454
  origin 225–264, 341

Moon—*contd.*
  accretion 221, 251, 252, 255, 260
  capture 241, 242, 252, 253, 260
  double planet 252, 237
  from Earth 221, 241, 242, 251, 261–263
  photography 258
  plains, material 439
  planetesimals, bombardment 248
  position 97–106
    observations 97, 98
    theory 99–106
  Procellarian System 435, 436
  profiles 182, 461
  radiation, heat 257
  radioactive abundances 126, 251
  radius 171
  Ranger 7 418, 462–468
  Ranger 8 418, 470
  Ranger 9 462, 464, 469
  retreat from Earth 242
    rate 225–228
  ring structures, hexagonal 467
  Roche limit 24, 216, 230, 238–242, 263, 264
  rotation 93
  shape,
    ellipsoid, triaxial 166, 168–172, 181
    geometrical 172, 179, 521
    terminator method, determination 183–186
    tidal bulge 180
  stratigraphy 433–444, 453
  structure, regional 431
  Sun 225
  surface 429
    altitude, inclination 183
    collisions 258
    composition, chemical 258
    dust cover 258
    iron content 259, 260
    photography 258
    reflections, properties 259
  Surveyor 258, 259
  tectonics 473–479
  tektites 249, 259
  temperature,
    initial 118
    of formation 255
  thermal history 116, 124–126
  tholeiite 316
  tidal friction 225, 229–234, 238
  tidal torques 225–230, 241, 252
  tides 230, 238, 241
    model 229–234
    oceanic 241
  topography 435
    maps 431, 432
  tuff deposits 439
  velocity, angular 93, 226
  Venus 225
  volcanic evidence 461–471
  volcanic features 446, 447, 449, 453–455, 461–463
  volcanoes 257, 462
  water 249
    permafrost 258
  Zond III 442
Mountain chains, formation 489, 513–518

Nepheline 293–298
Nepheline–melilite 269
Nepheline–olivine–albite 293
Neptune,
  angular momentum 217
  density 216, 242, 249
  mass 249
  moment of inertia 21
  rotation 217
  Triton 217, 235, 237, 238, 241, 245
New Zealand 483, 487
Niggli values 323
Niuafo'ou 461, 462

Oberon 237, 247
Oceans,
  geochemical studies 285–304
  heat flow 550–557
  ridges 489–498, 549–551
  trenches 298, 489–498, 517, 523
Olivine 293, 311
  chondrules 36–40
  nodules 297–299, 305–307, 321–328, 335
Orthoclase 297

Pacific Ocean 241, 341, 343, 344
  compression features 495
  convection currents 487
  East Pacific Rise 523, 550
  geoid 155, 158–161
  heat flow 550, 555–557
  gravity anomaly 521, 523, 560
  wrench faults 348
Palaeobotany,
  angiosperms 372
  glossopteris 372
Palaeoclimates,
  evaporites and salt, distribution 346, 347
  glaciation 373, 516
Palaeomagnetism 331–381, 515
  anisotropy 334
  continental drift, review of evidence 331–349
  Curie points 366
  data 351–381
    Africa 356
    America, North 337, 360, 369
    America, South 356
    Antarctica 362
    Australia 357
    Britain 365–367
    Canada 337, 360
    Europe 339, 358, 359, 364
    India 361
    Russia 339, 358, 359, 364
  demagnetization 332, 365, 368
  dipole field 333, 351
  Earth, expansion 336, 341, 379
  field tests 331, 369
  geomagnetic poles, virtual 331, 364, 365

Palaeomagnetism—*contd.*
  inclination error 333–335, 377
  lavas 334
  magnetic age 371
  polar wandering curves 341–348, 351–355
  quadrupole field 336
  remagnetization 367, 368
  remanence 331, 334
  sediments 331, 333, 377
  stability tests 332
Palaeomeridians 335–341, 344, 377
  America, North 340
Palaeopositions 515–517
Peridotite 287, 298–300, 315, 316, 321–323,
      327, 328
  analyses 298–307
  kimberlites 306, 308
  melting 308, 310, 311, 327
  rare-earth abundances 271, 279
  specific heat 308
Phlogopite 297
Pioneer 393
Phobos 77–84, 129, 246–248, 425–427
  discovery 77
  orbit 77–79
  perturbations 78
  precession 77, 427
  rotation 77
  solar torques 248
Planets,
  convection 483–566
  densities 115, 216, 249
  double 237, 238
  formation 113, 117, 214–217, 236–238,
      242–247
  gravitational energy 118
    potential 237
  masses 101, 249
  melting 316
  moment of inertia 216
  protoplanets 116, 117
  radioactive heating 118
  rotation 189–221
    asteroids 213, 214
    isochronic law 213, 214
    radar method 189
    rate 213, 214
  satellites 237, 247, 249
  segregation 316
  spin–orbit coupling 219–221
  structure, internal 216, 217
  temperature, initial 113, 117, 118
  thermal history 113–126
  tidal friction 115
Pluto 243, 253
Polar wandering, curves 341–348, 351–355
  Africa 352, 370–372, 375–377
  America, North 341–345, 354, 369–371,
      376–378
  America, South 345–347, 352, 371, 372,
      375–377
  Antarctica 373, 375, 378
  Australia 353, 372, 374–377, 515

Europe 341–345, 353, 354, 365, 368, 370,
      371, 376, 377
  India 355, 373, 375
Puerto Rico Trench 298
Pyroxene 308, 327
    chondrules 36–40
    nodules 308

Ranger 7 418, 462–468
Ranger 8 418, 470
Ranger 9 462, 464, 469
Raratonga 319
Rare-earth elements,
  abundances 267, 268
    achondrites 270, 273, 274, 281
    basalts 268, 269, 272, 276, 279, 281, 282
    chondrites 267–274, 281
    granites 268
    manganese nodules 268
    pallasites 270
    peridotite 269, 271, 279
    sediments 269, 272, 274
    trachyte 269, 272, 282
  fractionation 267–283
    fractional crystallization 272–276
    fractional melting 277, 278, 315
    partial melting 276, 277, 328
    zone melting 278–280, 314
  Goldschmidt ionic potential 268
Rhea 237, 247, 249
Ridges, oceanic,
  epicentres 489
  formation 489, 517, 518
  gravity anomalies 489
  heat flow 489, 549–551
  location 490
  spherical harmonic analysis 489–498
Rift system 483–487
  age 484, 485
  convection 483
  formation 489
  heat flow 489
  isostatic equilibrium 404
  location 483, 484
  magnetic anomalies 484
  seismic velocities 484
  spherical harmonic analysis 493
Russia,
  Chelekan Peninsula 335
  palaeomagnetism, data 339, 358, 359, 364

St. Helena 319
Samoa 319
Saturn,
  density 216, 249
  dust rings 241
  gravitational potential 237
  mass 101, 249
  moment of inertia 216
  rotation 216
  satellites 235, 237, 245, 247, 249
    Dione 237, 247, 249

Saturn—*contd.*
  Enceladus 237, 247, 249
  Hyperion 237, 247, 249
  Japetus 237, 247, 249
  Mimas 237, 247, 249
  Rhea 237, 247, 249
  Tethys 237, 247, 249
  Titan 237, 247, 249
Scotland,
  Midland Valley 366, 367
  seismic array 109
Seismology,
  arrays 109, 546
  core–mantle reflection 163
  earthquakes 109, 383, 487, 523
  epicentres 483
  gravity anomalies 383
  heat flow anomalies 383
  island arcs 383
  microseisms 109
  mid-oceanic ridges 383
  oceanic trenches 383
  shear waves 114
  travel-time anomalies 163
  velocities 111, 128, 136, 285, 484
  volcanoes 383
  waves 163
Serpentinites 287–292, 300
  amounts 289, 290
  analyses 298–300
Siberia, River Lena 483
Silicates, heat of fusion 308
Society Islands 319
Solar system,
  age 117
  asteroids 214, 215, 245, 286
  celestial body, formation 214–218, 235–239,
      242–248, 255–257
  chondrules 35, 37, 40, 45
  cosmic dust, origin 71
  dust rings 244
  Earth, rotation 226
  evolution 56
  gas density 242–244
  grains 215, 236, 244
  hydrogen, distribution 45, 46
  planetesimals 242, 244
  planets 215, 236, 245, 246
    Earth–Moon 237, 238
    Neptune–Triton 237, 238
  plasma 215, 236
  rare-gas abundances 49
  satellites 215, 236, 245, 246
  spin–orbit coupling 219–221
  tidal torques 193
    Jupiter 209
    Mercury 193, 195, 197, 201–205, 210
    Venus 205–207, 210
Star, formation 217
Sun,
  age 513
  density 243
  eclipses 226

  element abundances 253, 254
  hydrogen to oxygen ratio 45
  iron to silicon ratio 253
  mass 80, 133
  Moon 94
Surveyor 258, 259

Tectonics,
  activity, ages 520, 521
  features 489–498, 506, 514, 518–523
Tethys 237, 247, 249
Titan 237, 247, 249
Titania 237, 247
Tonga 383, 521
Trachyte 272
Trenches, oceanic,
  formation 489
  Japan 523
  Java 517
  location 490
  Mariana Trench 523
  Peru–Chile Trench 523
  Puerto Rico Trench 298
  spherical harmonic analysis 489–498
Tristan da Cunha 319
Triton 217, 235, 237, 245
  formation 237
  mass ratio 235, 237, 241
  orbit 238
  rotation 241
    sense 241

Ultrabasic rocks 305
  analyses 307
  composition 305
  definition 305
  formation 305, 307
  xenoliths 305
Umbriel 237, 247
Uranus,
  density 216, 243, 249
  mass 249
  moment of inertia 216
  rotation 216
  satellites 235, 246
    Ariel 237, 247
    Miranda 237, 247
    Oberon 237, 247
    Titania 237, 247
    Umbriel 237, 247

Venus,
  atmosphere 115, 116, 239
  atomic weight 116
  composition 131, 132
  core 116, 132, 261
  density 116, 216, 249
    internal 127–137
  Earth 194, 195, 205, 210, 226
  flattening 114
  gravitational potential 237
  gravitational torques 194, 205–210, 214
  hydrostatic state 524

Venus—*contd.*
  Jupiter 194, 195, 209
  magnetic field 116
  mass 101, 116, 124, 249
    core–mantle ratio 130–132
  Mercury 194, 210
  models 128
  moment of inertia 116, 132
  Moon 101
  radioactive heating 13
  radius 132
  rotation,
    evolution 205–207
    period 165
    rate 189, 194, 205, 216

  resonances 207–210, 219
  sense 189, 194, 195, 205, 206
  stability 196
  theory 193–211
Sun 193, 214, 205–207
temperature, internal 115
thermal history 115, 116
Volcanic rocks,
  from Hawaii 287, 288
  lead isotope ratios 319
  strontium isotope ratios 319

Wales, Cwmbran 366–368

Zond III 442